Foreword

Paul Philip
Chief executive
of the Solicitors
Regulation Authority
(SRA)

Andrew Langdon QC
Chair of the Bar

It gives me great pleasure to welcome you to The Training Contract & Pupillage Handbook. Although I am chief executive of the SRA, I was also called to the Bar, which I think makes me ideally placed to appreciate the challenges that lie ahead for you, regardless of which branch of the profession you hope to eventually join.

The standing of the legal profession in England and Wales is one of the highest in the world, with people coming from all four corners of the globe to access it. Solicitors, representing 85% of regulated legal service providers, clearly contribute greatly to this international reputation. We are therefore proud to play our part in making sure that all would-be solicitors reach the high standards expected of them before being allowed to enter the profession.

You will be aware that to achieve this we are introducing the Solicitors Qualifying Examination (SQE). This will make sure that, regardless of the training route potential entrants choose, everyone meets a consistent, high standard.

So what does this mean for you? Well, nothing immediately. The SQE will not be introduced until September 2020 at the earliest, so if you want to qualify as a solicitor through the current routes, you can continue to do so. Yet, depending on your plans, it might be an option you want to consider.

Regardless of whether you are looking at a training contract or pupillage, I wish you all the best in your training.

A career at the Bar offers both challenge and excitement. The Bar is the specialist advocacy profession in England and Wales, and its reputation for excellence, professionalism and legal acumen is recognised and respected around the world. Qualifying, and practising, as a barrister involves hard work, dedication, commitment and effort. But it is a profession which offers real fulfilment to those who succeed.

The attraction of a career at the Bar means that applying for pupillage is highly competitive. Pupillage is an important stepping stone to becoming a barrister and provides pupils with the skills required to practice at the Bar. The Bar and the Bar Council, the representative body of the profession, are committed to ensuring that we attract applications from the best candidates and from the widest talent pool possible, regardless of background.

This handbook will help you with your application for pupillage and guide you through the various stages. It contains a comprehensive account of the training required for a career at the Bar, as well as information to help you decide to which area of practice you are most suited. Further information about pupillage and the Bar can be found at www.pupillagegateway.com and www.barcouncil.org.uk.

Good luck with your pupillage application and in your future career.

Becoming a lawyer

Work experience

Postgraduate training

Solicitors

Training contract directory

Barristers

Pupillage directory

Useful information

Managing director	Sinead Dineen	sdineen@GlobeBMG.com
Content manager	Antonio Ignatius	aignatius@GlobeBMG.com
Communications and events coordinator	Bethany Wren	bwren@GlobeBMG.com
Consultant editor	Isla Grant	igrant@GlobeBMG.com
Senior editor	Josh Richman	jrichman@GlobeBMG.com
Deputy editorial services director	Jo Moore	
Business development director	Matthew Broadbent	mbroadbent@GlobeBMG.com
Group directors	Guy Davis, Tony Harriss, Mark Lamb	
Design & production manager	Neal Honney	nhonney@GlobeBMG.com
Design & production	Christian Aspreno	
Printer	Latimer Trend & Company Ltd, Plymouth	
Published by	Globe Business Media Group	
	New Hibernia House, Winchester Walk, London SE1 9AG	
Tel	020 7234 0606	
Email	info@tcph.co.uk	
	Copyright © Globe Business Media Group	
	All rights reserved	
ISBN	978-1-911432-08-1	
ISSN	1741-9395	

While every attempt has been made to ensure the accuracy of this publication, the publishers cannot accept responsibility for any errors, omissions, mis-statements or mistakes.

Further copies of this book can be ordered at www.tcph.co.uk.

Becoming a lawyer

How to use this book

The Training Contract & Pupillage Handbook (TCPH) is designed to be your companion and adviser throughout your journey to becoming a solicitor or barrister. It is important that you use it correctly to derive maximum benefit. You are embarking on a learning process: learning what lawyers do and the different types of law that they practise; learning about the different types of organisation involved in law; learning how to become a lawyer and – possibly most importantly – learning about yourself, what you have to offer the profession and how to sell your skills and personality to employers.

However, you mustn't run before you can walk and we advise you to think about dividing your research and planning into stages. If you complete each one in order, you should have the knowledge and understanding required to make an impact when it comes to recruitment and selection. You should also remember that you need to continually top up your expertise – it's much easier to learn steadily and gradually than try to cram in everything at the last minute.

Stage 1: The basics
A solid base of knowledge is important. Without this, your appreciation of your choices and opportunities will be severely diminished. The "Becoming a lawyer" section of the handbook introduces you to the core challenges ahead of you, while the "Solicitors" and "Barristers" sections explore the two main branches of the profession in more detail. Once you have done this preparatory reading, you should be able to answer the following questions with some authority:
- What are the differences between a solicitor and a barrister?
- Are there other types of lawyer?
- What are the different types of law firm and who do they serve?
- What are the different types of practice area?
- How is a set of chambers organised?

- What is the timetable for becoming a solicitor/barrister?
- Which postgraduate courses will you have to take?
- Which bodies regulate and represent lawyers?
- Why are vacation schemes/placements and mini-pupillages so important?

Stage 2: Getting up to speed
Once you have clearly established what needs to be done, you need to maintain an upward learning curve by regularly immersing yourself in the legal world and behaving, in effect, like a 'mini lawyer'. You need to read information provided specifically for wannabe lawyers such as LawCareers.Net's newsletter, LCN Weekly, but also the professional legal press (eg, *The Lawyer* and *Legal Week*), the national and international business press (eg, the *FT* and the *Economist*) and specialist websites such as LegalFutures.com. In doing so, you should begin to recognise the key news, themes and debates within the profession, see how the different parts of the law relate to each other and identify leading figures and organisations. Check out "The legal scene" in the handbook as a jumping-off point; your ultimate goal is to be sufficiently well informed that you could hold your own in a conversation among lawyers.
- What are the major developments in the legal profession over the last year?
- Have there been any major mergers recently?
- What do you know about new high-street legal brands?

Stage 3: Analyse yourself
Your investigations into the basics of the law and ongoing contact with the profession should already have given you a good idea of the attributes that employers are looking for. The exact skill set may vary, but you can rest assured that you will be expected to be intelligent and able to communicate well, show determination, possess close attention

to detail and operate well as part of a team. You need to review your experiences to pull out as many examples of these skills as possible and work out how to present them in the best possible light – employers like to see examples of go-getting, passionate, motivated people doing something constructive and interesting with their time. Read "Application technique" and "Interview technique" for more advice, and use LawCareers.Net's MyLCN functionality to build up your record of achievements and activities.

- Can you give a dozen concrete, detailed examples of activities in which you have participated that demonstrate skills relevant to working in the legal profession?
- Can you explain why you want to be a lawyer?
- What are the weaknesses in your case that you hope employers won't spot and what are you doing to address them?
- What is your USP?

Stage 4: Narrowing the field

We are only now getting to the stage of differentiating between employers. TCPH offers comprehensive listings of over 850 firms and nearly 200 chambers offering training contracts or pupillages. You can't apply to them all, so you need to refine your search – read "Types of law firm", "Types of chambers" and "Choosing where to apply" as a start. Use the indexing pages to identify firms/chambers by size, practice areas and location. Ideally, you should be able to identify a market sector you are interested in (eg, leading commercial firms in Northwest England) and work out which firms/chambers fall into this classification. Their directory entries in TCPH are your springboard for further research. You then need to look at organisations' own websites, explore legal press archives and indulge in some Google-based digging.

- What are their main work areas?
- Who are their clients?
- How do they make money?
- What is their ethos?
- Who are their competitors?
- Where have they come from and where are they going (ie, history versus ambition)?

What now?

The rest of TCPH expands on many of these themes. The sooner you start using it in earnest – understanding the challenge ahead, making a plan and acting on it – the better your chances. Most candidates who are unsuccessful fail because they have not followed the rules of the game. Do so and you'll be okay!

As ever, we wish you all the very best with your legal career and hope that the handbook can help you along the way. Happy reading!

Remember that you don't need to read this book cover to cover to get maximum benefit from it – it all depends on what path you choose, either before you open TCPH or as you read it. This diagram illustrates the basic process of using TCPH, from initial research to applying for a job – although don't forget that any specific information you need that is not covered by the chapters mentioned elsewhere in the diagram is likely to be in the more specialist chapters of the book. The colour scheme is the same as the colours used to separate each section of TCPH.

First steps
Learn about the legal profession and identify the career you want:

- Solicitor v barrister (p10)
- Alternative careers (p46)
- The legal scene (p14)
- Becoming a solictor (p144)
- The Chartered Institute of Legal Executives (p141)
- Becoming a barrister (p474)

Research
Find out more about the qualifications and work experience you will need for your chosen profession, and learn about different careers available within it:

- Career timetable (p13)
- Work experience (whole section)
- Postgraduate training (whole section)
- Solicitor practice areas (p151)
- Types of law firm (p149)
- Bar practice areas (p483)
- Types of chambers (p480)

Launching your career
Use TCPH for details of how to apply for the right training contract or pupillage for you:

- Choosing where to apply (p25)
- Application technique (p34)
- Interview technique (p39)
- Getting the best careers advice (p19)
- Training contract directory (whole section)
- Pupillage directory (whole section)

Solicitor v barrister

One of the most fundamental questions you must address when considering a career in the law is whether to become a solicitor or a barrister. Simply put, a barrister appears in court, while a solicitor works in a law firm.

However, the differences are much more complex. Some say that it comes down to whether you are an individualist (barrister) or a team player (solicitor). While it is true that a barrister is almost always self-employed and bound to other barristers only by convenience, and a solicitor may be just one worker in a law firm of thousands of people, in reality the situation is less black and white. Barristers are often involved in teamwork and some solicitors may spend many hours on their own drafting documents.

Here's a general guide to some factors which may help you to decide.

Academic performance
Fantastic academic results are the ideal underpinnings of every legal career. You will generally find a pretty close correlation between the best academic scores and the best (or at least the best-paying) jobs in the legal profession. This may be slightly more important for the Bar, as it is smaller and consequently even more selective. The Bar is also probably rather more weighted towards the traditional universities, to which the Oxbridge-heavy tenant lists at many chambers attest (although the Bar is doing its best to address this bias).

Positions of responsibility
Again, having been the head prefect is an impressive achievement whichever strand you choose. However, positions of responsibility are often concerned with keeping hierarchies in order and thus could be described as management training. For this reason, they may be more highly valued by firms of solicitors.

Sporting prowess
Even stevens on this one. Sporting prowess implies drive, teamwork and organisational skills. Some sports may lend themselves better to one branch of the profession or the other (eg, team sports for would-be solicitors) – but really, all are good for both.

Acting/performing
These are highly relevant skills for both branches of the profession. Whether you are a solicitor or barrister, you will be in the business of conveying information and ideas. However, the courtroom side of a barrister's work is a direct application of these attributes, so the Bar may value them slightly higher.

Commercial/business know-how
Whatever you do in the law, you will at some level be involved in running a business – be it as a small cog in a huge firm or as a self-employed person in sole practice or at the Bar. Furthermore, you will often be working to assist the businesses of others. Firms of solicitors no longer provide purely legal advice, but are employed as business advisers with an eye on overall strategy. Barristers are more typically 'hired hands' for advocacy or for preparing highly specific legal opinions, but those at the commercial Bar must still appreciate and prioritise the business interests of their clients when preparing to advocate on their behalf.

Legal work experience
At trainee or pupil level, nobody expects you to know the law inside out. What they do expect is for you to have a relatively sophisticated grasp of the profession, its activities and its rhythms, as a way of showing that you have thought sensibly about why you want to become a lawyer. One of the best ways of doing this is to find a law (or law-related) environment in which you can learn what it's all about.

Eloquence

As we saw above, the ability to communicate is *the* fundamental tool of the trade. The better you are at communicating, the better a lawyer you will be. Again, the fact that a barrister must regularly stand up and talk in court means that this skill is more important at the Bar.

Sociability

The law is a sociable profession in which you can expect to meet large numbers of people from all walks of life. Crucially, you must be able to get on with your clients and other lawyers with whom you work. The legal community is intimate and occasionally incestuous; it helps to be able to fit in and get on. Yes, there are legendary curmudgeons floating around (particularly at the Bar), but don't think it's advisable to become one of them.

Self-reliance

You'll need a fair amount of self-reliance and self-belief whatever you do in law. Solicitors generally have a more definite career structure, but after a certain point it's dog eat dog. As a barrister, though, you are literally on your own: it's your career and you've got to make it happen, make the most of it and deal with the quiet times. If you need more structure, then think again.

Intellectual curiosity

In reality, the area of law in which you end up will be the greatest driver of the intellectual content of your work. However, if you want to be a really serious analyst and provider of opinions on heavyweight points of law, then the Bar may be for you.

Finances

Quite clearly, it is right and proper that a career in the law should be available to all. That said, the relevant tuition fees (especially at postgraduate level) mean that it is not uncommon for individuals to end up with debts of well over £40,000. Before you rack up this kind of bill, be realistic about your job prospects.

Enthusiasm for dressing up

Do you like wearing gowns and wigs? Do you feel that panto should be staged all year round? The Bar values tradition above virtually any calling and the outfits reflect this. Solicitors' dress is, by contrast, dull, dull, dull (even on Fridays).

Commitment to social justice

There remain many commendable organisations and individuals in the legal profession who work tirelessly to beat injustice and ensure that right prevails. Furthermore, the grandest and greatest may well be involved in something socially useful (ie, pro bono). But don't be fooled: the law is an industry like any other and should be treated as such.

Further reading

Solicitors – www.LawCareers.Net/solicitors
Barristers – www.LawCareers.Net/barristers

Reality check: The decision as to which strand suits you best rests on a number of factors concerning your abilities, temperament and – dare we say it – financial circumstances. Choose wisely.

This table illustrates some of the factual differences between the two branches of the profession, including as they relate to demographics, working environments, career progression and salary.

Solicitors	Barristers
As of April 2017, there were 138,280 practising solicitors. The total number of solicitors on the roll was 181,000.	As of July 2015, 82% of barristers (ie, 12,757) were self-employed (not including those in dual practice, registered European lawyers or second six pupils). There were a total of 15,899 practising barristers.
Women make up around 47% of the profession. However, many fewer women than men are currently at partner level – an average split in private practice is 67% male partners compared to 33% female.	Around 35% of all practising barristers are women (ie, 5,660 women compared to 10,239 men).
BAME individuals make up 18% of all solicitors, as well as 18% at partner level.	BAME individuals make up 12% of all practising barristers (ie, 1,891).
Mostly employed in private law firms, so receive regular monthly salary.	Mostly self-employed, so receive irregular (but often substantial) fees.
Work mainly with individuals, companies and barristers.	Work mainly with solicitors and other barristers.
Office-based. Engage more in ongoing advisory and one-to-one client work.	Chambers and court-based. Engage more in one-off advocacy (ie, court cases).
Aspire to become partner (ie, part ownership of firm and entitlement to a percentage of its profits).	Aspire to become Queen's Counsel (QC) (ie, a top barrister, normally instructed in very serious and complex cases).
While there is no longer a minimum annual trainee salary, the average UK salary for a first-year trainee is around £27,000, while City firms pay considerably more – anywhere from £35,000 upwards.	The Bar Standards Board requires that all pupils be paid no less than £12,000 per annum. Many earn much more – upwards of £60,000 in some cases.

Career timetable

Confused about the career path to becoming a lawyer? With the simple career timetable below, there's no need to be!

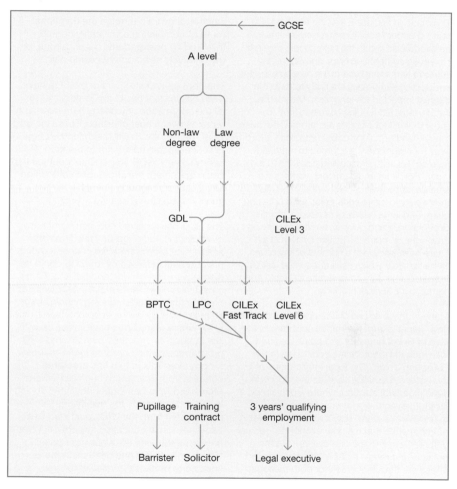

Further reading
For more on the solicitors' career timetable, see p146.
For more on the barristers' career timetable, see p476.
For more on the chartered legal executive timetable, see p141.
For more on legal apprenticeships, pick up a copy of our newest publication, *The Law Apprenticeships Guide*.

The legal scene

A period of radical change is underway across the legal profession and it is set to affect students and aspiring lawyers in several ways. The most immediate is that the teaching and training of both solicitors and barristers is to be overhauled within the next couple of years. However, competition from innovative new entrants to the market and the new possibilities enabled by technology are likely to have the biggest impact in the long term. Meanwhile, cuts to legal aid funding have had time to show their effects: courts are jammed because many members of the public, unable to afford legal representation, are forced to represent themselves, with proceedings slowing to a crawl. Solicitors and barristers working in this area describe their capacity, not to mention their ability to make ends meet, as at breaking point. And large numbers of people, afflicted by circumstance and poverty, are not accessing their rights through the justice system at all. There have also been a number of key cases in the last year which have concerned issues from parliamentary sovereignty, to employment rights, to intellectual property.

Many of these issues divide opinion, from the new 'super-exam' for trainee solicitors to the kind of Brexit deal that should be pursued following the electorate's vote to leave the European Union. The legal implications of the latter are as wide open as ever following June's general election, where a poll aimed at strengthening the prime minister's mandate to negotiate a 'hard' Brexit actually saw the government's thin majority evaporate – a very different result to the one everyone in the political and media establishment predicted. These are turbulent times for both the legal profession and the wider society it serves. Let's start with the most immediate issues facing prospective lawyers.

SQEsy does it?

From 2020, there will be a new assessment called the Solicitors Qualifying Examination (SQE) which all trainee solicitors will have to pass in order to qualify. The exam is being introduced to ensure that all qualified solicitors are of the same high standard whether they train through the traditional route of completing a university degree followed by postgraduate qualifications, or the relatively new apprenticeship path.

The content and structure of the SQE have been made clear (visit LawCareers.Net for all the information you need), but uncertainty remains over a host of issues. These include: what the new exam will mean for the Legal Practice Course (LPC), not to mention potential new 'SQE preparation' courses that could spring up; the affordability of training as a solicitor for young people; and the quality of solicitors' training overall.

The SQE has received criticism from many quarters, including top City law firms and academics. Some firms are concerned that the overhaul heralded by the SQE could be disruptive to their hiring and training. Firms have also voiced fears that the SQE will not provide the specialist training needed to be an effective City lawyer in comparison to the LPC, where many firms have linked up with law schools to offer their own tailored LPC programmes which prepare future trainees for practice. This in turn has prompted concern from academics such as Richard Moorhead, who has argued that introducing the SQE to separate the qualifying assessment from the LPC could lead to a two-tiered legal education system. Moorhead predicted that one tier would be Russell Group universities and other institutions seeking to protect the value of the law degree and LPC to employers, particularly the top law firms which are set to continue favouring traditional training contracts. On the other tier, Moorhead argues, would be all the other education providers teaching prep courses for the SQE. This may actually damage the diversity of the profession more than the current system, as Moorhead points out: "Unless the SQE assessment proves spectacularly successful at upsetting perceptions of law school hierarchy among law firms, then the SQE is likely to enforce a segmentation of the legal education market which will reinforce and exacerbate existing problems within the recruitment market for trainees." What the SQE's ultimate impact will be remains to be seen.

Fewer bars to the Bar?
With the Bar Professional Training Course (BPTC) costing around £19,000 in 2017 and only 39% of those who pass ever going on to become barristers, it is understandable that there have been sustained calls for reform in recent years. The Bar Standards Board's (BSB) Future Bar Training Consultation has been examining ways to make training more affordable and flexible, which it is hoped would make careers at the Bar more accessible to people from diverse backgrounds while maintaining the high standards required.

For now, the BPTC is set to remain in place unchanged, while the future of the Bar Course Aptitude Test (an exam which must be passed in order to be allowed onto the BPTC) has also been guaranteed. However, there could soon be more than one way to train as a barrister, with the BSB considering proposals which could be in place as early as Autumn 2018 – watch this space.

Hale progress
The shaking off of the legal profession's long-held reputation for being dominated by wealthy, privately educated white men is a long, ongoing process, but the past year has seen some good news for all those who don't fit into that extremely narrow demographic. One of the main progressive legal stories of 2017 is that a woman – Baroness Hale – has been elected as president of the Supreme Court for the first time in its history. Hale succeeds the outgoing president, Lord Neuberger, but a new policy of ensuring that a diverse range of candidates are considered for senior judicial roles should hopefully mean that this is just the start. And with three male Supreme Court justices set to reach retirement age in 2018 – Lords Hughes, Mance and Sumption – there may soon be further opportunities to ensure that the judiciary better reflects the society it serves.

Progress has been even more marked in the solicitors' profession, with law firms featuring heavily in gay rights charity Stonewall's Global Workplace Equality Index for 2017. Of the 12 organisations to be celebrated for their work to create inclusive workplaces, five were City firms – Baker McKenzie, Freshfields Bruckhaus Deringer, Herbert Smith Freehills, Pinsent Masons and Simmons & Simmons.

Tech revolution: most in the shell
Big changes resulting from new technology and competition are sweeping both the solicitors' and barristers' professions. In recent years, particularly following the financial crisis in 2008, firms and chambers have been under pressure from clients demanding lower or fixed fees, as opposed to the traditional model of billing by the hour, which is widely perceived as too expensive. This perception was reflected in the reforms to civil litigation rules drawn up by Lord Justice Jackson in 2013, which now mean that lawyers often cannot recoup limitless costs from the other side when they win a dispute as a way of making their work more financially viable – recovered costs and success fees must now be "proportionate" to the matters involved in the dispute.

In turn, technological advancements and their use by innovative new entrants to the legal services market are providing new competitive challenges to the law firm and chambers models, both of which have historically been slow to change with the times. This wider competitive environment, where corporations such as the Co-Op are now able to set up or buy stakes in law firms with funding from other areas of their business, has been facilitated by the profession's regulators, including the Legal Services Board and the Solicitors Regulation Authority, which believe that the legal profession should be run on the same free market principles as any other area of British commerce.

Technological progress also means that many of the tasks that were previously done by trainee and junior lawyers are now automated, with this prompting a number of changes that will directly affect those starting out in their careers over the next few years. Increasing automation, coupled with pressure from clients to keep fees down, means that those firms which keep their trainees busy with admin and low-value tasks will have to think again about their recruitment models – it is becoming simply unviable to take on trainees only to have them spend half their time photocopying or making the tea. Meanwhile in the barristers' profession, the prospect of greater automation and even online courts on the horizon could make it very difficult for junior barristers to secure enough work to make ends meet. In fact, the introduction of online courts, if it happens, would probably fundamentally change the Bar forever. On the other hand, the good news for prospective lawyers is that the training contracts and pupillages available should be, on average, of a higher quality.

One out, one in
The fact that we have had three justice secretaries in just over a year is an indication of the turbulent political times we are in. The latest politician to assume the role of justice secretary is David Lidington, who took over from Liz Truss following the general election in June. Truss was only in post for a matter of months herself after replacing Michael Gove, who in turn was sacked from the cabinet because of his unscrupulous scheming for the Tory leadership following the EU referendum,

when Theresa May became prime minister.

Lidington will hope to weather the storms facing his wider government – Brexit, the economy and social inequality – better than his predecessors, but he also faces acute challenges within his own brief. Perhaps the foremost of these is the state of Britain's prisons, which the president of the Prison Governors Association, Andrea Albutt, has said are in "crisis" due to a "toxic mix of pressures". Albutt's comments in August amounted to an unprecedented intervention from the prison governors' profession, but this is all the more reason to pay attention to her concerns. Prisons are now highly unsafe places for both staff and inmates alike, and the government's refusal to take seriously the increasing problems of overcrowding, violence, instability caused by prisoners and staff being constantly moved, and substance abuse has created a ticking time bomb regarding the likelihood of a major national incident. Many will watch anxiously for whether Lidington will use his position as justice secretary to push the prime minister to do more to tackle the crisis and its costly consequences for society.

Rich man's world
Another issue of huge importance for Lidington and the profession he oversees is legal aid (ie, funding for those who need legal representation but are unable to afford a lawyer themselves). Our justice system is supposed to ensure equality before the law whether you are rich or poor, but in recent years it has actually become more like the Ritz – anyone can go, as long as they have the money to get in. Cuts to legal aid funding have hollowed out and closed law centres across the country, denying the poorest and most vulnerable the access to essential legal services that they need. Meanwhile, more legal aid firms are having to turn down unviable work and many people are now being forced to represent themselves in court with no legal

training, even if the other side can afford a lawyer. Not only does this slow proceedings to a crawl and make the court system wasteful and inefficient; it also raises serious questions about our attitude as a society to justice – particularly whether it is right that those with the deepest pockets should be able to trample over those with very little in a legal system which is supposed to be equal. Many, including the chairman of the Bar and Lord Neuberger, the outgoing president of the Supreme Court, have argued that the situation is so unjust that it requires a complete rethink, with Neuberger saying of legal aid's decline: "Many people [are faced] with the unedifying choice of being driven from the courts or having to represent themselves… [it] verges on the hypocritical for governments to bestow rights on citizens while doing very little to ensure that those rights are enforceable."

Dial M for merger
While 2017 saw the high-profile, ignominious collapse of one law firm – RIP King & Wood Mallesons – it was more notable for a series of major mergers, as firms continue looking to exploit new markets or consolidate their practices. Eversheds merged with US firm Sutherland Asbill & Brennan at the tail end of 2016, giving transatlantic reach to a firm that was already one of the largest in the United Kingdom. And in May there was one of the biggest ever UK legal mergers, as CMS joined with Olswang and Nabarro to create a new 'super firm' (trading simply as 'CMS' for now) of 5,000 lawyers across 39 countries. Elsewhere, DWF launched in France through a merger with Heenan Paris, continuing the firm's expansion outside the United Kingdom, while in the South of England Coffin Mew cemented its position as a regional leader by merging with Charles Lucas & Marshall.

Legal developments – talking points
- While for some the vote to leave the European Union was an opportunity seized and for others it was a monumental act of national self-harm, what is certain is that the legal ramifications of leaving the European Union are highly complex, with relevance to a vast range of practice areas. One development that budding lawyers should keep a close eye on is the so-called 'Great Repeal Bill', which the government is expected to put forward to attempt to bring all the EU laws under which we currently live into English law. In theory, doing this will ensure legal and economic continuity on the day that Britain leaves the European Union, rather than a chaotic legislative void. And once those EU laws are under the sole sovereignty of Parliament, the architects and ideologues of Brexit can go about abolishing and changing those they don't like in a more relaxed fashion.
- In January 2017 the UK government pardoned thousands of gay men who had been convicted under archaic offences which used to criminalise homosexuality. The pardons were made under what has been dubbed 'Turing's law' – after the famous Second World War codebreaker who was later persecuted and chemically castrated by the authorities for having romantic relationships with other men. Like Turing's own pardon in 2013, many of the latest pardons were given posthumously. The pardons represented a welcome step toward equality, but some argued that they did not go far enough – not least because the term 'pardon' intimates forgiveness for some act of wrongdoing, when those convicted under old indecency laws understandably feel that they did nothing wrong.
- The Ministry of Defence (MoD) tabled controversial proposals concerning the concept of 'combat immunity' this year, in response to concerns that a culture has arisen of vexatious legal claims being made against soldiers for their actions on the battlefield. Ostensibly to protect soldiers from such claims, the MoD is expanding the concept of 'combat immunity', where soldiers cannot be held negligent for decisions made in the heat of battle and are

under no duty of care to avoid causing loss or damage to their fellow soldiers or anyone else in combat circumstances. However, the Law Society has argued that the MoD plans would extend combat immunity too far – to situations far removed from or long before actual combat – and are thus designed to prevent a wide range of negligence claims against the MoD being brought through the justice system. For example, it would no longer be possible to prosecute the MoD if inadequate equipment or training is to blame for injury or death. The argument remains highly controversial.

- Conditions in the so-called 'gig economy' have been under major scrutiny, with Uber drivers and Deliveroo drivers both challenging their assigned status as self-employed workers – a status which Uber and Deliveroo are keen to promote so that they don't have to give their workforce any of the employment rights enjoyed by employed workers. A report to the government by Matthew Taylor was pretty damning of these disingenuous practices in the gig economy which are exploiting workers, many of whom earn less than the minimum wage. However, trade unions and other critics have said that the recommendations to reform employment law in the Taylor report are nothing more than tinkering at the edges, and will create more loopholes for unscrupulous operators such as Uber to exploit.

Major cases

- January saw the Supreme Court rule that only Parliament has the power to trigger the Brexit process by invoking Article 50 of the treaty on European Union, which is the process a member state has to go through if it wants to leave. Theresa May and her government had tried to ensure that they could trigger Article 50 without a vote in parliament. However, a legal challenge brought by businessperson Gina Miller led to a court battle, with judges ultimately deciding that the power to trigger Brexit rested with

Parliament, not Theresa May. Some were bemused that the same people who had advocated Brexit to guarantee parliamentary sovereignty were the first to try to bypass Parliament on such a crucial issue.

- The plight of terminally ill baby Charlie Gard attracted worldwide attention as a result of the legal fight between his desperate parents, who wanted to take Charlie to the United States for experimental treatment with a very low chance of meaningful improvement, and his doctors who believed that experimental treatment would prolong his suffering and that Charlie should be allowed to die with dignity. The High Court, Supreme Court and European Court all agreed with the medical professionals, but that did not stop outside interests from interfering, with both Donald Trump and the Pope calling for Charlie to be given the experimental treatment. Charlie's parents eventually agreed not to pursue further treatment after another medical expert was consulted, and Charlie was allowed to die peacefully soon after.

- Digital piracy was struck a grievous blow in June when the Court of Justice of the European Union ruled that the activities of file-sharing sites such as The Pirate Bay constitute copyright infringement, meaning that many such sites could face being shut down.

Looking ahead

With both sides of the legal profession in a state of flux due to various economic, regulatory and social factors, and the entire country at a crossroads as it prepares to negotiate its new – perhaps diminished – place in the world after exiting the European Union, the next 12 months promise to be eventful. Prospective lawyers should pay close attention to the changes on the horizon for legal education and training, but also use their knowledge and critical thinking skills to take in and interpret developments in wider business and politics. Context is everything – especially when you are trying to think like a lawyer.

Getting the best careers advice

They say that forewarned is forearmed, and this is never truer than when you are considering a career in law. You will need the best advice you can get, given that competition for the legal profession is fierce and the outlay is high in terms of both time and money.

It's never too early to seek careers advice. You really do need it from the very beginning in order to be in the know about careers fairs, open days, campus presentations and crucial work placement scheme/mini-pupillage deadlines. Mirrick Koh, head of graduate recruitment and graduate development at CMS, has the following advice: "All the careers advisers I speak to are incredibly committed people with the best interests of the students at heart; but for whatever reason, some students do not use them as effectively as they could."

Available help

We suggest that you use every resource on offer at your university/college careers service in order to be as informed as possible. Usually, resources include:
- details of law fairs with visiting firms of solicitors and postgraduate course providers, and law firm open days;
- a programme of campus visits by firms;
- workshops on applications/CVs and interview technique;
- names of people in the profession who are willing to talk to you (eg, former students who are now practising law);
- up-to-date files on employers;
- information leaflets and brochures;
- recruitment literature for firms and prospectuses for postgraduate courses; and
- copies of the trade press and *The Training Contract & Pupillage Handbook* to keep you abreast of the legal scene.

Your adviser should also be able to give you some individual help with improving your CV, written applications and interview technique (eg, assisting with mock interviews). Careers advisers may also be able to help organise work experience.

Diana Spoudeas, graduate recruitment and development manager at Jones Day, thinks that a career adviser performs a vital role, including offering "practical assistance to help students secure jobs – some great careers services provide one-to-one specialist advice, job opportunities, employer visits and specialist sector knowledge". She does advise, however, against "step-by-step instructions on how to fill in an application form or answer interview questions – too much rehearsal can kill individuality and prevent your true personality from shining through at interview".

Claire Leslie, senior careers consultant at the University of Warwick, has this to say: "Your careers service should usually be able to offer you the following: one-to-one advice to help you decide the direction you should take and when things need to be done; practical help and advice on applications and interviews; and opportunities to meet recruiters. If you are away from campus, you can usually get advice from your careers service by email, telephone or Skype. Use the extensive information available to you – it's never too early to plan your legal career."

Puneet Tahim, senior graduate recruitment and development coordinator at Latham & Watkins, advises playing to your university's strengths: "If a university has a particularly active student law society that manages the recruitment events calendar and has an up-to-date website with information about firms and deadlines, you should become a member. Alternatively, you might attend a university where the careers service manages the events and have all of that information readily available."

Meanwhile, Andrew Pearson, a barrister at 7 King's Bench Walk, advises trying to get help from those already in the legal profession: "Contacts are perhaps the most difficult, but the most useful people to talk to. When you've worked out the basics, ask your careers service whether they can put you in touch with someone who works in a field which interests you. The better the careers service, the more likely they are to be able to do so. This person will be able to give you very useful, focused advice. Make the most of it by working out what you want to know and by following up any help that you get with an appreciative email or note. That way they'll be keen to help you again, or even to put you in touch with other people who might be able to give you advice or assistance."

A significant minority of students don't come to the profession straight out of full-time education. In the first instance, they should contact their local university and see whether they can get careers advice under the mutual aid scheme. Most universities are happy to provide any graduate with a period of assistance – in some cases, up to three years. They may find the careers service particularly useful in terms of obtaining tailored advice on ways to present previous experience to the greatest effect.

❝ Not only make sure that your writing is clear and grammatically correct in your application, but also provide actual evidence for your statements, be yourself at interview and be honest at all times ❞

Last, but by no means least, if you have a problem that's keeping you awake at night, simply log on to www.LawCareers.Net and click on "The Oracle". As its name suggests, this section of the website is the bearer of advice and wisdom. Check out the Oracle's back catalogue of questions (chances are, someone has been troubled by the same issue), and see whether the answers apply to you. If you have an original question, feel free to email us for individual careers advice. Click on "Ask the Oracle" or email oracle@lawcareers.net.

Common advice
Dates and deadlines
Stay clued-up about on-campus events and application deadlines. Laura Newton, a barrister at Brick Court Chambers, says: "Use your university/law school website as a first port of call. You will be able to stay on top of events and deadlines by setting up a Twitter account and following those who provide an active Twitter feed such as LawCareers.Net, Pupillage Blog, your career advice centres and the sets or firms you are interested in."

Puneet says: "It's pretty simple these days to keep on top of deadlines and events, as most firms will heavily publicise these on their own websites as well as on the university careers websites."

Don't rush
Dick Lidwell, freelance careers adviser and former careers adviser at the University of Oxford, advises against panicking if you are still uncertain as to which legal path to take: "If you're not sure whether it's a barrister or solicitor you want to be, don't rush into it. Take the time to explore; you can always come into the system a bit later. There's no point applying until you know, and this is where your careers service comes in. We can help and guide you right from the beginning – don't think that you can only go and see an adviser if you already know what you want to do! Obviously, we're also there to help at the next stage of actually applying: targeting, CVs/ forms and interview technique." Dick's top tips are as follow: "Not only make sure that

your writing is clear and grammatically correct in your application, but also provide actual evidence for your statements, be yourself at interview and be honest at all times."

Got what it takes?
Above all, what you want most from a careers adviser can be summed up in one word – honesty. One London barrister agrees on its importance: "Students should think about whether they stand a realistic chance of obtaining pupillage and forging a career at the Bar. If not, they should seriously consider whether it is worth undertaking the BPTC, with its attendant costs." Any careers adviser worth his or her salt should make it clear that you must have the following qualities and skills (without which you will find getting a training contract or pupillage much more difficult):

- Academic ability – the job is intellectually rigorous and demands that you be capable of clear and lucid thought, and able to process and assimilate large swathes of information. Most top-paying employers require at least a 2:1 degree and excellent A-level grades.
- Interpersonal skills – it is vital that you can interact with colleagues and clients alike to engender confidence, form lasting relationships and clearly explain complex situations.
- Written and oral communication skills – we know that lawyers are famed for their ability to use 20 words when five would suffice, but that is changing. Lawyers spend a large amount of their time talking to clients and drafting documents. The use of clear and

succinct language is appreciated by all.
- Personal responsibility and integrity – be true to yourself.

As an example of what firms are looking for in their prospective trainees, Sarah Stockley, international talent manager and former senior associate at Vinson & Elkins RLLP, says it is all about "good academics, an ability to present well and show knowledge about the firm and the sectors we practise in, and have a personality". On the Bar side of things, Laura highlights the following desirable attributes: "Intellectual ability, written presentational and advocacy skills are key. We will also try to gauge the applicant's motivation to become a barrister and their ability to build a successful practice in our chambers. As we operate in a highly competitive, client-focused industry, commercial awareness and interpersonal skills are crucial to success at the Bar: academic ability alone is not enough."

This brings us to that most crucial of assets: commercial awareness. Almost every recruiter we talked to mentioned this as vital. It is not enough just to know about strict legal principles; you have to be able to apply them to the commercial context within which your clients operate. It may also be important to have a sense of regional commercial issues.

Reality check: If you don't have all of the above qualities and you are considering doing the GDL/LPC/BPTC without the security net of a training contract or pupillage, think very carefully. For some postgraduate institutions, money is the bottom line. Putting it bluntly, they sometimes offer places to students who don't have the remotest chance of getting a training contract/pupillage. As one recruiter said: "Many institutions consider their course a licence to print money, forcing candidates into debt. They allow in students who are unlikely ever to get an interview, let alone pupillage."

Diversity in the legal profession

No one will be surprised to learn that the senior ranks of law firms, barristers' chambers and the judiciary are still overwhelmingly dominated by one particular group of people: white, upper-class men, predominantly public school and Oxbridge educated. Although this is widely acknowledged as a problem for the profession and many firms are attempting to redress the balance, doubts remain as to whether much progress is being made.

The vast majority of law firms have a diversity policy in place to guide their recruitment and promotion behaviours and many use affinity groups, targets and mentors to increase diversity and inclusion. The Bar is likewise making an effort, with its 'No Bar to the Bar' initiative, and with stats confirming that around 25% of pupils in 2014-15 were from a black and minority ethnic (BAME) background. The representation of women on both sides of the profession is also improving, with around 50% of pupils and trainees female. However, while there seems to be no problem attracting women to the law, retaining them is another matter and partners, QCs and judges are still mostly men.

A number of organisations have been set up to help students from underrepresented groups, including Aspiring Solicitors, Pathways to Law, PRIME, RARE, the Sutton Trust and SEO London. Many firms are also committed to making a change; all recognise the benefits to their firms of a diverse workforce. Below are some examples of best practices among firms keen to address the disparities in opportunity.

Gender
Baker & McKenzie was the first major global law firm to appoint a female head when Christine Lagarde became 'madame chairman'. It runs many affinity groups, including BakerWomen. Justine Thompson, inclusion and diversity manager, describes the breakfast event it held to coincide with International Women's Day: "We feel strongly that it is critical to engage everyone in the debate around gender, and the event attracted men and women from all levels of the firm in high numbers."

Disability
Twice winner of the Commendation for Diversity at the LawCareers.Net (LCN) Awards, Shoosmiths has been focusing on disability access, solidifying its commitment to being a government-backed 'Two Ticks' employer, which means interviewing all candidates with a disability who meet the minimum requirements. "We were doing it already, but hadn't been effectively communicating that to students, so made an effort to proactively talk about it," explains Samantha Hope, Shoosmiths' graduate recruitment manager.

Social mobility
The most recent winner of the LCN Commendation for Diversity, Hogan Lovells now uses a contextual recruitment system (CRS) for its vacation scheme and training contract applicants. The CRS tool hardwires social mobility metrics into the firm's existing recruitment system, allowing recruiters to quantitatively and consistently measure applicants' social mobility characteristics.

BAME
As well as setting up a number of ethnicity-specific affinity groups, Latham & Watkins has partnered with RARE, working directly with students from underrepresented minority ethnic groups on their applications. The firm also uses a CRS system to ensure that it "understands the context in which all candidates' experiences have been gained, ensuring that disadvantaged or underprivileged students are not ruled out for reasons of background rather than aptitude and skill".

Aspiring Solicitors

In just three years, diversity platform Aspiring Solicitors has created over 3,000 legal opportunities for its members, resulting in over 700 vacation schemes and training contracts. The organisation has three key objectives: to provide free increased access, opportunities and assistance to aspiring solicitors from all underrepresented groups; to educate and inform the next generation of the legal profession about the importance of diversity; and to promote and increase diversity within the profession. We interviewed Chris White, founder of Aspiring Solicitors, to get his thoughts on the current state of diversity in law.

What is the main aim of Aspiring Solicitors?

The three points above are key, but our ultimate goal is for there no longer to be a need for us to exist – that is the dream scenario! However, that is several years away, so our medium-term goal is to ensure that we are assisting individuals from underrepresented groups to penetrate the barriers that have created a very narrow pool of individuals getting to the top of the legal profession.

Why do you think the legal profession been slow to embrace the importance of diversity?

I think it would be easier to say what we have done wrong as a profession for many years, but I prefer to try to look forwards rather than backwards. The encouraging observation from our perspective is that more and more firms are joining Aspiring Solicitors and are consequently committing to increase diversity in the legal profession through working with us and our members.

What are some of the barriers those from underrepresented backgrounds face?

The most common theme running through all the groups is a lack of confidence – whether as a result of social background, such as having gone to a state school; or a disability that they're not confident about disclosing; or they're LGBT and don't want to come out to an employer. The perception is that difference is a negative, but we want to change that perception. We know that differences are what make us unique and can add value to client relationships.

How should firms ensure that their diversity policies have practical effect rather than just good intentions?

The firms that are making headway are those that reflect an increase in diversity throughout the firm – so not just graduates, but also mid and senior-level lawyers. If more firms were willing to publish their figures, students would have a better chance of recognising the leaders. No law firm is perfect in every way, but it is positive to see more firms referencing their results and improvements. Telling stories about successful experiences is also key.

Why should firms seek to attract a wide range of trainees?

Commercially, diversity is key. Law firms are businesses, so the central concern is how to be most profitable – keeping clients happy is part of that. Clients are extremely diverse and consequently you need a diverse legal team for them to relate to. You are also ensuring that you're fishing for candidates from an ocean rather than a pond; you're not going to get the best candidates if you restrict your pool.

Further reading:

- Diversity access schemes - www.LawCareers.Net/MoreLaw/ DiversityAccessSchemes
- Gender diversity – www.LawCareers.Net/ Information/Features/10052016-Feminist- lawyers-the-fight-for-gender-equality-in- the-legal-profession
- Aspiring Solicitors – www.aspiringsolicitors.co.uk

Don't miss a deadline!

The most comprehensive list of training contract deadlines is available on **LawCareers.Net**

www.LawCareers.Net/Solicitors/TrainingContractDeadlines

LawCareers.Net™

Choosing where to apply

Don't even think about applying to a law firm or set of chambers until you have figured out your own criteria for applying and done the relevant homework. The trick isn't to apply to loads of firms aimlessly in the hope that you will strike lucky with one. Similarly, don't follow the herd. Rather, identify the sort of organisation that you want to work for and then target those that fit the bill. Lucie Rees, graduate manager at Watson Farley & Williams LLP, advises the following: "Think about the opportunities you want during your training contract – for example, practice areas, client exposure and international seats. Many firms will offer you what you want, so one key thing to look at to help you narrow down your shortlist is the culture of the firm – is it somewhere you see yourself enjoying your time at work?"

What type of law?

Many firms and chambers specialise in one or more areas of law (eg, family, banking or media). They are pretty proud of this fact and a pet peeve is when applicants fail to mention the specialism or, worse, get it entirely wrong. In other words, don't write to a firm that is known for its family law expertise saying that you want to be a banking lawyer. The head of graduate recruitment at one City firm says: "What drives me insane is when applicants talk about a practice area we don't have – for example, 'your thriving media practice'. It comes across as sloppy and badly researched." So it pays to match your comments to the firm – achievable only by doing your research.

Meanwhile, Natalie Connor, a barrister at 11KBW, has this advice for those hoping to join the Bar: "Apply to places where members practise in the areas you are interested in. Many sets will advertise themselves as full service, when in reality they deal almost exclusively in one or two specialist areas. A good way of finding out what those areas are is to look at the 'news' and 'recent cases' section of each chambers' website to get an idea of the high-profile cases members are involved in."

Think about what broad sort of lawyer you want to be: do you see yourself as a human rights barrister? A commercial solicitor? A criminal lawyer spending lots of time in police stations? Or something else altogether? As an example, let's say that you want to be a human rights barrister – the best way of going about the application process is as follows:

- First, find out which sets specialise in human rights law (a search of www.LawCareers.Net and the legal directories at your careers centre will give you this info).
- Next, notice what is particularly special or exciting about the set and what separates it from its rivals (so look on its website to see whether there is a particular line of cases or a niche area of law that its tenants are developing).
- Finally, see whether you match the criteria that the set asks for from applicants. Be realistic – if it asks for applicants with a first, you are not going to get in with a 2:2.

If you meet all the criteria and the set has grabbed your interest, you should apply. Otherwise, keep looking, using the same step-by-step guide. This approach applies equally to other sets, law firms and practice areas.

However, it is generally important to keep an open mind about the exact area into which you will ultimately qualify. You won't know what you truly enjoy until you actually get some experience under your belt as a trainee or pupil, so don't narrow your focus too early, especially in your applications. If you have no idea about what you want your specialism to be, focus on getting into a firm or set that offers a well-rounded training contract/pupillage. Also, focus on firms and sets that offer a variety of seats and experience, and that have a good reputation generally (so scan the trade press for positive/negative coverage as well as looking at the glossy recruitment literature).

Where do I want to work?

Once you have figured out the sort of firm or set you want to target, you need to consider whether you'll be happy with the location. It's no use applying to a firm in the City if you don't like London; your heart won't be in it and this will be apparent at interview.

Often, regional firms prefer applicants with local connections. This is because they will be investing a lot of money in their trainees and, not unreasonably, they want to see a good return on their investment. In asking whether an applicant has local connections, they figure that those with ties to an area are less likely to leave for greener pastures after the training contract ends.

Also, regional firms want to be sure that you are not applying to them just because the London firms have passed you over. As one partner of a Yorkshire firm explains: "Does a candidate who has attended a prep school in Sussex, attended the University of Sussex and always lived in Sussex seriously expect us to believe that he or she wishes to move to Scunthorpe? There's clearly no long-term commitment and we've received the application for a training contract only because the candidate has been rejected by every practice in the Southeast."

What sort of working environment?

Many students find it difficult to distinguish between the different types of firm. However, many recruiters also talk about the need for students to have some idea of the culture of a firm, and whether it will match their needs and personalities. Puneet Tahim, senior graduate recruitment and development coordinator at Latham & Watkins, says: "It can be challenging for students to differentiate between firms, as many offer high-quality work. Students should

therefore consider which other factors will influence their experience as a trainee. These may include the size of the firm; if you are interested in multi-jurisdictional work, secondments or using any additional language skills, then a firm with offices in many jurisdictions could be for you."

Martha Jeacle, legal recruiting and associate development manager at Davis Polk & Wardwell London LLP, makes this point: "It is important to look at the size of the trainee intake. Being one of 100 as opposed to one of four will offer a very different experience, and each individual needs to decide what will work best for them. I also suggest that students find out what kind of training programme is in place for trainees, as a comprehensive formal training programme will ensure a more well-rounded period of training."

However, it is possible to generalise broadly about firms and chambers. For example, types of firm might broadly be categorised as international/City, national/regional and legal aid/general practice. For an in-depth explanation of what trainee life at each of these might be like, see "Types of firm" on page 149.

As for barristers' chambers, they can broadly be split into those that are in Central London and specialise by practice area – such as commercial, public law, common law and crime – and those in the regions, including the 'supersets'. Brian Lee, practice development and marketing director at 7 King's Bench Walk, says: "Students should make sure that the pupillage being offered is constructive and properly managed. A pupil supervisor should not only manage the workload for the pupil, in terms of who the pupil works for and when, but should also act as mentor. The pupil supervisor should also ensure that the pupil is not overworked. It is incumbent on all chambers to ensure that the pupil provides their best work for those they work for so that informed decisions can be made when a vote on tenancy is taken.

Students should make sure they know what is being provided before they apply."

Matthew Parker, barrister at 3 Verulam Buildings, says: "Bear in mind the differences in day-to-day practice at different parts of the Bar. For some kinds of barrister, the emphasis is on regular court work; for others, the volume of paperwork is much larger. And choose an area of law in which you have a genuine interest."

Sarah Stockley, international talent manager and former senior associate at Vinson & Elkins RLLP, urges students not to be swayed by the decisions of their contemporaries: "Students should ignore where their peers are looking to apply – what suits one person will not necessarily suit another." Laura Newton, a barrister at Brick Court Chambers, says: "Try to get a feel for different sets yourself, rather than relying solely on their reputation or word of mouth. You may find that a day or a week in chambers gives a completely different impression of a set from your preconception." For an in-depth explanation of what a pupil's life at each of these might be like, see "Types of chambers" on page 480.

What other factors are important?
When considering applying for a training contract or pupillage, you might also want to bear in mind the following factors:
- the nature of the training programme or pupillage;
- the way you will be treated as a trainee/pupil;
- the firm or set's overall reputation in the legal market;
- any awards received (www.LawCareers.Net has a list of firms recognised for training and recruitment);
- any impending changes such as mergers that may affect the firm or set's future;
- any financial help offered during postgraduate training;
- trainee/pupil retention rates;
- the firm or set's client base;
- the salary on offer and any benefits; and
- future opportunities and remuneration.

Caroline Lindner, global communications lead and former trainee recruitment manager at Norton Rose Fulbright, suggests not being too swayed by the much-touted "work-life balance" factor: "All lawyers work very hard and you will work long hours at times, so you need to accept this. Some firms, however, are better at encouraging their trainees to get involved with pro bono, social activities, sports teams and so on, so you should look at this aspect if it's important to you." Equally, don't be entirely swayed by salary, as Fiona Medlock, graduate recruitment manager at Mills & Reeve LLP, wisely urges: "A higher salary might be attractive but look at the long-term prospects and quality of training too."

Many firms and chambers will hold events at your university/college campus, such as workshops or seminars and/or social occasions at which you can learn about their working culture. You can also view graduate recruitment videos, browse their websites, attend open days and go on work placement schemes and mini-pupillages.

Michelle Ruddle, recruitment marketing manager at Hogan Lovells, explains that your first step must be to seriously analyse and think carefully about what you want from your career: "Ask yourself questions, such as: 'Why do I want to be a lawyer?'; 'What kind of work environment suits me?'; 'What motivates me?'; and 'What appeals to me about international, regional or niche firms?'"

With that in mind, let's leave you with a quick-fire checklist for easy reference:
- Type – commercial or high street?
- Size – law factory or local firm?
- Focus – highly specialised or a wide range of clients/practice areas?
- Location – London or regional?
- 'Feel' – pressured or relaxed?

Key competencies

Most legal recruiters want broadly the same thing – to hire excellent lawyers – and all look for key competencies when hiring to help identify who those potential recruits might be. It follows, therefore, that the trick to landing a training contract or pupillage is showing recruiters that you have as many of those key skills as possible.

So what does a successful lawyer look like? Different roles within the profession will place varying emphasis on the following skills, but you can be confident that all are extremely desirable when you are being assessed for suitability. Here, we take a look at the many ways you can sell yourself to recruiters and demonstrate that there are plenty of ways to identify the attributes that you have and that employers want.

Academic ability

Lawyers are involved daily with challenging material and work that stretches their intellectual capabilities. They need to have the mental capacity to process complicated information, draw inferences and form conclusions. Inevitably, your academic results are used by recruiters as the main indicator of your intellect; having impressive A levels and being on track for at least a 2:1 is a great first step (although be aware that this alone is no longer enough to distinguish you from the thousands of others who have also done well).

How to demonstrate: The obvious answer is your school and university performance – it is likely to be the first thing that a prospective employer looks at. Your results need to be good; don't shy away from highlighting the grades that show you off in the best possible light. For career changers, whose exam results are far in the past and don't necessarily reflect their current skills and experience, evidence of professional achievements and qualifications is valuable. Another way to prove your brainpower is to talk coherently about current affairs, showing that you have background knowledge, can understand context and draw rational conclusions.

Determination

Getting a job in the legal profession is much tougher than it used to be and a healthy dose of ambition is crucial to success. But securing a training contract or pupillage is just the beginning – the hard work and pressure really begin at that point, so you have to be able to show that you're the type of person who is determined to make it as a successful lawyer and can take the sustained heat.

How to demonstrate: Achievements of the highest order, ideally involving physical discomfort (eg, fell running, open water swimming, tractor pulling or playing the bagpipes) or tenacious perseverance. If there is anything you've done in the past that you can't quite believe you managed to do, mention it.

Attention to detail

A slipshod lawyer is a bad lawyer. Legal professionals must work accurately and concisely, spot and resolve mistakes, and go over everything with a fine-tooth comb. Proofreading is something that comes naturally to lawyers, as almost every element of the job involves accurate written work.

How to demonstrate: The best way to prove your eagle-eyed credentials is to produce a flawless and typo-free application form. Check, check and check again! Within your form, you could describe a computer program that you have written featuring thousands of lines of code, any one of which could have stopped it working; or discuss your organisation of a football league, including fixtures, results, pitch allocation and player registration. These are just two examples though – plenty of things require organisation and attention to detail, from managing the till behind a bar to taking a stock check.

Communication

Legal work is all about conveying advice. You need to prove that you can listen to what others say and ask of you, and communicate your thoughts and opinions effectively. After all, there's no point in being a genius if you can't express legal concepts to colleagues and clients.

How to demonstrate: We all communicate, all the time, so you should not be short of examples, but look for those where your communication skills made a material difference to a situation. These might include running a campaign (eg, student elections) involving written and oral communication, examples of journalism in which you present complicated ideas simply or debating and mooting.

Teamwork and leadership

In the law, teams are everything – while there is much solo work to be done, even the lone wolves (eg, top barristers) perform within the context of a team in which everyone contributes to the whole. You must be committed to working this way and, again, you've probably done more of this than you think – teamwork is how society functions.

How to demonstrate: Remember that we are talking about teamwork and leadership; show where you have led, but also show where you have bowed to the will of the group. Sports teams are the obvious examples, but any communal activity where different tasks contribute towards a shared goal can be used: orchestras and bands, clubs, Duke of Edinburgh, science projects or team debating.

Commercial awareness

Commercial awareness boils down to understanding individuals' or businesses' motives for acting in the way that they do. If you cannot understand your clients' motivations, goals and constraints, your advice on how they should act will be worthless. Furthermore, the place you will practise law is a business, be it a multinational corporation or a high-street firm. Your role within it will have a direct relationship to it achieving its goals.

How to demonstrate: Experience in the working world will come in handy here, as you are likely to have worked for a company of some sort and experienced how it functions from the inside. Talk about real-life business scenarios in which you have been involved, no matter how junior or peripheral you were. Demonstrate that you have followed commercial and business stories in the press over a protracted period and can comment on why a business or sector is expanding/contracting/changing.

Chances are, you will already have many of the above skills and the tough part may be coming up with the evidence to support your claims. Most of the examples above are drawn from the academic and extracurricular field. However, the richest pickings may well come from the work and work experience you have encountered. So, determine your goal (finding a career in law); take a body of material (you and your life); analyse it against a set of criteria (the skills that employers seek); and present your findings clearly and economically (make an application). Within your LawCareers.Net MyLCN account, the MySelf tool allows you to do this in a systematic fashion. The same applies to other activities; break them down and look for the nuggets of achievement and insight that demonstrate and have developed your skills.

Commercial awareness

Commercial awareness is one of the key skills that law firms look for in future trainees. This basically involves understanding the environment in which the firm and its clients operate, and then using your legal expertise to help both achieve their goals. To succeed in the law, you will need to demonstrate that you can think in this way.

To persuade a recruiter of your commercial awareness, you need to develop a genuine interest in the business world. Without this, you are unlikely to enjoy a career in commercial law or properly understand what your clients want to achieve. Even if you intend to train as a private client lawyer, you need to be able to speak the language of clients who are themselves business owners. Candidates who can enthusiastically engage with the vicissitudes of commerce prove themselves to have the potential to develop new client relationships, and perhaps even new legal products and services, further down the line. In short, they represent a safer investment.

What is it?

In a nutshell, commercial awareness is an understanding of the business environment within which a law firm and its clients operate. For commercial lawyers, it involves the ability to understand a client's business needs so that the legal advice you provide is constructive and tailored to achieving those aims. Whichever area of law you decide to go into, you will need to demonstrate that you can help drive your firm's business forward, beyond just securing your training contract. To break things down, you will need to show that you understand the importance of client relationships and the need for businesses to be cost effective. A commitment to your firm's strategic vision and a solid grasp of market factors (internal and external) are essential. With this in mind, you will need to show that you can:

- manage your time effectively;
- demonstrate initiative;
- work well within a team;
- develop strong client relationships; and
- demonstrate a good understanding of current economic conditions and in-depth legal knowledge.

Learning more

To this end, it is important to focus on the word 'awareness', and not mistake it for the word 'knowledge'. Remember that you are going to be a trainee and are not expected to know everything about the law firm or its clients' businesses from day one.

Commercial awareness for a future lawyer might sensibly be split into two categories: factors that relate to law firms as businesses themselves and factors that affect the clients for which they work. In the first category, prospective trainees should have at least a basic understanding of the purpose of the Legal Services Act 2007 and a general understanding of what a partnership is and how law firms are traditionally structured. A sense of how legal work and clients are sourced and charged is also helpful. For those keen to work at international law firms, an understanding of what the firm's network looks like and why it is shaped in this way is essential. This is easier if you have a reasonable understanding of the global economic landscape. What are the BRICS? What is an emerging market? What have been the consequences of the 2008 financial crisis for businesses and regulators? What caused that financial crisis? Why has austerity been the watchword of the decade in the United Kingdom so far? Has it really been an effective response to an ailing economy in comparison to the different approaches taken in countries such as the United States? And what about Brexit – with negotiations now underway, will it be possible for the United Kingdom to introduce stricter immigration controls and still access the single market? These topics are covered extensively in the mainstream media, often in great detail.

Radio: BBC R4 and the World Service	
Today programme	*Today* is the most influential news programme in the United Kingdom and sets the political agenda each morning. If you want to quickly build awareness of current affairs in politics, business and society, then listen to this.
The World Tonight	Broad coverage of international news and business.
The Bottom Line	Evan Davis's roundtable interviews get to the heart of business thinking.
Peter Day's World of Business	Veteran business journo Peter Day's show includes on-the-ground stories from around the world.
Today in Parliament	Learn how decisions in Parliament affect and are affected by the wider economy and the Overton window (look it up).
World Business Report	Daily stories from around the globe.
PM	Eddie Mair takes an irreverent, but probing look at the day's issues – excellent journalism and interviews with leading figures.
The World at One	One of BBC R4's main flagship news and current affairs programmes, along with *Today* and *PM*.
TV	
Channel 4 News	The hour-long show allows time for special reports to explain issues more deeply – by far the best news journalism on British TV.
Bloomberg TV	*Bloomberg West* is a tech-focused one-hour show, bringing all the news from Silicon Valley.

BBCs 1 and 2	The BBC's business and economics team contributes regularly to BBC News and also has blogs and stories on the BBC website. Look out for reports and blogs from Kamal Ahmed, and follow him on Twitter. Tune in to *The Andrew Marr Show* for interviews with leading figures from politics and business (or its ITV rival, *Peston on Sunday*). The Beeb also makes some good one-off documentaries/short series about world economics and business.
Press	
The Economist	Try discounted trial or student subscription for full access, or choose your limited free reads carefully. The app is free to download.
The Telegraph	Partial paywall. Many people (even lefties) really rate the Saturday edition.
The Times	Pesky pay wall! *The Times* law supplement is published on Thursdays.
Financial Times	Paywall (can read some material free). Good international features and interesting opinion pieces.
Guardian	The *Guardian* law section used to be very well regarded, although there are claims of a slip in quality since it lost its dedicated team of writers. But there's no paywall!
Reuters	Heavy on the financial markets and good for fast news reports.
Wall Street Journal	Interesting to read about European issues from another perspective.
BBC News website	Pitches many stories at the non-expert, but this can be really helpful.

However, a last-minute skim of the *Financial Times* before your interview will be of limited use. You should set yourself a routine and then stick to it, so that you can develop a genuine interest and a knack for spotting themes and trends. You will eventually be able to see things from a businessperson's perspective and develop a bigger-picture understanding of the impact of events. In short, you will adopt the media habits of a good legal professional before you become one.

On the previous page are some recommendations of good places to start learning.

Past experiences

Another way of assessing your commercial awareness is to think about what you already know. Consider your employment history and see whether you can identify any previous examples of commercial work experience. For example, have you worked in a service environment? Did you gain insight into how the business you were working within was run? Have you ever undertaken a specific project or devised a solution to a business problem? Was there a particular challenge that you had to overcome?

❝ Commercial awareness is an understanding of the business environment within which a law firm and its clients operate ❞

It is not only your employment history that counts as commercial work experience. Positions of responsibility can also demonstrate the necessary skills. Did you belong to any societies at university and if so, what was your role? For example, if you were the treasurer of a sports club, this can be used to demonstrate your ability to manage finances and budgets.

Not-for-profit work can also be used to demonstrate commercial awareness as, depending on your role, you may have been involved in promoting events or persuading companies to sponsor you or provide free products. These activities help to show that you have an understanding of basic business processes. Working in the family business or setting up and managing your own business (including online) can all point to commercial nous, as there is no better way to understand the fundamentals of a business than by running one yourself.

New experiences

In addition to looking at what you have done already, you may want to increase your commercial awareness by undertaking some useful employment while you study or after you have finished your degree or Legal Practice Course. The first step is to assess yourself. Consider the area of law that you wish to practise, the type of firm you want to work in and any skills which you may be lacking. Next, work out where you could gain the skills that may be relevant to your firm of choice. For example, if you are interested in banking or corporate finance, then consider gaining experience in a corporate setting (eg, an accountancy firm or tax office).

Commercial thinking can be developed in any employment setting, particularly if your role allows you access to the rationale for decisions made by your employer. For example, in the publishing industry, you might learn about the challenges faced by print media in light of the growth of online journalism. If you work in retail, logistics or warehousing during your holidays, you could develop an understanding of, say, the seasonality of demand or just-in-time purchasing principles.

Another option is to consider the types of client that you might be dealing with in a corporate law firm and try to gain some experience with those (eg, in a bank or financial institution). If you can gain insight into how potential clients run their businesses, this will be a strong selling point at interview. Alternatively, think about how a corporate firm is run and the skills you would need to work there (ie, working on large, complex deals as part of a large team). Use this basic idea to think laterally about other organisations which would allow you to work in the same way (eg, insurers or finance houses).

Ultimately, what matters is that you learn about and understand the environments in which you work. Even positions which appear very low level can produce great commercial insight. It just depends how you look at it and how well you can explain your understanding to a potential recruiter.

For more on developing commercial awareness, head to LawCareers.Net for weekly commercial news roundups, in-depth features and tailored advice from its Oracle email service. In particular, make sure you bookmark LCN's Commercial Question section, where each week solicitors from a different commercial or corporate firm analyse a topical issue from a commercial-legal perspective. Commercial Questions examine everything from intellectual property, to trends in international M&A, to the employment law implications of the gig economy, so reading them will help you to start thinking like a lawyer on a whole range of matters.

Commercial Question

Develop your business awareness

www.lawcareers.net

Application technique

By the time it comes to applying, you should have thoroughly researched the profession and know where it is that you want to apply. Wherever that is, mention why you are attracted to the firm or chambers in question (ie, the special/exciting things that you've found out about it after following our advice in the previous chapter), and how your skills and qualities match what they are looking for.

Andrew Campbell, a barrister at Queen Elizabeth Building and the current secretary to the pupillage committee, explains why your application is such a crucial step in the process: "An application form is in many ways a form of written advocacy. The case the candidate is presenting is why they should be offered a pupillage or mini-pupillage. Every question must be seen as an opportunity to impress, rather than a hurdle to overcome. The best answers will be like any good argument in court and will support the case with strong evidence."

Bear in mind the need to apply to a manageable number of firms or chambers. Ten well-researched and considered applications will serve you far better than 100 randomly fired-off CVs. Read on for targeted advice that will help you to create just such an application.

What's in a name?

Quite a lot, actually. Imagine how peeved you would be if you received a letter from a firm offering a training contract to someone else. Firms and chambers take offence when you get their name wrong. One graduate recruitment partner at a regional firm recalls a student who "sent an application and covering letter for a training contract stating that 'I would love to work at Withers.' Wrong firm!" Don't make this amateurish mistake. And don't take it upon yourself to change the name of the firm by shortening it – Caroline Lindner, global communications lead and former trainee recruitment manager at Norton Rose Fulbright, says: "Along with spelling and grammatical errors, abbreviating the name of the firm should be avoided at all costs." Equally, don't be the applicant who admitted to one City firm, on being called for interview, that "she couldn't remember applying to us – we were not impressed!". Keep a handle on which firms you apply to.

Timing

Many firms and chambers look to fill their training places two years in advance. For law students, this means applying during the summer vacation between the second and third year of your law degree. Non-law students should apply before starting the GDL.

While budding solicitors should apply directly to firms for training contracts, the recruitment process for the Bar is different. Certain applications must be made through the centralised online pupillage application system, the Pupillage Gateway (www. pupillagegateway.com). See "Training as a barrister" for further details.

Some smaller organisations accept applications just one year in advance. If you have left your application late or were unsuccessful in your first round of applications, use the "Jobs" section of www.LawCareers.Net to source up-to-date information and availability.

Many recruiters mention the importance of applying well before the official closing date: first, so you don't have to rush to get the application done; second, because the most popular firms may well fill their quota of trainees before the deadline. Mirrick Koh, head of graduate recruitment and graduate development at CMS, says: "Know your deadlines and find out whether the firm you are applying to recruits on a rolling basis, as this could influence when you submit your application." The message here is clear – don't let it go down to the wire.

Presentation

An application may be the first contact that you

have with prospective employers. Make a good impression by convincing them that you have the necessary skills, experience, qualifications and enthusiasm for the job in question.

Make sure that you know how the firm or chambers wants you to apply – the vast majority use online application forms, although some may still prefer CV and covering letter. Where possible, obtain the name of the person to whom your application should be addressed. Don't just send in a CV when the firm or chambers clearly wants you to tackle its application form.

We can't stress enough that the best applications are tailored to each individual firm or chambers. Tell a firm or set why you are choosing to apply to it rather than any of its competitors. Most recruiters complain about applications that are littered with misspellings and puffery about the nature of the organisation. A head of chambers in the Southeast agreed: "We had an application from someone allegedly impressed by 'the ethos of our set and the fact that it had kept it touch with its roots'. Our advice? Don't write guff like that on your applications. Flattery will get you nowhere – it's just padding and it doesn't impress."

Puneet Tahim, senior graduate recruitment and development coordinator at Latham & Watkins, adds: "Candidates should avoid using broad statements such as, 'I am a good team player, with excellent communication skills who is extremely ambitious and driven'. All these are valued skills and attributes, but you need evidence to back up your claims. You would be better placed to talk about a particular activity you are involved in and explain all of the skills you have developed as a result. Keep it simple and avoid unnecessary jargon. When you consider the volume of applications a firm receives, it's important to focus on the key information you want to convey. Don't use 10 words when five will suffice."

Competition is stiff and some firms and chambers receive thousands of applications for just a few places – never more so than in the current climate. Don't give recruiters the easy option to eliminate you from their lists – so no spelling mistakes, grammatical errors or casual language. And get someone who can spell to check the final version (errors through familiarity and repetition creep in otherwise). Alix Balfe-Skinner, HR manager at Taylor Vinters, says: "Attention to detail is everything – small things such as making sure you use capitals in the correct places are crucial. It makes an application seem more professional and as though more time and care has been taken."

Here are a few more top tips from recruiters:
- "Spelling and grammar are absolutely vital. Ask someone else to read through your form for you to check it makes sense. Copy and paste the text into Word and apply spellcheck. If you haven't got anyone to check it for you, review it. Leave it for a couple of hours then review again with fresh eyes before submitting" – Danielle White, graduate recruitment and development manager at Mayer Brown International.
- "Bear in mind that graduate recruiters will know little or nothing about you before receiving your application form. By the end of each form, candidates should have explained why they want to be a solicitor, why they are applying to that particular firm and why they feel the firm should hire them" – Puneet Tahim, Latham & Watkins.
- "You must check your spelling – otherwise it just looks sloppy. Where there is a word count, make sure that you are succinct. It's all about attention to detail and presentation, which is of course what we're looking for in our future lawyers – we wouldn't send out something with mistakes in it to a client" – Caroline Walsh, former head of legal trainee recruitment and development, Clyde & Co LLP.
- "Think carefully about what is distinctive about a particular set of chambers or area of

practice and explain why that interests you. You should also identify what is distinctive about you and why you should be picked above the other candidates" – Matthew Parker, barrister, 3 Verulam Buildings.

- "Be interesting, but not contrived. Interviewers have to read dozens of these forms. The more you can engage them, the better – but don't try to do so artificially. And be positive; being negative about anything on your application form can create a bad impression" – barrister at leading London set.

Application forms

Many students struggle with the open-ended or competency questions on application forms. These questions vary, but tend to focus on teamwork, problem solving, communication and judgement (eg, "Outside of your studies, describe a situation where you have worked with a group of people to achieve a goal"). As a rule, the best answers are as significant and unique to you as possible, easy to discuss at interview and relevant to the job. Tackle the question by breaking it down into the situation or context, the task or problem faced and the outcome or result.

Make sure that you read instructions very carefully. Don't be like this candidate for a regional firm: "We ask people to list their strengths and weaknesses. One student obviously did not read the question properly and listed her strengths as being 'honest, competent and hardworking' – so far, so good – but unfortunately went on to list her weaknesses as 'dishonest, incompetent and lazy'. Needless to say, she was not invited for an interview."

And keep an eye on word limits, as one barrister advises: "Brevity is key; don't waste words on things that are irrelevant, so abstract as to lack sense or by trying to be funny. Save your humour for interviews." Naomi Winston of Ten Old Square agrees: "Don't write reams and reams, just because you can – remember that someone has to read your application

(and maybe a couple of hundred others, too)."

Don't underestimate the amount of time it takes to complete an application form (hours rather than minutes). Plan to do them well in advance and don't leave it to the last minute on deadline day to submit. Lucie Rees, graduate recruitment & development manager at Watson Farley & Williams LLP, suggests "saving the form as you go along – there's nothing worse than spending hours doing something only for a technical hitch to mean you have to do it all again". Always read through the entire form, including the small print, which may contain important instructions; and practise on a photocopy of the form first. It may be time consuming, but it is crucial to approach each application individually, back up your work regularly and avoid the temptation to copy and paste. Michelle Ruddle, recruitment marketing manager at Hogan Lovells, says: "Tailor your answers; don't just copy and paste content from another application form, as you may end up referring to the wrong firm name in error, which shows lack of attention to detail. You should also have someone else check your application form before you click 'submit' to pick out any grammatical or spelling mistakes."

And while some recruiters say never copy and paste under any circumstances, others accept that you probably will, so take some advice on how to do it successfully, such as from this London barrister: "Be careful when copying and pasting. It saves time, but you won't endear yourself to a set if you are obviously describing how much you want to join their main rival." Similarly, Laura Newton of Brick Court Chambers says: "If you must copy and paste, do so with care! Make sure that the 'variable' parts get updated and that the text fits in with the rest of the form."

Covering letters

Unless the employer's instructions state otherwise, you should send a short covering letter with the application form (or CV). A covering letter gives you the opportunity to highlight your unique selling points, provide extra information in support of your application and convey your motivation for the job. The golden rule of covering letters is to keep them brief – no longer than one A4 page. The first paragraph should mention the position that you are applying for, the year of entry and, if it was advertised, where you saw the vacancy. The second paragraph should say why you want to work for the firm or set and what you can offer it. The third paragraph should close on a positive note, saying you look forward to hearing from the recruiter at his or her convenience, with your mobile number and any dates on which you are unavailable for interview.

Never write a standard covering letter to accompany all of your applications. 'Dear Sir or Madam' will not do. Be sure to tailor each letter to the firm/chambers to which you are applying. Clarity, neatness and courtesy are all equally important.

CVs

If one of your target firms or sets requires a CV rather than its own form, use this to your advantage. Unlike application forms, a CV gives you the chance to create your own personal record of achievements in a format that you control. The content of your CV should comprise the following.

- Personal details – include your name, address, telephone number and email address. Nationality and date of birth are optional.
- Education and qualifications – set out your most recent achievements in detail. Recruiters are more interested in how you performed in your year-end exams than how good you were at GCSE metalwork.
- Work experience/employment history – use reverse chronological order. Show the dates of work experience, including the name of the employer and the town/city it is based in. Mention any work experience, including any voluntary and seemingly less relevant jobs – for example, bar work can be sold as demonstrating your ability to perform a customer/client-facing role under pressure.
- Other skills and interests – non-academic skills include leadership, teamwork, flexibility, judgement, commercial awareness, imagination, adventurousness and diligence. They are often best illustrated and reflected through cultural, social, sporting, travel and independent activities and hobbies. But remember: the facts must ultimately support your application to become a lawyer. In particular, non-law graduates should highlight any legal work experience that they have in order to prove their commitment to law.
- Referees – it is standard practice to include two referees: one academic and one relating to work experience or general character. Check with your intended referees in advance that it's okay to mention them and offer to send them a copy of your application.

Further reading:
There is plenty more useful application advice on LawCareers.Net:
- Application master class – www.LawCareers. Net/Information/Features/04072017-Application-master-class
- Guide to formal application writing – www.LawCareers.Net/Information/Features/28062017-CVs-cover-letters-and-applications-LCNs-guide-to-formal-writing

Reality check: A key point when applying: tell the truth. Seems obvious, but sometimes it's worth reiterating, as one barrister we spoke to emphasised: "Don't lie and don't write about things that you don't know anything about. If you are caught out, it is incredibly embarrassing and the end of your chance of a pupillage." You have been warned.

Ten top tips for online apps

You should approach an online form exactly as you would a paper form – take your time, carefully prepare your responses and pay attention to detail. Here are our top 10 tips for online apps:

- Do read through the whole application form before you start, keeping a close eye on all instructions.

- Do plan where all your main boasts will be made. It would be a shame to work a slightly tangential skill or experience into one answer when you turn out to be questioned directly on the issue on the next page.

- Don't complete the form with your caps lock on, except where specified – it looks as if you're SHOUTING.

- Do take care with the layout of your application. Consider writing the longer sections using Word and then copying the text over, checking that the formatting (eg, bullet points) have transferred properly.

- Don't succumb to 'copy and paste' fatigue. This opens the door wide to calling the firm by the wrong name – recruiters' most-hated mistake.

- Do use the spell check, although not the US version, which will let annoying Americanisms through.

- Don't be tempted to use email or text talk (eg, 'It wld be wkd to work 4 u'). Write in full sentences and do not abbreviate words.

- Do make sure that there is some way of keeping a record of your application. Whereas previously you would have photocopied it, make sure you either save it, print it or copy it into a separate document.

- Do read through your completed application at least three times before you submit it. Boasting of your 'excellen eye for deetail' will not get you the training contract/pupillage.

- Do use a sensible email address that you will be able to access throughout the recruitment period. If you graduate in June, your university email address will be shut down, but firms will want to contact you throughout the summer.

Interview technique

So you've taken on board our advice from previous chapters, submitted your applications and – hooray! – have been invited to an interview. After five minutes of patting yourself on the back, The Fear will probably start to set in… What if I become a gibbering wreck? What do I wear? What questions will they ask?

Worry not: it's all about transforming your 2D application persona into a 3D person. Read on to find out how best to present yourself on the day.

Preparation

It's your application that has aroused the firm's/chambers' interest, so reread it. Try to imagine some of the things which your interviewers might focus on (eg, what you have gained from your experiences in terms of skills and personal development). Caroline Lindner, global communications lead at Norton Rose Fulbright, advises: "Interviewers will want to test how the candidate can respond to unseen materials or topics, so expect to be taken out of your comfort zone and be willing to debate and discuss topical commercial issues which you may not know a lot about. After all, we are looking for agile minds!"

Read the firm's/chambers' recruitment literature and browse its website. Read the trade press, such as *The Lawyer*, *Legal Week* and *Law Society Gazette*, as well as the law sections of *The Times* and *Guardian*, so that you are aware of current legal issues. If you can't face trawling through the broadsheets, go to www.LawCareers.Net for its News section.

Alix Balfe-Skinner, HR manager at Taylor Vinters, is keen to emphasise the importance of research and preparation: "It is vital that students understand and know as much as possible about the firm they are applying to and the challenges and opportunities currently faced by the firm. This is often a key questioning area in training contract and other interviews. You don't need to know everything, but you need to be able to give your opinion coherently and concisely. Reading the legal press is also essential, as candidates are likely to be asked about current affairs and the wider legal market."

On the day itself, arrive with time to spare. Being late is likely to be viewed as a sign of arrogance or rudeness, not confidence. Make sure you have a mobile phone and the number of the firm in case you are unavoidably detained, so you can let them know what's happening. Don't follow the example of the applicant from Leeds who turned up two hours late for an interview with a firm in London armed with several Harrods shopping bags, or the candidate who failed to show up for an interview without explanation, then rang the chambers a week later demanding to know why she hadn't heard from them.

Having done your preparatory homework and got yourself safely to the correct location, let's take a look at the sort of thing you can expect when you get there.

Assessment days

Firms and sets are increasingly using a variety of ways to assess your suitability to be a lawyer. Selection procedures can range from a series of interviews to a day of group exercises and tests, devised to ascertain whether you have the skills and qualities which they are looking for. In some ways, assessment days are a bit like a mini-vacation scheme – they are a chance for the firm to put you through your paces in a variety of different ways rather than just talking to you at an interview.

A typical assessment day (if there is such a thing) might include group exercises, ability tests, presentations and in-tray exercises. In a brutal twist, there may even be a cull at lunchtime where poorer performers are sent home, while the remainder might have a formal panel interview in the afternoon. One recruiter mentions an incident that occurred during the chambers' assessment day: "We do an X-Factor style goodbye halfway through the day, inviting only a few to stay for lunch and second interview. We were joined at lunch one year by someone we had rejected, but who could not understand the word 'goodbye'." The lesson here is to learn when to take a hint!

❝ Don't ask a question that, had you done any research on the firm, you would have found out the answer ❞

Remember that although they might sound intimidating, the exercises generally aren't set to trick you, but rather are intended to reveal what sort of person you are and the sort of lawyer you might become. One firm likes to test applicants' initiative by asking in a written assessment whether you know its address and phone number (the answers are on the pen you are given to write the answer!). Be your best self on the day and don't let nerves get the better of you. Lucie Rees, graduate recruitment and development manager at Watson Farley & Williams, offers some reassurance: "Assessment centres are designed to put candidates at their ease and give them the best chance to showcase the skills we are looking for. More times than not, successful candidates tell us they actually enjoyed the day, which is great to hear. There is a mix of group and individual work, all of which fits into a client scenario that runs throughout the day. Try to relax and be yourself – you're more likely to perform well and find the firm that is right for you."

Each firm/chambers will have its own way of going about things and, with a bit of luck, will brief you properly in advance. If it doesn't, there's no harm in asking, but don't be too pushy as surprises might be a deliberate part of the day.

Psychometric tests

Psychometric tests are supposedly the Holy Grail, bringing science into the recruitment equation. With employers seeking not only ability, but also candidates with an appropriate temperament and character profile, psychometric tests are designed to work this out. While they are somewhat imperfect and should always be used in conjunction with other methods, it is fair to say that they represent a useful tool for recruiters. Fiona Medlock, graduate recruitment manager at Mills & Reeve, says that psychometric tests can provide "a strong indication of a participant's potential".

The key to psychometric tests is that there is no 'right' answer. Often, similar questions are asked in a number of ways. The aim is to discourage candidates from trying to guess what answer is expected and instead give a genuine picture of themselves. As such, it is hard to offer advice on how to approach them, beyond being honest. Some firms will even give an identical test immediately after the first, to ensure that people are being honest – as one recruiter says: "Nobody can remember how they responded previously if they were trying to suppress their true nature!"

Interviews
During

An interview is a two-way process, designed for both you and the interviewer to decide whether you meet each other's needs. Sarah Stockley, senior associate and member of the trainee recruitment team at Vinson & Elkins, says: "An interview day at our firm starts with candidates arriving an hour before their interview slots. They are given a written question and asked to orally present the advice they would give in that scenario for five minutes at the start of the interview.

The remainder of the interview is spent discussing the application form and the candidate in general, as well as the firm."

During the interview, you should do the following:
- Listen carefully to all questions and think for a moment before answering.
- Speak in a clear voice and be positive and alert throughout.
- Remember your manners. One City firm recruiter mentions an interviewee who asked "whether there were any David Brent characters in the office – it might have been funny if the candidate hadn't been performing so badly".
- Be aware of your body language. Look the interviewer in the eye when speaking to him or her, but without staring psychotically.
- In a panel interview, make eye contact with everyone, not just one person throughout. And do try to get people's names right – one interviewer recalls "making such an impression on the candidate that she called me David; my name is Robert!"
- Try to be relaxed and enthusiastic, without being too laid-back. One partner at a City firm recalls the candidate who swore during the interview, but had no recollection of doing so: "It just goes to demonstrate that people are often oblivious to how they come across."
- Be yourself, urges Danielle White, graduate recruitment and development manager at Mayer Brown International LLP: "It's always nice to see someone who is passionate and motivated, and who is able to show his/her personality as well as capability during the interview."

We mention eye contact for a reason. Talking to graduate recruiters, it's an issue for many candidates. Whether you want to or not, you must make eye contact with the interviewer(s). Simply put, avoiding eye contact makes you look shifty, whereas making it projects confidence and self-assurance. Fiona says: "Try to sit still – being nervous often causes fidgeting which you may not be aware of. This can be off-putting to interviewers, so be self-aware." Another London recruiter, giving an example of how not to do an interview, recalled in horror "the candidate who spent 40 minutes staring at a speck on the wall because she just could not make eye contact with us". Equally bad was the interviewee who "listed effective communication as one of his main strengths, but did not once make eye contact, rather disproving his claim".

66 Try to sit still – being nervous often causes fidgeting which you may not be aware of 99

Although there is no way to find out the interview questions in advance, you can make an educated guess about some of them (the box on p43, which lists some of the most commonly asked questions, is a good place to start). Prepare your answers accordingly and think about one or two clever questions that you can ask your interviewers. Remember also that there is not necessarily always going to be a 'correct' answer – some of the questions will be asked in order to gauge how well you express yourself. Puneet Tahim, senior graduate recruitment and development coordinator at Latham & Watkins, says: "Candidates should try to pre-empt what an interviewer might ask them and prepare for these questions. In doing this they will be able to engage in a meaningful discussion/debate which demonstrates their communication and influencing skills."

You're likely to get asked at least one question designed to assess your business understanding, advises Danielle:

"Commercial awareness is very important and will almost certainly be tested at some point during the process. It is of fundamental importance that candidates understand what is happening in the business world and how this will potentially impact on the legal industry."

We know it's hard, but do try to speak intelligently while thinking on your feet during the interview. Examples of how not to do it include naming Lauren Goodger when asked whom in the world you most admire; declaring that you don't know who David Lidington is or whether Nigel Farage is leftwing or rightwing; and mentioning the importance of presenting a professional appearance while sporting zebra-striped hair, a skirt with the hem hanging off, a creased jacket and scuffed shoes.

On the question of attire, matching neon green tights and nail varnish do not go down well with the rather staid legal profession. One regional recruiter gives this sartorial example: "One candidate arrived dressed more appropriately for nightclubbing than an interview. She wore a very orange, very short skirt and a low-cut pink top with a low-slung belt around her hips. When she stood up to leave her belt fell to the floor, leaving her face as pink as her top!"

Ask questions to which you genuinely want to know the answers – but not those for which you could have found out the answer beforehand. One northwest graduate recruitment adviser comments: "Don't ask a question that, had you done any research on the firm, you would have found out the answer. There are no brownie points for asking the obvious."

We asked recruiters what sorts of questions would impress them. Most said anything that reflects an interest in and understanding of the commercial world, clients and their business needs, or something that demonstrates specific knowledge of the firm without merely parroting the graduate recruitment literature or the firm's/chambers' website. Amy Kisser, barrister at QEB and a member of the pupillage committee, says: "Candidates always seem to think that they need to ask an 'impressive question' of their interviewers – we think this is nonsense. We want them to use this part of the interview as an opportunity to ask us any questions they may still have – having looked at our website already – rather than for us to use it as an opportunity to assess them. We are clear that interviews are very much a two-way street; our candidates are assessing us as much as we are them!" It is also important to remain unfazed and appear confident.

❝ Reading the legal press is also essential, as candidates are likely to be asked about current affairs and the wider legal market ❞

Some recruiters mentioned being both impressed and flummoxed by questions about why they like their job and what would make them leave!

After

Try to end things on a positive note, shaking hands with your interviewer(s) and thanking them for their time. If you feel comfortable doing so, ask for some feedback. Ways not to end an interview? One candidate concluded by saying: "I like to try lots of things, but rarely succeed at any of them." We suspect that didn't leave a very positive impression. Another barged back into the room, interrupting another interview, to ask whether the interviewers had his bus ticket.

As soon as you come out of the interview,

it's a good idea to find somewhere quiet to sit and write down all the questions you can remember being asked. Then write down what you gave as an answer. Later, work through the questions again, this time writing out what you would have said, given time to think and no interview nerves. By taking time to reflect on the interview, you'll be making the most of the experience (whether good or bad) and preparing yourself for the next one.

Offers

You will hear back from most recruiters quickly. If you receive an offer, most firms will give you four weeks in which to respond. If you are certain that you want to accept, respond in writing as soon as possible. If you are unable to give a decision at the time of receiving an offer, let them know and give a date by which you should have a final answer. Once you have accepted an offer, inform all other firms/chambers that have invited you for interview or that have made you an alternative offer. If no deadline is given, don't feel pressured to give an answer if you think that other offers may still be forthcoming.

Further advice appears throughout TCPH. In particular, be sure to read the profiles of individual solicitors and barristers in the practice area sections, many of whom offer their take on the application and interview process.

Further reading
There is plenty more useful interview advice on LawCareers.Net, including:
- Training contract interviews made easy – www.LawCareers.Net/Information/LCNSays/Training-contract-interviews-made-easy
- A dedicated guide to pupillage interviews – www.LawCareers.Net/Information/Features/03012017-Acing-that-pupillage-interview

Reality check: Remember that you won't be successful in your interview endeavours without preparing thoroughly, dressing smartly, arriving punctually and making eye contact.

Ten top interview questions
Naturally, what you will be asked in interviews can vary from firm to firm and set to set. However, here are 10 commonly asked questions to give you an idea of what recruiters are keen to know:

- Why are you applying to this firm/chambers?
- What are your long-term objectives in terms of career development?
- What do you really want in life?
- Are you satisfied with your academic achievements to date?
- What sorts of qualities do you feel you can bring to a job or career?
- What do you see as your personal strengths?
- What do you see as your faults or weaknesses?
- What is the worst mistake you have ever made and what did you learn from it?
- Have there been any commercial stories in the news over the last week that have interested you?
- Is there any aspect of the law or criminal justice system you would like to change?

Scotland and Northern Ireland

As we already have a firm handle on how things work in England and Wales, let us now look at how lawyers are trained in other parts of the United Kingdom. Here follows a brief explanation of what happens in Scotland and Northern Ireland.

Scotland

Over the last few years, legal education and training in Scotland have undergone a major review. This included the introduction of a requirement that all prospective solicitors complete a Foundation Programme – which for the time being remains exclusively the LLB, but leaves room for the potential of some variation in the degree undertaken – and renaming the Diploma in Professional Legal Practice and the traineeship as Professional Education and Training (PEAT) Stage 1 and Stage 2, respectively. However, PEAT 1 is still commonly referred to by students, universities and legal professionals as the Diploma in Professional Legal Practice. At the time of writing, the Scottish Law Society website still referred to both the LLB and the diploma in its main education section, so for the purposes of this chapter, we use both terms. For the most up-to-date information, visit www.lawscot.org.uk.

Undergraduate study

It is possible to study for an LLB in Scots Law/Foundation Programme at 10 universities in Scotland. The ordinary degree takes three years, while the honours degree takes four. There are also accelerated degree options, which can be taken if you have a non-law first degree. Students on the Scottish law degree at either the University of Dundee or the University of Strathclyde can take enough English law modules to earn a dual-qualified law degree, enabling them to progress to qualification in England and Wales or Scotland.

If you do not wish to do an LLB, it is possible to do a three-year, pre-diploma training

contract with a qualified Scottish solicitor, at the end of which you sit the Law Society of Scotland's professional exams. During the three years you must receive training in various prescribed areas.

Vocational study

All those who intend to practise as a solicitor or advocate (the equivalent of a barrister) must complete the Diploma in Legal Practice/PEAT 1, a 26-week full-time course offered at six universities, namely Aberdeen, Dundee, Glasgow, Strathclyde, Edinburgh and Robert Gordon. The course imparts knowledge and skills necessary for working life, with an emphasis on practical application and much of the teaching carried out by practising lawyers.

Training

Solicitors

To qualify as a solicitor, individuals must complete a two-year training contract/PEAT 2. Trainees are usually paid by the training firm at least the minimum amount set by the Law Society of Scotland (from June 2017 £18,000 in the first year, £21,500 for the second year). During the training contract, trainees must complete a minimum of 60 hours of trainee continuing professional development, which is structured learning over and above the trainee's office work. It is possible to be admitted as a solicitor after one year of training (especially useful if the trainee is to appear in court on behalf of clients); but normally, at the end of the two years – and provided that all conditions have been met – the trainee is admitted as a fully qualified solicitor.

Advocates

The body that administers the Scottish Bar is the Faculty of Advocates. Having completed the diploma, a trainee advocate (or 'intrant') must undertake a 21-month period of paid training in a solicitors' office (as for a trainee solicitor above, although slightly shorter), followed by a nine-month period 'devilling' as an unpaid pupil to an advocate. The intrant must then pass an exam set by the Faculty of Advocates covering written and oral advocacy. At this stage, he or she is admitted as an advocate.

Prospective students should note that a law degree from an English university will not form part of the qualification process in Scotland. Nor will a Scottish law degree be recognised by the Law Society of England and Wales as part of its qualification process. If you train in, say, Scotland, you will have to retrain to practise in England and Wales or Northern Ireland, and the same applies for movement in the opposite direction – unless you hold the special dual-qualified degree on offer from the universities of either Dundee or Strathclyde.

For more details visit www.lawscot.org.uk and www.advocates.org.uk.

Northern Ireland
Undergraduate study
Law degrees are offered at Queen's University Belfast (QUB) and the University of Ulster in Northern Ireland. However, law degrees from a number of other universities in England, Wales and Ireland are also accepted as qualifying law degrees for the purposes of passing on to the next stage: apprenticeship.

Non-law graduates must complete a two-year master's in legal science at QUB before they can progress to their apprenticeship.

Vocational study/training
Solicitors
The vocational study and practical training aspects that are found separately in England, Wales and Scotland are combined in Northern Ireland. Trainee solicitors must undertake a two-year apprenticeship under a supervising solicitor (called a 'master'). The practical component comes first, with a

four-month period of office-based training. This is followed by one year studying for the Certificate of Professional Studies at the Institute of Professional Legal Studies at QUB or the Graduate School of Professional Legal Education at the University of Ulster. This is then followed by a further eight months of office-based work.

There is a reciprocal arrangement whereby English and Welsh-qualified solicitors may transfer to Northern Ireland without taking further qualifications or examinations. They need only complete an application form, supply any proofs asked for and pay a fee. However, Scottish solicitors are required to take further examinations and complete a period of apprenticeship before they can be admitted in Northern Ireland.

Barristers
Trainee barristers must undertake the Bar Postgraduate Diploma in Professional Legal Studies at the Institute of Professional Legal Studies at QUB. They are then called to the Bar; but before they can practise, they must enter into one year of pupillage with a practising barrister of not less than seven years' standing.

For more details visit www.lawsoc-ni.org and www.barofni.com.

Alternative careers

Nobody ever said that having a law degree condemns you to life as a lawyer – far from it, in fact. There are many alternatives to becoming a solicitor or barrister, and routes to qualification other than the standard training contract or pupillage. Employers will value the skills you have learned through your legal training, such as the ability to research, collect and analyse large amounts of information, and to create a logical argument and reasoned conclusion from a set of facts. The ability to communicate clearly with the public and the profession alike is another sought-after skill. Discretion and a first-class memory are all highly valued in the general careers market.

Read on to see whether any of these alternative careers or routes to law tickle your fancy.

Alternative professions
Accountancy and taxation
Many accountancy firms recruit law students to specialise in tax work because, arguably, there are few differences between the job of a tax accountant and that of a tax lawyer. In addition, three of the 'big four' accountancy firms – PricewaterhouseCoopers, KPMG and Ernst & Young – have secured alternative business structure licences, allowing them to launch and run their own law firms.

Accountancy exams are tough, but the potential rewards – both professional and financial – are excellent. A move into accountancy also offers the opportunity to branch out into other careers (with positions in industry, management and consultancy). For further details of careers in accountancy, contact the Institute of Chartered Accountants in England and Wales or the Chartered Institute of Taxation (see "Useful addresses").

Finance
Banks are keen to recruit law graduates, as are building societies, insurance companies, stockbrokers and related professions. Those who thrive in a competitive, high-pressure environment may find a financial services or City career attractive. Most of the leading financial institutions offer summer work placement programmes, which are a good starting point for you to explore this further.

Civil service
There are opportunities throughout the civil service. Law graduates may wish to pursue a career in the Home Office, the Ministry of Justice, the diplomatic service or the Foreign Office. Her Majesty's Revenue and Customs employs tax inspectors and those with an ability to understand the intricacies of tax law are especially suited to such jobs. The UK Border Agency also welcomes applications from candidates with a legal background. It is worth investigating the Civil Service Fast Stream, an accelerated training scheme for graduates (www.faststream.gov.uk).

Media
Writing about the law can be a creative way in which to use your legal knowledge. Specialist publishers occasionally advertise for law graduates or qualified lawyers to train as legal editors. There is a wide variety of potential employers, ranging from international publishing houses with large legal departments to small companies that produce legal news and features, reference works and directories. In addition, a number of international law firms have publishing departments that provide newsletters and briefings for clients.

Newspapers and television and radio stations all employ legal correspondents. Here, an understanding of how the law works is invaluable.

Police
Those with a keen interest in law and order may wish to consider joining the police force; opportunities abound for graduates to achieve accelerated promotion. For further details, take a look at recruit.college.police.uk/pages/home.aspx.

European Commission

The European Commission often advertises for law graduates to work in its directorates. To get a taste of what that might be like, the commission offers five-month periods of in-service training (known as 'traineeships') for people who have recently obtained a university degree/diploma. The programme has been running for over 50 years and tens of thousands of people have benefited – in fact, many of them have gone on to become European civil servants and even European commissioners. Although traineeships are only open to EU nationals and the United Kingdom has voted to leave the European Union, Britain will still be a full member until March 2019, throughout the long and complicated process of leaving. This means that these opportunities should still be open to UK graduates. For more information, contact the European Commission's London office (see "Useful addresses").

Court reporting

Court reporters record verbatim court hearings for official transcripts of court proceedings. Increasingly, reporters use a computer-aided transcription system rather than traditional shorthand. Court reporters need not be legally qualified to enter the profession, although it is an advantage. Details of training and careers are available through the British Institute of Verbatim Reporters (see "Useful addresses").

Conveyancing

Licensed conveyancers deal with property transactions worth nearly £10 billion each year. Conveyancing is the process of legally transferring title or ownership of property from one person to another. A licensed conveyancer is a specialist lawyer qualified in all aspects of property law in England and Wales. They are also commissioners for oaths and more and more of them do probate, which is the process for enacting someone's will after their death. They work in a wide range of organisations, including specialist firms, landowning estates and local authorities, and are regulated by the Council for Licensed Conveyancers (CLC) (see "Useful addresses").

The Scottish Qualifications Authority has developed a range of new diplomas in partnership with the CLC, which replace the previous CLC qualifications. It is possible to study to become a licensed conveyancer while working, by either distance learning or part-time study. Most students spread the course over three to four years, although it is possible to complete it in two. To find out more, call the CLC on 020 7250 8465 or email traineelawyer@clc-uk.org.

Alternative qualification opportunities
In-house lawyers

Approximately 25,000 lawyers work in-house in commercial and industrial organisations in the United Kingdom. The main characteristic of the in-house role is that lawyers deal exclusively with their employer's legal business. This close involvement enables the lawyers to develop detailed knowledge of all aspects of their employer's business and provide advice that is in tune with the employer's commercial needs.

Although commercial organisations are usually the main employers of in-house lawyers, an increasing number of non-profit making bodies (eg, charities and trade unions) are hiring legal advisers to work in-house. One interesting aspect of working as a lawyer within a non-profit-making organisation is that many of its legal concerns relate to its own particular interests, in addition to the general laws that affect other companies.

However small, most in-house legal departments are expected to provide cost-effective, commercially attractive and legally correct solutions to problems. Common to most legal departments is a requirement to draft and maintain up-to-date standard contract documents. In-house lawyers may also be involved in planning business strategies with commercial colleagues and negotiating the terms of deals with customers or other lawyers. Other responsibilities could include advising on the supply of goods and services, leases, mortgages, mergers and acquisitions, and cooperation agreements for research, production, distribution or marketing, as well as litigation stemming from disputes arising from any of these activities.

Ensuring the company's compliance with UK and EU law is an important part of the in-house lawyer's remit. Specialist knowledge of the law relating to the employer's business may be necessary (eg, financial services, pharmaceuticals or telecommunications). Besides a thorough and analytical approach to business and the relevant law, it is also important for in-house lawyers to have excellent communication skills, a flexible and confident attitude, the ability to work as part of a team and sound commercial awareness.

For more information contact the Commerce and Industry Group (www.cigroup.org.uk) or the Bar Association for Commerce, Finance and Industry (www.bacfi.org).

Government lawyers

The work carried out by government lawyers covers virtually every aspect of the law you can think of. The diversity of the work reflects the range of activities within government, including related to issues of national and international significance and across public and private law (covering advisory and legislative work, litigation, commercial and a wealth of specialist areas).

Jenny Underhill at the Government Legal Service Secretariat says: "Lawyers and legal trainees within government will advise and represent their client, the government of the day, on a huge range of domestic and European matters. Government lawyers advise not only on what the law is, but also on what it should be. This type of work is quite simply unique. Approximately 40 trainee solicitors and pupil barristers positions are advertised each year. What many of our trainees find attractive is that they are given a high level of responsibility at an early stage and have the option to work in a variety of fields of law throughout their career."

For those who are successful in obtaining a training contract or pupillage, government departments will pay LPC or BPTC fees in full, provided you have not yet started either course. Where the course has already begun, they will pay the fees for the remainder of the course. Those intending to study the LPC or BPTC on a full-time basis can also expect to receive a bursary of between £5,400 and £7,600 for the vocational year.

Crown Prosecution Service

The Crown Prosecution Service (CPS) is the largest legal employer in England and Wales, with around 2,500 lawyers who conduct criminal prosecutions on behalf of the Crown.

Crown prosecutors weigh up evidence and public interest factors in all cases and decide those which should be heard by the courts. They also advise the police on matters relating to criminal cases. CPS caseworkers assist prosecutors in case management as well as attending court, dealing with post-court administration, assessing professional fees and liaising with witnesses and other organisations within the criminal justice system.

Martin McKay-Smith, training principal and director of pupil training at the CPS, says: "The CPS offers a varied, challenging and interesting career for those focusing on criminal litigation. The role of the modern prosecutor provides a true public service, encompassing charging decisions, advocacy and victim and witness care. Our mission is to deliver justice transparently, through the independent and effective prosecution of crime, fostering a culture of excellence in the way we analyse, advocate and progress our cases, reflecting always on what we do to learn and improve."

Applicants for the role of lawyer within the CPS must be solicitors admitted in England and Wales with a full current practising certificate or barristers called to the English Bar who have completed pupillage. In addition, the CPS recruits annually through a Legal Trainee Scheme, with up to 40 training contracts or pupillages available. Those interested in applying are advised to visit the CPS website (www.cps.gov.uk/careers).

Law centres

For over 40 years, law centres have provided an invaluable service to those in need of legal help and advice, often in deprived inner-city areas. With around 45 centres nationwide, the non-profit-making service is free for clients and centres are funded through local authorities. The nature of the work is dictated by local needs; workers are likely to need to know something about the law relating to immigration, employment, crime and landlord and tenant. Jobs are advertised in the local and national press, and in specialist publications such as the Legal Action Group's magazine or the *Law Gazette*.

Although not financially rewarding, law centre work is one of the most satisfying ways in which a lawyer can use his or her legal expertise. For more information, contact the Law Centres Federation (see "Useful addresses").

Citizens Advice

Citizens Advice is a professional national agency offering free, confidential, impartial and independent advice. In operation since 1939, Citizens Advice provides a service similar to law centres at around 2,700 community locations throughout England and Wales. Information and advice are dispensed in person, and by telephone and email, to millions of people every year – 2.6 million in 2016-17 alone.

Advisers can help to fill out forms, write letters, negotiate on behalf of clients and represent them at courts or tribunals in matters ranging from debt and benefits to housing, employment and immigration. Most centres offer legal advice and some employ their own lawyers. Contact Citizens Advice for further information (see "Useful addresses").

Court work

Over 95% of all criminal cases are dealt with by magistrates. Her Majesty's Courts and Tribunals Service employs many qualified solicitors and barristers as justices' clerks. Clerks advise lay magistrates on law and procedure, and are key figures in the daily running of the courts and the administration of justice. They also play a vital role in the management and administration of the service, organising the arrangement of court time, payment of fines and other related matters.

Stipendiary magistrates are largely chosen from practising solicitors and barristers, although it is possible for a lawyer to progress through the magistrates' courts to the circuit bench and beyond. Clerks who are interested in administration can work towards becoming a justices' chief executive, with responsibilities for increasingly large groupings of magistrates' courts. Further information is available from the Magistrates Association (see "Useful addresses").

Her Majesty's Courts and Tribunals Service also provides administrative support to the higher courts and tribunals. More information can be found at www.gov.uk/government/organisations/hm-courts-and-tribunals-service.

Alternative routes into law

Paralegals

There are a number of other opportunities to work in a solicitors' firm other than as a trainee. As well as administrative, business support and specialist non-legal fee-earner roles, many graduates get work as paralegals. The standing of paralegals is rising, especially as many firms are favouring paralegals over trainees or even some junior solicitors. This is particularly true in alternative business structure law firms, which are permitted to have paralegal partners. Paralegals with paralegal practising certificates under the Professional Paralegal Register have the added credibility of a voluntary regulator behind them, making them ideal as freelancers. Paralegals with sufficient experience can now also apply for junior judicial office.

While it is now possible to complete a paralegal apprenticeship, it is not in fact essential to have any legal qualifications whatsoever to work as a paralegal – according to the website of the Institute of Paralegals (www.theiop.org), of the approximately 60,000 paralegals working in solicitors' firms, most do not have any legal qualifications and only a minority are graduates.

Rita Leat, chief executive of the IoP, says: "There has never been a better time to become a professional paralegal, as they are now recognised as the fourth arm of the legal profession. Paralegals make up the highest proportion of legal service providers in the United Kingdom, many of whom are self-employed or paralegal businesses. Many law graduates seeking careers as barristers or solicitors may find that working as a paralegal will enable them to develop their knowledge and experience if they wish to resume their progress towards qualifying as a solicitor or barrister at a later date."

Rita's advice is especially apt as in July 2014 the Solicitors Regulation Authority (SRA) announced changes to the training regulations that allow LPC graduates to qualify as solicitors without doing a training contract – provided that they can show to the SRA's satisfaction that they have achieved equivalent training elsewhere. In April 2015 Robert Houchill of Bates Wells Braithwaite became the first paralegal to qualify in this way.

Most paralegals specialise in one type of law – commonly personal injury, family, criminal, conveyancing, debt recovery, probate or commercial law – so most vacancies are in these practice areas (there is more variety if you work for an in-house legal department). Unless you have previous practice experience, you will be applying for entry-level positions, even as a law graduate. As entry-level positions tend not to be advertised, you should apply direct to the firms you would like to work for.

Competition is fierce and preference tends to be given to those who have some experience or practical legal training. Optional training valued by employers is available from a variety of providers, including CLT (www.clt.co.uk/paralegal) and the Chartered Institute of Legal Executives (CILEx) (www.cilex.org.uk). You should also look out for the IoP's new training arm that will be launched this year, with specialist paralegal training and qualifications being made available.

CILEx legal executives

CILEx was established in 1963 with the aim of recognising the skills offered by lawyers' clerks in England and Wales. CILEx now represents around 20,000 individuals who are employed in various legal institutions in the United Kingdom, including private practice law firms, local government, and commerce and industry.

Chartered legal executives are qualified lawyers who have at least three years' experience of working under the supervision of a solicitor and who have passed the CILEx exams. Their daily work is similar to that of solicitors, but they have a narrower training than that of a qualified solicitor. They often specialise in one or two areas of the law.

Depending on his or her area of specialisation, a chartered legal executive may brief barristers, advise a party to a matrimonial dispute, draft a will or draw up documentation for the formation of a company. Chartered legal executives are recognised by the Ministry of Justice as qualified lawyers and are eligible for judicial appointments and partnerships in law firms, and can also be advocates.

There are certain suggested minimum qualification requirements, but an introductory qualification course is provided for those who do not have the necessary grades or legal background. Most aspiring chartered legal executives combine study for their CILEx exams (through evening classes, day release or distance learning) with the practical experience of working in a firm, building up a client base and becoming a fee earner.

A representative from CILEx told us: "CILEx gives individuals the opportunity to study for a career in law without incurring huge debts and at the same time gain worthwhile on-the-job experience. Any gap between the day-to-day work of a solicitor and a chartered legal executive lawyer is ever closing. CILEx is even currently applying for greater independent practice rights. There has never been a better time to be a chartered legal executive lawyer."

Most employers will pay for CILEx tuition and examination fees and, of course, the trainee is earning a living as he or she progresses. For further information contact CILEx (see "Useful addresses"). For more detail, see the CILEx chapter on page 141.

Legal apprentices

A legal apprentice is an individual who joins a law firm straight from school, rather than going to university, to work in a role similar to that of a paralegal. Apprentices also receive on-the-job training that takes them towards a formal qualification – for example, as a chartered legal executive, paralegal or solicitor.

Over the past few years, a number of firms have launched their own internal apprenticeship schemes (including DWF, Kennedys, Clyde & Co and Browne Jacobson). There are currently four separate levels of legal apprenticeship – Intermediate, Paralegal, Chartered Legal Executive and Solicitor. Both the Paralegal and the Solicitor Apprenticeships require three A levels graded C or above.

This area of the legal market is relatively new and constantly changing, so if you are seriously considering doing an apprenticeship, you will find much more information about the work involved and the different possible career paths in *The Law Apprenticeships Guide 2018*. Pick one up from your careers adviser or read the guide online at www.LawCareers.Net.

Chartered secretaries

Chartered secretaries work as company secretaries and in other senior positions in companies, charities, local government, educational institutions and trade bodies. They are qualified in company law, accounting, corporate governance, administration, company secretarial practice and management. They are trained to deal with regulation, legislation and best practice, and to ensure effective operations. See the website of the Institute of Chartered Secretaries and Administrators at www.icsa.org.uk.

Where did it all go wrong?

As you may have already discovered, finding a training contract or pupillage involves careful planning and application. It's a case of ensuring that what you have to offer is presented as efficiently and attractively as possible, while avoiding the kind of faux pas that will haunt you for years after the event. Inevitably, you will make mistakes, but rest assured: whatever has gone wrong for you has been trumped many times over. Here we look at some of the pitfalls encountered in the past, based on a survey of actual recruiters. We urge you not to reprise them!

First impressions…

…or falling at the first hurdle. While it's important for your application to stand out from the pack, bear in mind that grabbing the interviewer's attention should only be for the right reasons. You don't want your well-crafted application to end up being forwarded around the firm for giggles.

One firm was dismayed to be confronted with an inspirational quote from *The Lion King* at the head of an application. Meanwhile, one recruiter at a commercial firm describes with horror two cringe-worthy instances of applicants trying a bit too hard to stand out: "A candidate once set out her application in the format of a play, with Act One, Scene One featuring a lost law student looking for a training contract and Act Three, Scene Three 'still to be written'. Another applicant began her covering letter with a line about how she flailed her arms around when excited. She then elaborated to say that friends had commented that our firm was the only one that was making her flail! There are better ways to demonstrate enthusiasm and commitment to a firm. My advice? Don't go with quirky!"

One well-known commercial and chancery London set was bemused by the applicant who, when asked about his motivation to apply for pupillage, wrote "I have always wanted to work for a leading tax chambers."

Nice sentiment, "except tax was not one of our core areas of law; obviously, this was a copy and paste job that had gone horribly wrong", recalls the chambers' marketing and business development manager.

On a more mundane level, recruiters are adept at spotting mass applications, even if the candidate has managed to match up firm, recruitment contact and the type of work the firm does (apparently quite an achievement for many; one hapless applicant included the names of three other firms – yes, three – in her application to a fourth). Published example letters should likewise be treated as a guide and shouldn't be copied out verbatim. You really aren't the only one who's found that website, you know.

Equally, sometimes a strikingly original example or an answer that is just a bit too candid can be just as damning, as one recruiter recalls: "One hot Friday afternoon, I reviewed two applications which had been sent in from the same address, although in two different names with different details and experiences. The first applicant, answering the question about their greatest achievement, wrote something so blue, it is unrepeatable. The second applicant, answering the question about extracurricular activities, said that they spent their time 'going down the pub and drinking lots of beer'. It gave me a laugh, but perhaps their time could have been better spent."

And make sure that you use decent examples when trying to demonstrate that you have the necessary skills. One recruiter recalls a candidate who really scraped the barrel: "The applicant described how his parents went on holiday and left him in charge of the house and his younger siblings. The story ended with him changing a lightbulb, which he said he had not expected to have to do. The applicant claimed that 'the fact that I did this successfully shows that I react to challenges well', but I'm afraid we're looking for slightly bigger challenges than that!"

Face to face

So you've made it to interview. Well done, but don't be complacent. You can rewrite an application, but once you've got it very wrong in front of an interviewer, there's not a lot you can do, so stay focused. There are three main ways that an interview can go awry on the interviewee's part: nervousness, rudeness and inappropriateness.

Lawyers are generally a sociable breed whose work involves a high degree of interaction with both colleagues and clients. This means that recruiters are looking for a modicum of social ability, confidence and grace. Nervousness at interview is understandable and all but the most callous of interviewers will allow for this.

Before you go to the interview, think about your appearance. As with your application, it's best not to stand out for the wrong reasons: don't wear anything too outlandish and do check everything's done up properly! On your arrival, remember to be respectful. One junior tenant on a set's interview panel went to the door to meet the applicant, who later described the tenant as "just a receptionist".

Once in the interview room, remember all that experience you've had of sitting on – not falling off – chairs and drinking glasses of water rather than pouring them down your front. Similarly, it's best to wipe clean your specs if they've misted up (unlike one candidate who conducted his whole interview through a fog). And remember, the firm wants to interview you; if you bring your mother along, it is unlikely that you, or she, will get a training contract.

Think about what you say, too: a candidate who claimed to have a lifelong love of shipping and the sea (in an application to a shipping firm) eventually revealed that this 'love' amounted to a one-week family cruise 15 years previously; while the candidate who admitted to informing herself of current affairs via the tabloids (apparently she found broadsheets boring) was rather ill-advised. It also pays to pay attention at all times – a recruiter at a large, full-service national firm shares this example of how switching off can lead to embarrassment: "Following a series of talks given by our lawyers at an open day, an attendee casually asked one of the speakers (a senior associate) if she thought she might apply for a training contract with the firm following the experience of the open day. Clearly, this individual had been sleeping through the talks!" Further, don't massively confuse things by answering "Why do you want to be a lawyer?" with "I don't want to be a lawyer"!

One recruiter from a US firm recalls this tricky encounter with an interviewee who was asked for an example of using their initiative: "The candidate talked about working in insurance, cold calling an elderly lady and essentially ripping her off by selling her all of the insurance under the sun! The initiative part related to making more money for the business without being asked to!" Don't forget that ethics play a big part in a successful lawyer's career.

There are lots of old interview chestnuts that you can expect to be asked, so have an answer ready. These include (with less than ideal answers): what is your greatest achievement? ("Stopping biting my nails.") What are your hobbies? ("Playing with my girlfriend.") Why do you want to become a lawyer? ("I used to be a doctor, but I'm tired of having to use my judgement.") Why are you applying to this firm? ("My zodiac sign is Libra, the symbol for justice.") Having something positive to say about the town or city you are in is helpful – definitely don't be like the candidate who, when asked why he wished to move to Norwich, replied: "This is Norwich?" And possibly not best to tell the partners interviewing you how very hungover you are.

Outright rudeness will make you the stuff of legend at a firm or chambers, but won't get you a job. One City firm tells how an interview was interrupted by the candidate's mobile phone ringing (bad). The candidate answered her phone (very bad) and then asked for some privacy while she conducted her conversation (very, very, very bad). Another candidate, when asked why he had applied only to City firms, bar the northern firm interviewing him, replied: "You must have slipped through the net!"

Remember that you're not in your living room. One top national firm describes how a candidate was making a presentation in front of a panel of recruiters, but "decided to demonstrate a particularly flamboyant cricket move and split his trousers". And the interviewer certainly isn't your "mate": especially not when you try to stretch a personal contact by saying: "I'm a great friend of your wife, you know."

Accidental disaster
It happens. You've covered every angle, done your research, arrived hours early and while you're waiting, you manage to spill coffee on your shirt. Don't panic. Tell somebody what has happened. Don't be like the woman who walked into her interview in an inappropriate party dress for this reason, but only told the firm after the interview, or the man who arrived covered in blood from a stress-induced nosebleed and likewise gave no explanation. Pouring a cup of scalding tea into the lap of the interviewer can also be a tricky situation, as a candidate in Yorkshire discovered. As long as you apologise for any mistakes, you should be OK.

Hopefully this chapter puts things in perspective. If you do have a rush of blood

to the head and pull off something similar to the above, don't despair – just move on to the next application. And remember, mishaps don't only happen to candidates. A recruiter in Bath conducted an interview using the wrong candidate's name throughout and then fell down the stairs while showing her out.

Work experience

Work experience

Here at *The Training Contract & Pupillage Handbook*, we like to tell it to you straight. The bottom line is that without relevant work experience, you are not going to get a training contract/pupillage.

You see, dazzling academics and personality are not enough to satisfy recruiters in the legal profession. They also want hard evidence that you are committed to a career in law. This is for two reasons. First, they want to know that law isn't so much a passing fancy for you as a serious ambition. Second, they want your decision to be an informed one, based on your experience to date.

An ideal start to your career is to get a place on a formalised work placement scheme/mini-pupillage. You know the drill: they are run by firms and chambers, and no expense is spared during your two weeks (most even pay you to be there!). In an ideal world, everyone who wanted a place on one of these would get one. They're the perfect foot in the door of a firm/chambers: you get to make crucial contacts and put across the real you, rather than the tongue-tied version that recruiters tend to meet at interview. However, there just aren't enough places to go round. Fear not, though, as we will show you how to create your very own work placement.

How do I get involved?
Formal schemes
During formal work placements and mini-pupillages, firms and chambers will make every effort to ensure that you get a wide range of experience and a real taste of life as one of their own. The schemes normally offer a chance to get involved with real legal work, meet trainees, associates and partners, and enjoy an array of social events. All this and you get paid as well – usually between £200 and £300 a week, but sometimes more. On these sorts of scheme you're effectively becoming a trainee for two weeks, dipping your toe in the water, seeing if you like the firm and vice versa. The same goes for a good mini-pupillage, which will give you the chance to attend court and conferences with members of chambers, see barristers at their day-to-day work and get a flavour of how the particular set operates. During assessed mini-pupillages, you may be asked to prepare a piece of written work in order to develop a feel for the practical application of law. Generally, you should see the two to three weeks as a time to get a sense of the work, the people and the culture, while being sure to make the best possible impression. Katie Makey, recruitment officer at Shearman & Sterling, says: "Being a trainee is not all glamour, so when we see candidates who have done comprehensive stints in comparable law firms, we hope that they have seen the true picture of trainee life – if they are still keen on applying to us, then we are reassured that they have carefully considered the career and are committed."

With any luck, your positive impression will lead to the offer of a training contract or pupillage. Fiona Medlock, graduate recruitment manager at Mills & Reeve, says: "Many firms use their placements as part of their training contract recruitment process. It is an opportunity for you to see first-hand if a firm is the type of place you can envisage yourself starting your career, while the firm has the opportunity to assess whether you have the potential they are looking for." But can we suggest that you don't follow the lead of one work placement student at an international firm who "constantly posted his experiences with us on the satirical RollOnFriday website. Sadly, his efforts to remain nameless failed!" Equally, we think it may not be sensible to resort to violence, as one placement student did on a night out with a Newcastle firm: "The candidate picked a fight with one of our trainees on a social night during a work placement. We didn't take his application any further and he didn't ask for any feedback!"

Work placement: case study
Adam Blin, who until March 2017 was an associate in Linklaters corporate team, remembers his work placement at the firm well: "The tasks you get involved in as a vacation scheme student are very similar to what you would undertake as a trainee. You'll get involved in a wide range of work, with the support of a principal and a trainee buddy, which really helps you to understand the role of a trainee within the firm. You are given the opportunity to learn a lot about Linklaters, our culture and the work we do through various seminars and workshops throughout the vacation scheme. The best advice I can give to students is to always ask questions when visiting a firm; everybody is really friendly and wants you to make the most of your time here. It's a two-way process, which people can sometimes forget."

> ** Non-legal work experience can be incredibly valuable to students in terms of developing their wider skillsets **

The experience has also stood Adam in good stead when bringing through subsequent generations of vac schemers: "I was a trainee buddy during this year's summer vacation scheme and was really impressed by the quality of the work the students were able to produce. I managed to get involved in some of the scheme's social events, which provided an informal environment for students to network with lawyers from across the firm while also showcasing some of the fun opportunities that sometimes come our way."

Another former vac schemer, now an associate at a City firm, gave this advice: "Get stuck in to the work; I was certainly made to feel that I could ask any questions.

Also, get to know the people, from your fellow schemers to the graduate recruitment team to the associates and partners. Go to as many of the social events as you can. You are trying to work out whether that firm is right for you, so make the most of your time there. The placement is a two-way process, for them to impress you as well as you to impress them. I found it a very beneficial experience." He also points out that it takes you one step closer to a training contract, as most firms will guarantee you an interview if you attend their work placement scheme.

Mini-pupillage: case study
One barrister-to-be says of his mini-pupillage experiences: "Mini-pupillages were an invaluable part of the pupillage application process. By doing them, I was able to get a proper feel for the work that a chambers did and the set's atmosphere. Mini-pupillages (though they are often unassessed) also give chambers the opportunity to have a look at you and see whether you could be a good candidate for pupillage. I would strongly advise anyone applying for pupillage to do several mini-pupillages – particularly at the sets they might end up applying to. My favourite mini-pupillage was at the set where I ultimately ended up doing pupillage and getting tenancy."

Alternative experience
Those of you who aren't lucky enough to get a place on one of the formalised programmes must be resourceful. It's not the end of the world if you don't get a place, but you will have to take the initiative and create opportunities for yourself.

Lucie Rees, graduate manager at Watson Farley & Williams, says: "All experience is relevant and shapes you into the person you are. Firms are looking for well-rounded candidates and experience in a variety of areas will help with this. All the work experience you have will build your knowledge and transferable skills – it's how you then choose to make it work for you on your application form that counts."

Puneet Tahim, senior graduate recruitment and development coordinator at Latham & Watkins, agrees: "Non-legal work experience can be incredibly valuable to students in terms of developing their wider skillsets. Where they can sometimes let themselves down is not really thinking about using it in their application forms to sell themselves. Rather, they need to take the time to explain what they were doing, the skills they developed and how these will be useful to them in a career in law."

Andy Creer, barrister at Hardwicke Chambers, adds: "We recognise that people have different opportunities according to their socioeconomic backgrounds. It is therefore more important to demonstrate what you have got out of your work experience, than what you have done *per se*."

Alternative work experience in the business world can also help you to build your commercial awareness, as Matthew Parker, barrister at 3 Verulam Buildings, points out: "Non-legal work experience is very useful if it involves skills that are important at the Bar, such as public speaking, collecting and presenting information or dealing with clients. For the commercial Bar, it is often very helpful to have had some experience in a business environment, which will help develop commercial awareness and enable you to engage with clients' concerns on their level."

Citizens Advice

One option is to volunteer at your local Citizens Advice Bureau (CAB). Maxine Cole, a senior crown prosecutor at the Crown Prosecution Service, volunteered for about a year at the Barking and Dagenham CAB following her master's. She comments: "I provided advice on housing law, landlord and tenant issues, claims for disrepair and welfare law. When it came to applying for training contracts, I was able to talk about some of my experiences at CAB – for example, when asked to discuss how I dealt with a difficult situation, I referred to an incident at the CAB involving a client with Alzheimer's. I would certainly recommend CAB work because the training is excellent: you are trained in all the areas that they expect you to advise on and in how to use their files to find information. It teaches you how to apply the law in reality and hones your interview and advice skills."

Even a two or three-week stint at the CAB could work to your advantage. Like Maxine, you will be able to include the experience on your CV and then talk about it at interview.

Court work

Court work is another option. Fatim Kurji, a barrister at Birmingham superset No5 Chambers, explains what marshalling involves: "The point of marshalling is to spend some time with a judge to see the litigation process from a judicial perspective. I spent my time reading the skeleton arguments and papers before the court and then watching the trial unfold. The process is immensely useful: you quickly learn which advocacy styles are effective and which to avoid. When it came to applying for pupillages, my marshalling experience in particular helped me to answer those standard interview questions, such as 'What makes a good barrister?' I would recommend it as a good introduction into seeing how trials are run and putting into perspective the roles of the advocates and the ultimate aim – persuading the judge."

Free Representation Unit

Other options include volunteering for the Free Representation Unit (FRU), a charity that provides free legal representation to those who cannot afford it. FRU trains you to represent its clients at tribunals. Lots of barristers/solicitors look favourably on this practical experience, which is invaluable when applying for pupillage and training contracts. We spoke to a pupil at Blackstone Chambers, who said: "I volunteered at FRU for almost two years while on the GDL and BPTC. Outside studying, I think it was the most useful thing I did. FRU gives you the opportunity to get stuck into practical elements of law in a way that not many other pro bono organisations do. You have to meet and advise clients, run a piece of litigation on your own and ultimately may have to argue a case before the Employment or Social Security Tribunal. In short, you get real experience of what being a barrister is like."

The first step in volunteering is to attend an induction day for the area in which you are interested. They are usually held eight times a year, with four of the days focused on training in employment law and the other four in social security. You can attend either employment, social security or both, depending on your level of experience. To undertake employment training, you must be at least a master's, GDL, LPC or BPTC student. To undertake social security training, you must be at least a final-year LLB or GDL student.

To read an interview with a former FRU volunteer and the charity's chief, see our "Free Representation Unit" chapter in this section. Find out more about FRU at www.thefru.org.uk or by ringing 020 7611 9555.

Pro bono work
Many universities and postgraduate study providers operate pro bono clinics, which are a great chance to get involved in providing legal advice at the front line. John Watkins, director of employability at The University of Law, talks about the University's schemes and their benefit to both students and the wider community: "Pro bono at the University consists of three broad programmes: legal advice clinics, where students answer legal enquiries from the general public under supervision; external opportunities, where students gain experience of working for not-for-profit organisations; and public legal education, raising legal awareness in communities through schemes such as the Streetlaw initiative. All our students are encouraged to participate, and with a wide range of over 3,300 opportunities and placements available each year, students can get involved whatever their field of interest. Students appreciate the many benefits that flow from developing their knowledge and skills in a challenging but secure real-life setting. The additional benefits to the wider community reinforce the positive nature of the work."

Sarah Stockley, member of the trainee recruitment team and former senior associate at Vinson & Elkins, says of pro bono: "Pro bono is an excellent way for students to practise giving legal advice and also giving something back to the community. A lot of firms offer pro bono services, so it is a good skill to learn early on."

Martin Barnes, chief executive of LawWorks, adds: "I would encourage every law student to get involved in pro bono activities. There is a range of potential opportunities available, including helping people with real-life issues as well as developing legal and practical skills."

For more on LawWorks and what it does, see the "LawWorks" chapter in this section. For more on getting involved with pro bono in general, see www.lawworks.org.uk and www.studentprobono.net.

European Union
Although no one knows what the outcome of the Brexit negotiations will mean, currently graduates might like to consider doing a traineeship (formerly known as a 'stage') at

the EU institutions. The European Parliament, the Council, the European Commission, the European Court of Justice, the Social and Economic Committee, the Committee of the Regions and the European Ombudsman all organise traineeships, each lasting between three and five months. Traineeships may be paid or unpaid. For further details visit http://ec.europa.eu/stages/index_en.htm.

> **ɢɢ Work of all types – including cleaning and waiting – shows grit and determination, as well as a willingness to roll up your sleeves and get on with the job ɟɟ**

What else can I do?
Staying closer to home, you could send a speculative letter to local high-street law firms asking to shadow a partner (or a trainee) for a few days or offer to answer the phones at a nearby legal advice centre. Court ushering at your nearest magistrates' court and outdoor clerking are suggested for those unable to get on a formal mini-pupillage.

We asked graduate recruiters how non-law graduates in particular can get a foot on the ladder if they cannot get onto a formal work placement. All said that non-law graduates should at least make the effort to research the profession, speak to solicitors/trainees about their experiences and visit firms or attend open days. In addition, they suggest using personal contacts to obtain work experience, either in law or in a related field (eg, banking or accountancy). Diana Spoudeas, graduate recruitment and development manager at Jones Day, says: "Work of all types – including cleaning and waiting – shows grit and determination, as well as a willingness to

roll up your sleeves and get on with the job. We recruit candidates with wide interests and if you have experienced other careers, you can speak from the heart at interview about the reasons you have excluded those careers and feel propelled towards law."

One recruiter talked about the non-law student candidate who was studying business management, but joined his university law society and enjoyed the benefits it gave him.

Best suggestion of all: write speculatively to firms for experience in some sort of support capacity (eg, legal secretarial work or paralegalling). Commercial experience, perhaps in-house, is also regarded as valuable. A recruiter at one international firm says: "Previous non-legal work experience can help students understand businesses or individuals that they are working with and the challenges they face."

A graduate recruitment assistant at another international firm suggests: "Try to get other business experience in order to develop yourself in all areas. It's worth trying to make contact with the firm you're interested in (eg, attend a law fair or phone up the graduate recruitment team), so that your name is remembered positively. In relation to extracurricular activities, we like to see anything that demonstrates commitment and an ability to take something to a high level. Activities that show responsibility, leadership or team cooperation are also valued."

Students with disabilities would do well to contact the Lawyers with Disabilities Division. This division of the Law Society aims to achieve equality of opportunity for people with disabilities, whether they be qualified solicitors, trainee solicitors, law students, clients or members of the public. One of the things that the division does is contact firms to encourage them to offer work placements to disabled students. For more details visit www.lawsociety.org.uk/support-services/practice-management/diversity-inclusion/lawyers-with-disabilities-division.

When should I do it?

It's never too early to start. In terms of formal schemes, law students should try to secure a placement in the summer before their final year at university at the latest; non-law students should apply during the summer following their third year. In fact, more firms than ever are running schemes aimed at first years, so you need to be on the ball right from the beginning of your university career.

Most formal schemes last between two and three weeks. Take a look at the "Insider reports" chapter for a selection of application deadlines for formal work placement schemes. Otherwise, check individual firms' websites.

With regard to informal DIY experience, just get writing!

How do I get the most out of it?

Without a shadow of a doubt, most firms use their formal and informal work experience schemes as part of the recruitment process. A solicitor at national firm Freeths says: "You can only learn so much from an application form and interview. However, a week or two spent with lawyers and support staff is the best way for both firm and student to make an informed decision about each other. Because they are so useful, I suggest you treat your applications for summer schemes as seriously as – if not more seriously than – your training contract applications."

This is your opportunity to show off your skills and charms to their very best advantage. So while there, make sure that you really do all you can to be your best possible self. That means:

- asking questions;
- showing enthusiasm and initiative;
- taking advantage of all opportunities that are offered;
- behaving professionally; and
- acting appropriately (so no getting drunk or being rude!).

Equally, if you are at a firm or chambers, you should be assessing whether it is the sort of place in which you can imagine working. If you are at one of the other voluntary schemes (eg, Citizens Advice or a pro bono clinic), make sure you are taking mental notes about how you respond to the type of work to which you are being exposed. What sparks your interest? What makes you switch off? What would you like to learn more about? Don't forget, it's a two-way process.

What about afterwards?

Send a brief letter thanking the recruiter for your placement/mini-pupillage/DIY work experience. Add a personal touch along the lines of how you think the experience has helped you at the outset of your career and what you most enjoyed.

It may be worth jotting down some thoughts and impressions of the experience to focus your mind. This will allow you at interview to talk about how it helped in terms of your future plans and overall knowledge of the legal profession.

Reality check: A large number of firms recruit trainees directly from work placements, so it is worth getting onto a scheme if possible. In addition, you should be asking family members, friends, teachers and even friends of friends if they know anyone working in the legal profession who might be able to help you get some work experience. Introductions are important!

LawWorks

There is a long history of lawyers doing pro bono work, going back to medieval times and beyond; for many people, pro bono was the only means to seek redress or justice. Restrictions in the scope of legal aid and the impact of local authority spending cuts on law centres and advice agencies have contributed to a contemporary access to justice crisis, with those who cannot access legal aid and who cannot afford to pay potentially being denied advice or representation.

Pro bono is not, and should not become, an alternative to a properly funded system of legal aid – it simply cannot fill the vacuum and need caused by policy change and cuts – but its importance and value have never been greater.

Any lawyer has the ability (with the right temperament and commitment) to do pro bono that makes a difference, whether you become a lawyer in private practice or an in-house lawyer working for a company or a charity, or in local or central government. You may have legal expertise or knowledge which can help an individual or a charity to resolve a legal problem. What you definitely will have is valuable training, skills and aptitudes that are readily translatable to real-life situations and problems. And you can make a valuable pro bono contribution as student, trainee or pupil – early experience of pro bono can instil a passion and commitment that lasts a career and beyond.

Pro bono for students

LawWorks launched its Students and Law Schools Project (funded by the Law Society) in 2007. Since then, pro bono has strengthened and grown, and is increasingly seen as a key part of legal education. The benefits of pro bono as a student, trainee or pupil can include developing legal skills, such as interviewing clients and drafting letters; gaining practical research skills, based on real legal problems for real clients; exploring practice in new areas of law; developing contacts and links to legal professionals, firms, charities and others; and making a contribution to your local community.

> **❝ You can make a valuable pro bono contribution as student, trainee or pupil. Early experience of pro bono can instil a passion and commitment that lasts a career and beyond ❞**

There are different ways to get involved in pro bono as a student:

- Legal education for the public – your law school may have links with local community groups or schools interested in knowing more about areas of law or the legal system. You could research relevant topics and prepare for or contribute to presentations and workshops.
- Student placement – your law school may not be able to support pro bono opportunities internally, but may arrange for you to volunteer with a local advice agency or community group.
- Legal advice clinic – your law school may run or be part of a legal advice clinic (including being part of the LawWorks Clinics Network, as below). With supervision, pro bono activity may include drafting letters, researching legal problems and face-to-face advice.
- Tribunal representation – the Free Representation Unit (FRU) provides a good opportunity for students to acquire advocacy experience. FRU volunteers help with case preparation and representation in tribunal cases (see p65 for more on FRU).
- Internships with charities – legal and pro bono organisations such as LawWorks,

the Bar Pro Bono Unit, the Access to Justice Foundation and the London Legal Support Trust are often looking for interns to support the work of their organisations. There may be opportunities with other charities and organisations.

The Bar Pro Bono Unit acts as a clearing house, matching barristers prepared to undertake pro bono work with those who need their help. Applications are reviewed by one of a number of senior barristers and the unit then makes a decision as to whether to try to find a volunteer barrister to assist.

LawWorks supports the development of law school clinics and also organises the annual Student Pro Bono Awards, run in partnership with the attorney general. By providing support and encouragement for student pro bono, it hopes to facilitate an interest and passion that will last and grow.

Pro bono for qualified lawyers
Opportunities for pro bono volunteering continue during training and pupillage. Increasingly, aspiring lawyers see opportunities for pro bono as informing their career decisions. For many, pro bono is an essential part of being a lawyer. It can help to build skills and confidence, develop teams and team spirit, and offers the chance to test oneself as a lawyer, perhaps in a new environment or a different area of law.

LawWorks is the operating name of the Solicitors Pro Bono Group. Established in 1997, it is a charity providing support for local independent pro bono advice clinics and supporting the pro bono work of our members – largely law firms and in-house teams – and others. In Scotland pro bono is supported by its sister charity, LawWorks Scotland.

LawWorks connects volunteer lawyers in England and Wales with people in need of legal advice who are not eligible for legal aid and cannot afford to pay, and with community groups and not-for-profit organisations that support them or their communities.

Our programmes include the following:
- The LawWorks Clinic Network – LawWorks supports a network of over 220 independent clinics, providing free advice to individuals, predominantly in the area of social welfare law (eg, social security benefits, housing, family and employment). Advice is delivered face to face, over the phone and via Skype.
- The Not-for-Profit Programme – LawWorks connects smaller charities and community groups with the skills and expertise of lawyers, strengthening their capacity and avoiding or resolving problems.
- Secondary specialisation – In response to growing need for legal advice and representation, LawWorks supports more in-depth pro bono casework and representation, including training and supervising lawyers to develop expertise in areas of social welfare law. This includes a project for solicitors taking on first-tier social security tribunal cases, and working with the charity Together for Short Lives to provide legal advice for families and carers of children with life-limiting conditions.

LawWorks is also developing a 'policy voice' for pro bono, drawing on the experience of clinics, our members and the wider profession, to inform and influence change to better enable access to justice for all.

Working together to achieve more
In recent years, the coordination of pro bono in England and Wales has strengthened.

The annual National Pro Bono Week celebrates the breadth and impact of pro bono work (including internationally) undertaken by the legal profession throughout the year. Sponsored by the Law Society, the Bar Council and the Chartered

Institute of Legal Executives, a range of events, including with a student focus, are held across the country.

In 2016 the Law Society launched a Pro Bono Manual (to support solicitors to develop or extend pro bono practice) and a Pro Bono Charter, encouraging the profession to make a public commitment to pro bono.

The National Pro Bono Centre was established in Chancery Lane, London, to house and support national pro bono organisations and others working to maximise access to justice. The centre represents the creation of a single, physical hub for the coordination and development of national pro bono services (www. nationalprobonocentre.org.uk).

Conclusion

Pro bono has an important and significant contribution to make in enabling access to justice. The important debates about legal aid provision and policy reform will continue. Whatever direction your future career may take, you can personally make a difference through pro bono. It truly is part of being a lawyer.

Martin Barnes is the chief executive of LawWorks. For more information about LawWorks, visit www.lawworks.org.uk.

Free Representation Unit

The Free Representation Unit (FRU) is a charity that provides individuals with representation that they could not afford otherwise and gives junior lawyers a valuable opportunity to get practical advocacy experience.

FRU represents clients in employment tribunals, social security tribunals and a small number of criminal injuries compensation cases. FRU has a handful of staff to oversee the cases and provide advice and support to the representatives, run the office and raise funds; but the volunteers take responsibility for case preparation and advocacy in the tribunals. Cases are passed on by over 200 referring agencies or by self-referral for some employment cases.

David Abbott has been the charity's chief executive since June 2017. He says: "FRU owes its success to a simple model, matching unrepresented clients facing tribunals with junior lawyers seeking the opportunity to handle cases. In bringing together these two parties, we promote access to justice and help junior lawyers gain experience that will be valuable in their future careers. Without our service, some clients might not attend their hearing or would be left with the daunting prospect of representing themselves. We don't operate a merits test when accepting referrals, but our volunteers still have a high success rate."

FRU's office is in Holborn, close to the heart of the legal profession and several law schools. Volunteers use the office to prepare their cases, carry out research, make use of its facilities, seek advice from the legal officers, hold conferences with clients and discuss cases and tactics with fellow volunteers. FRU has secured funding to make both training and case preparation more accessible and flexible through its digital strategy and will be implementing this over the next 12 months.

With over 300 volunteers working on cases in any given year, FRU has a rigorous training process. Would-be volunteers must attend a day-long technical training course in one of FRU's practice areas and then must complete a test. "Only about two-thirds of the volunteers pass this test at the first attempt," explains David. "People who pass then have to observe a tribunal case and attend an office induction, at which point they are ready to take on their first case. Volunteers can take on as few or as many cases as they wish, although many enjoy building on the skills gained in their first case and the buzz created by knowing that they did a great job for their client."

Allison Crabtree started volunteering with FRU when she was studying for the GDL at The University of Law in Moorgate, continuing through her LPC year. "I attended a training day and was attracted by the chance to do a real case," recalls Allison. "I took the test, which was challenging but very much like one of the practical scenario based problems I was set on the GDL. FRU has been flexible in a way that many volunteering opportunities aren't; you have to meet with your new client quickly, stay in touch with them as things progress and be available for the tribunal date, and you often need to put in many hours of preparation, but there are no specific days or weeks to be in an office. That has made it possible for me to combine it with studying full time."

Allison explains why FRU is useful for both would-be barristers and solicitors: "Most of the other FRU volunteers I've met hope to become barristers and are drawn to FRU because of the advocacy experience, but I think it's just as helpful for aspiring solicitors. Volunteers interview clients and witnesses, draft documents and prepare bundles. And of course many solicitors do a lot of advocacy; in employment cases, the employer's representative in tribunal is quite often a solicitor."

FRU's legal officers maintain close contact with the volunteers, particularly during the ratification process for the first case. "The legal officers oversee cases, provide support to the volunteers throughout and are always available to talk things through," comments David. "It is a big step to take your first case to tribunal and we are very keen to ensure that representatives do not feel that they have been thrown in at the deep end. We encourage volunteers to share their experiences and try to promote a collaborative learning experience. We always remember that we are providing a service to clients who need to be confident that their FRU representative will do the best possible job on their behalf."

Allison confirms the important role that the FRU legal staff play: "They are a major reason I wanted to volunteer, as they are passionate about the work and an absolute goldmine of information. But the staff are there to help you get things right; they will not hold your hand through the work. No one will be in your client conference or at tribunal with you. It is your case and your responsibility. You need to develop a sense of when to ask for help and I think that's a useful skill to take to a training contract or pupillage."

David explains why volunteering for FRU is such a good experience for people who want a career at the Bar: "The essence of being a barrister is advocacy, which is something you can only learn through practical experience. Although you practise cross-examination and making submissions on the BPTC, it does not compare to the experience FRU offers by giving you the opportunity to appear as a representative in a tribunal. When you are in front of the judge, you know that it's down to you and this makes it particularly rewarding, whatever the outcome. In addition, FRU provides essential experience in client care and in taking on a case that may have been prepared by the client themselves or another agency."

Allison adds: "FRU work helps you to develop a real feeling for the strengths and weaknesses of a case, and then see it play out with all the unpredictable things that spring up along the way. Clients and cases are very diverse – for example, you might have a seriously mentally ill client in a social security case, who would struggle to attend their tribunal without your help, and then an employment client with a professional background who is legally knowledgeable and well prepared. Sometimes the work is about helping a client present the facts in the clearest way and sometimes there are points of law or complicated evidential issues – I have cross-examined a HR director over the calendar settings on his IT network!"

FRU helps volunteers to develop the ability to put someone at ease and listen to them, while keeping the legal issues in mind and getting the necessary information, explains Allison: "Clients may be very angry about how they've been treated at work or embarrassed to be applying for benefits and discussing personal medical issues with strangers. There can be a lot at stake financially too."

Finally, it feels great to be praised for your work by a member of the judiciary, reflects Allison: "One of the most rewarding aspects has been the respect and appreciation I've received from many judges. Judges know about FRU and some have even been volunteers themselves. They appreciate that we help tribunals run more smoothly and fairly."

For more information about FRU and how to become a volunteer, visit www.thefru.org.uk.

Vacation scheme insider reports

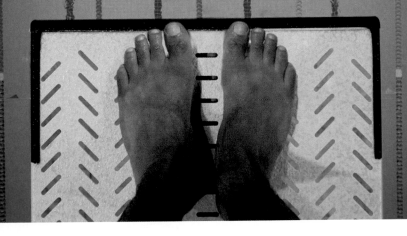

ALLEN & OVERY

It's your heart going faster.
Your knees going weaker.
Taking that one big deep breath.
IT'S TIME.

A career in Law

Our industry is changing faster than ever before. New ways of working create new opportunities, and we're looking for people who aren't afraid to challenge the status quo. If you want to realise your full potential, supported by a world-class development programme and mentored by some of the industry's leading experts, we want to hear from you. Search Allen & Overy Graduate to find out more.

A career in Law
Visit aograduate.com

@AllenOveryGrads   /allenoverygrads   AllenOveryGrads

Nassim Ikhlef is in his final year of a mathematics degree at Imperial College London. He attended a winter vacation scheme at A&O in December 2016 and will start at the firm in March 2019.

Insider report
Allen & Overy LLP

What did you do while on the vacation scheme?

Most of my time was spent at my seat which was in the banking practice of the firm. It was a busy period for the group which meant that there was no shortage of tasks I could help out with, despite my limited knowledge of the law. I reviewed contracts and updated documents as part of a due diligence for a deal, as well as researched and summarised particular areas of law. The graduate recruitment team organised a range of networking events, allowing us to meet people from different practice areas, at all levels within the firm. On the first day, we had a lovely lunch with the trainees, as well as a Q&A session with the managing partner.

What did you feel that you gained from the placement?

This experience offered a fascinating glimpse into the fast-paced work environment of an international commercial law firm. After the scheme, I felt I had a much better understanding of the type of work a lawyer performs and how they manage responsibilities. I was also able to appreciate the importance of the collective effort required to close a deal or complete a case.

It was the best way to understand the culture at A&O: it's clear that everyone works really hard and despite the pressures that can come with tight deadlines, people enjoy their work. You are working alongside an amazing set of people who derive a lot of satisfaction from what they do. They are all at the top of their profession too, so you learn an incredible amount just by sitting with them.

Which were the most enjoyable – and most challenging – aspects of the scheme?

It was a pleasure getting to know the other people on the scheme; I felt part of a very friendly, diverse and capable group. I really enjoyed working with them on the team tasks, which got me excited at the prospect of working together as trainees at the firm.

Coming from a non-law background, it was a challenge adjusting to the nature of the tasks that I had been assigned - maths is a stark contrast to law! But with the guidance and reassurances of the trainees and my supervisor, I became more confident as the week went on, and soon relished the fact I was making real contributions, however small, to the live deals that were going through.

Did the scheme end with a training contract interview or some other kind of further recruitment process?

There was no training contract interview at the end of the scheme; but we completed two tasks during the week, and there was a lot of emphasis on personal development. I know that the graduate recruitment team asked my supervisor for detailed feedback, so instead of completing the same interview I did to get on the scheme, the focus was on my performance during the week.

Is there one key thing that you took away from the experience that you would pass on as advice to others?

I would definitely encourage you to talk to as many different people as possible within the firm and ask plenty of questions! Everyone I met was kind, helpful, and happy to share their experiences of working at the firm. The trainees and the graduate recruitment team were great at putting you in touch with other people, so that you can meet up for a quick coffee and a chat. It gave me invaluable insight into the firm, the work they do and the culture, which you just can't get from a brochure or website.

No of scheme places
50

Location of schemes
London

Length of schemes
Varies

Remuneration (per week)
Competitive

Dates of schemes
Winter:
11-15 December 2017
Summer:
25 June – 6 July 2018

Closing date for applications
Winter:
31 October 2017
Summer:
31 December 2017

Application procedure
Online application form
www.aograduate.com

For full contact information and details of Training Contract, see the firm's full entry in the main directory on p280

Remember to cite *The Training Contract & Pupillage Handbook* on your application form if you apply to this law firm.

MOVE
YOUR MIND

Aim beyond pure legal knowledge. Beyond commercial advice.
Be known for something more: a clarity of thought and an instinct
for problem solving that can influence governments and leading
businesses the world over. Join us and we'll help you enrich and
expand your worldview, grow your skills and influence new ways
of thinking. In other words, we'll help you move minds.

Begin now at www.ashurst.com/en/careers

 AshurstGraduates   AshurstGraduates in Ashurst

ashurst

Matthew Vine studied law at the University of Nottingham. He attended Ashurst LLP's December 2016 winter scheme, will begin the LPC in September 2017 and start his training contract in September 2019.

What did you do while on the vacation scheme?

I helped trainees with various tasks, including drafting and taking documents to another firm for signing. I sat in on a very useful training session, where the team recapped on what was happening with a large restructuring deal; it was particularly useful to hear from the trainees about their role in that process. There were some great social events, including Bounce ping pong with trainees, ice-skating and a very nice dinner with partners. All were great opportunities to chat to a wide variety of people and learn more about their work and the firm.

What did you feel that you gained from the placement?

I gained true insight into the firm; it can be hard to distinguish between different firms on paper as you can't really know what each is like until you're there, so getting first-hand experience was invaluable. I also met so many people at the firm who seemed genuinely interested in me as a prospective trainee. Overall, my experience at the firm went beyond my expectations. I met people from all levels, including partners who took the time to talk to me about my career path and discuss their own professional experiences.

Which were the most enjoyable aspects of the scheme?

Again, meeting people at the firm was the most enjoyable part for me. There was so much effort put into ensuring that we had maximum exposure to lots of different people and experiences, through events and talks, including from the managing partner of the London office.

Did the scheme end with a training contract interview or some other kind of further recruitment process?

Once we had completed the vacation scheme, we were encouraged to send off a new training contract application, updated with more targeted knowledge and experiences that we'd gained through the scheme. We then had an hour-long interview with two partners. Having been lucky enough to receive an offer, I then felt instantly involved with the firm. All future trainees received telephone calls and regular email updates about the firm and future opportunities – which is how I applied for and got a paralegal role with a client of the firm.

Is there one key thing that you took away from the experience that you would pass on as advice to others?

Don't be shy; get out there and engage with people at all levels of the firm. It's the best way to find out what the culture is like, which is one of the most important things to know when deciding where is going to be a good fit for you. If you're polite and enthusiastic, you will get on well. And even if you don't end up working at that particular firm, you are likely to have made some useful contacts for the future.

No of scheme places
110

Location of schemes
London

Length of schemes
Spring: 1 weeks
Summer: 3 weeks

Remuneration (per week)
£400

Dates of schemes
Winter:
11-15 December 2017
Spring:
9-13 April 2018
Summer:
25 June-13 July 2018
23 July-10 August 2018

Closing date for applications
Winter:
5 November 2017
Spring and Summer:
7 January 2018

Application procedure
Online application accessed via the firm's website at www.ashurst.com/en/careers

For full contact information and details of Training Contract, see the firm's full entry in the main directory on p285

Remember to cite *The Training Contract & Pupillage Handbook* on your application form if you apply to this law firm.

WORK EXPERIENCE 71

OPPORTUNITY

If you're one of the handful of graduates who join Bristows LLP as trainee solicitors each year, you'll be exposed to a world of opportunity right from the start…

…opportunity to get involved with top tier work for clients in the most innovative industries.

…opportunity to work side-by-side with some of the most respected lawyers in their fields.

…opportunity to build your career in an environment where you'll be stretched but also get plenty of support and encouragement.

If we sound like the firm for you and you want to find out more, please visit training.bristows.com.

BRISTOWS

Sophie French is a law graduate from the University of Oxford. She attended a two-day workshop at Bristows in July 2016 and will start her training contract in September 2018.

What did you do while on the vacation scheme?

Although Bristows is particularly known for its IP expertise, the workshop provides great insight into the work done by the entire firm. We had presentations by partners from lots of different departments, including commercial, technology and copyright disputes; competition and real estate. We were also given info on live cases and heard from the managing partner on Bristows' strategy for the future. There was a group exercise, where we looked at different steps of a patent dispute, and a technical case study I found that particularly interesting because we had the chance to look at the apparatus at the centre of the dispute. In terms of networking, we had lunch with the trainees on the first day and partners on the second day, and drinks one evening with all the trainees, where we were able to ask questions about the firm in a very relaxed setting.

What did you feel that you gained from the placement?

Most importantly the placement confirmed my reasons for applying in the first place. For example, I'd never done any IP law before, so it was a great chance to learn more about what that involves. We also got insight into the day-to-day activities of a Bristows lawyer and I was able to experience first hand the innovative and collaborative working environment, which felt quite different to some of the other schemes I'd been on. As the firm has a relatively small intake, trainees definitely get more involved with the cases, which is something I was looking for.

Which were the most enjoyable – and most challenging – aspects of the scheme?

One of my favourite parts was a speed networking session where we had five minutes to speak to a range of employees, including secretaries and IT staff, as well as associates and partners.

It was a challenge to keep up with the intensity, as it was spread over just two days. We had a massive number of sessions and events, and to get the most out of it, you had to be on the ball. But I suppose that was good training for being a trainee!

Did the scheme end with a training contract interview or some other kind of further recruitment process?

We had a presentation from the grad rec team, with information on the next steps and really useful application and interview tips. We then had to submit a letter of update if we wanted to apply for a training contract, explaining what we'd learnt in the workshop, how our views of the firm – or what we were looking for – might have changed. If successful at that stage, you were then invited to two further interviews and an assessed exercise.

Is there one key thing that you took away from the experience that you would pass on as advice to others?

I found that having done some research into Bristows' current cases and clients really helped me to get the most out of the experience. I focused on learning about things that I was particularly interested in, which meant that I was able to ask questions in presentations to deepen my knowledge of the firm. I also had some handy topics of conversation when speaking with partners, which can be daunting if you're not sure what to discuss!

No of scheme places
36

Location of schemes
London

Length of schemes
Winter: workshop
(two days)
Spring: workshop
(two days)
Summer: workshop
(two days)

Dates of schemes
Winter: December 2017
Spring: April 2018
Summer: July 2018

Closing date for applications
See website

Application procedure
Online application form

For full contact information and details of Training Contract, see the firm's full entry in the main directory on p303

Constance O'Conor completed a vacation scheme at Clifford Chance in July 2016. She studied philosophy at Durham University.

What did you do while on the vacation scheme (eg, type of work, networking, presentations or social events)?

I spent the first week of the vacation scheme in the litigation department, which I had put forward as a preference. The work was hugely varied – I proofread documents, condensed a judicial report, did a costs submission and conducted some research for Save the Children, a pro bono client of the firm. In the second week I sat with the corporate funds team, which I hadn't requested in my application, but which I really enjoyed – it goes to show the importance of keeping an open mind and trying new things. In corporate funds I had fewer formal tasks, but sat in more on conference calls and spent more time with my supervisor on the work that she was doing. The firm also put on networking breakfasts with all the departments and there were also lots of coffees, lunches and dinners with the other vac schemers and people from across the firm.

What did you feel that you gained from the placement (eg, insight into the firm, useful contacts or an appreciation of a trainee's workload)?

The main thing I gained from the experience was confidence. I found the application process quite daunting and on the first day of the scheme, I arrived feeling almost like an impostor – particularly as I'm not a law student. But as soon as I arrived, I was made to feel like I fitted in – people were so generous with their time, while my fellow vac schemers were a diverse group of people.

Which were the most enjoyable – and most challenging – aspects of the scheme?

One of the most enjoyable aspects of the scheme for me was attending a pro bono session in Battersea. Clifford Chance lawyers commit to a certain number of pro bono hours and I went along with a couple of trainees from corporate funds. It was great to see the firm engaging with and helping the local community, especially as I have previously volunteered for the Citizens Advice Bureau. However, probably the most enjoyable aspect of the scheme in general was all the people I met and getting to know their interests.

There was one moment where I felt that I hadn't been at my best – I was asked to do a piece of research and I struggled with it. I wasn't happy with what I handed in, but that night I went home and redid the research with new information that I found, and handed that in the next day, after which I felt a lot better.

Did the scheme end with a training contract interview or some other kind of further recruitment process?

Yes. I was so nervous beforehand, but the interview took the form of a really interesting conversation with a female partner, which took in what I had learned on the scheme as well as my interests outside law. It was much more relaxed than the interview process for a place on the vacation scheme in the first place.

Is there one key thing that you took away from the experience that you would pass on as advice to others?

Talk to everybody and do everything with the greatest possible energy. And remember to be enthusiastic, as you will be working with people who are giving up valuable time to show you the ropes.

No of scheme places
30

Location of schemes
London

Length of schemes
2 weeks

Remuneration (per week)
£450

Dates of schemes
2-13 July 2018

Closing date for applications
3 January 2018

Application procedure
Via our website www.cliffordchancegraduates.com

For full contact information and details of Training Contract, see the firm's full entry in the main directory on p313

Remember to cite *The Training Contract & Pupillage Handbook* on your application form if you apply to this law firm.

74 THE TRAINING CONTRACT & PUPILLAGE HANDBOOK

Dorothea James studied philosophy at the University of Durham and the GDL at BPP. She attended the two-week summer scheme at Ince & Co in June 2016 and will start her training contract at the firm in September 2018.

What did you do while on the vacation scheme?
I spent both weeks of the scheme in the shipping department, which was a great opportunity to get deeply involved, while carrying on my work throughout the duration of my vacation scheme. I had the chance to meet some of the shipping clients, as well as sit in on a mediation, which was a fantastic experience. Further to this, I was involved with a client drinks event hosted by the firm, which was a great chance to engage with clients in a social environment. To top the scheme off, an event was held for all on the scheme and trainees at the firm; this was a brilliant way to get to know more about life at the firm as well as find out about other people's experience on the vacation scheme.

What did you feel that you gained from the placement?
The biggest thing I took away was what I learnt about the firm's ethos; it is very hard to differentiate between firms on paper, so once you're there you can see how it all works as a cohesive whole. Ince promotes a social and comfortable, yet professional working environment, meaning that I felt able to speak to anyone at the firm, and find out about their career and experiences there.

Which were the most enjoyable – and most challenging – aspects of the scheme?
The most enjoyable experience was being party to the mediation hearing; it was thoroughly interesting to see the lawyers and their clients in action, to see the way they interacted and seeing the mediator at work was also very intriguing. Having not seen this before, I learnt a lot through seeing a different set of skills in use. I felt privileged having the opportunity to have such an invaluable experience so early on.

One of the challenges I was warned about early on was taking on too much work, and with the amount of opportunities offered to me, it was a tough job managing this when the temptation to get involved with so many things is so great. You needed to work out what you can realistically manage with the time you had available, say yes to as much as you can, but realise it is a balancing act and you don't want to spread yourself too thin.

Did the scheme end with a training contract interview or some other kind of further recruitment process?
At the end of the two weeks you are invited for an interview with a partner and HR. During the interview you discuss the firm, what you've done during the scheme and what you have gained from it overall. You are also tested on your commercial awareness.

Is there one key thing that you took away from the experience that you would pass on as advice to others?
Be proactive; you've got an amazing opportunity in front of you at the firm, so make the most of it. Ask as many questions as you can, absorb as much as you can, and get involved with as much as possible. It's a fantastic two weeks, and to make the most of it you have to put yourself out there.

No of scheme places
10

Location of schemes
London

Length of schemes
2 weeks

Remuneration (per week)
£350

Dates of schemes
Spring 2018

Closing date for applications
31 January 2018

Application procedure
Apply online at incegraduates.com

For full contact information and details of Training Contract, see the firm's full entry in the main directory on p370

Remember to cite *The Training Contract & Pupillage Handbook* on your application form if you apply to this law firm.

Global game-changers

Space &
Satellite
New York

Technology
Transactions
Silicon Valley

Fin-Tech &
Blockchain
London

Driverless Cars
Paris

Cybersecurity
Sydney

Renewable
Energy
Johannesburg

Privacy
Hong Kong

Drones
Washington

The world is changing. So is business. Every day there are new technologies, new
medicines, new routes to cleaner power. Our global team of lawyers works across
practice areas to help clients to think ahead and shape the future. Find out how you
could make innovation possible with a career in law at

hoganlovells.com/graduates

Georgia Davies is in the final year of a psychology degree at the University of Durham. She took part in a spring 2017 vacation scheme at Hogan Lovells and will commence her training contact at the firm in September 2019.

Insider report

Hogan Lovells

What did you do while on the vacation scheme?
The entire scheme was very well structured. We spent the two weeks in two different departments – my first week was in corporate, then in capital markets. I gained technical insight into two of the firm's leading practices by attending internal meetings, listening in on client calls and helping with trainee-level work. I was asked to complete some independent research and answer specific legal questions set by my supervisor. In addition I helped the trainees with pro bono drafting, which gave me insight into another side of their work. There were presentations specifically for the vacation scheme students, including corporate and finance case studies, a session on advocacy skills, and a presentation on the firm's international and business strategy. There were also plenty of networking opportunities; we had an assortment of trainee mentors in each department and we were able to get to know them over coffee, drinks and even taking part in an underground cookery school! We were also able to chat to the partners, including at a celebratory meal at the end of the scheme, where we could ask informal questions and get advice.

What did you feel that you gained from the placement?
Coming from a non-law background, it definitely improved my knowledge of the law from a technical and practical perspective, as I was able to really integrate into the departments and see the work done by lawyers at all levels. I also gained a more specific insight into the firm's culture; everyone I talked to – partners, trainees and business staff – was so friendly and there is a true open-door policy; you are encouraged to seek advice and speak to everyone. I was impressed by how much time my supervisor took to explain things to me.

Which were the most enjoyable – and most challenging – aspects of the scheme?
Undoubtedly, the most enjoyable part of the scheme was the group presentation; we were split into two teams and our brief was to pitch a business development idea to a selection of partners. We had to collaborate with each other and seek advice from the different departments, and come up with something tangible by the end of the scheme. It was a great way to get to know each other better. I was with a real mix of students, including some who'd already done the GDL and LPC, so it was great to compare experiences and get advice from people at different stages of the process. The most challenging, but also one of the most enjoyable aspects, was getting stuck into the intricacies of the law, especially in capital markets – you have to fully immerse yourself in the subject matter. However, once you've done this, it's really enjoyable.

Did the scheme end with a training contract interview or some other kind of further recruitment process?
On the final Thursday we had an interview with two partners, with notes from our original interview and references from our supervisors about how things had gone in the different departments. It was a discussion about the work we'd done and skills gained, focusing on the reflective journal that we had been encouraged to keep during our time at the firm.

Is there one key thing that you took away from the experience that you would pass on as advice to others?
The most important thing is to be yourself; if you are, it will all go smoothly. This is a two-way process and you need to find a complementary fit. You also need to make the most of all the opportunities, both formal and informal – be enthusiastic and confident, speak to people and ask tons of questions.

No of scheme places
65

Location of schemes
London

Length of schemes
2-3 weeks

Remuneration (per week)
£400

Dates of schemes
Winter:
4-15 December 2017
Spring:
9-20 April 2018
Summer:
19 June – 6 July 2018
16 July – 3 August 2018

Closing date for applications
Winter:
31 October 2017
Spring:
7 January 2018
Summer:
7 January 2018

Application procedure
Visit our website at www.hoganlovells.com/graduates to find out more information and complete an application form online

For full contact information and details of Training Contract, see the firm's full entry in the main directory on p364

Remember to cite *The Training Contract & Pupillage Handbook* on your application form if you apply to this law firm.

Leonie Ghirardi studied law at University of Reading. She completed a vacation scheme at Jones Day in Spring 2016 and will start her training there in September 2018.

What did you do while on the vacation scheme?

Mirroring the non-rotational nature of training at Jones Day, there were no 'seats' during the vacation scheme. I wasn't assigned to a department or supervisor; instead I was required to 'walk the floors' – a term often used at Jones Day – to seek my own work. As well as helping me get to know the lawyers of the firm, it also gave me exposure to a wide variety of practice areas, which is one of the great benefits of the firm's training model. I was involved in renegotiating the terms of a partnership deed and actually found myself drafting the notes that were to be sent to the client, which was an exciting level of responsibility. I carried out some financial due diligence for a multijurisdictional deal and was involved in a data protection breach case, as well as in tasks with the real estate, IP and competition law teams. I also sat in on client conference calls and even attended an external investors' meeting with a firm associate. In addition to this 'live' work, all vacation scheme candidates participated in a group negotiation exercise – which was a lot of fun – and a one-on-one business discussion where we had to pitch a client we thought the firm should represent and justify our arguments to a partner. The scheme was also packed with social events, including firm receptions and a ping pong social where the graduate recruitment team got really involved! I also attended an optional workshop which discussed the ethical issues solicitors could face and professional conduct, which was enjoyable and insightful.

What did you feel that you gained from the placement?

I gained a great insight into the firm. I left with a real understanding of the practice areas and working culture of the office. I also got a real appreciation of the non-rotational training contract structure and a sense of a trainee's role within the firm, as well as the demands that trainees face within a fast-paced, commercial environment.

Which were the most enjoyable – and most challenging – aspects of the scheme?

Walking the floors was the best aspect of the scheme, for me. Every day I arrived knowing that I would meet new people and try something new. Lawyers at Jones Day know that trainees and vacation schemers will be knocking on their doors to ask for work – it is ingrained in the culture at the firm – so they were all friendly and happy to get me involved in their work. The flipside to the non-rotational system was having to manage conflicting priorities, which was challenging to get to grips with in two weeks. But I felt that this gave an accurate reflection of how life as a lawyer in the City would be.

Did the scheme end with a training contract interview or some other kind of further recruitment process?

Candidates knew we were being assessed throughout the scheme on our work product. All vacation schemers are guaranteed a training contract interview. This is conducted during the scheme rather than at the end to allow candidates to take feedback on board and still have a chance to secure a training contract before the scheme concludes. This assessment approach was very holistic, which I valued.

Is there one key thing that you took away from the experience that you would pass on as advice to others?

Be yourself as much as possible, because the environment at Jones Day is one which can really bring out the best in you.

No of scheme places
72

Location of schemes
London

Length of schemes
2 weeks

Remuneration (per week)
£400

Dates of schemes
Winter:
December 2017
Spring:
April 2018
Summer:
July 2018

Closing date for applications
Applications open on 1 September 2017. We recruit on a rolling basis and cannot guarantee availability, so apply early.
Final deadlines:
Winter:
27 October 2017
Spring:
15 December 2017
Summer:
10 January 2018
We recruit nearly all trainees from our placement candidates.

Application procedure
Online at www.jonesdaylondon.com

For full contact information and details of Training Contracts, see the firm's full entry in the main directory on p373

Remember to cite *The Training Contract & Pupillage Handbook* on your application form if you apply to this law firm.

WORK EXPERIENCE 79

WHAT IF YOU WANT TO STAND OUT FROM THE CROWD?

At Kirkland & Ellis we keep our trainee intake small giving you the chance to shine.

We hire just 10 trainees each year and provide them with high quality work from day one. You will be treated as a lawyer from the start and be given every opportunity for success.

Graduate careers in law
UKGRADUATE.KIRKLAND.COM

KIRKLAND & ELLIS INTERNATIONAL LLP

The Gherkin, 30 St Mary Axe, London

Adrian Kilercioglu studied politics, philosophy and law at King's College London. He completed a vacation scheme at Kirkland & Ellis in June 2016.

What did you do while on the vacation scheme (eg, type of work, networking, presentations or social events)?

There was a healthy mix of work and social events, alongside daily presentations on each of the firm's practice areas which were interesting, honest and informative, especially for those of us who had not spent much time in a law firm before. I sat in the finance team, where among other things I was asked to look at a template loan agreement and take out certain clauses, which was a challenging, but very interesting task. It was useful to experience what a trainee in the finance team might do on a day-to-day basis.

We were paired up with both a trainee buddy and an associate supervisor. The trainees and associates often took us out for lunch, where we could ask lots of questions in a more relaxed environment. We went out one day near the Gherkin to play mini-golf and were also invited to the firm's summer party on the last day of the scheme, which was really fun.

What did you feel that you gained from the placement (eg, insight into the firm, useful contacts or an appreciation of a trainee's workload)?

This wasn't my first vacation scheme or experience of corporate law, so the main benefit of the scheme for me was the chance to experience the culture at the firm – how colleagues interact with each other and so on. There are twin benefits to securing a place on such a scheme – experiencing the kind of work that solicitors do and getting a feel for a firm as a place to work, which was the most important thing for me when choosing a firm.

Which were the most enjoyable – and most challenging – aspects of the scheme?

Both the most enjoyable and most challenging aspect of scheme related to the work I was given. Most importantly, the work very interesting and varied – I absorbed so much useful information in the space of 10 days. Aside from the tasks set by our associate supervisors and trainee buddies, we were strongly encouraged to go out and seek work from others too. This meant I was able to complete work and gain an insight into different teams during my time on the scheme.

The work I was set was also challenging, as there were many unfamiliar concepts, particularly related to finance. Luckily, my associate supervisor and trainee buddy were great at explaining things, and really took the time to walk through my assignments with me.

Did the scheme end with a training contract interview or some other kind of further recruitment process?

Yes, everyone was interviewed over the last two days of the scheme.

Is there one key thing that you took away from the experience that you would pass on as advice to others?

The most important thing when applying is to be concise. Recruiters read hundreds of applications, so you need to make sure that they can see your key information easily and quickly to get through the first sift. And when on the scheme, bear in mind that you are in an assessment – even though the experience itself is really enjoyable. You have beaten hundreds of people to get onto the scheme, so at that point it really is yours to clinch.

No of scheme places
30

Location of schemes
London

Length of schemes
2 weeks

Remuneration (per week)
£500

Dates of schemes
Spring and Summer 2018

Closing date for applications
/ January 2018

Application procedure
Apply online at
ukgraduate.kirkland.com

For full contact information and details of Training Contract, see the firm's full entry in the main directory on p379

LawCareers.Net™

Delivering your future in law

LCN Weekly is packed with news, profiles, opinion and advice about becoming a lawyer, and delivered to your inbox for free every Tuesday.

Don't miss out on this essential source of information!

Subscribe to LCN Weekly at
www.lawcareers.net/mylcn/

Sanaa Mekki completed a vacation scheme at Linklaters in July 2016. She studied law at the London School of Economics.

Insider report
Linklaters LLP

What did you do while on the vacation scheme?
I sat in two departments over the four-week scheme: capital markets and banking. The scheme was comprehensive, with a good mix of work and social events. As well as after-work socials twice a week, we also regularly met up for working breakfasts and lunches. I attended a number of talks about the firm, learning about its practice areas and strategy. There was always help at hand as I sat next to an associate or managing associate, and I was given plenty of interesting work to do. I even received work from associates in other departments.

What did you feel that you gained from the placement?
A lot of people don't know what working in commercial law really involves as it's not generally taught at university. So it was great to experience it first-hand. I realised how complex and intricately connected the firm's different departments are. Overall, the experience really confirmed that this was the kind of career I wanted.

Which were the most enjoyable – and most challenging – aspects of the scheme?
The group work I did with my fellow vacation schemers was one of the highlights. Teamed up, we were tasked with pitching work to a panel of partners. They were playing the roles of potential clients so that it was a realistic simulation of a commercial solicitor's role.

Trying to balance priorities was a challenge. For example, I would be given work to do by an associate just as I was about to attend a presentation. And throughout the scheme each of us had to work on a personal project in addition to all the different things we were doing each day.

Did the scheme end with a training contract interview or some other kind of further recruitment process?
There is always an interview with a partner at the end of the scheme. Nothing about it is fixed, so it was unlike the interview process to get onto the scheme, which was split into a competency interview and a technical interview. Instead, I was asked questions which ranged from technical matters to finding out a bit more about me. Although an interview like that is difficult to prepare for, the experience itself wasn't daunting at all. The partner wanted to give me the opportunity to demonstrate my skills, not to catch me out.

Is there one key thing that you took away from the experience that you would pass on as advice to others?
Take everything in and make sure that you're focused on learning as much as possible about Linklaters, for example, the firm's strategy and future plans for different areas of practice. It's really important to demonstrate your specific interest in the role and the firm.

No of scheme places
110

Location of schemes
London

Length of schemes
Winter: 2 weeks
Spring: 2 weeks
Summer: 4 weeks

Dates of schemes
Winter, Spring, and Summer (penultimate-year and final-year undergraduates, graduates and postgraduates)

Application procedure
Online application form, critical thinking test, case study and two interviews

For full contact information and details of Training Contract, see the firm's full entry in the main directory on p385

MACFARLANES

EXCEPTIONAL LAWYERS.
WITHOUT EXCEPTION.

Louise Thompson completed a vacation scheme at Macfarlanes in Spring 2017. She studied economics at the University of York.

What did you do while on the vacation scheme (eg, type of work, networking, presentations or social events)?

I sat in two different departments – commercial real estate and competition – and experienced a wide variety of work in each. This included research tasks on specific points of law, working on documents and contacting various organisations to help the trainee I was shadowing. The scheme was also broken up with talks by members of the firm's different departments, while there were also lots of social events with trainees, associates and partners, which enabled me to meet people of various levels of seniority right across the firm.

What did you feel that you gained from the placement (eg, insight into the firm, useful contacts or an appreciation of a trainee's workload)?

Although it feels like you're trying constantly to impress the firm, a vacation scheme is equally about assessing whether the firm is right for you. Before attending the scheme I knew that I was interested in Macfarlanes, but I needed to quantify and prove that my reasons were sound, which is why the vacation scheme was key. My experience wasn't daunting at all and I gained a good understanding of the firm's culture, as everyone I came across was friendly and helpful. Even if you attend a vacation scheme and don't like the firm in question, you have still learned something.

Which were the most enjoyable – and most challenging – aspects of the scheme?

The most enjoyable aspect was the combination of working full-time in a professional environment, but with fellow vacation schemers going through the same, new experience alongside me. It was great to be able to bond with the other students, share our questions, and support each other. The most challenging aspect of the vacation scheme is making sure that you are on top of all the work that you are given. During the second week there was a training contract assessment as well as a negotiation exercise, both of which were ancillary to the work I was doing for my supervising trainee. It was very important to be organised and keep a note of every task that I was assigned, so that I didn't forget anything.

Did the scheme end with a training contract interview or some other kind of further recruitment process?

There were three different assessments spread over two days, which was welcomed rather than having them all on the same day. First there was a written exercise which posed a problem and asked for a logical solution, with little legal knowledge needed. The second assessment was a competency interview, which was essentially a relaxed chat with a partner about my experiences on the scheme. The third and final stage was another interview on a case study, which absolutely flew by as there was a lot to get through in just 25 minutes. In contrast to some of my friends who experienced schemes at other firms before attending interviews at a later date, I found that having the assessment process during the scheme itself made it much less daunting, as I was used to the environment and had already met many people at the firm.

Is there one key thing that you took away from the experience that you would pass on as advice to others?

Ask other people for help and advice, whether friends who have experienced a vacation scheme before, or people at the firm who you may not have met before. It is more than likely that a trainee whom you have only just met will be very happy to help. I would also advise using the services of diversity organisations such as Aspiring Solicitors, which were so instrumental in getting me where I am today.

No of scheme places
55

Location of schemes
London

Length of schemes
2 weeks

Remuneration (per week)
£330

Dates of schemes
Easter:
3-13 April 2018
Summer:
25 June – 6 July 2018
9 July – 20 July 2018

Closing date for applications
31 January 2018

Application procedure
Online application via our website www.macfarlanes.com/graduates followed by an open day

For full contact information and details of Training Contract, see the firm's full entry in the main directory on p387

Thierry Houle-Graham completed a vacation scheme at Mayer Brown in April 2017. He studied law at University College London.

Mayer Brown International LLP

What did you do while on the vacation scheme (eg, type of work, networking, presentations or social events)?

During my first week I sat in banking and finance, and during the second week I was in the insurance litigation department. In finance, I worked on the financing of a copper mine in Panama, which was really exciting. My tasks included comparing term sheets from three previous transactions involving the same party to highlight conditions that other counterparties had agreed to in previous transactions. Mayer Brown used these previous transactions to illustrate why the counterparties involved in this transaction should agree to the same conditions that other parties had agreed to in the past.

The firm's graduate recruitment team organised various social events. On the last day we visited Mayer Brown's Paris office, which gave us the opportunity to understand how the firm's offices across the globe collaborate with one another. The trainees were also very proactive.

What did you feel that you gained from the placement (eg, insight into the firm, useful contacts or an appreciation of a trainee's workload)?

You never know what the firm's culture is like until you experience it yourself. At Mayer Brown I found I could approach anyone with a question, from trainees to partners. Experiencing the niche, technical, international work that I undertook during my time in the finance department gave me a great insight into what I could expect from a career as a commercial solicitor.

Which were the most enjoyable – and most challenging – aspects of the scheme?

The investment reports that I drafted for various African countries were particularly interesting, as I was in completely new territory. I summarised key legal points related to mining rights and corporate governance in Zambia, Ghana and Namibia.

While working on the financing of the mine, I was asked to check documentation sent by our Panamanian counterparts. My supervisor had given me the list of documents we needed, which was in English. However, the documents I received from Panama were all in Spanish, so I had to use my very limited Spanish to translate the documents enough to figure out whether they were the right ones. That was certainly a challenging moment!

Did the scheme end with a training contract interview or some other kind of further recruitment process?

There is a formal interview to get onto the scheme and at the end of the two weeks, you have a 30-minute talk with two partners and a member of graduate recruitment. It is less of an interview and more of a chance to talk about what you have learned and ask any questions that you might have.

Is there one key thing that you took away from the experience that you would pass on as advice to others?

Be enthusiastic and don't be afraid to volunteer for work, particularly if there is a piece of work you are interested in. As I mentioned earlier, most of my work throughout the scheme centred on the financing of a copper mine in Panama. The only reason I worked on that transaction was because I volunteered to do a simple document review when the senior associate on the transaction first asked for help. Once I finished that task, I asked her if there was anything else I could do, and every day from then she gave me new tasks, because she knew I was interested.

No of scheme places
30

Location of schemes
London

Length of schemes
2 weeks

Remuneration (per week)
£275

Dates of schemes
Spring 2018
Summer 2018

Closing date for applications
31 January 2018

Application procedure
Online

For full contact information and details of Training Contract, see the firm's full entry in the main directory on p391

Achieve more. Together.

At Mills & Reeve we believe our culture is truly unique. We have made a commitment to providing an exceptional platform for personal growth for all our people. The training and support they receive is second to none.

If you want to start your career working with world-class lawyers, delivering sector-leading legal advice to an international client list, then get in touch.

How to apply:
Online at www.mills-reeve.com/graduates

Application closing dates:
Summer placements - 31 January for 2018
2020 training contracts - 31 July 2018

Number of vacancies:
36 summer placements
20 training contracts

Contact:
Fiona Medlock,
Graduate Recruitment Manager
01223 222336
fiona.medlock@mills-reeve.com
www.mills-reeve.com/graduates

MILLS & REEVE

Achieve more. Together.

Jonathan Christy studied law at the University of Nottingham and is currently on the LPC. He attended a two-week summer vacation scheme at Mills & Reeve (Cambridge office) in July 2016 and will start his training contract in September 2017.

What did you do while on the vacation scheme?
The scheme is split into four mini seats. I sat in the employment, real estate, corporate and family departments. You're allocated a supervisor in each, who looks after you and ensures that you're given a broad range of work to do from everyone in the team. On my first day, I attended the Employment Tribunal in London, and on day two I was at the Crown Court recording a plea, on my own! I was thrown straight in at the deep end, which was great. I also attended meetings, analysed case reports, helped to amend a company's articles of association, and researched the law on boundaries.

On the social side, all the vac schemers went out for a meal, which ensured that we got to know each other. I played in a seven-a-side football match against local businesses, went punting and took part in a variety of other social gatherings with the trainees. They were all great opportunities to ask questions and get to know people.

What did you feel that you gained from the placement?
I gained true insight into the firm, including its culture and working practices, which enabled me to understand the expectations it has of its trainees and how they can expect to be treated while here. It also helped me to understand why the firm has been in the Sunday Times 'Best 100 companies to work for' list for the past 14 years! The non-hierarchical set-up was reflected in the open-plan office and the fact that everyone I spoke to was approachable and willing to help.

Which were the most enjoyable – and most challenging – aspects of the scheme?
I both enjoyed and was challenged by being invited to client meetings. It wasn't just a 'fly on the wall' scenario; the partners would ask me questions on strategy and legal matters afterwards, so that was a challenge – but it also gave me the chance to show my understanding and social intellect, and my ability to interpret the environment I was in. It was a real confidence builder, because you're being treated as someone with something useful to contribute.

Did the scheme end with a training contract interview or some other kind of further recruitment process?
On our last day we had an informal meeting with graduate recruiter Fiona Medlock, where we discussed feedback from the teams and were asked for our evaluation of the scheme. The assessment centre and partner interview occur before the scheme, so having secured a spot, you're automatically being considered for a training contract. If you're a good match for the firm you're in with a good chance.

Is there one key thing that you took away from the experience that you would pass on as advice to others?
You should recognise that completing tasks to a high standard is a must, but a key part of the experience is for the firm to see if your personality is a good match with its ethos. So be enthusiastic, get involved in all opportunities and show them what you have to offer as a future colleague and member of the firm.

No of scheme places
36

Location of schemes
Birmingham, Cambridge, Manchester, Norwich

Length of schemes
2 weeks

Remuneration (per week)
£300

Dates of schemes
June and July 2018

Closing date for applications
31 January 2018

Application procedure
Firm's online application form

For full contact information and details of Training Contract, see the firm's full entry in the main directory on p396

Aidan Coghlan studied history at the University of Oxford. He completed a vacation scheme at Osborne Clarke LLP in Summer 2015.

What did you do while on the vacation scheme?
I spent two weeks with the firm. In my first week, I sat with the equity capital markets branch of the corporate team and in the second, I sat with the restructuring and insolvency team. I had previously expressed an interest in both areas, so it was kind of the firm to give me the opportunity to experience them first hand. The majority of my work comprised of preparing documents for live matters brought by real clients. This included compiling company search reports; running a winding-up check on a company; proofreading an equity subscription agreement; and drafting a response to a client query. I was given regular and extensive feedback on what I had done by senior associates, while on one occasion a partner in the banking team took me through the lending documentation process and spent a good hour explaining to me what the client was looking to achieve. On top of that, the trainees were tireless in supporting me, so I was able to improve as the placement progressed.

What did you feel that you gained from the placement?
I gained three key things from the placement. First, I gained a valuable insight into the day-to-day life of a trainee, as the majority of what I participated in was real work delegated to the trainee looking after me. Second, the vacation scheme has allowed me to form relationships with people at the firm before I commence training, as I was able to meet many great people through internal networking events, including the firm's summer party. Third, I discovered that Osborne Clarke has a really warm, non-hierarchical and supportive culture, along with its rigorous processes and systems. I knew that it was important to find a firm that would be a great cultural fit for me, so experiencing life at the firm was a big win for me, as I wanted to join a firm that I would be happy working in, but I also want to do very high-quality work.

Which were the most enjoyable – and most challenging – aspects of the scheme?
I wanted to learn what life as a trainee at the firm is really like, while everyone wants to feel that what they are doing is useful, so I really enjoyed being involved in the firm's real work. The most challenging part of the scheme was learning to prioritise tasks and to perform them efficiently, while still being precise and thorough within the time constraints.

Did the scheme end with a training contract interview or some other kind of further recruitment process?
There were a number of assessed elements to the scheme, including group presentations, aptitude tests, an appraisal of written work, a psychometric evaluation and an end-of-placement interview. They were pretty thorough – I slipped through the net somehow!

Is there one key thing that you took away from the experience that you would pass on as advice to others?
Try to relax, because my impression is that at Osborne Clarke, people want you to succeed and they also want to get to know you as a person. Be yourself – that's what a trainee advised me, so it is worth passing on.

No of scheme places
35

Location of schemes
Bristol, London and Reading

Length of schemes
2 weeks

Remuneration (per week)
£275

Dates of schemes
June – July 2018

Closing date for applications
15 January 2018

Application procedure
Please visit our website www.osborneclarke.com/ trainees and complete our online application form.

For full contact information and details of Training Contract, see the firm's full entry in the main directory on p406

Insider report
Reed Smith

Alice Powell studied European studies and French at King's College London. She completed a vacation scheme at Reed Smith in Summer 2016.

What did you do while on the vacation scheme (eg, type of work, networking, presentations or social events)?

I experienced two different seats over the course of the two weeks. I spent the first week with the energy and natural resources team, and the second week with the shipping team. The scheme involved a mix of real work and learning. I drafted emails, sat in on meetings and listened in on conference calls; I also attended useful workshops on presenting and negotiating. Vac schemers also took part in a mock employment tribunal, in which we split into two teams and argued the case in front of a former judge, which was so much fun! Finally, there were plenty of opportunities to socialise throughout the two weeks, with welcome drinks and other socials. I felt that I gained a strong overview of the firm – I met a variety of people and really developed an understanding of the work the firm does.

What did you feel that you gained from the placement (eg, insight into the firm, useful contacts or an appreciation of a trainee's workload)?

I gained a good appreciation of what a law firm does in terms of day-to-day work and how different departments interact. Perhaps the main benefit of the scheme was the opportunity I was given to see what working at the firm is really like and whether I would fit in. The scheme really immersed me into life at the firm and made me feel included and part of everything that was going on.

Which were the most enjoyable – and most challenging – aspects of the scheme?

I enjoyed meeting all the people at the firm and made the most of all the social opportunities – I even joined the netball team for the two weeks that I was on the scheme. I also loved all the activities and opportunities that were provided, including the mock employment tribunal. It all ensured that even if I didn't secure a training contract, I would still come away with a really valuable experience that would stand me in good stead for the future.

Getting my head around all the legal concepts which were quite new to me was certainly challenging, but everyone was so supportive and always had time to explain things, so help was always available if I needed it.

Did the scheme end with a training contract interview or some other kind of further recruitment process?

Yes, the fourth day of the second week was focused on our assessment – half of us went in the morning and the others went in the afternoon. The assessments involved a previously unseen exercise, an interview and a group exercise. The firm was very prompt in providing feedback – we all heard back within a few days.

Is there one key thing that you took away from the experience that you would pass on as advice to others?

If you secure a place on a vacation scheme, the firm will already know that you are intelligent, having seen your academic achievements already. Doing well on a vacation scheme is therefore not so much about proving that you are clever, but showing that you are hardworking, reliable and someone with whom others want to work. If you want to be there, show it by joining in and taking all the opportunities that arise.

No of scheme places
20

Location of schemes
London

Length of schemes
2 weeks

Remuneration (per week)
£330

Dates of schemes
End of June and end of July

Closing date for applications
31 January 2018

Application procedure
Online application form via our website
www.reedsmith.com/ukgraduates

For full contact information and details of Training Contract, see the firm's full entry in the main directory on p418

Remember to cite *The Training Contract & Pupillage Handbook* on your application form if you apply to this law firm.

92 THE TRAINING CONTRACT & PUPILLAGE HANDBOOK

Joseph Akwaboa completed a vacation scheme at RPC in July 2016. He studied law at the University of the West of England.

What did you do while on the vacation scheme (eg, type of work, networking, presentations or social events)?

The two-week scheme was divided in half, with one week spent in an insurance seat and the next in a commercial seat. I sat with the professional and financial risks team during my first week and the construction and projects team for the second. In my insurance seat I attended client meetings and took attendance notes, while during my commercial seat I undertook a lot of research tasks and also drafted a number of letters. The experience gave me a great insight into what solicitors at RPC do and how interesting – not to mention time-sensitive – the work is. There was also an opportunity to write for the firm's trainee-run blog, 'RPC trainees take on business', which puts out regular content via the firm's website. On the social side, we had a karaoke night in the first week and went bowling in the second week – a lot of the trainees attended both events and it was nice to get to know them while winding down in the evening. There was also a 'speed networking' session which was a good way to meet trainees from across the firm and learn about the different departments.

What did you feel that you gained from the placement (eg, insight into the firm, useful contacts or an appreciation of a trainee's workload)?

Throughout the two weeks I was officially an employee of the firm and I was treated as one, rather than someone on work experience. That was evident in lots of small things, from how I arrived to find my own desk set up and personalised in exactly the same way as the associates' and partners' desks, to being invited to play football as part of the firm's 'inter-house system', which facilitates friendly competition between those assigned to the Reynolds, Porter and Chamberlain 'houses' within the firm. I was also afforded an excellent insight into RPC's work – it is one thing to read about what firms do and quite another to get involved yourself and see it first-hand.

Which were the most enjoyable – and most challenging – aspects of the scheme?

The most enjoyable part of the scheme was sitting in on a client meeting with a partner and a senior associate, as well as the client's head of legal. It was my job to write up the attendance notes for circulation to the client and it was fascinating to see how lawyers discuss ideas and the different aspects of a transaction – commercial and legal – from different perspectives. The most challenging aspect of the scheme was juggling the various priorities.

Did the scheme end with a training contract interview or some other kind of further recruitment process?

All of the vacation schemers attended a training contract interview with a partner and a member of HR on the last day of the scheme.

Is there one key thing that you took away from the experience that you would pass on as advice to others?

The main thing I have learned is that it is so important to ask lots of questions and engage with all the aspects of the firm. Engaging with the work goes without saying, but you should also make the most of all the social opportunities given to you.

No of scheme places
24

Location of schemes
London

Length of schemes
2 weeks

Remuneration (per week)
£300

Dates of schemes
Summer:
18-29 June 2018
2-13 July 2018

Closing date for applications
19 January 2018

Application procedure
Recruitment for our summer schemes usually takes place in either January or February. Shortlisted candidates will be invited to one of our assessment days during which they will meet our existing trainees, associates, legal directors and partners

For full contact information and details of Training Contract, see the firm's full entry in the main directory on p423

Remember to cite *The Training Contract & Pupillage Handbook* on your application form if you apply to this law firm.

WORK EXPERIENCE | 93

The Law Society

GO FOR GOLD!

THE LAW SOCIETY HAS JUST CONFIRMED OUR 'GOLD' STATUS IN ITS DIVERSITY AND INCLUSION CHARTER

BIRMINGHAM | BASINGSTOKE | BELFAST | EDINBURGH | LEEDS | LONDON | MANCHESTER
MILTON KEYNES | NORTHAMPTON | NOTTINGHAM | SOUTHAMPTON | THAMES VALLEY

SHOOSMITHS

WWW.SHOOSMITHS.CO.UK | WWW.TWITTER.COM/SHOOSMITHSGRADS
WWW.FACEBOOK.COM/SHOOSMITHSGRADUATES | WWW.INSTAGRAM.COM/SHOOSMITHSGRADS

Hannah Howard is in the fourth and final year of a part-time law degree at the University of Buckingham. She attended a one-week scheme at Shoosmiths in April 2016.

What did you do while on the vacation scheme?
My placement took place in the employment team. I had the chance to do research for a senior associate, check contracts against precedent documents, review client amendments to contracts, as well as sitting in on training and interdepartmental case law updates. In terms of assessment, we had a mini-assignment and a presentation to fit in around the other work that we were given. On the social side, we had lunches with the trainees and other colleagues – Shoosmiths really encourages everyone to take time away from their desks, which was refreshing.

What did you feel that you gained from the placement?
I gained an excellent insight into the ethos of the firm. On paper, it sounded perfect – I'm a career changer and wanted a firm that valued work-life balance, with a focus on hiring individuals, not carbon copy trainees. I was hoping that my experience would live up to those expectations but it more than surpassed it. Everybody – paralegals, trainees, associates, partners – was so accommodating and willing to give me tasks and feedback, ensuring that I understood what I was doing. I also learnt how Shoosmiths works as a business, the different practice areas and the way these interlink. Having the opportunity to visit different departments to get a sense of what they do and talk to trainees about their experiences was really useful. The entire scheme was incredibly well organised – it was seamless from start to finish.

Which were the most enjoyable – and most challenging – aspects of the scheme?
Making contacts and talking to current employees about their experiences was invaluable; everyone was more than happy to chat. We were included as part of the firm for the entire time that we were there. It is a credit to the firm that the values it claims to have on paper translate to reality; they were palpable.

The presentation that we had to do in front of partners, senior associates and trainees was a challenge, especially as it wasn't something I'd done before and I felt pressure to impress! But I was pleased to have put it together, delivered it and received good feedback. It was enjoyable, in retrospect!

Did the scheme end with a training contract interview or some other kind of further recruitment process?
It was made clear that we would find out whether we had made it onto the firm's assessment day along with all the other candidates, and that there were no guarantees just because we had spent time on the vacation scheme. The firm operates a CV blind assessment process, so we certainly weren't fast tracked in any way – we simply went into the pool along with all the other applicants.

Is there one key thing that you took away from the experience that you would pass on as advice to others?
If you're fortunate enough to get a place on a scheme, take the opportunity to talk to as many people, and get involved with as many tasks, as you possibly can. You want to try to get a feel for the firm and whether it's right for you. Above all, enjoy it and make the most of it, especially in terms of meeting people – that really helps on the assessment day, and beyond, to settle your nerves. Shoosmiths really does value individuality, so just be yourself and make sure that your personality shines through.

No of scheme places
60

Location of schemes
Birmingham, Edinburgh, Manchester, Milton Keynes, Northampton, Nottingham, Reading, Solent

Length of schemes
1 week

Remuneration (per week)
£285

Dates of schemes
June 2018

Closing date for applications
28 February 2018

Application procedure
Apply online at www.shoosmiths.co.uk

For full contact information and details of Training Contract, see the firm's full entry in the main directory on p428

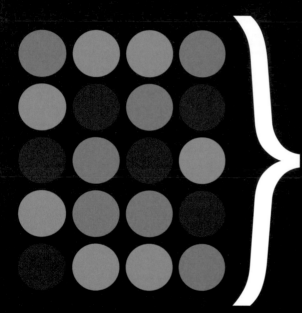

Alex Plant completed a work placement scheme at Stephenson Harwood in July 2016. He studied law at the University of Durham.

Insider report
Stephenson Harwood LLP

What did you do while on the placement scheme (eg, type of work, networking, presentations or social events)?

I spent the first week of the scheme in the marine and international trade (MIT) group. The work was every bit as interesting and varied as I'd hoped – I sat in on a case which was being heard in the Court of Appeal, and conducted research on a niche point of law for a shipping dispute case. In the second week I sat in the finance group, where I worked closely with a trainee and supervising partner on the final stages of a restructuring project. Working with both teams gave me a broad perspective of what goes on at the firm and enabled me to try my hand an equally wide range of tasks, from compiling letters and amending documents to taking notes during conference calls. Each day was broken up with lunch with trainees and supervisors, while mornings were often spent attending introductory talks with associates from the various practice groups. We also went out for drinks with other placement scheme students and trainees in the evenings.

What did you feel that you gained from the placement (e.g. insight into the firm, useful contacts or an appreciation of a trainee's workload)?

The scheme gave me a genuinely honest insight into the atmosphere and feel of the firm. Every student knows that there is usually a lot of corporate speak on firms' websites and in their brochures, but participating in a placement scheme cuts through that to enable you to see what a firm is really like. For example, the introductory talks given by associates felt like a two-way process where our questions were encouraged and answered honestly – while it was clear that they all enjoyed working at the firm and value the culture, it didn't feel as though they were sugar coating anything.

Which were the most enjoyable – and most challenging – aspects of the scheme?

One particular highlight was a talk given to us by the firm's chief executive, Sharon White. It was great to be able to ask questions about the growth and future strategy of the firm, and I think it is pretty rare for placement scheme students to have the opportunity to quiz someone at such a senior level. The most challenging aspect of the scheme was definitely time management and managing people's expectations. At university, I was used to having several days or even weeks to complete assignments; the time frames are obviously much tighter at law firms. I enjoyed the challenge though and definitely learned from it.

Did the scheme end with a training contract interview or some other kind of further recruitment process?

An assessment day was held midway through the second week of the scheme, which alongside your general performance over the two weeks helps the firm to decide on training contract offers.

Is there one key thing that you took away from the experience that you would pass on as advice to others?

Invest real effort in speaking to as many people as possible, whatever their level of seniority. Not only will this give you a well-rounded feel for the firm, but the enthusiasm you show will naturally make a lasting impression on people.

No of scheme places
40

Location of schemes
London

Length of schemes
Winter: 1 week
Spring and Summer: 2 weeks

Remuneration (per week)
£350

Dates of schemes
Winter:
11-15 December 2017
Spring:
3-13 April 2018
Summer:
11 June – 22 June 2018
25 June – 6 July 2018
9 July – 20 July 2018

Closing date for applications
Winter:
12 November 2017
Spring and Summer:
31 January 2018

Application procedure
Apply online at www.shlegal.com/graduate

For full contact information and details of Training Contract, see the firm's full entry in the main directory on p434

Remember to cite *The Training Contract & Pupillage Handbook* on your application form if you apply to this law firm.

SULLIVAN & CROMWELL LLP

AN EXCEPTIONAL OPPORTUNITY

Sullivan & Cromwell provides the highest quality legal advice and representation to clients around the world.

The results we achieve have set us apart for more than 130 years and serve as a model for the modern practice of law.

If you are considering a career as a solicitor, interested in working with the world's leading companies on their most challenging matters, and feel that you have the qualities we are looking for, we encourage you to apply for a place on the 2018 summer vacation scheme or for a training contract in our London office, to commence September 2020.

Please send a copy of your CV (including a full classification and percentage breakdown of all academic results) and a covering letter to: traineesolicitors@sullcrom.com. We will be accepting applications for the 2018 summer vacation scheme from **1**st **November 2017** through **12**th **January 2018**, and applications for our 2020 trainee intake from **1**st **May 2018** through **13**th **July 2018.**

www.sullcrom.com

LONDON · PARIS · FRANKFURT

NEW YORK · WASHINGTON, D.C. · LOS ANGELES · PALO ALTO

TOKYO · HONG KONG · BEIJING · MELBOURNE · SYDNEY

Dermot Costello is studying law with American studies at King's College London. He is in his final year. He attended a two-week summer placement with Sullivan & Cromwell in 2016 and will commence his training contract in September 2018.

What did you do while on the vacation scheme?

One thing that distinguished Sullivan from other schemes was that we didn't have 'make-work' activities; we were involved with tasks that contributed to actual, live work. For example, a client had a medium-term note programme, issuing debt on a rolling basis. I was asked to work with a precedent document, check various elements and change the terms as necessary. I did other bits of research and looked at the partner comments on an associate's piece of work.

We sat in on some presentations, with other members of the firm, where different lawyers talked through how their various deals were progressing. It was great to hear about complicated transactions and get a sense for what the firm does. On the social front, we had cocktails with the trainees, dinner with lots of different people from the firm and one of the grad rec partners also took us all out for lunch. Another nice thing was that all the junior lawyers tend to eat lunch together in the canteen, so there was a real communal feeling, especially when compared to some other firms.

What did you feel that you gained from the placement?

I definitely got great insight into how some transactions are run, being given the chance to sit and read actual documents. And because I was also asked to do some minor drafting jobs, I got a sense of what you actually do as a lawyer; you're not just writing fake memos.

Which were the most enjoyable – and most challenging – aspects of the scheme?

I enjoyed having to develop my research skills, under time pressure, and breaking work down for someone else's benefit. We also went on a great tour of the Lloyd's Building and the Royal Courts of Justice, which I really enjoyed – it was an interesting jaunt to learn more about legal and insurance history.

The only thing I found difficult at the beginning to get used to was having to email trainees or associates to ask for work. That was a challenge as I had to really manage my time, juggle different tasks, seek work and prioritise my workload. It was a step up from managing my studies and other commitments at university.

Did the scheme end with a training contract interview or some other kind of further recruitment process?

At the end of the scheme I met for a brief chat with both grad rec partners, who wanted to know how I'd found the process and if I had any questions – it seemed more for my benefit than theirs. I then submitted a document with a list of everyone I'd worked and they were contacted for their impressions of me. It wasn't a daunting process at all.

Is there one key thing that you took away from the experience that you would pass on as advice to others?

On the scheme itself, try and ask as diverse a group of people as you can for work; if you've chatted over lunch, then ask them if you can help with something. Be proactive and chase as many different types of work as you can; don't sit and twiddle your thumbs hoping work will come to you!

No of scheme places
6-8

Location of schemes
London

Length of schemes
2 weeks

Remuneration (per week)
£500

Dates of schemes
July 2018

Closing date for applications
13 January 2018

Application procedure
By CV (including a full classification and percentage breakdown of all academic results) and a covering letter to traineesolicitors@ sullcrom.com

For full contact information and details of Training Contract, see the firm's full entry in the main directory on p437

Remember to cite *The Training Contract & Pupillage Handbook* on your application form if you apply to this law firm.

WORK EXPERIENCE **99**

Insider report
Vinson & Elkins RLLP

Freddie Wright completed a one-week scheme at Vinson & Elkins in June 2016. He studied law at the University of Bristol.

No of scheme places
Approximately 25

Location of schemes
London

Length of schemes
1 week

Remuneration (per week)
£250

Dates of schemes
Summer 2018

Closing date for applications
31 January 2018

Application procedure
Online application form

For full contact information and details of Training Contract, see the firm's full entry in the main directory on p449

What did you do while on the vacation scheme (eg, type of work, networking, presentations or social events)?
The vacation scheme is structured to mirror the non-rotational nature of the training contract. The firm places vacation schemers in groups of two, with each scheme lasting a week. I was able to undertake a broad variety of work, from M&A, to tax, to dispute resolution. The tasks I was involved in included researching and presenting on a case on *Sharia* financing and VAT, and analysing and interpreting a sale and purchase agreement for a private equity transaction. I was also invited to present my research during the tax team's update meeting over breakfast, which for me highlighted just how involved vacation schemers are in the real work that the firm does. This was helped by the fact that the firm's vacation scheme intake is relatively small, which meant that I was valued as an individual in terms of being given interesting, valuable tasks to do on my own, rather than trying to shine as one of a large group of vacation schemers.

What did you feel that you gained from the placement (eg, insight into the firm, useful contacts or an appreciation of a trainee's workload)?
The scheme enabled me to gain an appreciation of the work I would be undertaking as a trainee. Similarly, I also formed an accurate impression of what the office is like and how the firm works as a whole – it was a holistic experience and we were not just given mock exercises to do, as might be the case at some firms. The culture was warm and welcoming from the first day of the scheme, when I was introduced to each member of the firm. All this meant that I was able to form a good idea of what it would be like to train at the firm.

Which were the most enjoyable – and most challenging – aspects of the scheme?
The most enjoyable aspect was the firm's informal approach to networking and events, which allowed for a more natural approach to networking and integrating into the office over the course of the scheme. I was able to get to know people and seek out work independently, and there wasn't any of the 'enforced fun' that I've previously experienced. The most challenging aspect of the scheme was managing the various streams of work that came from independently establishing those connections with people from across the firm. I had to prioritise tasks and be comfortable enough to say no to something if I was at full capacity.

Did the scheme end with a training contract interview or some other kind of further recruitment process?
There was an exit interview which partly involved discussing an essay that all vacation schemers are set at the start of their placement, as well as my wider experiences on the scheme. Usually the firm makes training contract offers based on that interview and how candidates have performed over the week, but I was invited back for a second interview later in the summer.

Is there one key thing that you took away from the experience that you would pass on as advice to others?
My one key piece of advice is to spend as much time getting to know your assigned buddy as possible. Your buddy is the person with whom you will work most closely, meaning that a lot of your sense of the firm's culture will come through those interactions.

Jake Smith completed a one-week vacation scheme with Walker Morris in April 2016. He studied law at the University of York.

Insider report
Walker Morris LLP

No of scheme places
48

Location of schemes
Leeds

Length of schemes
1 week

Remuneration (per week)
£175

Dates of schemes
April and June

Closing date for applications
31 December 2017

Application procedure
Online application form

For full contact information and details of Training Contract, see the firm's full entry in the main directory on p451

What did you do while on the vacation scheme (eg, type of work, networking, presentations or social events)?

There is a myth that only City firms in London do the most interesting work, but my experience at Walker Morris confirmed that this is not true at all. The firm is proud of its single-site Northern strategy and having the entire firm based at one office does not restrict the range of work that trainees and vac schemers are exposed to. I sat with the banking and insolvency team, where I spent time looking at the different types of securities that banks take out when they lend money, and the ways that those securities can be enforced. Trainees in the banking and insolvency team often review such securities to ensure that everything is in place before a transaction. There were also two group presentation tasks during the week which were used for assessments.

On the social side, several lunches took place during the week with trainees and partners in attendance. These were great opportunities to get to know people from other departments in the firm. However, I would advise that someone on a vacation scheme should be looking to network throughout the placement, not just at these arranged sessions. There were also other social events to attend, including an ice breaker on the first evening and an evening out in the middle of the week.

What did you feel that you gained from the placement (eg, insight into the firm, useful contacts or an appreciation of a trainee's workload)?

I felt comfortable within the firm's working environment and could envisage my career at Walker Morris, which is a level of insight that you can only gain through first-hand experience. I also gained an appreciation of trainee life at the firm through working closely with trainees and my supervisor over the course of the placement. Everyone I met at the firm was happy to offer guidance and point me in the right direction, which is something I know I can also rely on if I have any queries and need to get in touch while I'm studying for the LPC.

Which were the most enjoyable – and most challenging – aspects of the scheme?

I was delighted with how welcome I was made to feel at the firm – I can't emphasise enough that the atmosphere of a workplace should have a significant bearing on where you choose to apply for a training contract. A lot of the work that I experienced on the scheme was very different to anything I had done before at law school, so getting up to speed and identifying where the knowledge I already had fitted into certain tasks was challenging initially, in the same way that I expect most vac schemers are challenged when they start a placement.

Did the scheme end with a training contract interview or some other kind of further recruitment process?

I wasn't interviewed personally at the end of the scheme, as the firm decided to offer me a training contract based on how I got on during the placement.

Is there one key thing that you took away from the experience that you would pass on as advice to others?

As clichéd as it sounds, it's so important to be yourself. The scheme is a great opportunity to take a detailed first-hand look at a firm and decide whether you like the environment, the work, the people and so on, but you will only get out of it what you put in.

Remember to cite *The Training Contract & Pupillage Handbook* on your application form if you apply to this law firm.

WORK EXPERIENCE **101**

WATSON FARLEY & WILLIAMS

INQUISITIVE MINDS MEETING GLOBAL CHALLENGES EVERY DAY

Vacation Schemes
Apply by
26 January 2018

Training Contracts
Apply by
27 July 2018 for 2020 start

See our website for
open day details
wfw.com/trainee

Kaajal Shah graduated with a degree in law with international legal studies from the University of Southampton in 2016. She attended a two-week Easter vacation scheme at WFW and will commence her training contract in September 2019.

What did you do while on the vacation scheme?
I sat in the energy department for two weeks, where I shared an office with a partner who was also my supervisor. Throughout, he took the time to explain things to me and gave me the opportunity to sit in on conference calls. I was paired up with a trainee buddy, who was so welcoming and approachable. He gave me real insight into life as a trainee, sharing his honest views on everything. I was given a variety of work, including legal research and drafting documents from various members of the department. The vac scheme students were also assigned a group project, which meant that we worked together throughout, preparing a pitch in front of the audience on the last day.

What did you feel that you gained from the placement?
I got to see first hand how a legal team works together; it was an exciting time because they were closing a big project, so I was invited to all the group meetings and made to feel a part of the team. I helped out by preparing the documents for signing. Along with sitting in our preferred department, we had lunchtime presentations from associates across the departments, to gain deeper understanding of their work and how everything ties in with the firm's key sectors. There was also a very useful talk on overseas secondment, which all WFW trainees are guaranteed. I learnt a lot hearing about the trainees' different experiences.

Which were the most enjoyable – and most challenging – aspects of the scheme?
I really enjoyed getting to know all the trainees, as well as the other vac scheme students, at the social events. The events were very well organised by the grad team, which included Escape Rooms, an evening at Jamie's Italian and a nice farewell lunch on the last day. The most challenging aspect was finding time in the day for everyone to work together on our group project, as we were all sitting in different departments with varied workloads. We set up a group chat, arranging short meetings daily, which really helped us bring our presentation together and go into the pitch with confidence.

Did the scheme end with a training contract interview or some other kind of further recruitment process?
Towards the end of the scheme, we had a formal interview with a member of the grad rec team and a partner. While preparing for the interview really helped me, I was definitely put at ease by my interviewers and it was an enjoyable conversation! I was delighted to receive an offer soon afterwards.

Is there one key thing that you took away from the experience that you would pass on as advice to others?
Treat it like a two-way process; take the time to assess if you like the culture and can imagine working there. The firm is looking for the right fit, so don't be afraid to show your personality and get stuck in. WFW really values teamwork, so use the scheme as an opportunity to develop those skills, working alongside your fellow vac scheme students, rather than treating them as the competition.

No of scheme places
Up to 30

Location of schemes
London

Length of schemes
2 weeks

Remuneration (per week)
£325

Dates of schemes
March, June and July 2018

Closing date for applications
26 January 2018

Application procedure
Online application

For full contact information and details of Training Contract, see the firm's full entry in the main directory on p453

Martha Male studied English at the University of Bristol before undertaking the GDL at The University of Law. She attended a two-week vacation scheme at Withers in Summer 2016 and will commence her training contract in September 2018.

What did you do while on the vacation scheme?
We were able to request to sit in a particular department that we were interested in; I asked for family and had one week there, followed by a week in the rural real estate department. Among other things, in family I carried out legal research on topics such as prenuptial agreements and attended a High Court divorce case, while in real estate I helped to investigate property titles. It was great to see two very different departments and made the entire experience really useful. Throughout the scheme we worked on a case study that revolved around a mock dispute where we were split into two groups and asked to act on behalf of a client. We had to work on a variety of tasks, including a client interview and drafting an attendance note. We then took part in a mock mediation, which was a fantastic way to get to know the other vac schemers and put into practice the skills we had learnt in our two weeks at the firm. We had a lovely, informal dinner with some of the business leaders and trainees, which was a great way to get to know people, ask some of the questions we hadn't yet had a chance to, and get to know them as people. We also had lunch with the trainees regularly, so there were lots of opportunities to socialise throughout.

What did you feel that you gained from the placement?
While doing research into a firm beforehand is useful to a certain extent, first-hand experience and the chance to meet people face to face is much more valuable in terms of understanding the firm's ethos. For example, everyone at Withers is friendly, as well as hard-working, and I noticed it had a really supportive atmosphere.

Which were the most enjoyable – and most challenging – aspects of the scheme?
I found the entire scheme enjoyable, but I was surprised by how much I enjoyed the case study. Activities surrounding the case study were evenly spread throughout the duration of the scheme, so there was always something to think about and work on. It was a great way to get to know the other vac schemers and something you could ask people in your department about – it was a great conversation starter! At times it was tricky to organise and manage my workload as I had to complete work from multiple people and also prepare for the scheme's activities, but it was also a great chance to learn how to prioritise work and manage competing deadlines.

Did the scheme end with a training contract interview or some other kind of further recruitment process?
I was invited to an assessment centre after the vacation scheme. On the day, we had to deliver a 10-minute pre-prepared presentation, had an interview with two partners and did various other assessed activities. I was offered my training contract shortly after!

Is there one key thing that you took away from the experience that you would pass on as advice to others?
Try to enjoy every single minute – you have two weeks to talk to leading lawyers and get involved in real work, all of which helps you to determine what type of practice area and department might suit you. It's so useful for applications and interviews, as well as for self-development. At the same time, the firm has two weeks to see who you really are, and you can show off your skills and strengths far beyond your online application. If you throw yourself into everything with enthusiasm and a big smile, you'll learn so much and find it rewarding in many different ways.

No of scheme places
18

Location of schemes
London

Length of schemes
2 weeks

Remuneration (per week)
£350

Dates of schemes
Easter
3-13 April 2018
Summer
18-29 June 2018
2-13 July 2018

Closing date for applications
31 January 2018

Application procedure
Online application form

For full contact information and details of Training Contract, see the firm's full entry in the main directory on p461

Firms that offer work placement schemes

Firms in **bold** have provided detailed information in the directory section
Firms in **purple** have provided an Insider Report

Abode Solicitors
ACA Law Ltd
Acuity Legal Limited
Addleshaw Goddard
Adlams LLP
Akin Gump Strauss Hauer & Feld
Allan Janes
Allen & Overy LLP
Amicus Solicitors LLP
Ams Solicitors Limited
Anglo-Thai Legal (ATL)
Anthony Collins Solicitors
Anthony Jacobs & Co
AP Law Solicitors Ltd
Arlingtons Sharmas Solicitors
Arnold & Porter Kaye Scholer LLP
asb law LLP
Aschfords Law
Ashfords
Ashton Bell
Ashtons Legal
Ashurst LLP
Aston Bond
Atkins Hope
Atteys Solicitors
Austin Kemp Solicitors Limited
Avadis & Co Solicitors
Avery Emerson
B P Collins LLP
Baker McKenzie
Baron Grey
Bastian Lloyd Morris LLP
Bates Wells Braithwaite
Berg
Berwin Leighton Paisner
Bevan Brittan LLP
Beviss & Beckingsale
Bhatt Murphy
Bhogal Partners Solicitors
BHW Solicitors
Bilton Hammond
Bircham Dyson Bell LLP
Bird & Bird
Birkett Long LLP
Birketts LLP
Blacks Solicitors LLP
Blake Morgan LLP
Blandy & Blandy LLP
BLM
Bond Dickinson
Boodle Hatfield LLP
Bosley & Co
Boyes Turner
BPE Solicitors LLP
Brachers LLP
Bridge McFarland

Bridger & Co Solicitors
Bristows LLP
Bross Bennett
Browne Jacobson LLP
Bryan Cave
BS Singh & Co LLP
BTMK Solicitors LLP
Burges Salmon LLP
Burton & Co LLP
Cains Advocates Limited
Caldicotts
Campbell-Taylor Solicitors
Camps
Canter Levin & Berg
Capital Law
Cartmell Shepherd
CFG Law (part of the client first group)
Charles Russell Speechlys
Chatham Chambers Solicitors
Churchers Bolitho Way
Cleary Gottlieb Steen & Hamilton LLP
Clifford Chance
Clyde & Co LLP
CMS Cameron McKenna Nabarro Olswang LLP
Cohen Davis Solicitors
Coles Miller
Collyer Bristow LLP
The Commercial Law Practice
Conrad King & Solomon Solicitors
Cooley (UK) LLP
Covington & Burling LLP
Cripps LLP
Cunningtons
Curtis Law Solicitors LLP
Curzon Green Solicitors
DAC Beachcroft
Darbys Solicitors LLP
Darlingtons
David Gray Solicitors LLP
David Phillips & Partners
Davis Polk & Wardwell London LLP
Dawson Cornwell
Daybells LLP
De Marco Solicitors
Dean Manson LLP – Solicitors
Debevoise & Plimpton LLP
Dechert LLP
Dexter Montague LLP
Df Legal LLP
DH Law Solicitors Ltd
DLA Piper UK LLP
DMH Stallard LLP
Donald Race & Newton
Druces LLP
Duncan Lewis Solicitors Ltd
DW Law

DWF LLP
Eb Legal
Edmondson Hall
Edwin Coe LLP
Elliott Bridgman Limited
Ellis Jones Solicitors LLP
Emery Johnson Astills
The Endeavour Partnership LLP
Eversheds Sutherland (International) LLP
Express Solicitors
Faegre Baker Daniels LLP
Faradays Solicitors
Farrer & Co LLP
FBC Manby Bowdler LLP
Fellowes Solicitors LLP
Field Seymour Parkes
Fieldfisher
Foot Anstey LLP
Forbes Solicitors
Forsters LLP
Fountain Solicitors Limited
Franklins Solicitors LLP
Freeman Johnson
Freshfields Bruckhaus Deringer LLP
Furley Page LLP
Gamlins Law
Gateley Plc
GHP Legal
Gibson Dunn & Crutcher LLP
Glaisyers Solicitors LLP
Goody Burrett LLP
Gowling WLG (UK) LLP
Greenberg Traurig LLP
Greenhouse Stirton & Co
Greenwoods Solicitors LLP
Gregg Latchams Limited
Gregory Abrams Davidson LLP
Guile Nicholas Solicitors
Harding Evans LLP
Harris Waters & Co
Harrison Clark Rickerbys Solicitors
Hatton
Hay & Kilner Law Firm
Henry's Solicitors Limited
Herbert Smith Freehills LLP
Hewitsons LLP
HFW
Hibberts LLP
Hill & Abbott
Hill Dickinson LLP
HKH Kenwright & Cox
hlw Keeble Hawson LLP
Hogan Lovells
Horwich Farrelly
Howarth Goodman
Howes Percival LLP

Hugh James
Humphreys & Co
Humphries Kirk LLP
Hunters
Huttons
Ince & Co LLP
Inghams
Irena Spence & Co
Irwin Mitchell
Jeremy Roberts & Co
John Hodge Solicitors
Johns & Saggar LLP
The Johnson Partnership
Jones Day
Joseph Hill & Co
Joves Solicitors
K&L Gates LLP
KC Law Chambers Solicitors
The Keith Jones Partnership
Kennedys
Kesar & Co Solicitors
Kingsley Napley LLP
Kirkland & Ellis International LLP
Kiteleys
Kotecha & Co
Kuit Steinart Levy
Kundert Solicitors LLP
LA Steel
Langleys Solicitors LLP
Latham & Watkins
Latimer Lee
Laytons Solicitors LLP
Leathes Prior
Lee Bolton Monier-Williams
Lester Aldridge LLP
Lewis Silkin
Linklaters LLP
Lodders Solicitors LLP
London Solicitors LLP
M Olubi Solicitors
Macfarlanes LLP
Major & Co
Makka Solicitors Ltd
Makwana Solicitors
Malcolm C Foy & Co Ltd
Malik & Malik
Malik Legal Solicitors Ltd
Malletts
Marriott Harrison LLP
Martin Cray and Co
Matrix Solicitors
Maurice Turnor Gardner LLP
Mayer Brown International LLP
McDermott Will & Emery UK LLP
McMillan Williams Solicitors
Meikles

Firms that offer work placement schemes

Firms in **bold** have provided detailed information in the directory section
Firms in purple have provided an Insider Report

Michelmores LLP
Middleton Solicitors
Middleweeks
Milbank Tweed Hadley & McCloy
Milburns Solicitors Limited
Millan Solicitors
Mills & Co. Solicitors Limited
Mills & Reeve LLP
Mincoffs Solicitors LLP
Minster Law Solicitors
Mishcon de Reya LLP
MLP Law LLP
Mohammed & Co
Moosa-Duke Solicitors
Morgan, Lewis & Bockius UK LLP
Morrison & Foerster (UK) LLP
Moss & Co
Muckle LLP
Murrell Associates Limited
Myerson Solicitors LLP
Noble Solicitors
Nockolds
North Yorkshire County Council
Norton Rose Fulbright
Obaseki
O'Melveny
Osborne Clarke LLP
Osbornes Solicitors LLP
Osmond & Osmond
Ozoran Turkan
Palmers
Paragon Law Limited
Paris Smith LLP
Parker Bullen LLP
Paul Hastings
Penningtons Manches LLP
Peters & Peters
Philcox Gray Ltd
Pinsent Masons LLP
Pope & Co
Premier Solicitors LLP
Prettys
Punch Robson
PwC
Quality Solicitors J A Hughes
Quality Solicitors John Barkers
QualitySolicitors Mirza
Rai Solicitors
Ratcliffe & Bibby Solicitors
Rawal & Co
Reed Smith
Rest Harrow & Co Solicitors
Reynolds Colman Bradley LLP
Riaz Solicitors
Rippon Patel & French LLP
Rix & Kay Solicitors LLP

Roberts Jackson Solicitors
Rollits
Ropes & Gray International LLP
Royds Withy King
Roythornes Solicitors
RPC
Samuel Phillips Law Firm
Samuels
SAS Daniels LLP
Savas & Savage Solicitors Limited
Schofield Sweeney LLP
Sentinel Solicitors
The Sethi Partnership Solicitors
Shearman & Sterling (London) LLP
Sheikh & Co
Shoosmiths
Sidley Austin LLP
Sills & Betteridge LLP
Silverdale Solicitors
Simkins LLP
Simmons & Simmons LLP
Sintons LLP
SJP Law
Skadden, Arps, Slate, Meagher & Flom (UK) LLP
Slaughter and May
Smith Llewelyn Partnership
Sonn Macmillan Walker
Spelthorne Borough Council
Spence & Horne
Squire Patton Boggs (UK) LLP
Sri Kanth & Co
Steeles Law LLP
Stephens Scown
Stephenson Harwood LLP
Stephensons
Stevens & Bolton LLP
Stone King
Stowe Family Law LLP
STS Solicitors
Stuart Miller Solicitors
Sullivan & Cromwell LLP
Surrey Law Centre
Sweetman Burke & Sinker
Talbot & Co
Tassells
Taylor Vinters LLP
Taylor Walton LLP
Taylor Wessing
Teacher Stern LLP
Tees Law
Thaliwal & Co Solicitors
Thomson Snell & Passmore LLP
Thorne Segar Ltd
Tim Johnson / Law
TLT LLP
TMJ Law Solicitors

TMJ Legal Services Ltd
Toussaints
Tozers LLP
Tranters
Travers Smith LLP
Trethowans LLP
Trowers & Hamlins LLP
TV Edwards Solicitors
Veale Wasbrough Vizards LLP
Vinson & Elkins RLLP
Vodafone Group Services
Vyman Solicitors Ltd
Wainwright & Cummins
Wake Smith Solicitors
Walker Morris LLP
Walter Wilson Richmond
Walters & Plaskitt
Ward Hadaway
Watkins Solicitors
Watson Burton LLP
Watson Farley & Williams LLP
Watson Legal
Watson Watson Solicitors
Wedlake Bell LLP
Weightmans LLP
Weil, Gotshal & Manges (London) LLP
White & Case LLP
White & Co
Whitworth & Green Solicitors Ltd
Wilkin Chapman LLP
Wilsons Solicitors
Wilsons Solicitors LLP
Winckworth Sherwood LLP
Winston & Strawn London LLP
Withers LLP
WLL Solicitors
Woodfines LLP
Wright Hassall LLP
Young & Pearce
Zyda Law

Chambers that offer mini-pupillages

Chambers in **bold** have provided detailed information in the directory section

Albion Chambers
Angel Chambers
Apex Chambers
Arden Chambers
Atkin Chambers
Atlantic Chambers
Bank House Chambers
2 Bedford Row
7 Bedford Row
9 Bedford Row
25 Bedford Row
36 Bedford Row
42 Bedford Row
29 Bedford Row Chambers
Blackstone Chambers
4 Breams Buildings
One Brick Court
4 Brick Court
Brick Court Chambers
Broadway House Chambers
Carmelite Chambers
1 Chancery Lane
Charter Chambers
Chartlands Chambers
Citadel Chambers
Cloisters
12 College Place
Coram Chambers
Cornerstone Barristers
Criminal Defence Solicitors
Crown Office Chambers
One Crown Office Row
Crown Office Row Chambers
Deans Court Chambers
Dere Street Chambers
Devereux
Doughty Street Chambers
2 Dr Johnson's Buildings
Three Dr Johnson's Buildings
Drystone chambers
East Anglian Chambers
Enterprise Chambers
Erskine Chambers
39 Essex Chambers
One Essex Court
5 Essex Court
Essex Court Chambers
23 Essex Street
Exchange Chambers
Falcon Chambers
Farrar's Building
Fenners Chambers
Field Court Chambers
187 Fleet Street
Foundry Chambers
Fountain Court Chambers

Francis Taylor Building
1 Garden Court
Garden Court Chambers
Goldsmith Chambers
9 Gough Square
Gough Square Chambers
4-5 Gray's Inn Square
1 Gray's Inn Square
Gray's Inn Tax Chambers
Guildford Chambers
Guildhall Chambers
Hailsham Chambers
2 Harcourt Buildings
Harcourt Chambers
Hardwicke
1 Hare Court
3 Hare Court
7 Harrington Street Chambers
Henderson Chambers
1 High Pavement
Hogarth Chambers
Invictus Chambers
Iscoed Chambers
One ITL
KBG Chambers
KBW
11KBW
6KBW College Hill
KCH Garden Square Barristers
Keating Chambers
Kenworthy's Chambers
1 King's Bench Walk
2 King's Bench Walk
2 King's Bench Walk
4 King's Bench Walk
5 King's Bench Walk
7 King's Bench Walk
9 King's Bench Walk
12 King's Bench Walk
Kings Chambers
Lamb Building
Landmark Chambers
Lincoln House Chambers
Linenhall Chambers
Maidstone Chambers
Maitland Chambers
1 MCB
Monckton Chambers
New Court Chambers
New Park Court Chambers
3 New Square
4 New Square
8 New Square
11 New Square
New Square Chambers
No5 Chambers

Northampton Chambers
Ten Old Square
15 Old Square
Old Square Chambers
Old Square Chambers
Oriel Chambers
Outer Temple Chambers
Five Paper
4 Paper Buildings
5 Paper Buildings
9 Park Place
30 Park Place
Park Square Barristers
Parklane Plowden Chambers
3PB
4 Pump Court
5 Pump Court
6 Pump Court
Pump Court Chambers
1 Pump Court Chambers
Pump Court Tax Chambers
QEB Hollis Whiteman
Quadrant Chambers
Queen Elizabeth Building
Queen Square Chambers
Radcliffe Chambers
5RB
Red Lion Chambers
Selborne Chambers
Serjeants' Inn Chambers
Serle Court
South Square
11 South Square
5 St Andrew's Hill
St Ives Chambers
9 St John Street Chambers
18 St John Street Chambers
St John's Buildings
St John's Chambers
St Mary's Chambers
St Paul's Chambers
St Philips Chambers
Staple Inn Chambers
Three Stone
4 Stone Buildings
5 Stone Buildings
9 Stone Buildings
Stone Chambers
Stour Chambers
Sussex Chambers
Tanfield Chambers
Fourteen
Temple Garden Chambers
3 Temple Gardens
2TG
Thomas More Chambers

Trinity Chambers
Trinity Chambers
3 Verulam Buildings
Westgate Chambers
Wilberforce Chambers
15 Winckley Square
XXIV Old Buildings

Postgraduate training

Postgraduate training

Broadly speaking, the Solicitors Regulation Authority (SRA) and the Bar Standards Board (BSB) are responsible for laying down the training requirements for qualification as a solicitor or barrister in England and Wales. The past few years have seen a lot of change in the postgraduate training world, for both would-be solicitors and barristers, especially since the publication in 2013 of the cross-profession Legal Education and Training Review (LETR). The final report offered 26 key recommendations related to the effectiveness of legal teaching and training methods, including a number of ways in which quality, accessibility and flexibility must be enhanced. Since then, both the SRA and BSB have released plans and consulted on how to implement the recommendations, and some important changes have been made in the last two years.

Changes ahead

As of 2015-16, firms are now allowed to recruit solicitors from the second year of university onwards (previously training contracts were only supposed to be offered in the final year). Most firms are sticking broadly to the traditional 31 July application deadline, but others are recruiting earlier in the year and directly from their vacation schemes. Another change has been to abolish the term 'training contract' in favour of the less specific 'period of recognised training' (although confusingly, most firms and providers still refer to 'training contract'!). In practical terms, this means that law firms and aspiring solicitors have been given much greater flexibility in how they gain the necessary skills and experience to qualify. For example, it is now possible to apply to the SRA to be granted qualification if you have completed a law degree or the Graduate Diploma in Law (GDL), the Legal Practice Course (LPC), and gained all the necessary skills and experience (as set out by the SRA) while working as a paralegal. Meanwhile, it is no longer necessary to gain a mixture of contentious and non-contentious experience in order to qualify and changes have also been made to continuing professional development training, which you undertake when you start practising.

Another major development is the proposed introduction by the SRA of a Solicitors Qualifying Examination (SQE), which all prospective solicitors – whether coming through the university, equivalent means (see explanation under GDL heading) or apprenticeship routes – would have to take in order to qualify. The proposal met with widely published opposition, particularly from universities and academics, but the SRA has confirmed that the SQE will go ahead – the exam is expected to be introduced in 2020.

The Bar, too, is looking at the future training of barristers and has decided to introduce a limited number of new routes to train as a barrister, which could be in place by 2019. A central tenet is that training as a barrister needs to become more flexible and accessible to a more diverse range of candidates. As of August 2017, what those new routes will be exactly has not yet been revealed. And in a big timetable change, as of January 2017 the Pupillage Gateway now opens for applications in January rather than April. This change has been made to stop the application season clashing with exams and to allow students to know whether they have secured a pupillage before committing to the expensive Bar Professional Training Course (BPTC). Find detailed information about the SQE and the planned changes at the Bar on LawCareers.Net.

So things are very fluid at the moment; but as they stand, the below describes the postgraduate training landscape.

Two-stage training

For both solicitors and barristers, training comprises two stages: academic and

vocational. The academic stage can be completed in one of three ways:
- a law degree;
- the GDL for non-law graduates; or
- the CILEx exams for those wishing to qualify as chartered legal executives, which enable people who are already in legal employment to qualify while they are working (see "Alternative careers").

The vocational stage involves completion of the LPC or BPTC, plus a two-year training contract or one-year pupillage.

GDL
The GDL is a conversion course that non-law graduates can take to enable them to apply for an LPC or BPTC place. It is normally a one-year, full-time course designed to enable non-law graduates to fulfil the academic stage of legal training. The course can also be taken over two years, either part time or by distance learning.

If you intend to study full time, you should apply through the Central Applications Board (www.lawcabs.ac.uk) from September onwards in your final year at university. There is no closing date for applications; rather, applications are dealt with as they are submitted and institutions are notified weekly of new submissions. Applications for part-time courses must be made directly to the provider.

To be eligible for the GDL, students must hold a degree from a UK university or recognised overseas university. As a non-graduate, it may still be possible to commence the GDL based on the SRA's "equivalent means" test, which assesses whether the individual holds other "academic or vocational qualifications that the SRA considers equivalent to a degree". Subject to various criteria, the following people may be eligible for exemption: mature students; chartered legal executives; assistant

justices' clerks; and those with professional qualifications equivalent to a degree (eg, obtained through the Institute of Chartered Accountants). If you think you might fall within one of these categories, you should contact the SRA (www.sra.org.uk/contactus or 0370 606 2555) or consult its "Equivalent means information pack" page.

Course content
The GDL is an intensive, demanding programme focusing on the seven foundations of legal knowledge, which are:
- contract;
- tort;
- criminal;
- equity and trusts;
- European Union;
- property/land; and
- public.

Be aware that this stage of training is widely regarded as extremely difficult. Specific course content is set internally by individual institutions. However, for full-time students, the final examination will normally comprise a three-hour paper in each of the seven core areas. All papers will usually need to be passed on the same occasion. Although you have up to three years to complete the GDL, you will not be allowed to attempt any paper more than three times. Part-time and distance-learning GDL students must attend a recognised course which lasts two years and must complete the course in not more than four years.

As an alternative to the GDL, a two-year, senior-status law degree can be studied. After this degree, students go straight on to the appropriate vocational stage of legal training (ie, LPC or BPTC). A number of UK universities offer senior-status degrees. To check whether your preferred university offers a senior status degree, visit the SRA website (www.sra.org.uk) and go to the "Qualifying law degree providers" page in the "Students" section.

Finally, it is worth taking into account the fact that many institutions teaching both the GDL and LPC will automatically offer you a place on the latter if you successfully complete the former.

LPC

All institutions that offer the full-time LPC are managed by the Central Applications Board. You should contact them for an application form or apply online at www.lawcabs.ac.uk.

The LPC is the vocational stage of training to be a solicitor. It aims to provide students/trainees with sufficient knowledge and skills to ensure that they are well equipped to undertake the work of a solicitor. It is a one-year, full-time (or two-year, part-time) course designed to bridge the academic degree and training contract. Although the length of time it takes to complete remains the same, it is possible to split the course into core and elective stages, enabling you to start your training contract sooner (ie, after having completed the core stage only).

The LPC focuses on practical skills and the instilling of professional conduct and ethical standards. Teaching methods are no longer just academic: the emphasis is on workshops, continuous assessment, independent research and group discussions. The course also permits some specialisation through a range of optional subjects.

In Stage One, the core subjects cover litigation, property, business, professional conduct and regulation, taxation, wills and the administration of estates. This stage also teaches students specific skills such as advocacy, drafting and writing, interviewing and advising, problem solving and legal research. This stage is completed at law school.

It is now possible to complete Stage Two during your training contract or while working at a law firm in another role (eg, as a paralegal or legal secretary), should you wish to do so. This stage consists of electives from a range of subjects in private and corporate client work, including commercial law and practice, employment, intellectual property, consumer, housing, family and immigration.

BPTC

Anyone wanting to become a barrister must pass the BPTC, which effectively bridges the gap between the study of law and work as a pupil. Students seeking a place on the BPTC must go through the centralised online application process at www.barsas.com.

The full-time BPTC is a one-year course; the part-time course takes two years. All students must be admitted to an Inn of Court before registration on the BPTC. The BSB also requires that applicants must:
- hold at least a 2:2 degree (in either law or non-law plus the GDL);
- gain a score of at least 7.5 in all subjects of the British Council's IELTS test, if English is not their first language; and
- pass the Bar Course Aptitude Test (BCAT), which tests critical thinking and reasoning, and is designed to assess chances of success at the Bar. Applicants must pay £150 to sit the test.

The main areas of knowledge taught on the BPTC are civil litigation and remedies, criminal litigation and sentencing, evidence and professional ethics. It also teaches skills related to advocacy, conferencing, drafting and resolution of disputes out of court. Students are then allowed to choose two optional subjects from areas that include family, intellectual property, immigration, personal injury and employment law. Assessment varies from institution to institution. However, the BSB sets three standard exams in civil litigation, criminal litigation and professional ethics.

If a BPTC graduate seeks to pursue a career as a solicitor, he or she may be granted exemption from attendance and assessment in several areas of the LPC, including litigation, advocacy, drafting, practical legal research and two vocational electives. Students must have completed the BPTC no earlier than five years before enrolling on the LPC.

LLM
A master's in law is a popular option as the profession grows more competitive and students seek to add an extra edge to their CV. The LLM is a sure-fire way of developing your expertise in a niche area of the law, but be aware that it is unlikely to make the difference that lands you a training contract or pupillage. This is especially so if you see doing an LLM as the way around a lower-than-expected first degree result in order to get a training contract/pupillage. Few law firms/chambers will take account of an LLM if your first degree result falls below their entry requirement and you have no genuine mitigating circumstances.

In marketing your LLM to potential employers, you will be able to point out that you have not only gained a thorough knowledge of a particular area of law or legal practice, but also improved your communication and research skills. But do bear in mind that while most firms don't mind where you have studied the GDL, this isn't the case with LLMs. LLM programmes are governed by snobbery as much as undergraduate law degrees, and there is no point pretending otherwise. Thus, our advice for LLMs is to use the same principles for selecting a course as you would at undergraduate level.

What to look for in a postgraduate provider
You have a wide range of choice when it comes to the postgraduate law courses. There are over 30 institutions – some with more than one site – offering the LPC alone. Whether you are about to do the GDL, LPC or BPTC, a number of factors should guide which law schools you apply to. Those of

you with the easiest choice have already secured a training contract or pupillage and your future firm/chambers will have specified the provider that you should attend. It is also possible that your prospective firm/chambers is paying your fees, in which case you don't have to pay too much heed to financial considerations.

The rest (and the majority) of you should pay close attention to each of the factors listed below.

Course fees
This boils down to how much money you can afford to hand over for the privilege of attending the course. Fees for a one-year course can be as much as £19,070 (for the BPTC in London in 2017-18). However, do not make the mistake of thinking that the more expensive the course is, the better it will be. That's not always the case.

Both BPP and The University of Law have recently made financial offers to LPC and BPTC students who have failed to secure either a training contact or pupillage having completed the course. First, BPP's 'career guarantee' says that if within six months of graduating no training contract or pupillage is forthcoming, a student will be given the chance to study another of BPP's courses for free (from an approved list). Next, The University of Law's 'employment promise' provides that if a student fails to secure a job within nine months of graduating, he or she will get all of the course fees back, made up of 50% cashback and 50% credit towards any further courses. A note of caution: both these offers are heavily caveated, so it is worth reading the small print before basing your decision to apply to either on this reason alone.

Course structure/type
It is essential to do an LPC or BPTC that reflects the type of law you wish to practise.

The LPC at its core remains the same course for everyone, but institutions offer versions with different emphases. For example, BPP Law School offers a business-focused LPC, developed in conjunction with leading firms that include Clifford Chance, Freshfields Bruckhaus Deringer, Allen & Overy and Herbert Smith Freehills. It also now offers High Street Extra, an optional programme on the areas of law that are key to high-street or small firms. The University of Law's standard LPC is now the LLM LPC, offering students the chance to gain both a master's and the LPC during the one-year course. It also offers firm-specific LPCs to future trainees at firms that include magic circle stalwart Linklaters. Ask potential providers what they have to offer and how this differs from what is available elsewhere.

Teaching quality
Some courses have better teachers and teaching methods than others. The SRA continually monitors course quality and rates LPC courses, focusing on six different areas:
• teaching, learning and the curriculum;
• assessment;
• students and their support;
• learning resources;
• leadership and management; and
• quality assurance and enhancement.

Contact the SRA to find out more (www.sra. org.uk/contactus or 0370 606 2555).

Facilities
Not all courses and institutions offer the same level of facilities, resources, support and class sizes. Some institutions include books and materials, while at others these are additional costs. Don't be afraid to ask questions about what you get for your money.

Housing/living costs
London is an expensive city in which to live, while the rest of the country is (mostly) cheaper. This should be factored in when you consider how much you will be paying for the course. Ask the questions and do your research.

Location
If you study somewhere near home, you can live there and save on costs. If you are keen to move elsewhere, first work out whether you are likely to be happy there – a preliminary visit is a good idea. The BPTC and LPC are usually completed in a year, which is a manageable amount of time wherever you are, but be sure to consider the factors that are important to you.

Reputation
This is possibly the most nebulous of considerations. There are plenty of people whose opinion you can elicit (potential employers, tutors, careers advisers, friends, relations, colleagues and fellow students). With all that advice, you should garner a fair amount of insight into the best place of study for you. Just remember to pay more heed to those who actually know what they are talking about!

Further reading on LawCareers.Net:
• GDL – www.LawCareers.Net/Solicitors/GDL
• LPC – www.LawCareers.Net/Solicitors/LPC
• BPTC – www.LawCareers.Net/Barristers/ BPTC

Financing the vocational courses

Training to be a lawyer is not cheap. The reality is that if you have to pay for all your university tuition fees and vocational courses, you could incur debts of many tens of thousands of pounds. And it's not just course fees that have to be taken into account – there are also the other expenses of books, accommodation, food, transport and at least one good suit!

So with that in mind, how do you go about financing the vocational stage of your study? Thankfully, there are a variety of options. For those who secure a training contract or pupillage before they begin their vocational training (which is recommended), sponsoring firms or chambers may pay fees and/or a maintenance grant. For those who are self-funding this stage, careful financial planning is essential. In 2017-18 Graduate Diploma in Law (GDL) course fees were as much as £10,890. Fees for the Legal Practice Course (LPC) and the Bar Professional Training Course (BPTC) were even higher, with the LPC costing as much as £15,685 and the BPTC up to £19,070. Clearly, these fees represent the upper limits of what you can expect to pay, but the courses are always a significant financial undertaking – especially given the rising cost of living throughout the country.

Sponsorship
An increasing number of firms and chambers offer financial assistance to their future trainees and pupils, from full payment of fees and maintenance for up to two years of postgraduate study to the provision of an interest-free loan towards LPC/BPTC course fees. One thing to remember is that the terms of sponsorship may tie you to the firm for a period of time after your training contract. Details of individual policies can be found in the directory section of this book.

Local authority grants
Such grants are available, but funds are extremely limited. In addition, grants are discretionary for the GDL and LPC, which means that they are difficult to get. As a result, you should contact your local authority as soon as possible to find out the situation and apply immediately. Local authorities will supply a booklet describing the details of their award policies. Most authorities require you to complete an application form with details of your education history and financial circumstances.

Law Society
The Law Society lists a variety of trusts and scholarships designed to support the development of individuals who can demonstrate exceptional academic ability and potential as a solicitor. For application details, visit the Junior Lawyers Division website.

The Law Society also runs a Diversity Access Scheme, which provides support to talented people who will have to overcome a specific obstacle in order to qualify. Such obstacles might include social, educational, personal or financial factors. The scheme provides scholarships to cover LPC course fees and successful applicants will automatically qualify for support through the Law Society's mentoring scheme.

Inns of Court
In recent years the four Inns have dished out millions of pounds in awards. They all seem to use the umbrella term 'award' to describe scholarships, bursaries and grants. Inner Temple even calls them 'exhibitions'. Curiously, most wannabe barristers know little about the awards available and although the Inns' websites provide some information, there's a complex web of requirements and application procedures, meaning that working out exactly what is available can be a challenge.

Eamonn O'Reilly is the scholarships and students manager at Inner Temple: "All the four Inns are different and it's difficult to get your head around all the different awards. We all have a scholarships fund and we all give

Financing the vocational courses

money out, mostly on merit, using different kinds of means testing to fine tune that. The scholarships committees think: 'Does this person have a good chance of succeeding at the Bar?' That's the bottom line."

The Inns' websites have application forms for you to complete and send to the relevant person. The forms ask for character details, legal experience, income/funds and references. You can only apply for scholarships at one Inn. If the scholarships committee likes your application, it will invite you to an interview.

Here is a breakdown of what's on offer.

Lincoln's Inn

Lincoln's Inn offers 32 scholarships ranging from £3,000 to £8,000 for those studying the GDL and 110 scholarships and bursaries for those on the BPTC. The total value of the Inn's awards is just over £1.5 million. Individual scholarships and bursaries range from £3,000 to £18,500. Lincoln's Inn has many other awards and bursaries available, from its £60,000 fund for up to 50 awards of up to £1,500 for pupillage to the £3,500 Peter Duffy Human Rights Award for young barristers to spend three months at the European Court of Human Rights in Strasbourg. There are also scholarships of £3,500 to the other European courts in The Hague and Luxembourg. Finally, there is a Continuing Education Fund of £26,500 for BPTC graduates undertaking overseas internships. Students are recommended to apply for awards in their third year at university or the year before starting the GDL or BPTC. The Inn's website (www.lincolnsinn.org.uk) has clear instructions and a downloadable application form, which should be submitted to the scholarships coordinator (scholarships@lincolnsinn.org.uk).

Inner Temple

Probably the Inn with the most accessible information, Inner Temple handed out £1,736,306 in awards in 2017. The number of awards is not fixed, but the Inn usually offers 80 to 100 scholarships per year for those on the BPTC. These vary in value, with a maximum award of £22,000. For those on the GDL a number of scholarships are available, of values up to £10,000. A small number of pupillage awards are available, as well as small entrance awards and disability grants. The Inn has a scholarships and students manager, Eamonn O'Reilly (eoreilly@innertemple.org.uk). Its website (www.innertemple.org.uk) has all the info you need and you can apply online.

Middle Temple

Middle Temple makes awards worth around £1.1 million every year. The biggest portion goes to those on the BPTC, with most of the rest awarded to GDL students. Although the exact number of scholarships varies from year to year, the Inn helped over 100 students in 2015, with amounts ranging from £1,000 to £18,000. While the awarding of scholarships is based purely on merit, the sizes of the awards are based on the applicant's financial means. The Inn also has a pupillage hardship fund for pupils who experience severe, unforeseen financial difficulties and a pupillage support scheme for pupils on low awards in publicly funded areas of law. The website (www.middletemple.org.uk) tells you a lot about the scholarship scheme and has a downloadable application form with clear instructions. Scholarships are part of the education department within the Inn's Treasury and Christa Richmond is the director of education. Contact the education services manager, Sally Yorke (s.yorke@middletemple.org.uk), with questions.

Gray's Inn

Although Gray's Inn is the smallest of the four Inns, in 2016 (the most recent statistic available at time of writing) it awarded in excess of £895,000 in scholarships, awards and prizes. In 2015-16 the Inn awarded £120,000 in CPE/GDL scholarships, and £645,000 to scholars undertaking the BPTC. Four residential scholarships totaling £32,000 and a number of international and domestic internship awards amounting to £8,000 were made, ranging from £100 to £3,000 per award. Students were awarded prizes for mooting, debating and essays ranging from £250, £350, £500, £1,000 and £1,500. Gray's also awarded £80,000 in pupillage and £10,000 in new practitioner scholarships. Detailed information on all of Gray's Inn's scholarships can be found at www.graysinn.org.uk/education/scholarships. Mairi Wilson and Vicky Hanson are in charge of scholarships at the Inn. All enquiries should be sent to scholarships@graysinn.org.uk.

College access funds

College access funds are available to postgraduate students at universities and publicly funded colleges, mainly to provide additional assistance to meet living costs. The funds are available at the discretion of your college and are intended for those who are experiencing particular difficulties in meeting their living costs. Students should contact the student support department of their institution for further details.

Loans

Some high-street banks offer specialised loans for those wishing to study for professional qualifications. However, there does seem to be an increasing unwillingness to lend to students, with NatWest withdrawing its Professional Trainee Loan Scheme in 2011 and the Royal Bank of Scotland (which owns NatWest) cancelling its loans for students before having to be bailed out by the government. Along similar lines, in 2014 Metro Bank announced a deal with The University of Law, offering its GDL, LPC and BPTC students a professional studies loan for legal studies. However, as of 2016, this was no longer available.

Career development loans are deferred repayment loans that are available to help pay for vocational courses, including fees and any related expenses, not exceeding a total of £10,000. One month after finishing the course, you must begin to repay the loan to the Cooperative Bank – the only bank that offers the loan – over an agreed period and at an agreed rate. Applicants must show that they intend to use the resulting qualification for the purposes of finding employment in the United Kingdom or European Union. In 2016 The University of Law announced that it would also be providing loans to its master's and LPC students, via the Student Loans Company, for up to £10,280.

Worth noting is that career development loans cannot be used to fund a course that leads to another course rather than employment. This means that banks cannot offer them to help students fund the GDL.

More information and an application form may be obtained from participating banks, the National Careers Service helpline on 0800 100 900 or the www.gov.uk website (search for "career development loan").

Charities and grant-making trusts

Some grant-making trusts and charities may offer financial assistance to those seeking to qualify as a lawyer. The application criteria for these awards vary enormously, but they are often so specific that eligibility is limited to just a few and only small amounts of money are available. The best place to find a full list of such organisations is in the reference section of a local library. Try publications such as *The Guide to Educational Grants, The Directory of Grant-Making Trusts, The Grants Register, A Guide to Grants for Individuals in Need* and *Charities Digest*.

Reality check: The road to becoming a trainee or pupil is a huge financial investment, with no guarantee of a training contract or pupillage at the end of it. Make sure you've got what it takes before committing thousands of pounds to the process.

Course directory

Bristol Law School

University of the West of England, Coldharbour Lane, Frenchay, Bristol BS16 1QY
Tel: 0117 328 3333
Email: admissions@uwe.ac.uk
Web: www.uwe.ac.uk/professionallawcourses
f uwebristol 𝕏 uwebristol

College overview UWE Bristol Law School is widely recognised as one of the leading providers of professional legal education in the UK. We have a reputation for excellence and for delivering courses of the very highest quality. UWE Bristol Law School offers the full range of professional law programmes. Our courses are taught by the tutors who design and write them; experienced solicitors or barristers teaching within their own subject areas. From our dedicated law facilities to our events and pro bono activities, we have everything you need to enhance your career prospects and have a very strong track record of assisting students that have not secured training contracts or pupillage.

Our benefits: regional law fair and meet the employers fair; networking and careers events (including our distinguished executive address series); dedicated professional law teaching and common rooms; mock courtrooms (used by legal practitioners and students); comprehensive online resources, including recorded lectures; extensive law library; virtual world case study option; pro bono unit, with a range of award-winning activities.

Graduate Diploma in Law Our GDL enables you as a non-law graduate to progress with confidence to the LPC/BPTC, and is supported by a dedicated team of tutors who understand the demands of the GDL route. Teaching is not shared with undergraduates. The curriculum is divided into two teaching blocks with assessments after each block, which greatly assists our students in managing workload. Tuition will develop you for the demands of the legal profession, equipping you with the necessary legal skills to thoroughly apply the law to a set of facts and the ability to solve legal problems.
Places offered: 150 split between full time and part time.

LLM Advanced Legal Practice Whether you are intending to practise in a commercial or high street firm, the practical, wide-ranging Legal Practice Course leading to a Masters qualification will provide the broad and rigorous foundation you need to be 'practice ready'. Workshop teaching happens in small, interactive groups with an emphasis on intensive, personal tuition. Here, you will learn by doing within a supportive, friendly environment, developing the skills and knowledge to excel in your role as a solicitor. You will benefit from flexible modes of study and a choice of timetabling options. There are strong links to local and regional practice, including a placement scheme run in conjunction with Bristol Law Society and an innovative legal simulation case study run in conjunction with local solicitors. There are different options to complete the Masters programme, and these focus on continuing your professional development, as a reflective practitioner with responsibility for your own development and learning.
Places offered: 320 (full time) 80 (part time).

LLM Bar Professional Training Studies With its reputation for teaching excellence, high levels of student satisfaction and outstanding pastoral care, our BPTC leading to Masters qualification is highly commended by the Bar Standards Board (BSB) and will equip you with key skills to excel in practice. There are exceptional links with the local Bar which provide four advocacy and mooting competitions annually sponsored by local chambers and an additional Western Circuit sponsored advocacy prize. As part of the programme you have the opportunity to become an accredited civil commercial mediator.
Places offered: 120 (full time) 48 (part time).

CPE/GDL	150
LPC	400
BPTC	168

Apply to

GDL Central Applications Board (full time), direct to UWE Bristol (part time)
LPC Central Applications Board (full time), direct to UWE Bristol (part time)
BPTC Bar Professional Training Online

Contact names

GDL
Wendy Swinscoe
wendy.swinscoe@uwe.ac.uk

LPC
Jane Waddell
jane.waddell@uwe.ac.uk

BPTC
Delyth James
delyth.james@uwe.ac.uk

PSC/CPD
Ben Reeves
benjamin.reeves@uwe.ac.uk

The City Law School, London

City, University of London, Northampton Square, London EC1V 0HB
Tel: 020 7040 3309
Email: law@city.ac.uk
Web: www.city.ac.uk/law
f thecitylawschool **𝕏** citylawschool

University overview The City Law School is one of London's major law schools. Part of City, University of London, a member college of the University of London, we provide legal training for anyone interested in pursuing a career in law. Located in the heart of legal London our exceptional legal courses are delivered by our team of highly respected and well known academics and practitioners, sharing their experiences and real life skills of working in the legal profession.

Graduate Entry LLB (full time) Our Graduate Entry LLB (GE LLB) degree is designed for non-law graduates looking to convert into law. Taught over two years, the course teaches you the seven core foundation subjects that are usually covered in an undergraduate law degree. The course also gives you the opportunity to explore a specific area of law by offering a range of specialist elective subjects.

Graduate Diploma in Law (full time) Our Graduate Diploma in Law (GDL) has a strong academic focus, providing a solid foundation in law, teaching you the seven core foundation subjects covered in an undergraduate law degree, in just one year. It is one of the largest and most respected GDL courses in the UK and benefits from specialist staff with unrivalled experience, including visiting academics from Oxford, Cambridge and other universities.

Legal Practice Course (full time) Our Legal Practice Course (LPC) has been designed to ensure that you are fully prepared to meet the demands of the modern legal profession. We teach you the core legal skills and knowledge that you need to be a successful solicitor and also give you the opportunity to develop a specialist interest in a particular area of law by offering a range of vocational electives. The LPC is also available with an LLM option, so it is eligible for the government's postgraduate loan funding.

Bar Professional Training Course (full or part time) Our Bar Professional Training Course (BPTC) delivers effective training for future barristers and equips you with the key skills and networking opportunities to progress onto pupillage and forge a successful career at the Bar. The core skills of advocacy, opinion writing, drafting, alternative dispute resolution and client conferencing are taught in the context of procedural and evidential knowledge in both criminal and civil practice. The BPTC is also available with an LLM option, so it is eligible for the government's postgraduate loan funding.

Master of Laws (LLM) The LLM at The City Law School is a flexible masters programme which enables students to develop a critical understanding of specialist or linked areas of the law. Students embarking on the LLM are able to select from a range of different programmes that can be tailored according to your career goals, choosing to either gain a Master of Laws, selecting electives from a range of modules, or to gain a specialist LLM, selecting electives from one specialist area. Specialisms include civil litigation, international banking law, public international law, dispute resolution, international commercial law, international human rights and more. Other LLMs include: LLM International Business Law (distance learning) and LLM Maritime Law (Greece).

GE LLB	46
GDL	190
LPC	111
BPTC	362
LLM	150

Contacts

LLB (Graduate Entry)
020 7040 3309
law@city.ac.uk

Graduate Diploma in Law
020 7040 3309
law@city.ac.uk

LPC
020 7040 5787
lpc@city.ac.uk

BPTC
020 7040 5787
bptc@city.ac.uk

LLMs
020 7040 5787
masteroflaws@city.ac.uk

THE CITY
LAW SCHOOL
CITY, UNIVERSITY OF LONDON
—— EST 1894 ——

Remember to cite *The Training Contract & Pupillage Handbook* if you apply to this law school.

The University of Law
BUSINESS FOCUSED
LAW COURSES
Our range of law courses focus on building practical legal skills so you have the best opportunity to achieve your career ambitions.
From the GDL, MA Law, LPC and BPTC for aspiring lawyers, to Professional Development courses for trainee solicitors and qualified lawyers.
NATIONAL STUDENT SURVEY 2016
1ST
FOR OVERALL STUDENT SATISFACTION
NATIONAL STUDENT SURVEY 2016
97%
STUDENT SATISFACTION
Find out more
law.ac.uk/postgraduate

The University of Law

Braboeuf Manor, Portsmouth Road, St Catherines, Guildford GU3 1HA
Tel: 0800 289997
Email: admissions@law.ac.uk
Web: www.law.ac.uk/postgraduate
f universityoflaw 🐦 universityoflaw

University overview The University of Law (ULaw) is the UK's longest-established specialist provider of legal education. Our business-focused courses are designed and taught by experienced lawyers with strong emphasis on building the practical skills that today's employers are looking for. You'll have access to the country's most varied pro bono programme with over 3,700 opportunities to put your legal skills into practice. Not to mention the UK's largest legal mentoring programme, with the support of over 500 practising lawyers. Helping you become employable is a central aim of our legal training programmes. Since 2013 over 90% of our full-time summer LPC graduates have secured legal positions within nine months of completing the course, the majority with training contracts.

Graduate Diploma in Law (full time/part time/online) Our GDL is designed to build knowledge and skills that more than match a law degree. Academic training is built around real life examples with research assignments that directly reflect the way you'll work as a lawyer. Our structured study pattern means that the foundation module assessment and teaching is spread out so you can focus on selected modules each semester.

MA Law (full time)) Our MA Law is designed specifically for non-law graduates to gain a legal qualification at Masters level. The MA Law is an internationally recognised qualification, so it's ideal for a career path in or outside of the legal sector. MA Law students may also be eligible for a student loan.

Legal Practice Course (full time/part time/online) We're confident that our LPC is the best preparation for entering legal practice by offering you the skills to succeed in the business world. Our client focused LPC course enables you to develop commercial awareness, critical thinking, project management and networking skills. Study our LPC and you can gain an MSc in Law, Business and Management or an LLM in Professional Legal Practice at no extra cost. LPC Masters students may also be eligible for a postgraduate student loan.

Bar Professional Training Course (full time/part time) Our BPTC is uniquely structured to mirror the real life experience of a barrister in practice. We're the only legal training provider offering a live selection process. Study in small groups with plenty of opportunities to test your advocacy skills. With our BPTC LLM you can gain additional practical experience representing real clients in courts and tribunals. Masters students may also be eligible for postgraduate funding.

LLM Legal Practice (Conflict Resolution) (Intellectual Property) (full time/online) Our Masters programmes provide an excellent way to develop in-depth knowledge and specialist skills in your chosen study area of either conflict resolution or intellectual property. LLM students may also be eligible for postgraduate funding.

MSc Law, Governance, Risk and Compliance (online) - MSc Law and Financial Crime Compliance (online) Building on expertise gained from the International Compliance Association (ICA) Professional Postgraduate Diploma, develop your international legal and compliance knowledge with our career enhancing Masters qualifications.

Events We run events of all types, including open days, law fairs and insight days, as well as lawyers den, barrister insight days and our annual national law fair. Check them out at www.law.ac.uk/events/postgraduate.

Contact

Admissions
Freephone 0800 289997
International
(+44) (0)1483 216000
admissions@law.ac.uk

Apply to

GDL, MA Law and LPC full time
Central Applications Board
www.lawcabs.ac.uk

GDL and LPC part time and online
www.law.ac.uk/postgraduate

BPTC full and part time
Bar Student Application Service
www.barsas.com

LLMs and MSc
www.law.ac.uk/postgraduate

Locations
Birmingham, Bristol, Chester, Exeter, Guildford, Leeds, London (Bloomsbury and Moorgate), Manchester, Reading

The
University of
Law

LawCareers.Net™

Delivering your future in law

LCN Weekly is packed with news, profiles, opinion and advice about becoming a lawyer, and delivered to your inbox for free every Tuesday.

Don't miss out on this essential source of information!

Liverpool John Moores University

Redmonds Building, Brownlow Hill, Liverpool L3 5UG
Tel: 0151 231 5175
Email: apsadmissions@ljmu.ac.uk
Web: www.ljmu.ac.uk
🐦 ljmulaw

College overview Liverpool John Moores University (LJMU) is a contemporary university in one of the most famous cities in the world. We aim to give people the opportunity to maximise their potential in an environment that is stimulating, challenging and exciting, but also caring and supportive.

The School of Law offers a broad portfolio of academic, vocational and professional programmes in both full-time and part-time modes. The School provides undergraduate, postgraduate and professional programmes in law, legal practice and criminal justice. It also offers opportunities to study for an MPhil or PhD by research. School staff are engaged in a wide range of law and criminal justice research, and the School hosts the Centre for Criminal Justice.

The School of Law has invested significantly in staff development, with an emphasis on enhancing the status and quality of teaching and learning, and also in providing excellent information technology facilities.

The School is part of the Faculty of Arts, Professional and Social Studies, based in the £38 million Redmonds Building close to the heart of Liverpool City Centre. Liverpool is a vibrant city and the cultural capital of the North of England.

Legal Practice Course (full and part time) The LPC at LJMU has been designed to meet the requirements and needs of the legal profession in the 21st century. The LPC aims to produce a highly skilled, commercially aware and effective trainee solicitor, who is prepared for the rigours and demands of a training contract. Students will join a team of professional lawyers who are highly committed, enthusiastic and skilled teachers.

LPC students are able to volunteer for the School of Law's pro bono Legal Advice Centre. The service, which is open to residents around Merseyside, gives students real-life client and case management experience working across a variety of legal areas, from family to employment and commercial law.

LLM Qualifying Law The School of Law is now recruiting to the new LLM degree, which offers students a broad range of learning options selected from across the School of Law's diverse module portfolio. The LLM Qualifying Law degree replaces the GDL and offering candidates a fully validated (SRA/BSB) masters qualification. The degree can be studied in both full-time and part-time patterns and offers excellent preparation for a professional legal career.

Other postgraduate courses (one-year full time or two-year part time)
LLM in Legal Practice (top-up masters allows you to convert your existing LPC or BVC/BPTC Postgraduate Diploma to an LLM)
LLM in International Business, Corporate and Finance Law
LLM Global Crime, Justice and Security
MA Criminal Justice

LJMU also offers a range of postgraduate and professional programmes in business, arts, humanities and media. For further details visit our website www.ljmu.ac.uk/courses or telephone 0151 231 5175.

LPC   144

Apply to

Full time Central Applications Board

Part time Apply direct

Admissions contact LPC
Fiona Fargher
f.l.fargher@ljmu.ac.uk
0151 231 3930

Admissions contact LLM
a.r.harvey@ljmu.ac.uk
0151 231 3955

Admissions contact LLM Qualifying Law
Anita Ellis
a.ellis@ljmu.ac.uk
0151 231 3936

Admissions contact LLM in Legal Practice
Laura Samaroo
l.samaroo@ljmu.ac.uk
0151 231 3832

Admissions contact LLM International Business, Corporate and Finance Law
Dr Tony Harvey
a.r.harvey@ljmu.ac.uk
0151 231 3955

Admissions contact LLM Global Crime, Justice and Security
Dr Gary Wilson
g.wilson@ljmu.ac.uk
0151 231 3397

Admissions contact MA Criminal Justice
Dr Noel Cross
n.cross@ljmu.ac.uk
0151 231 3902

STUDY AT A UK
TOP 25 LAW SCHOOL*

*Guardian University Guide 2018

Multi-award winning, Northumbria Law School is one of the largest law schools in the UK**, with a national and international reputation for excellence in legal education.**

We offer courses for law graduates who want to be barristers or solicitors and conversion courses for non-law graduates. With full-time, part-time and distance learning study options available – why not pursue your passion at Northumbria to get ahead in your law career?

GDL / LPC / BPTC / GDL / LLM

Discover more northumbria.ac.uk/law
0191 227 4494
law@northumbria.ac.uk

WANT IT.
MASTER IT.

THE QUEEN'S
ANNIVERSARY PRIZES
FOR HIGHER AND FURTHER EDUCATION
2013

northumbria
UNIVERSITY NEWCASTLE

Law School

Northumbria Law School

City Campus East, Newcastle upon Tyne NE1 8ST
Tel: 0191 227 4494
Email: law@northumbria.ac.uk
Web: www.northumbria.ac.uk/law
f northumbrialaw **𝕏** northumbrialaw

University overview Northumbria Law School is one of the largest law schools in the UK, with a national and international reputation for excellence in legal education. We are a multi award winning law school, having received the highly prestigious Queen's Anniversary Prize for the outstanding work of our student law office – the largest university law clinic in the UK. We have also won the prestigious 'Best Law School' accolade at the Attorney General's Student Pro Bono Awards a record three times. We focus on law in practice and are committed to ensuring that students develop the knowledge and skills needed to become successful legal professionals.

Graduate Diploma in Law GDL (full time or distance learning) Our GDL is taught using a practical, student-focused approach providing a solid grounding in the major areas of law. It covers the foundations of legal knowledge, which are taught by means of lectures, other large group sessions and seminars. Students are provided with comprehensive study materials, webcasts and step-by-step workbooks to support their studies. Successful GDL students who continue to study at Northumbria are guaranteed a place on the Legal Practice Course (LPC).

Legal Practice Postgraduate Diploma LPC (full or part time) Our LPC provides vocational training across a range of subjects and practical skills, enabling students to learn how to apply their legal knowledge in a practical context. The well-established, highly successful programme offers a strong staff/student ratio, a guaranteed legal placement or professional mentor and a wide range of electives tailored to both general and commercial practice.

LLM Legal Practice (full or part time) This programme will enhance the students' legal knowledge and allow them to develop the skills and values necessary to become an effective and successful legal professional. This Master's degree offers students the opportunity to gain an internationally recognised LLM qualification in addition to the LPC and will prepare students for the demands of the legal profession and prepare them for a training contract and life as a solicitor.

Bar Professional Training Course BPTC (full or part time) Our BPTC is student-centred with skills taught in small group sessions. During the programme students' develop a range of essential skills, which include advocacy, drafting, opinion writing, conference skills and resolution of disputes out of court. Evidence, criminal and civil litigation are also taught as discrete subjects, as well as been integrated with the five main skill areas. All subjects and skills are developed through practical sessions, in which students work on case studies and carry out a range of tasks, which are typical of pupillage.

LLM Bar Practice (full or part time) This programme allows students to enhance their BPTC qualification by enabling them to gain a Masters (LLM) award as part of the BPTC course. The LLM can be obtained by completion of a project, which provides students with the opportunity to explore in great depth areas of law in which they may wish to practice. This programme will also enable eligible students to apply for postgraduate funding.

LLM Advanced Legal Practice (distance learning) Designed for qualified lawyers (solicitors and barristers, or their international equivalent) who want to develop their knowledge in a specialist area of law. Students develop their skills in legal research and its written presentation, through an in depth study of an agreed legal topic under individual tutor supervision. We offer a range of other LLM programmes taught by leading academics and experienced practising lawyers.

LPC	150 (full time)
	50 (part time)
GDL	100 (full time)
	50 (distance)
BPTC	100 (full time)
	48 (part time)

Contact

Admissions
0191 349 5600
er.admissions@
northumbria.ac.uk

Apply to

GDL & LPC (full time)
www.lawcabs.ac.uk

BPTC & LLM Bar Practice (full and part time)
www.barsas.com

GDL (distance learning, LPC (part time) and LLM
Direct to Northumbria
www.northumbria.ac.uk/law

northumbria
UNIVERSITY NEWCASTLE

Law School

Remember to cite *The Training Contract & Pupillage Handbook* if you apply to this law school.

TAKE THE NEXT STEP AT AN AWARD-WINNING LAW SCHOOL

NOTTINGHAM LAW SCHOOL IS ONE OF THE LARGEST UNIVERSITY LAW SCHOOLS IN THE UK WITH A LONG-ESTABLISHED REPUTATION FOR MODERN LEGAL EDUCATION.

Why choose Nottingham Law School for the next step in your legal career?

- Consistently high pupillage and graduate employability rates
- Teaching delivered by qualified practitioners and expert staff
- Internationally recognised LLM award in addition to the LPC and BPTC
- Eligible for UK Government postgraduate loan scheme
- Excellence in legal education for over 50 years
- Work experience opportunities in our Legal Advice Centre
- Dedicated careers and recruitment service
- An award-winning pro bono scheme

Find out more at
www.ntu.ac.uk/nls
and start training for your
successful legal career

NOTTINGHAM LAW SCHOOL
NOTTINGHAM TRENT UNIVERSITY

Nottingham Law School

Burton Street, Nottingham NG1 4BU
Tel: 0115 848 4460
Email: nls.enquiries@ntu.ac.uk
Web: www.ntu.ac.uk/nls
f ntulawschool **𝕐** lawnls

School overview One of the largest and most diverse law schools in the UK, Nottingham Law School has been delivering excellence in legal education for over 50 years. We seek to ensure that all of our clients, from students to experienced practitioners, receive the best practical legal education and training. You will be taught by a unique mix of qualified lawyers with a proven track record in practice and legal education. As an acknowledgement of our commitment to legal education, we were voted Legal Education Provider of the Year at the 2016 *Solicitors Journal Awards*.

Nottingham Law School has an excellent record of graduate employability. Our focus on practical skills and our dedicated careers and recruitment service ensures that you get the best possible start to your career. We have an award-winning pro bono scheme and our commitment to practical legal education is epitomised by the purpose-built Nottingham Law School legal advice centre. This centre provides a multitude of opportunities for students as well as access to justice for a variety of clients.

Graduate Diploma in Law (full time or distance learning) This conversion course is designed for any non-law graduate who intends to become a solicitor or barrister in the UK. The intensive course effectively covers the seven core subjects of an undergraduate law degree in one go. It is the stepping stone to the LPC or the BPTC and to a legal career thereafter.

Legal Practice Course (full time or part time) At Nottingham Law School we strive to provide you with the practical knowledge and insight that employers regard as essential. This is why we have enhanced our LPC so that the successful completion of all its elements will result in the award of a Masters degree. As well as providing you with an internationally recognised qualification, our LLM Legal Practice Course will provide enhanced insight into the legal profession. On the LLM part of the course you will have the opportunity to complete a project or dissertation, focusing on aspects of legal practice that interest you. You will also benefit from a series of lectures delivered by experts within the legal profession, a bridge to practice module and commercial awareness training.

Bar Professional Training Course (full time) Nottingham Law School designed its BPTC to develop a range of core practical skills, and to equip students to succeed in the fast-changing environment of practice at the Bar. We have enhanced our BPTC so that the successful completion of all its elements will result in the award of a Masters degree: LLM Bar Professional Training Course. Particular emphasis is placed on the skill of advocacy and Nottingham Law School is home to the UK's first centre for advocacy. The BPTC is taught entirely by qualified practitioners, and utilises the same integrated and interactive teaching methods as all of the school's other professional courses. Essentially, students learn by doing. Students are encouraged to realise, through practice and feedback, their full potential.

Other postgraduate courses We offer LLMs in a number of subject areas including international trade and commercial law; oil, gas and mining law; human rights law; intellectual property law; health law and ethics; corporate and insolvency law and sports law. We also provide intellectual property courses for practitioners and a professional doctorate in legal practice.

Apply to

GDL (full time)
www.lawcabs.ac.uk

GDL distance learning
www.ntu.ac.uk/apply

LPC (full time)
www.lawcabs.ac.uk

LPC (part time)
www.ntu.ac.uk/apply

BPTC
www.barsas.com

Other postgraduate law courses
www.ntu.ac.uk/apply

Location
Nottingham

NOTTINGHAM LAW SCHOOL
NOTTINGHAM TRENT UNIVERSITY 🎓

Remember to cite *The Training Contract & Pupillage Handbook* if you apply to this law school.

POSTGRADUATE TRAINING 133

Course providers

Institutions in **bold** have provided detailed information in the course directory section

Institutions that offer the GDL
Birmingham City University
Bournemouth University
BPP Law School
University of Brighton
Bristol, University of the West of England
Brunel University
Cardiff University
The City Law School
De Montfort University
University of East Anglia
University of Central Lancashire
The University of Law
Leeds Beckett University
London Metropolitan University
London South Bank University
Manchester Metropolitan University
Northumbria University
Nottingham Law School
Oxford Brookes University
University of Plymouth
Roehampton University
University of Sheffield
Staffordshire University and Worcester College of
Technology at Worcester
University of Sussex
Swansea University
University of Westminster

Institutions that offer the LPC
Anglia Ruskin University
Birmingham City University
Bournemouth University
BPP Law School
Bristol, University of the West of England
Cardiff Law School
The City Law School
De Montfort University
University of Derby
University of Central Lancashire
The University of Law
Leeds Beckett University
Liverpool John Moores University
London Metropolitan University
Manchester Metropolitan University
Northumbria University
Nottingham Law School
University of Plymouth
University of Sheffield
University of South Wales
Staffordshire University
University of Sunderland
Swansea University
University of West London
University of Westminster
University of Wolverhampton

Institutions that offer the BPTC
BPP Law School
Bristol, University of the West of England
Cardiff Law School
The City Law School
The University of Law
Manchester Metropolitan University
University of Northumbria
Nottingham Law School

Solicitors

BARRISTER

IN-HOUSE

SOLICITOR

CHARTERED LEGAL EXECUTIVE

PARALEGAL

LEGAL APPRENTICE

Find your career in law with

*Law**Careers.Net*™

LawCareers.Net is the number one resource for everything you need to know about a legal career, offering news, features, lawyer and recruiter profiles, advice, blogs and videos, along with a comprehensive directory of over 1,000 employers.

www.lawcareers.net

The Law Society and the Junior Lawyers Division

Law Society

The Law Society is the professional body that represents, promotes and supports solicitors in England and Wales. Our commitment is to put members at the heart of everything we do. Whether we are seeking to influence governments, campaigning for justice, delivering training or promoting solicitors to the public, we are committed to making sure that your voice is heard, your needs are met and your business is supported.

Whether you are working in a high-street practice, a commercial, regional or City firm, an alternative business structure (ABS) or in-house for a private, public or charitable organisation, the Law Society exists for you. We also fulfil, on behalf of the solicitors' profession, an important public interest role of enabling access to justice, upholding individual rights and freedoms, supporting public education and upholding the rule of law.

We are committed to ensuring that you can make the most of opportunities and can respond to the challenges of a changing legal sector. Our aim is to deliver value for money for the public interest funding contribution that you make as part of your practising fee and when you choose to pay for additional products and services.

Supporting students and solicitors

We provide a range of services for students, trainees and newly qualified solicitors, including information and training. Our weekly *Law Society Gazette* includes news, commentary and features on different areas of law. Our website is a comprehensive and regularly updated source of information for the entire profession.

Every year we run over 400 national and regional conferences, workshops and seminars, including careers workshops for undergraduates and LPC students. Once qualified, members can subscribe to a range of networks. Benefits include exclusive access to training events, conferences and seminars, dedicated web areas and web-based forums, newsletters and alerts, practice toolkits and quarterly magazines.

As the sole national representative body for all solicitors in England and Wales, we are the voice of the profession, making sure that its members' views are heard by regulators, government and other decision makers. We campaign for better law, lobby and work with parliamentary members, and challenge the government where necessary.

Promoting equality and diversity

Our Diversity Access Scheme helps talented, committed people to overcome social, economic or personal barriers to becoming a solicitor. It funds LPC places at a number of teaching institutions and offers mentoring support and work placements.

Junior Lawyers Division

With approximately 70,000 members, the Junior Lawyers Division (JLD) is one of the largest communities within the Law Society. It represents, supports and provides services to junior lawyers at the start of their careers to help them develop, progress and diversify within the legal profession. Membership of the JLD, which is free and automatic, includes LPC students, LPC graduates such as those working as paralegals, trainee solicitors and solicitors up to five years' qualified.

A local presence

Local JLD groups exist across the country. They run events ranging from lectures to monthly meetings and social events, and offer an opportunity to socialise with junior lawyers who work and live in the area. They can often be a lifeline for trainees who may be alone in their firms, as well as giving junior lawyers the chance to connect and build their professional networks.

Campaigning on key issues

The JLD ensures that members' views are heard and campaigns to bring about real change to further members' interests. JLD campaigns and lobbying activities over the years have covered issues such as the trainee minimum salary, work experience, cuts to legal aid, student funding and successfully lobbying the Solicitors Regulation Authority to amend their proposals for a centralised assessment.

Events

The JLD offers opportunities to attend national events and engage with support services. The main events include the following:

- Forums – one-day careers events, held around the country, focusing on issues that affect the membership, from how to get a training contract to practical skills and advice for junior lawyers in the work environment.
- Conference – an annual event, featuring interesting speakers and lively debate with the focus on taking control of your career.
- International weekend – once a year the JLD, the Young Barristers' Committee, the European Young Bar Association and the London Young Lawyers Group organise a two-day training conference that is attended by lawyers from around the world.
- Essay competition – a 2,000-word essay competition that gives the JLD's student, paralegal and trainee members the chance to compete for prize money, as well as honing their drafting skills on a subject of professional relevance.
- International networking – opportunities to meet and network with junior lawyers from other legal jurisdictions through membership of international organisations.

Advice and information

The JLD aims to be a source of information on everything you need to know about becoming a solicitor and the issues facing junior members. Its website includes information about legal career paths, national and regional events, ongoing policy projects, webinars, initiatives involving junior lawyers and articles of interest to the junior profession. Its social media pages – on Twitter, Facebook and LinkedIn – provide updates on JLD activity and upcoming events.

Getting involved

The JLD is always looking for active participation; its committee has positions available each year, including a specific LPC student seat.

This information is provided by the Law Society. Learn more about the Law Society at www.lawsociety.org.uk. Learn more about the JLD and sign up for the JLD e-newsletter at www.lawsociety.org.uk/juniorlawyers, or contact them via email at juniorlawyers@ lawsociety.org.uk.

The Solicitors Regulation Authority

The Solicitors Regulation Authority (SRA) is the regulator of solicitors and law firms in England and Wales, protecting consumers and supporting the rule of law and the administration of justice. It does this by overseeing all education and training requirements necessary to practise as a solicitor, licensing individuals and firms to practise, setting the standards of the profession and enforcing compliance against these standards. Further information is available at www.sra.org.uk.

In order to practise, all would-be solicitors need to be admitted to the roll. Under current regulations, you must have satisfactorily completed:
- the academic stage of training (ie, a qualifying law degree (QLD), the Graduate Diploma in Law (GDL) or the Common Professional Examination (CPE));
- the Legal Practice Course (LPC);
- a period of recognised training (formerly referred to as 'training contract'); and
- the Professional Skills Course (PSC)

This is known as the domestic route to qualification. Alternative routes may be available to those who have CILEx qualifications, or who have already qualified in another jurisdiction.

You must also satisfy the SRA that you are of the right character and suitability to be a solicitor. As part of this, you must undertake screening, which includes a standard disclosure from the Disclosure and Barring Service (DBS).

The SRA will be changing its qualification requirements (see 'Changes ahead' below). However, the following information sets out the current requirements for admission as a solicitor.

LPC
If you are planning on becoming a solicitor through the domestic route outlined above, you need to complete the LPC or demonstrate that you have met the SRA's requirements for this stage by "equivalent means" (see www.sra.org.uk/students/resources/equivalent-means-information-pack.page). Before enrolling on the LPC, you need to have met the academic requirements for admission.

Period of recognised training
The period of recognised training is a period of supervised training with an SRA-registered training establishment (eg, a firm of solicitors, local authority or legal department within a commercial organisation). It usually lasts for two years, but can be completed over a longer period if working or studying part time.

During this time, you will develop your understanding of legal practice and the responsibilities you will take on when you are admitted to the roll. The following criteria must be met:
- You will gain experience in at least three areas of English or Welsh law and develop your skills in contentious and non-contentious areas of practice.
- You will need to keep a record of the work you have done and the skills you have gained.
- You will have informal performance reviews with your training principal or supervisor.
- You will have at least three formal appraisals over the period.

You may also demonstrate that you have met the requirements of the period of recognised training through equivalent means (see SRA website, as above).

The SRA may monitor training establishments to ensure that the quality of training is adequate. As a result, during your period of recognised training you may be asked to complete a questionnaire about your training and your firm.

Admission to the roll

Approximately 10 weeks before the end of your training, the SRA will contact you to complete a declaration agreeing to screening checks. This includes financial and identity checks plus a standard disclosure from the DBS. The fee for this is £42.

Eight weeks before the end of your training, you will be sent an application for admission. Applications must be received at least 28 days before the date on which you wish to be admitted (see www.sra.org.uk/trainees/admission/admission.page).

Once admitted, solicitors are under a professional duty to make sure they can offer a proper standard of service to their clients. They must therefore address any learning needs they identify through appropriate training and development.

Changes ahead

In April 2017 the SRA announced that it would introduce a new national licensing exam for intending solicitors – the Solicitors Qualifying Examination (SQE). The target date for the introduction of the SQE is September 2020. The SRA believes that the SQE will provide a mechanism for all candidates to be assessed on a consistent and fair basis.

Once the SQE is introduced, the SRA will no longer require aspiring solicitors to take the QLD, GDL or LPC. Instead, candidates will be free to do the training they need to prepare themselves for the SQE.

The SQE will consist of a functioning legal knowledge test and a skills test. It is likely many candidates will take SQE stage one at or shortly after they complete their law degree. Candidates will need to complete a substantial period of legal work experience in order to be able to pass stage two (the skills test).

There will continue to be a requirement for two years' work experience before admission. However, the SRA will recognise a wider range of legal work experience, not just formal training contracts, but also working as a paralegal or in a student law clinic.

It is likely that anyone who has started a QLD or GDL before the SQE is introduced will have the choice about whether to qualify under the existing route to qualification, or to qualify under the SQE.

More information about the SQE can be found on the SRA's website at www.sra.org.uk/sra/policy/training-for-tomorrow.page.

Further information

This is a broad outline of what you need to do to start your career as a trainee solicitor. If you need more details, please visit www.sra.org.uk/students and www.sra.org.uk/trainees, where comprehensive student and trainee sections include the training regulations in full, a list of training firms and organisations, institutions that provide academic and vocational courses, and more. If you need to talk to someone, call the SRA's contact centre on 0370 606 2555 or email contactcentre@sra.org.uk.

The SRA works closely with the Junior Lawyers Division (JLD) throughout the year in hosting events for students and young lawyers, such as webinars, to help address some of the issues they face. For example, it has held sessions with JLD members to discuss the SQE. For more on the JLD, see www.lawsociety.org.uk/juniorlawyers or page 137.

This information is supplied by the SRA.

The Chartered Institute of Legal Executives

The Chartered Institute of Legal Executives (CILEx) is the professional association representing around 20,000 qualified chartered legal executive lawyers, paralegals and other legal practitioners. Changes in legislation mean that chartered legal executive lawyers are increasingly on a level playing field with solicitors or barristers, as they can now become judges, coroners, advocates and partners in law firms.

CILEx is recognised as one of the three professional bodies of the legal profession, alongside the Bar Council (see page 466) and the Law Society (see page 137). The role of a chartered legal executive lawyer is now so similar to that of a solicitor that the average client is unlikely to be able to distinguish between them. In fact, many chartered legal executives supervise solicitors. The difference is that a chartered legal executive is a qualified lawyer who is trained to specialise as an expert in one or two particular areas of the law, whereas solicitors have a broader, more general legal training.

There are alternative academic routes to becoming a chartered legal executive lawyer. If you don't have a law degree, you will need to take the traditional CILEx route, which is comprised of the level 3 CILEx qualification (set at A-level standard) and the level 6 CILEx qualification (studied to the same standard as an honours degree). This full CILEx route costs on average around £9,500, depending on where and how you choose to study. This will typically take four years to complete part time and can be completed alongside full-time working. Timescales can be flexible and study can be tailored according to your personal and professional needs.

If you already have a qualifying law degree, irrespective of when this was achieved, CILEx offers a cost-effective alternative to the LPC or BPTC through its graduate fast-track diploma, which usually takes around a year to complete part time and costs approximately £3,250.

Regardless of whether you follow the traditional CILEx route or the graduate fast-track diploma pathway, you will need to complete a three-year period of qualifying employment and submit a portfolio of evidence called work-based learning. Work completed as a paralegal, while studying, may be used towards part of this requirement; a minimum of one year of your qualifying employment needs to fall after you've completed your CILEx academic qualification. The last two years of your qualifying employment must be continuous.

If you already hold an LPC or BPTC, you will be exempt from all CILEx qualifications and can immediately apply to become a graduate member of CILEx and use the designatory letters 'GCILEx'. You will still need to complete the qualifying employment requirement. On successful completion of the academic stage, and the qualifying employment stage, of training, you will become a fellow of the CILEx and have the right to call yourself a chartered legal executive lawyer.

CILEx has a network of over 80 accredited study centres in England and Wales that are approved to deliver CILEx courses and quality assured to CILEx standards. CILEx examinations take place twice a year, in January and June, and may be taken at separate examination sittings to suit your plans and study needs. Distance learning is offered through specialist study centres, including at CILEx Law School.

Training to be a solicitor

A career as a chartered legal executive lawyer is a worthwhile, rewarding and fulfilling career in its own right, but CILEx does recognise that there are those who have more traditional ambitions. CILEx qualifications can be used to count towards qualifying as a solicitor.

As a fellow of the institute, you may be exempt from the Solicitors Regulation Authority (SRA) training contract. It is important that you contact the SRA to get full details, as this exemption is wholly at its discretion.

Salaries

Salaries will vary according to your location and legal specialism. Starting salaries are usually up to £20,000 per year while qualifying. Many trainee CILEx members report that they are on higher salaries than the trainee solicitors they work alongside. After completion of your CILEx qualifications, you can expect to earn on average up to £26,500.

Once fully qualified (having completed three years of qualifying work experience), you can expect to earn on average up to £45,500; if you work in a big city or become a partner in a firm, you can earn much more (salaries of over £100,000 have been stated).

CILEx qualifications are highly valued by employers and, as such, recent surveys have found that around 67% of CILEx students have their membership fees paid for by their employers.

What chartered legal executive lawyers do

Professional responsibilities increase with experience. Fully qualified and experienced chartered legal executives are able to undertake many of the legal activities that solicitors do and often supervise solicitors and other legal staff. They will have their own clients and represent them in court. Although chartered legal executives can be involved in many areas of law, the most common areas of specialism are:

- conveyancing – the legal side of buying and selling property;
- family – advising on divorce and matters affecting children;
- crime – defending and prosecuting people accused of crimes;
- company and business law – advising on legislation that affects clients' businesses such as tax, contract and employment law;
- litigation – advising clients who are in dispute with someone else;
- probate – dealing with wills, trusts and inheritance tax; and
- personal injury – handling accident claims.

All CILEx members are independently regulated and must adhere to a code of conduct. They are required to continue training throughout their careers in order to keep abreast of the latest developments in the law.

The move to allow CILEx fellows to apply for judicial positions has seen the appointment of the first chartered legal executive judges. Additionally, a growing number of chartered legal executives are acquiring their own advocacy rights in higher courts. Many are partners in legal practices.

Where chartered legal executives work

Chartered legal executives are found in over 60% of The Lawyer's list of top 200 UK law firms, but it is not just legal firms that employ them. Such lawyers fill key legal roles in a wide variety of government bodies, local authorities, charities and business organisations, including Caterpillar, HSBC, Admiral Insurance, Disney Corporation, UK Border Agency, Ministry of Defence, Crown Prosecution Service, the NHS, county councils, RSPCA and The Peabody Trust.

Partnership is the aspiration of most solicitors in private practice and that ambition is also shared by chartered legal executives. The legal market has seen many changes since the Legal Services Act 2007, which formally recognised chartered legal executives as fully fledged lawyers and enabled them to become partners in law firms.

The future

The quality of chartered legal executives as specialist lawyers is increasingly being recognised. Since early 2015 CILEx has been able to grant its members additional rights to conduct litigation in civil, criminal and family matters, and provide probate and conveyancing services, as well as immigration advice, independently of solicitors.

Combined, these will essentially give chartered legal executives all the rights they need to practise on their own without being in partnership with a solicitor or under supervision.

If you are looking for an affordable and flexible career in law, CILEx is worth serious consideration.

Sharon Bruty is head of communications at CILEx. For all the latest information, visit www.cilex.org.uk. For details on becoming a chartered legal executive, visit www.cilexcareers.org.uk.

Becoming a solicitor

Solicitors provide legal advice and representation. They work directly with their clients and are usually the first point of contact for anyone seeking legal advice. In general practice, solicitors may be called on to advise on issues ranging from crime, personal injury, contracts and wills to buying houses and taking over a business.

Increasingly, solicitors and firms specialise in certain areas of law. A run-down of various specialisations can be found in "Solicitor practice areas".

One important thing to note: in April 2017 the Solicitors Regulation Authority (SRA) confirmed that in 2020 it would be introducing the Solicitors Qualifying Examination (SQE), which all prospective solicitors will have to pass in order to qualify. The SQE will bring about fundamental changes to the way that would-be solicitors are educated and trained, but for now, the information below remains current. To learn more about what the SQE will mean, read the SRA chapter on page 139 or go to www.sra.org.uk/home/hot-topics/Solicitors-Qualifying-Examination.

Training contract/period of recognised training

The traditional training contract – or 'period of recognised training', as it is now termed by the SRA – is a two-year employment contract with a law firm or other approved organisation. The two years provide an opportunity for trainees to put into practice all the knowledge and skills they have acquired so far, with the firm assessing the trainee's suitability for retention on completion of the training period. Trainees may also study elective LPC modules if they choose to begin the training contract on completion of the initial core LPC modules.

The SRA implemented a number of changes to its training regulations in 2014, including a move to a more outcomes-focused approach which allows firms greater freedom to design the structures of their own training contracts. However, trainee solicitors are still required to meet the SRA's competence statement (released in March 2015 and forming the basis of the proposed SQE) and most training contracts are still based on the following format.

Structure

The training contract format varies between firms. Most (although not all) firms operate a 'seat' system, in which trainees spend six months in four different departments. This gives trainees exposure to different practice areas so that they can make an informed choice as to their preferred qualification area. As far as possible, firms will try to accommodate the individual wishes of trainees in terms of seats, although they have to consider the overall needs of the firm. The SRA has a number of guidelines that must also be followed. In some firms, trainees may also have the opportunity to spend a seat in an overseas office or on secondment to a client.

Training contracts may be less structured in smaller and high-street firms than those with the larger commercial firms – an approach that might appeal to those who fear a 'conveyor-belt' training mentality in the City firms. As many small firms cannot offer detailed training over a wide spread of specialisations, trainees are sometimes permitted to undertake consortium training, fulfilling different training seats in different firms.

Content

What trainees learn during the training contract will depend on the type of firm. Clearly, the practice areas at a commercial firm in the City are going to differ from those at regional high-street firms. The smaller firms that mainly concentrate on a single area of work will obviously provide the most limited experience, but conversely can offer the most responsibility.

Assessment and support

Almost without exception, firms have three and six-monthly appraisals for each training contract seat. In this way trainees get good feedback about their performance both during and after a seat. Nobody will expect you to know everything from day one of your training contract; indeed, some firms dedicate the first few weeks to induction lectures and presentations to get you up to speed with the firm, its clients and its different practice areas. Most of your work will involve drafting, writing and researching, with everything being checked by a qualified solicitor and your supervision overseen by a partner (many trainees share an office with their supervisor during their seats).

Other training opportunities exist with the Crown Prosecution Service and within the government, and with some companies outside private practice in commerce and industry (see "Alternative careers").

LPC electives

Trainees who have completed only Stage One (the core modules) of the LPC will also need to complete Stage Two (the elective modules) during their training contract. Some postgraduate course providers now offer different ways of doing this, from flexible tutor time (weekends and evening classes) to online tutorials.

Equivalent means

The changes in 2014 to the SRA regulations allowed for qualification via "equivalent means", which in practice means that in some circumstances it may be possible to qualify as a solicitor without having done a training contract. Instead, the individual is required to prove that he or she has the necessary skills and training to become a solicitor by evidencing his or her achievements while working in other, non-solicitor legal roles – most obviously as a paralegal. Again, this is in its infancy and is the exception rather than the rule, but that may change when the SQE is introduced.

Professional Skills Course

You cannot qualify as a solicitor without passing the Professional Skills Course (PSC). This is a modular course which aims to ensure that you have reached the appropriate level of skills and knowledge during the LPC and the training contract. Firms must pay for their trainees to attend the PSC.

The three core modules are:
* financial and business skills;
* advocacy and communication skills; and
* client care and professional standards.

You will also need to complete 24 hours' worth of elective modules. If it is taken full time, the PSC will last up to 12 days. However, each module can be taken individually. Many of the larger firms run the PSC in house as part of their ongoing training programmes.

Non-graduates

Non-graduates can qualify as a solicitor by way of the Chartered Institute of Legal Executives (CILEx), which involves completing several years' qualifying employment (usually in a law firm), passing specific CILEx exams to qualify first as a member, then as a fellow, and then applying to the SRA to be considered as exempt from various of its qualification requirements. For more on CILEx, see "Alternative careers" and the CILEx chapter on page 141.

> **Reality check:** Remember that although most firms currently use the four-seat training contract model described here, this could change over the coming years – a few also run training on a non-rotational basis. A smaller number of firms also choose to operate a six-seat training system, exposing trainees to a wider variety of practice areas.

Career timetable: solicitors

Before we launch into this chapter, you need to be alert to the fact that in April 2017 the Solicitors Regulation Authority (SRA) confirmed that it would be going ahead with its new 'super exam', which all prospective solicitors will have to pass in order to qualify. The Solicitors Qualifying Examination (SQE) is to be introduced in 2020; for now, all students and trainee solicitors will still be able to qualify by the current route, while those who commence training just before or at the point at which the SQE is introduced will also be able to continue via the traditional route. All those who begin legal education and training once the SQE has been introduced will have to train under the new system and pass the SQE.

This means that as things stand, the information below is correct, but fundamental change is not far away. For more on the SQE and what it requires, read the SRA chapter on page 139 and keep alert to things by going to the SRA's website, at www.sra.org.uk/home/hot-topics/Solicitors-Qualifying-Examination.

First-year law and second-year non-law students

What does it mean to be a solicitor? Am I cut out for the work? Why do I want to be a solicitor rather than a barrister? Do I want to practise in London or the regions? In which practice area? These are the questions to be asking around this time. Answers can be gleaned by delving into the law section of your university careers centre, attending your university's law fair (usually held in October/November) and undergoing a healthy dose of self-analysis.

You should try to arrange some summer work experience to begin checking out the different types of firm. In addition to informal work experience, some of the bigger firms now run formal work placement schemes specifically aimed at first-year law students, so keep an eye out for these. Above all, work at achieving and maintaining good grades – when it comes to applying for work placement schemes and training contracts, firms will definitely want to know your first and second-year grades.

Second-year law and final-year non-law students

Autumn term, winter holidays and spring term
Decide whether you genuinely believe that law is a career which will suit your character and skills through further research into the profession. Go to the careers advice service and discuss the profession generally with a careers adviser. Attend law firm presentations on campus and at firms' offices, and research and apply for work placement schemes for your summer vacation – 31 January is a significant deadline. It's a good idea to do a few schemes in order to get a feel for the range and types of practice available to you. Some firms also offer winter and spring holidays work schemes.

Worth noting is that as of July 2015, the Voluntary Code of Practice for the Recruitment of Trainee Solicitors (which most firms adhere to) was amended to "reflect modern practices". The most significant change is that firms may now:
- set their deadlines for training contract applications at any point, although not before candidates' penultimate year of undergraduate study; and
- make training contract offers at any point during candidates' penultimate year of undergraduate study.

In essence, this means that the traditional deadline of 31 July may change, as more firms recruit and offer earlier. However, for now a very large number of firms still place their application deadlines on 31 July.

As mentioned above, virtually all university law career fairs take place in October/November. They represent your best chance to meet firms face to face. It is sensible to have done some preliminary research so that you can ask intelligent questions. Many firms also organise on-campus presentations during these two terms.

Look into the funding possibilities for your postgraduate legal training (eg, local education authority grants) and check closing dates for applications.

Non-law degree students will need to apply for a place on the conversion course, known as the Graduate Diploma in Law (GDL). If you intend to study full time, you should apply through the Central Applications Board (www.lawcabo.ac.uk) from September onwards in your final year at university. There is no longer a closing date for applications; rather, applications are dealt with as they are submitted and institutions are notified weekly of new submissions. Applications for part-time courses must be made directly to the provider.

Spring holidays
Apply for further work placements for the summer vacation. Thoroughly research the applications procedure for training contracts, especially those at firms you are interested in. By now, you should be beginning to shortlist the firms to which you want to apply.

Summer holidays
Most major law firms have training contract application deadlines during this period, although note the point above in relation to the revised code of conduct; the major deadline of 31 July could change as more firms set their own deadlines and choose to recruit earlier. Gain some further work experience, either on a formal work placement scheme or through other means. You may also be interviewed for training contracts during this period.

Final-year law and GDL students
Autumn term
You must also apply for a place on the Legal Practice Course (LPC) through the Central Applications Board from September onwards in your final year at university. As described above, the application system has changed so that there is no longer a closing date for applications; rather, applications are dealt with as they are submitted and institutions are notified weekly of new submissions. Applications for part-time courses must be made directly to the provider.

Spring term
The SRA runs character and suitability checks on students wishing to train as solicitors, and requires people to disclose any information related to this. If you do have such issues (eg, a police caution), you need to disclose these at the earliest opportunity – and at least six months before you would anticipate starting a training contract. Undergoing a character and suitability check before starting the LPC costs £100.

Summer term
If you have not succeeded in obtaining a training contract, keep applying! You might want to consider delaying starting the LPC if you are yet to find a training contract, given the competitiveness of the job market; time spent gaining experience and focusing on applications should give you a better chance of success.

LPC
If you have yet to find a training contract, keep making further applications throughout your LPC year until you get one. Attend as many law fairs as possible and check for adverts in the *Law Society Gazette* and on www.LawCareers.Net.

The SRA requires providers to split the LPC in half, separating the compulsory Stage One subjects from the elective Stage Two subjects, which can then be completed during the training contract. However, the one-year option remains the most popular way of doing the course.

Training contract/period of recognised training

The traditional training contract – or 'period of recognised training', as it is now termed by the SRA – is a two-year employment contract with a law firm or other approved organisation, akin to an apprenticeship. In July 2014 the SRA implemented a number of changes to its training regulations, including a move to a more outcomes-focused approach which allows firms greater freedom to design the structures of their own training contracts. However, trainee solicitors are still required to meet the SRA's competence statement (released in March 2015 and forming the basis of the proposed SQE) and most training contracts are still based on the following format.

Year one

Ensure that your training contract has been registered with the SRA (your firm will usually do this for you). Most firms operate a series of departmental rotations (usually four seats in separate departments, each lasting six months). On-the-job training is provided throughout and is supplemented by courses and lectures during the two-year training period. If you've so far only completed Stage One of your LPC, you'll need to complete Stage Two during your training contract.

Year two

Around the middle of your second year, most firms will run through their post-training job offer process and you will know whether you are going to be offered a position at the end of your training – hopefully in your preferred department. Approximately 12 weeks before your training contract is due to end, the SRA will send you the necessary forms so that you can apply to be formally admitted to the roll of solicitors. Provided that all necessary training conditions have been satisfied, you will be admitted to the roll. Congratulations – you are a solicitor!

Types of law firm

There are many different kinds of law firm, and where you train has a significant influence on your career, as the style, size and clientele of each will vary. Consider the following broad categories to establish which type of law firm might best match your career goals and working style.

International firms

These are mainly located in the City of London. For the UK-born 'Anglo' firms, London is the hub of their international operations, which can range from just a couple of strategically located offices to a sprawling global network – Clifford Chance, for example, has 35 offices in 25 countries. Among these Anglo firms are some of the world's legal giants, reflecting the fact that English law governs complex, big-ticket transactions across the globe, and is the law of choice for high-value disputes. UK firms also reap dividends from the ubiquity of the English language, the City's status as a key financial centre and the convenience of European time zones for coordinating cross-border deals.

A firm's footprint determines the availability of overseas secondments for trainees. Wherever you are based, expect to work mostly on multi-jurisdictional matters for either UK or foreign-based corporate clients. Each will have its own strong suits; for example, Allen & Overy is dominant in all things finance-related, while Clyde & Co excels in disputes. It's important to understand the key practice areas and client sectors of the firms you apply to.

People sometimes refer to the 'magic circle' and 'silver circle'. These expressions have historical resonance, but no real significance. The magic circle comprises Allen & Overy, Clifford Chance, Freshfields Bruckhaus Deringer, Linklaters and Slaughter and May. The so-called silver circle firms are not quite as big as their magic circle peers.

US firms in London used to be viewed as a separate category, having offered English law advice only since the mid-1990s. However, there are now around 75 US-born firms in the United Kingdom and around a dozen more hybrid Anglo-US firms. Approximately 40 run training schemes, some with 30-plus trainees and others just a handful. Yet small in London need not equate to small globally: Arnold & Porter Kaye Scholar LLP, for example, employs some 1,000 lawyers across 14 global offices, but takes on just two UK trainees each year.

Staff work long hours in return for top dollar. A trainee's starting salary will be in the high £30,000s to low £40,000s. If you join a big London office, you'll have resources, amenities and peers aplenty, and probably a relatively bureaucratic working environment. While potential seat options will be abundant, competition for the most popular ones will be stiff and you will have to spend time in core departments.

For a profile of a solicitor at an international firm, see Michael Hossack of Allen & Overy LLP in the "Capital markets" chapter, p154.

UK-focused City firms

Exclusively UK-based firms typically offer a broad commercial training, emphasising one or two specialist areas; some will also have a private client practice, reflecting longstanding relationships with wealthy individuals and trusts. Bristows, for example, is a market leader in IP law; meanwhile, Boodle Hatfield LLP has a real estate focus, resulting from its connection to vast landowner The Grosvenor Estate. Most domestic firms cultivate relationships with overseas lawyers and this attracts some multi-jurisdictional work. Starting salaries are typically in the high £20,000s to low £30,000s.

For a profile of a solicitor at a UK City firm, see Mark Watts of Bristows in the "Technology, media and telecommunications" chapter, p200.

National/regional firms

Beyond London, the most active cities are Manchester, Birmingham, Leeds, Bristol, Liverpool, Cardiff, Newcastle and Nottingham. National firms have offices in several cities (and perhaps also Scotland), whereas a 'regional' firm might limit itself to say, the north or the southwest, perhaps with an additional office in London. A regional firm could have just one office or several. Clients are mostly UK public and private companies, local and public authorities, and possibly also international businesses with UK interests. Smaller firms are also likely to prioritise private client work.

Expect to spend your training contract in a single region, potentially visiting different offices. Salaries vary by location, with Birmingham, Manchester and Bristol faring relatively well (low £20,000s to low £30,000s) compared to, say, Wales or Kent (from around £16,500 to mid £20,000s). Regional trainees typically work more manageable hours than their City counterparts. Available seat options will depend on the firm's business model, so do your research.

For a profile of a solicitor at a national/ regional firm, see Grace Malone of Burges Salmon in the "Employment" chapter, p172.

General practice, legal aid and advice centres

Law on the high streets is undergoing a revolution as a result of the Legal Services Act 2007. Some predict that thousands of tiny partnerships and sole practitioners will give way to large franchises (eg, QualitySolicitors) and alternative business structures. Some firms now market their services at kiosks or pop-up stands in shopping centres. Your clients will be ordinary people with a house to buy, a spouse to divorce, an ex-employer to sue, a will to write or an injury to be compensated for. Some will be entrepreneurs in need of a steer through an exceptional phase of their business plan. You will need good time management and people skills, and must be a confident decision maker.

It's been a torrid decade for lawyers assisting publicly funded clients and opportunities for new trainees are fewer than ever. Legal aid has become unprofitable – so much so that many practitioners who remain in the field must bolster their income from privately paying clients, while the government has plans to cut legal aid even further. This kind of work is only for those truly committed to universal access to justice. You will encounter abusive neighbours, rogue landlords, recidivist teens, individuals struggling to cope with disability or debt and endless need in your local community.

For an example of a solicitor at a general practice firm, see Tom Lawrence of Howes Percival LLP in the "Private Client" chapter, p192. And for an example of a solicitor working in the legal aid sector, see Jocelyn Cockburn of Hodge Jones & Allen in the "Human Rights" chapter, p180.

Reality check: In 2014 the minimum trainee salary was abolished and firms are now entitled to pay trainees the national minimum wage. While many – particularly in the commercial sector – will continue to pay their trainees well above that, it is likely that some increasingly squeezed high street and criminal firms will make use of the rule change.

Solicitor practice areas

Banking

Banking and finance is a global industry involving a wide variety of financial products, ranging from simple bank loans to companies to highly structured financing arrangements across multiple jurisdictions. The rise of internationalisation and the development of increasingly sophisticated financing structures mean that modern banking law and practice is becoming ever more complex. In the post-financial crisis era, banking and finance lawyers find themselves at the forefront of the evolution and recovery of the industry.

Despite an inkling that life at the Bar might suit him, Sam Sherwood ultimately opted for the more commercially driven life of a solicitor: "I wanted frequent client contact and was keener on working in a team as a business adviser, as opposed to the perhaps more solitary existence of a barrister." He recalls the "sometimes disheartening" process of making training contract applications, but advises that keeping focused is the key. He joined a top City firm as a trainee in September 2012 and Kirkland & Ellis (K&E) as an associate in the debt finance team in 2015.

PE at K&E
K&E's debt finance work is almost exclusively centred around leveraged finance. Sam explains what this means day to day: "At K&E, we don't often act for banks – our clients are predominantly private equity (PE) sponsors. A lot of our work centres around leveraged buy-outs – essentially, helping a sponsor to borrow money through private loans or in the capital markets to enable it to acquire a business or asset – but we also assist on large restructurings and are frequently instructed on lender-side mandates by the credit arms of PE houses. You are always given a lot of responsibility, but at my level you are expected to handle the ancillary and security documents, as well as overseeing the conditions precedent process. However, it is not uncommon to assist with the drafting of commitment papers and, if a bid is successful, to put together the first draft of the credit agreement."

The nature of these deals is that they are, almost without exception, international. "I am currently working on deals for a sponsor that hopes to acquire two businesses, one in Norway and another in Germany," says Sam. "We're in the process of putting the financing commitment papers together – the documents under which a lender agrees to lend and the key terms on which they are willing to do so – so that the sponsor can present them to the vendor as part of its bid. It is very international work – I've been here for two years and I've only done one deal where the acquired business was located in the United Kingdom. Our clients have global reach and look at opportunities all over the world, although being in London, most of our deals involve European companies. That said, I recently worked on a deal where our client acquired a portfolio of assets in Australia and New Zealand. This gave me the opportunity to travel and allowed me to work in our Hong Kong office for two months, as well as spending time in Sydney. The international angle is exciting and it gives you a truly global perspective."

The Antipodean deal was a career highlight for Sam – he explains why: "Doing that particular deal was fascinating because it involved a strategic acquisition by a key client and I got to travel, attend meetings overseas and take a prominent role. It was just me and two partners on the entire deal, so it was great exposure. I got to know the client really well and understand how they operate internally – something which lawyers of my level often don't experience."

Get the buzz
Sam also enjoys the adrenaline rush that comes with short timeframes: "I remember a

For more firms that work in this practice area, please use the "Training contract regional indexes" starting on p205.

Name: **Sam Sherwood**
Firm: **Kirkland & Ellis International LLP**
Location: **London**
University: **University of Nottingham**
Undergraduate degree: **Law**

deal where we were instructed on Thursday and had signed the credit agreement the following Tuesday! It was hard work with long days, but a real rush and the client was very happy. Working across time zones can also have an impact on the length of your day as it's often difficult to schedule calls without inconveniencing someone – although luckily, being in London, you're often in the middle!"

❝ Our clients expect us to know which terms are achievable, especially in our sector where shifts can happen quickly; you are seen as a business adviser rather than just a black-letter lawyer ❞

Sam notes a continued convergence between the way deals are financed in Europe and the United States: "Working in leveraged finance means that you're always at the forefront of new developments and we're continuing to see appetite for capital structures that are traditionally more commonplace in the US market." The vicissitudes of the economy more generally are mitigated by the firm's core strengths: "As K&E is PE-focused, our clients are always active throughout the economic cycle; when there's a boom we're busy with buyouts, but when there's a downturn, we are brought in to advise on restructurings. PE houses are flexible and are adept at finding value regardless of the economic environment."

Take an open-minded approach
The qualities that will stand you in best stead in the world of banking are resilience and enthusiasm, claims Sam: "The hours can be unpredictable and you have to maintain

good attention to detail, but enthusiasm goes a long way. If you're on the fence about whether to do a banking seat, it's better to just jump in and see. You get real responsibility early on and will genuinely play a crucial role in the deal, even as a first-seat trainee, which is hugely exciting. More generally, try and keep an open mind during the training contract; your skillset and what you enjoy in practice may be very different from your initial perceptions or your experiences from law school. In addition, don't shut down if you find yourself in a seat you think you're not going to like – it's better to give it your best shot and you will inevitably take something away from it, even if you don't want to qualify there."

Commerciality is also key, as you would imagine working in the financial sector: "Commercial awareness is important and our clients expect us to know which terms are achievable, especially in our sector where shifts can happen quickly. You are seen as a business adviser rather than just a black-letter lawyer. This happens naturally in practice but it's important to get a general appreciation of what's going on before you start. The business pages in the broadsheets are generally more user-friendly than the *FT* and there are countless blogs on developments in the legal sector."

In terms of how to prepare and learn more, Sam advises getting out there for some much-needed face time. "Go to law fairs, speak to trainees, have frank conversations about what their days are like – all of which will give you a good idea of what's ahead," he says. "You can read all the promotional literature in the world, but talking to people who have gone through the process and are currently training is a much better indicator of whether a firm is a good fit for you. You'll get great training and good quality work at most City firms, but it's just as important to enjoy it!"

Capital markets

'Capital markets' is the term used for financial markets where debt or equity securities are traded. Capital markets lawyers work primarily with transactions involving the issue of debt or equity securities either to the public or to a group of investors. Capital markets practice is closely connected to derivatives and financial regulation. Capital markets lawyers conduct due diligence review on the issuer of the securities, draft the prospectus and other disclosure documents describing the issuer and its securities to the potential investors, negotiate agreements between the issuer and its advisers and navigate the transaction through regulatory hurdles. London's pivotal position in the global debt and equity markets makes this a significant element of the City's legal activity.

The idea of a career in law began to take shape for Michael Hossack when he was still a history student; while the cut and thrust of the commercial world ultimately drew him to the solicitors' side of the profession. "I was attracted to the corporate sphere by the opportunity to apply my legal knowledge in a commercially practical and constructive way," he explains. "It interested me far more than the narrower, arguably more academic focus that working as a barrister seemed to entail."

Michael began training at Allen & Overy (A&O) in 2013 and qualified in March 2015. "I had a very positive training contract," he recalls. "The trainees were given a lot of freedom to pursue areas of law that interested them – the training principal and graduate recruitment team always listened to what trainees wanted and were flexible in trying to accommodate them, which I appreciated."

It was during his training contract that Michael's interest in capital markets emerged. "I spent my second seat in our debt capital markets team, which at A&O is called the general securities group," he explains. "The area focuses on standalone bond issues and medium-term note programme updates and drawdowns, as well as liability management. Another attraction of joining the capital markets practice was that A&O tops the league tables in this area. Our partners are leading experts and some, such as Geoff Fuller, have literally written the books on capital markets law and practice that are used as reference guides across the City – I wanted to work with and learn from the best."

Early responsibility

Capital markets involves the issuing and trading of instruments such as shares and bonds. It is a particularly rich environment for trainees and junior lawyers, because many smaller transactions can be managed solo. "As a junior associate, I am often given full responsibility for drafting all the documents for a transaction, as well as reviewing in cases where the documentation is being put together by another firm," explains Michael. "On a typical bond issue, these would include the subscription agreement, the trust deed, the agency agreement and the prospectus, as well as smaller documents such as legal opinions, board minutes and authorisations. The negotiation stage follows that, where those documents are reviewed and negotiated with the client and the other side. This may be down to A&O and how the department is organised here, but it is great to work in an area which enables so much responsibility for junior lawyers. Being trusted to manage deals gives me a great sense of achievement and purpose in my work."

From markets to politics

The time-sensitive nature of many deals can mean late nights in the office. However, having to burn the midnight oil is usually a result of something really important – and exciting – happening, such as finding yourself caught up in Eastern European politics. "One deal that I remember particularly well concerned a

For more firms that work in this practice area, please use the "Training contract regional indexes" starting on p205.

Name: **Michael Hossack**
Firm: **Allen & Overy LLP**
Location: **London**
University: **University of East Anglia**
Undergraduate degree: **Modern history**

standalone bond issued by the government of an Eastern European country, our client," recalls Michael. "We were dealing with the finance ministry of that country, which was interesting in itself, especially for me as a junior lawyer. As we were planning the execution phase of the transaction one Friday evening, we received a message from the client requesting an immediate conference call, which is quite unusual for 6:00pm on a Friday, even in my line of work. We ended up holding the conference call with the country's minister of finance and all his team at around 9:00pm, when we were informed that there had been a political crisis in the government and that there had been a significant reshuffle, with members of the opposition coming into the government. We essentially had to figure out what the impact would be on the transaction and how to manage the situation, which had gone from being a purely financial matter to a political issue as well. Such things have happened on other deals that I have worked on, too – as the name suggests, the transactions we work on in capital markets are market driven, so whatever is going on in the world at the time can affect what we are working on. It is definitely interesting to read in the press what could come up in your own work later in the day."

Its direct influence on the wider world is a key appeal of the practice area for Michael: "I enjoy working in an area where I can really see the effects of the work that we do. Our work actually has an impact on the outside world."

Shadow banking

A trend to be aware of in capital markets and the finance sector generally is the rise of so-called 'shadow banking', as Michael explains: "It is linked to general banking, but it also has relevance for capital markets. Shadow banking is different from the traditional banking modeled by big banks, in that borrowers bypass those banks to go directly to investors such as pension funds and hedge funds, which you wouldn't typically think of as lenders. The normal model in debt capital markets is that companies look to raise money by issuing debt securities, which are bought by banks and then sold on to investors. What is happening now is the development of a market where companies can issue debt securities directly to investors, cutting out the banks – this is known as private placements. There is an established private placement market in the United States, but it is yet to really take off in Europe and the partner with whom I work most frequently is taking the lead in driving this forward."

Business skills are just as important as legal knowledge in order to succeed as a capital markets lawyer. "The ability to project manage is essential, although it is not something that gets mentioned often in advice for aspiring lawyers," explains Michael. "We are usually working on a number of deals at the same time, most of which will be cross-jurisdictional, involving various teams working in different time zones. We in the London office are usually the people coordinating the transaction between the A&O teams in other offices around the world, as well as between the client and lawyers at other firms who might be involved. Often a transaction is a case of organisation, structuring and negotiation."

Michael's advice to anyone hoping to enter the world of commercial law is to gain as much legal work experience as possible: "Almost all law firms run vacation schemes, which are an excellent way to experience what life as a trainee is like and get your foot in the door. However, places on these schemes are very difficult to secure. I found it hard to gain experience myself, so I went out in my hometown and knocked on the doors of the local solicitor firms to ask if I might do a little work experience or shadowing. Most of them were friendly and were happy to have me around. It was a world away from what Allen & Overy does, but it was still valuable experience which really supported my future applications."

Commercial

A commercial lawyer's practice covers many sectors from financial services, energy and infrastructure, consumer and retail, digital, health and life sciences to industry and transport. Typically they undertake a wide variety of work, which includes advising on IP rights, IT deals, procurement contracts, digital banking and payments work, outsourcing and manufacturing, supply chain and advertising arrangements. As a result, clients often range from sole traders and start-ups to FTSE 100 companies and global financial institutions, all of whom require their commercial lawyers to have a deep understanding of both their individual business and the markets in which they operate.

Fiona Ghosh has enjoyed what you might call a grand tour of the legal profession, including vacation schemes at two magic circle firms, a stage at the European Commission, legal work experience in Washington, pupillage and qualification as a barrister, and working as a solicitor at both US and UK firms. Now dual qualified, she is a solicitor advocate and partner in the commercial team at the City office of Addleshaw Goddard. She comments on her route: "My vacation schemes gave me a good idea of what to expect, but they also made me realise that I didn't want to train at a magic circle firm. Then I was fortunate to be offered pupillage at Cloisters, my dream set. I completed that, and was then offered a role at a major US law firm (Weil Gotshal) and was advised by the clerk in chambers that I would be silly to turn the offer down. I worked there for several years and then moved to Leeds for a couple of years before moving back to London and working here at Addleshaw Goddard. I was offered partnership by Eversheds' City practice at six years PQE in 2006, and then returned here in 2014 as an equity partner. Although I have moved around somewhat, my reasons were always deliberate – if a

great opportunity was on offer and I felt that I had told my story in my current job, then there was no reason not to accept and move on. It's also worth bearing in mind that those moves happened over a period of 14 years and not overnight!"

This unique vantage point of both sides of the profession has given her a unique insight into the advantages of life as a lawyer: "As a solicitor, I really enjoy the ongoing client relationship and the greater emphasis on day-to-day teamwork; it can be a more solitary lifestyle at the Bar. I also enjoy the international aspects of the role, the fast-paced nature of the work and greater emphasis on the pragmatic application of the law. Frankly, I really enjoy doing deals and being a strategic business adviser."

Cutting-edge work

While her practice as a commercial lawyer focuses predominantly on the financial services market, Fiona enjoys being at the cutting edge of that field. "I engage in a wide variety of commercial work, mostly involving large, complex financial transactions of regulated entities," she explains, "but a big part of my practice is around digital payments. I have recently been involved with the launch of mobile wallet programmes for banks, including Apple Pay, Android Pay and Samsung Pay. I also give advice in relation to joint ventures and strategic alliances between big brands in this market. That naturally brings me to advice on data, its use and exploitation."

She offers more detail on the fast-paced world of digital banking: "The launch of Apple Pay has been great; we acted for more issuing banks than anyone in Europe, so as a team and a firm we feel very proud to be involved. It is ground-breaking work, challenging the status quo of the financial services retail market – that is an exciting and innovative thing to be a part of. I am lucky to do a lot of work for interesting and compelling

For more firms that work in this practice area, please use the "Training contract regional indexes" starting on p205.

Name: **Fiona Ghosh**
Firm: **Addleshaw Goddard**
Location: **London**
University: **University of Oxford**
Undergraduate degree: **Jurisprudence**

clients, and the financial services market is changing very fast. Not a day goes by when we don't talk about something disruptive or challenging, a new concept, idea, legal problem or risk. There's never a dull moment!"

In-depth access to and knowledge of this market makes Fiona and her ilk true specialists in the field, and much sought after: "I recently chaired the plenary session panel at PayExpo, the largest payment get-together in the United Kingdom. I have been invited to speak at a cross-parliamentary forum on payments technology, an Africa fintech event in the City and sit as an expert on the board of a leading fintech legal journal. It's always interesting to meet players from all sides of the fence."

While this all sounds very exciting, there are downsides to a senior role in such a dynamic international field, as Fiona explains: "The hours can be unpredictable. I have two young children and balancing a challenging career with the needs of a young family can be hard. However, if you're passionate about your time spent working and enjoy it, have the talent and tenacity, it is eminently doable. I never thought it wasn't worth pursuing after having children; but that's not to say it's for everyone nor that it's easy, or that there aren't sacrifices involved. That's the role of many parents today, in all walks of life."

A fintech revolution

Fiona muses on some of the big changes ahead in the burgeoning fintech sector and the ways in which her work – and clients – might need to adjust: "In the next five to 10 years, we will see a significant change in the way we all transact on a day-to-day basis. The focus on regulation of this market will continue, but it will also continue to shape the market and present new opportunities for those who are agile and quick to respond – mainly the non-traditional financial market players. The advent of the General Data

Protection Regulation in 2018 will likely cause nervousness in the market as people get to grips with a new framework for the retention and exploitation of data. We will continue to see challenges in the way in which tech companies use data. These exciting times present opportunities for clients, but also challenges, and that's where we step in."

❝ I am lucky to do a lot of work for interesting and compelling clients, and the financial services market is changing very fast ❞

The nature of the work means that it often features in the press, so if this sounds like the type of lawyering you'd like to do, you need to keep up to date with current affairs and tech developments – "you only need to open the paper to read something about Blockchain or Bitcoin" – and do as much work experience as you can: "Gain exposure to as many different types of legal environment as possible – in London, regionally and at the Bar, small and large – because for a graduate who hasn't been in the workplace you don't yet know what will push your buttons. The more experience you can have in different working environments, the better. You are then armed with information when you come to make the decision about which way to jump."

And she speaks from personal experience: "I had experience as a solicitor, but wanted the technical rigour of the Bar. I worked in the regions, the City, a US firm, a UK firm – it was all good experience. The most important thing on starting out is that you don't make a decision that shuts doors which you may one day want to re-open. The world was a small place when I started, but it truly is connected now – you should never forget how important the power of the network can be."

Commercial property

Commercial property (or real estate) lawyers act for a variety of domestic and international clients – including investors and developers, governments, landowners and public sector bodies – on a wide range of transactions, involving everything from offices to greenfield and retail developments, infrastructure projects and the management of shopping malls. The work itself focuses on the sale, purchase and lease of land; development; investment; and leasehold management. This touches on a range of other legal disciplines, including planning, environmental, construction, litigation and tax law. Property may also be a key component of other projects, including mergers and acquisitions, property finance and commercial projects. It crosses most sectors: investment, banking, insolvency, education, hotels, health, transport, agriculture, charities and private wealth.

Working out how best to convert the experience he had gained in the financial services sector saw Tom Newborough consider life as a lawyer, as he explains: "A couple of years after I graduated, I was working in a senior customer services role in a financial company. I enjoyed it, but wondered how I could use the skills I had developed in a more challenging setting, so I decided to take the plunge in to law." Still focused on skills, being a solicitor made the most sense: "Going to the Bar was never something that I really considered because I thought that my skills leant themselves more to the solicitor route. I also had the – possibly wrong – impression that becoming a barrister was less accessible for someone with no prior legal background."

Tom describes his year doing the GDL as predictably tough. "I was working part time at the same time as studying full time, and the pressure really kicked in the last couple of months, with exams and my dissertation due in," he recalls, "but it was the same for everyone. And it's a good test of what to expect as a lawyer – you need to be able to manage your time well."

A training contract at Shoosmiths beckoned, where Tom was happy to be thrown in at the deep end: "I was given responsibility where I asked for it and showed that I was capable. It was a very focused training contract, where I realised quite early on that transactional work was my preferred option." After a stint first in property litigation, followed by corporate, he spent his two final seats in commercial property, where he went on to qualify.

Retail heaven

The wide-ranging nature of this practice area – due in part to the many different types of client that the firm serves – is one of the things that Tom particularly values about his career: "The work you do is often dependent on the type of client. For example, we currently deal with lots of retail clients, including a number of household names in relation to tenancy leases. We also act for institutional landlords and investors. One example is a client who owns a large shopping centre which requires a lot of asset management work, including new leases, lease variations or granting licences. You very rarely get the same sort of work, and retail leasehold work has built my experience up quickly and keeps me on my toes!"

Tom identifies a few of the key developments from the past couple of years in commercial property: "In city centres, the rise of trendy retail and leisure spaces continues, such as gastro pubs, craft ale bars and pop-up shops and restaurants. Distribution warehouses are also a big thing, with ever more demand for online shopping. In Nottingham there is increased investment in infrastructure, particularly around transport hubs, that is linked to the general rejuvenation of the city centre."

A career highlight centred on being part of the team selling a large property portfolio on

For more firms that work in this practice area, please use the "Training contract regional indexes" starting on p205.

Name: **Tom Newborough**
Firm: **Shoosmiths**
Location: **Nottingham**
University: **University of Leeds**
Undergraduate degree: **Psychology**

behalf of an investment client. "It coincided with my starting as a third-seat trainee and finished near the end of my fourth seat," explains Tom. "Being involved with all the elements and seeing the first large-scale project all the way through was great, especially seeing it all come together." But it's not just the headline, big-deal work that makes it mark: "I got as much satisfaction from the first time I negotiated a lease over the phone with a solicitor or explained some complicated legal issues to a client in a conference call. Although these matters are smaller scale for the firm, they're big for a trainee or NQ."

One of the downsides to such a challenging – and rewarding – job is the obvious demands it can make on life beyond the office, as Tom explains: "Especially in real estate, you never feel that you're completely in control of your workload. There is always something more you could be doing, so it can be a challenge to decide when to go home! It comes down to prioritising the urgent work, but also finding time to fit in everything else that's required of you. That can be difficult and stressful, and you need to become comfortable with not being able to tick everything off your to-do list each day!"

The full implications of Brexit remain a mystery (to us all!), but it is the one thing that Tom and his colleagues are keeping the closest eye on, especially in terms of their investor clients: "It's mostly about what decision making is going on during the negotiation process – for example, are clients holding back until they know what the outcome of the UK deal? Will they move their head offices elsewhere? From a property perspective, it's about those clients potentially being less active in the market."

Commercial experience
So what do clients need from their lawyers right now? Tom thinks there are several key

skills: "Commerciality is really important; clients want to get stuff done and it's your job as their lawyer to assess the risks and work out how to do things in the best possible way. Also important are soft skills such as time management and an ability to deal with pressure. Both your verbal and written communication skills need to be strong; the worst thing you can do is give an ambiguous response. You have to be very clear, even down to the way you structure your emails and present information; you could reel off all the legal issues to a client, but they only really care what the outcome is. Anything superfluous should be left out."

In terms of getting ahead of the pack at training contract application time, work experience is non-negotiable. Tom explains: "It can be hard when applying for a training contract, having come straight from university, to provide practical examples to go with your application. Don't get hung up on it having to be legal experience; any work experience, even in shops or restaurants, is great if you're learning about the commercial aspect of the job." If you can get legal experience, all the better: "I did a placement at a criminal firm with a solicitor specialising in mental health; it wasn't my preferred type of law, but having got something on my CV, it set the ball rolling. Also, don't panic if you're not hired straightaway – I was 25 when I received my training contract offer".

Remain open to what working in a law firm is going to be like: "My preconception was perhaps that law firms were fairly stuffy and people were likely to be unapproachable; the reality is of course completely different. I felt relaxed here from the very beginning. You are learning quickly and you don't need to have all the answers straightaway. It is better to say that you don't know and go and check. Ask questions as often as you need to, as everyone wants you to learn and progress."

Competition

Typically, competition and regulatory work includes merger control under the Enterprise Act 2002 and the EU Merger Regulation, regulatory and court proceedings under the Competition Act 1998 and EU legislation, issues arising from sector-specific regulation, state aid, public sector and utility procurement issues. There has been significant reform of both UK and EU competition law and practice in recent years, and further proposals are being considered. An interesting recent development in the area is the reform of the cartel offence giving rise to criminal liability for individuals. Private competition law actions are a particular area to watch, with both the UK and EU authorities keen to encourage such suits, and where the Consumer Rights Act introduces an "opt-out" class action regime to the United Kingdom.

Although Paul Gilbert enjoyed his time a budding classicist at university, he finished higher education ready for something different. Talking to his peers – among them law students and young lawyers – about what to do next sparked an interest in law as a career destination. "I learned what my contemporaries were doing in the field, and the work and collegiate culture sounded ideal, so I did some more research into the legal profession," he explains. "I considered all the options, but it quickly became apparent that there was never much debate between the solicitors' and barristers' professions in my mind. I enjoy the buzz of working in a team within an office environment."

Paul went on to train at magic circle firm Slaughter and May. "My training contract was a hugely valuable experience, for three reasons," he recalls. "First, I experienced five very different areas of law, as I was able to split one of my seats in two; and second, all my supervisors were excellent. I think the quality of supervisor at any law firm can vary and I was very lucky with

mine. Finally, I benefited greatly from having direct client contact almost from day one."

Industry expertise

After qualifying and spending several years at Slaughters, Paul worked at the Office of Fair Trading – today part of the Competition and Markets Authority – where he gained extensive experience of UK competition law. This insight means that, as counsel at US-headquartered firm Cleary Gottlieb Steen & Hamilton LLP, Paul is now a key asset to the firm and its clients. "My role as a competition lawyer covers both UK and EU competition law," he explains. "I work on a wide range of matters and cases, including merger work, cartel investigations, abuse of dominance cases and competition litigation. The variety is one of the main attractions of the job."

Spending time with clients in order to understand their businesses is a key aspect of the role. "As competition lawyers, it is our job to get under the skin of a commercial enterprise, which we then present to competition authorities, courts and others as convincingly and persuasively as we can," explains Paul. "Essentially, depending on the case, we are arguing either that something will not have an adverse effect on the economies within a particular market or that it will."

Those arguments are largely conducted though written and oral advocacy. "I spend a lot of time preparing papers to submit to competition authorities such as the European Commission, advocating why certain practices or transactions should be permitted or, sometimes, not permitted," Paul explains. The stakes are high – and in some cases can break new legal ground. Paul highlights the following example: "One of the most satisfying and enjoyable cases that I have ever done was the *Metlac* case, which we won for a great client and which also enabled us to be quite innovative in the way that we applied the law. The case concerned a family-owned Italian

For more firms that work in this practice area, please use the "Training contract regional indexes" starting on p205.

Name: **Paul Gilbert**
Firm: **Cleary Gottlieb Steen & Hamilton LLP**
Location: **London**
University: **University of Oxford**
Undergraduate degree: **Classics**

company which was subjected to a hostile takeover by AkzoNobel, a very large Dutch conglomerate; we were able to use the UK antitrust process to block that hostile takeover. It was novel because it was the first time that UK antitrust law had been the sole legislation preventing a hostile takeover, and also because it was the first time that UK antitrust law had been used to block a merger between two foreign companies, with the Italian company not having a permanent base in this country. The case went to the Court of Appeal and there was an application to the Supreme Court, but ultimately we were successful and set new precedents in the process."

Always something different

But although success is sweet, Paul mostly looks forward, rather than backward – there is always something new to focus on. "Whenever we begin a case with a new client, there is always a very steep learning curve, which is part of what keeps us fresh," he says. "The key thing about practising competition law, which most people don't realise, is the need to constantly jump from industry to industry – one day you could be dealing with banking regulation; another with pharmaceuticals; and another with a tech company, such as Google."

The cross-jurisdictional nature of competition law means that the Brexit debate has been watched by Paul and his colleagues with professional, as well personal interest. However, Paul is philosophical about the outcome. "Like many of my colleagues, I was of the view that we should stay in the European Union. But with Brexit, there will only be more competition law to do. At the moment, a lot of cases that are dealt with in Brussels go through a one-stop shop – there aren't simultaneous UK investigations because the UK parts of the case are reviewed by the European Commission. Brexit is likely to mean that some cases will need to be looked at in the United Kingdom as well as the European

Union, and there may be certain areas of the law where the United Kingdom could decide to take a slightly different approach from Brussels. This is unlikely to have an adverse effect on competition lawyers professionally, as competition work will increase, not decrease, as a result of Brexit."

Another issue surrounding competition law currently is just as existential as Brexit. "There is a constant policy debate about how interventionist the competition authorities and competition law should be," explains Paul. "There is a feeling across some sectors that competition law is becoming quite interventionist – more so than the terms of the broad economic regulation that it was originally intended to be – so it is here that we could see things changing in the foreseeable future."

Embrace ambiguity

If a career as a competition lawyer appeals, Paul has this to share: "What trainees find when they arrive for their competition seats, in contrast to others, is that in competition law we often don't have right and wrong answers. This is not to say that all other areas of law are black and white, but generally there is a bit more clarity in terms of what is the right approach. Anyone considering a career as a competition lawyer needs to be comfortable with ambiguity and be prepared to express their own informed opinions. There is also a real onus on competition lawyers to get up to speed with their clients' businesses, perhaps more quickly than in other areas of law."

Paul also has some salient advice that all budding lawyers would do well to take on board: "It is so important for lawyers to take charge of their own careers. Particularly for trainees and young lawyers joining big firms, there is the temptation to just stay on the conveyor belt; but I would advise anyone thinking of joining the legal profession to think carefully about what they want to do and not be afraid to be proactive in pursuing it."

Construction

Contentious construction work involves the resolution of disputes by way of litigation, mediation, adjudication or arbitration. Non-contentious work involves drafting and negotiating contracts and advising on projects, insurance, health and safety, environmental matters and insolvency. Clients range from industry associations, insurers, contractors, architects, engineers, public authorities and government bodies to major companies and partnerships.

While it is self-evident that the majority of solicitors follow the most common route to professional qualification – undergraduate degree, law school (GDL and/or LPC) and training contract – it should always be remembered that other paths do exist, and that law is a career that remains accessible to those who commit to practising it at various different stages of their professional lives.

Paul Hargreaves is one of those who took "a more alternative route", although his career with his current law firm Walker Morris began long before his formal legal education. "I started working for Walker Morris in 1999, in what was then WM Claims, our personal injury unit," he explains. "I had no formal legal qualifications; a lot of personal injury firms will have a select number of qualified lawyers, the rest will be case handlers/fee earners, and I started as a case handler. In 2001 I left Walker Morris because I wanted to travel; I visited a variety of different countries and ended up in Australia working for Aon Insurance. When I returned to the United Kingdom, I came back to Walker Morris and decided that law was the career for me. I did a law degree part time at Leeds Metropolitan University (as it was called then). It was two evenings a week for a four-year period. While studying, I was working full time."

Hard work pays
All the hard work and effort paid off; Paul did the LPC in 2008 and was offered a training contract with Walker Morris which began

in 2009. Two years later Paul qualified as a solicitor, was shortlisted for "Associate Solicitor of the Year" at the British Legal Awards 2015 and is now a director at the firm. He admits that he did consider training at a few other firms, but Walker Morris won out. "It was an easy choice, really," he says. "I knew the people, I knew and liked the firm, and I liked what it stands for. I knew my training contract would provide me with close personal supervision and also a high level of responsibility to get involved in cases and run my own files. Although I did research other firms and thought about going down to London, at heart I knew that what I was looking for was here."

> ❝ What I find in construction is that it's a great area in which to be a litigator as there are still a large number of disputes ❞

At the start of his training contract, Paul thought that his previous experiences would mean he would specialise and qualify into a litigation role, but during his six-seat rotation he briefly dabbled with the idea of regulatory law, before settling in the firm's construction and engineering department.

Big ticket to ride
"It was the big-ticket litigation that did it," he recalls. "What I find in construction is that it's a great area in which to be a litigator as there are still a large number of disputes, which is great for us. Walker Morris is quite unique in its approach at getting junior lawyers more involved at an earlier stage than other firms; since qualification I have been involved in a number of significant cases, including representing 96 claimants in a claim involving issues arising out of the Defective Premises Act 1972 and which included a four-week trial before Mr Justice Edwards-Stuart in the Technology and Construction Court."

For more firms that work in this practice area, please use the "Training contract regional indexes" starting on p205.

Name: **Paul Hargreaves**
Firm: **Walker Morris LLP**
Location: **Leeds**
University: **Leeds Beckett University**
Undergraduate degree: **Law**

Not all trainees will be lucky enough to get involved in such high-rolling cases, of course, but Paul assures us that there is very real work to keep them busy: "We make sure that the trainees are part of the team from the word go. You are given work to do and you're certainly not spending your days photocopying – we see that as a waste of talent. We want them to be trained up as quickly as possible, working as quickly as possible and fee-earning as quickly as possible. One of the things I know from speaking to peers at other firms is that we are known for giving trainees a large amount of responsibility. This means that trainees can hit the ground running in the departments into which they qualify."

The construction and engineering team as a whole does a mix of contentious and non-contentious work, such as drafting building contracts, bond guarantees and warranties. This insulates it to a degree from the infamous changes of fortune that characterise the construction industry, which are traditionally closely linked to the political and economic climate.

"No one really knows how Brexit will affect things," muses Paul. "I think it is going to be quite challenging for all sectors, including construction. There certainly needs to be a lot more building within the United Kingdom – certainly more houses, as there is a massive shortage – but to be able to do that we need money. That said, in construction, when it's boom time we are dealing with a lot of development work and we are doing a lot of non-contentious work. As soon as you get a recession, people are more inclined to revisit issues and that is when you get involved in litigation. So you get both ends, and at the moment we have a good mix here at Walker Morris."

Fledgling lawyers keen to get involved in the non-contentious side of the practice should show an interest in construction work in general, Paul believes, so they should be looking at the building press and architectural journals to find out what is happening in the sector.

As for those interested in the contentious side of construction – which, as Paul confirms, is an excellent place for litigation-hungry lawyers – they need to be able to process large volumes of technical data. "In law generally there is a significant amount of information that you have to be able to digest and assimilate," he explains. "But certainly in construction work, and defect work in particular, you can be faced with 300-page reports about a subject in which you have limited knowledge and you have to be able to pick that up relatively quickly and be able to put it to your client in a succinct manner that they will understand. That is a skill in itself."

Paul finishes with a word of warning for those who are not sure they are cut out for the legal profession: "If you don't really like this job, don't do it! That applies to all areas of the law. It's not a soft option. It is hard work and long hours sometimes. But it can be incredibly intellectually satisfying and worthwhile – or at least I think so; but then I am very interested in the law."

Corporate finance

Corporate finance lawyers advise companies on all aspects of the buying and selling of whole businesses or business assets. This requires guidance on how to comply with company law procedures, the raising of funds and, in the case of cross-border transactions, compliance with foreign laws. It is possible to work primarily on mergers and acquisitions (M&A) with public or privately owned companies. Alternatively, a corporate lawyer may focus on the private equity, venture capital or hedge fund sectors, or spend his or her whole career as a generalist assisting SMEs and small-scale entrepreneurs.

First-hand experience is the best way to decide whether a career path is really for you, and work placements at both solicitors' firms and barristers' chambers informed Michael Mountain's choice to become a solicitor. "I was attracted to a career as a solicitor by the team-focused nature of the role, as opposed to the more individualistic nature of working as a barrister," he explains. "I also liked the idea of being involved in deals from start to finish, which involves a closer working relationship with the client – in contrast, barristers usually receive their instructions from solicitors. Barristers get involved at quite a late stage and while they are then involved at the "business end", I find that contributing from a deal's inception all the way through to completion provides a certain satisfaction that is hard to match. Solicitors often have a broader mandate than barristers, which is something that I believed I would enjoy."

After graduating from his law degree and completing the Legal Practice Course, Michael trained at magic circle firm Slaughter and May. "It is an excellent place to train and my experiences there instilled the highest standards into my work," he recalls. "My training set up a really good foundation for my career and I think that would be the case whether I stayed in law or decided to do something else. I qualified into the corporate department at Slaughters – I gained exposure to a wide variety of work and enjoyed the dynamics of deals in this practice area."

“ It is unpredictable from day to day, but I like the build-up to completing a transaction, which necessarily involves different stages and different levels of intensity ”

Michael later joined international law firm White & Case. "I specialise in M&A, including advice on joint ventures, minority investments and also do a range of general advisory corporate work. Of late, this has particularly involved working for investment funds."

Investment funds

A key aspect of Michael's role, inevitably, is documenting the transactions that his team shepherds to close. "There is often both an equity and a debt component in the deals that we help to execute on behalf of investment fund clients, as their investments take the form of ownership in entities, as well as debts which have been lent to those entities," he explains. "Part of the strategy for many investment funds is to invest in the asset in a variety of different ways. Any deal will involve negotiating with the other stakeholders invested in the asset and carrying out due diligence. As a lawyer on the transaction, you will often be documenting two principal aspects: the purchase agreement for the acquisition itself and then the shareholders'/investment agreement, which concerns the ongoing relationship between the shareholders/stakeholders invested in the asset."

Michael has been heavily involved in the expansion of this area of White & Case's

For more firms that work in this practice area, please use the "Training contract regional indexes" starting on p205.

Name: **Michael Mountain**
Firm: **White & Case LLP**
Location: **London**
University: **University of Oxford**
Undergraduate degree: **Law**

corporate practice in London. "Perhaps the highlight of my career so far is being part of forming a new unit within the corporate team, which focuses on investment fund clients and works in tandem with the restructuring and private debt teams," he explains. "It has been challenging, but satisfying and enjoyable to help this part of the firm's practice grow and thrive over the last 18 months."

Ebb and flow

The workload in this transactional area is not necessarily steady or predictable – it inevitably involves a lot of peaks and troughs. "It isn't for everyone – it depends on how you like your working days to ebb and flow," says Michael. "It is unpredictable from day to day, but I like the build-up to completing a transaction, which necessarily involves different stages and different levels of intensity. The moments that bring the most happiness and satisfaction are when you get recognition from clients with whom you have been working for a number of weeks or months on a deal – appreciation from people you have come to really respect is a great reward for hard work, and it feels good to be seen as a valued adviser."

A familiar bugbear of working in commercial law is time recording. "It's certainly not a highlight – trying to accurately account for every minute of your day is quite challenging," observes Michael. "It is also quite particular to the legal profession, as the work of many other professional advisory firms is accounted for in a different way."

Commercial lawyers are currently weighing up the consequences of Brexit and how it might transform the landscape. "It has already had an impact on M&A and will continue to do so," explains Michael. "That isn't to say that M&A activity is just going to stop, or indeed that other areas in which corporate lawyers play a part are not going to continue to thrive, but certainly clients are assessing the impact of Brexit and will be taking that into account

in their investment strategies and transaction planning. I would also say more generally that, in terms of the business we are in, London is a very competitive legal market, so it is becoming increasingly important for firms and lawyers to stand out from their competitors anyway. Finding innovative ways to develop your business is a constant challenge."

Quick off the mark

To succeed in corporate finance and M&A, you need several key skills, not least the ability to remain calm under pressure. "As I mentioned, the way that deals can ebb and flow means that there is usually a crescendo to the transaction which is very busy and intense, so you need to be able to remain focused under those conditions," explains Michael. "You also need to be able to quickly identify the key issues in any situation. You may have more time to deal with them, but finding the crux in a matter in short order is expected, which is a real skill. Flexibility and the ability to multitask are also important, as you need to be able to manage multiple transactions at once, which could be of a completely different nature."

Michael also has the following general tips for those keen to embark on a career in law: "It is a great idea to meet and talk to lawyers at law fairs, open days and the other opportunities available. The day-to-day job can be very different depending on which type of firm you join, so it's useful to do your research and speak to a broad range of people at different kinds of firm. One thing I would also recommend is not to be afraid to take time out to travel or work in a different environment before you start your legal career. These experiences can be beneficial when you're writing applications and attending interviews, and I don't think that you would miss out by coming to the profession a year or two later. However, it can be difficult to drop your responsibilities and take that kind of time out further down the line. You certainly don't have to rush in."

Corporate tax

Virtually all commercial transactions have tax implications. Corporate tax is thus an important practice area for any major law firm. Working in corporate tax involves advising on the most tax-efficient means of acquiring, selling or restructuring assets, negotiating and documenting the transaction, and ensuring the smooth completion of the deal. On the contentious side, corporate tax lawyers advise on all aspects of tax litigation and investigations, including negotiating with tax authorities.

While finding a direction or vocation in life can be a challenge for many, Alicia Thomas had no such difficulties, as it seems her family mapped out her future for her – and she was only too happy to oblige. "When I was really small, around seven years old, I was at my Gran's house and she asked my cousin and me what we were going to be when we grew up," she recalls. "My cousin said he was going to be a doctor, so I declared – perhaps rather pompously at the time – that I was going to be a lawyer. It sort of stuck and when I got to secondary school, it suited my personality, so I went with it. At that time, I was pretty good at maths and my uncle suggested that if I was going to be a lawyer, I should be a tax lawyer. It turns out, of course, that being a tax lawyer doesn't involve that much maths at all; but by the time I found that out, it was too late! It seems I am influenced far too easily by my family members!"

Having taken the advice of her nearest and dearest to heart, Alicia set her sights firmly on her goal. After completing a double degree in English and French law at King's in London and the Sorbonne in Paris, she applied for a vacation scheme at Macfarlanes (on the advice of an aunt, of course) and was offered a place on a training contract. Before taking it up, Alicia worked to shore up her tax credentials, completing a master's in tax law and taking the chartered tax adviser exams.

Not open all hours

Once on the training contract, Alicia was pleasantly surprised to find that the horror stories she had heard about working hours were somewhat exaggerated in the case of Macfarlanes. "The hours were better than I expected them to be as a trainee," she says. "I think I have done one all-nighter in my entire career. I don't want to say you don't have to work hard and it depends on who you speak to, I suppose; but I had heard all sorts of scare stories about people not going home until 4:00am every day. When I got here, I found that it's really not that bad."

Luckily for Alicia, she also discovered that she very much enjoyed the practice of tax law outside academia, as it is an intricate and fast-moving area of law that requires multiple skills. "I enjoy it because it constantly changes and presents a challenge," she explains. "Every year something new comes up and you have to think your way through new problems. There is a lot of actual law involved, as well as lots of negotiation on the corporate side. I think you get the best of both worlds: the practical work with clients, where you just have to get the deal done; and the legal side, where you are trying to work out the solution to a particular problem in a way that isn't egregious or going to cause them problems in the newspapers."

Starting simply(ish)

Due to the relatively large amount of legislation involved, trainees are likely to be eased in gradually – perhaps working on tax covenant sections of corporate documents that deal with the various tax liabilities when companies change hands. That way, trainees can gain an understanding of the key issues that arise for companies on a day-to-day basis, within the practical context of a sale. It also encourages them to start thinking about the different taxes that apply to companies, such as corporation tax on income and capital gains and value added tax.

For more firms that work in this practice area, please use the "Training contract regional indexes" starting on p205.

Name: **Alicia Thomas**
Firm: **Macfarlanes LLP**
Location: **London**
University: **King's College London and the University of Paris 1**
Undergraduate degree: **Law**

With more experience, trainees may be asked to contribute to more complex pieces of work. "Once you have got yourself used to those things, they start giving you more advanced work," suggests Alicia. "On larger matters, such as an acquisition or the setting up of a fund, you often draft something called a structure paper, which sets out the steps needed to accomplish the goal and their tax implications. As a trainee, you probably won't do very much of the structure paper itself; but you might be asked to read through it and update the diagrams or update small sections of the paper. The idea is for you to start reading things in more depth and, as time goes on, start becoming responsible for drafting bigger bits of that paper."

A lot to remember
Alicia readily admits that corporate tax law is in the public eye much more today than when she was a law student. With this heightened scrutiny comes increased political attention and this means that the legislation can change very quickly. She points out, however, that it is often better to have a broad overview of the changes rather than spending too much time committing the fine print to memory.

"Tax is now very much at the forefront of the public consciousness," she acknowledges. "I think back when I was a student, people thought of tax as quite boring. However, since the financial crisis, it has become much more a part of the political sphere and that is represented in the frequency with which we have changes coming about nowadays. While it might seem that you would need an encyclopaedic knowledge to retain everything, I'd say that it is safer not to try to remember it all. The best thing to do is to have an awareness of all the things that happened and check the statute for each matter, as every time you read the legislation, there is a new nuance. If you assume that you have memorised it and know what is

going on, you may be more likely to miss those points in the context of the particular transaction you are dealing with."

Those, like Alicia, who are committed to a life as a tax lawyer should able to demonstrate a genuine interest at interview and justify the reasons for that interest – whether through further academic study, sector knowledge or practical experience. However, she also suggests it is important not to appear too set in your ways.

"When I went for my training contract interview, I got the feeling that they thought it was a bit naive of me to think I could possibly know where I want to qualify before I started working in practice," she recalls. "Generally speaking, people prefer trainees to have an open mind so that they are willing to go and do their best in every seat. So if you have a view about what you want to do, great – but come prepared to justify that. And you still need to show you're willing to keep an open mind; otherwise you might be shooting yourself in the foot. It is one thing to show yourself as being prepared; it is another to show yourself as being inflexible."

Crime

Criminal solicitors advise and appear in court on behalf of both accused persons and the prosecution, handling the full spectrum of offences, from minor motoring misdemeanours to more serious crimes, including murder. They deal with all aspects of the criminal justice system, from the initial police interview to trial before the court.

Despite being a history graduate, Matthew Hardcastle had always had an eye on a legal career – and in fact feels that his non-law background has enhanced his day-to-day lawyering: "I always had an interest in law but I enjoyed my time as a history student, particularly the research aspect of it. I found it an attractive prospect to spend my professional life in a job that would allow me to continue to use those skills; a career in law has allowed me to continue with a mix of research and practical application. I find that a history background has helped me to take a rounded approach to cases."

The courtroom side of a barrister's career initially appealed, but further research revealed that he was better suited to life as a solicitor: "Advocacy was something I was interested in, but after speaking to several people about which route to take, there was a consistent theme of the difficulties faced by junior members of the criminal Bar. I thought that the solicitor route offered more stability and, in some ways, a more traditional route to advocacy with a greater exposure to the magistrates' courts at an early stage."

Matthew joined TV Edwards, a large high-street practice specialising in criminal defence, first as a paralegal and then as a trainee. "I absolutely loved it – Anthony Edwards, who was head of the firm, teaches other lawyers about criminal law, so the training I received was first rate," Matthew recalls. "It was very hands-on experience, which you would expect in a publicly funded firm. I couldn't have asked for anything more."

After three years post-qualification at TV Edwards, Matthew moved to Kingsley Napley. He describes his current practice: "My work is split between white collar cases and more traditional criminal cases. There is a very supportive atmosphere at Kingsley Napley with the partners working very much as a team with their associates; this allows a good balance on every type of case."

ff You can have a fantastic knowledge of the law, but if you can't connect with your client then it will be very difficult to practise effectively ff

Part of what appeals to Matthew about his career is the variety afforded by a mix in type and size of work: "As a profession we get pushed more and more into specialising at a very early stage of our careers, but for me, I think the combination of large financial crime and general crime is a nice balance. Large matters can take on a life of their own and develop slowly, so they require a different approach. Having said that, underneath it all, it's the same law and rules of evidence."

Human beings on trial
Reflecting back on some of the most significant professional moments of his career, Matthew recalls a long-running case, acting for an individual "who was essentially in the wrong place at the wrong time". He expands: "He had been very good at his job, without realising that his job involved working for a firm that was practising illegally. He had everything to lose and when the jury acquitted him, the relief for him and his family was palpable."

The human element is one of the most satisfying aspects of the job, but also the one that requires a lot of skilled handling. "I

For more firms that work in this practice area, please use the "Training contract regional indexes" starting on p205.

Name: **Matthew Hardcastle**
Firm: **Kingsley Napley LLP**
Location: **London**
University: **University of Hull**
Undergraduate degree: **History**

meet people from varied backgrounds, who find themselves in need of advice for many different reasons," explains Matthew. "But, if you are going to do the best job for your client then you have to understand their individual needs as well as the specifics of the case."

He expands on the need for finely honed people skills: "You can have a fantastic knowledge of the law, but if you can't connect with your client then it will be very difficult to practise effectively. You are often meeting them at the most stressful point in their life and you have to build a sufficient relationship so that they are able to trust your judgement – that includes when you give tough advice." It also includes your perception of what the 'best' strategy would be: "You must always be alive to your client's desired outcome as any disconnect can lead to a pyrrhic victory."

Criminally underfunded

For Matthew, the consistent underfunding of the criminal justice system is one of the most troubling aspects of the job: "There is an extreme lack of funding at the moment and that causes systemic issues. Many good lawyers – be that for the prosecution or for the defence – are unable to progress a case in the way that they would want to because they have too much work and too little time. There is no certainty or stability in the system and a delay at any point can have a knock-on effect during the life of a case. That can be difficult to manage and I suspect it will only get worse."

Some have suggested that the increasing digitalisation of criminal legal proceedings may help alleviate some of the problems of underfunding: "At some point, a decision will have to be made about how publicly funded work, and criminal justice as a whole, will be funded. Will there be a new approach or will there be sufficient savings derived from digitalisation to carry on in the same way?"

Getting work experience to learn more about the profession you hope to join is important, explains Matthew, but it needn't be on a formal vacation scheme: "I got my training contract at TV Edwards, following work experience and a period paralegalling there. However, I had also walked around the area where I lived, clutching a copy of my CV, and knocking on the doors of local firms, hoping to get some experience. I managed to secure one day a week at a firm, which was invaluable in terms of what I learnt. People think that way of getting experience has gone out of fashion and it's not for everybody – you have to have the spare time to do it for one thing – but especially in criminal law, you can learn so much from high-street experience."

On that point, Matthew is keen to emphasise that career progression from trainee upwards is possible in the publicly funded side of the profession. "It's a shame that some don't consider the high street an entry point anymore because there is real expertise in the high street firms – some of the most remarkable lawyers I know are on the high street. And it is also possible to progress from the high street to the City, if that's what you choose. Equally, I have seen first hand how consistently impressive the new qualified solicitors are at Kingsley Napley; their ability on qualification is a clear result of high-quality training they receive. Overall, the single most important factor is to ensure that you receive excellent training – it is what frames your career."

Dispute resolution

Commercial litigation involves the resolution of disputes in the corporate and commercial sphere, including those arising out of joint venture projects, civil fraud, commercial and banking transactions, corporate governance, financial services regulation and professional negligence. The Jackson Reforms, which came into force in April 2013, have significantly changed the court process, including the way litigation is managed, especially in relation to directions and costs.

Always keen to keep her options open, Karla Sheerin-Griffin launched her career with a BA in legal science and French, followed by a one-year LLB conversion course: "I wanted to ensure law was the right course for me, which is why I chose a BA with legal science rather than going down the law degree route. I really enjoyed studying law and from early on was attracted to the role of a solicitor, as I thought it was a good match with my personality. I wanted to work as part of a team, learn from experienced lawyers and be in a role that would allow me to develop strong working relationships with clients."

Contentious v non-contentious
Having spent some time as a paralegal in Stephenson Harwood's Paris office in the asset finance team, Karla completed law school and began her training contract with the firm in London. Before starting, she wasn't sure whether she would pursue the contentious or non-contentious route. "I knew I wanted to work in the City, but I didn't yet know if I wanted to be a transactional lawyer or a litigator," she recalls. "My first seat as a trainee was in litigation and I loved it from day one. I got a real buzz from the work. I enjoyed the legal research and the wide variety of cases. I felt that we were advising clients on matters that were key to their businesses. I enjoyed managing competing deadlines and keeping various plates spinning. My third seat sealed the deal; I was seconded to work for a client. The work was a mix of commercial contracts and disputes, and I particularly enjoyed the disputes side. It made me determined to go down the contentious route."

Now fully qualified and part of the commercial litigation department, Karla deals with a wide range of disputes, but the majority of her work falls into three categories, as she explains: "The first is civil fraud, which includes working on applications for freezing, disclosure and search orders – the work often requires us to take action at short notice to protect a client's position. The second is financial disputes, in which I predominantly act for banks. I like this type of work because, in addition to advising on disputes, you may also be advising clients on the risks of pursuing a particular course of action or transaction and how to manage those risks. You really need to understand the client's business in order to do that. The third is art law, which is quite a niche area. The work is fascinating and covers a wide range of issues. I have worked on disputes relating to authenticity and title, as well as export licence applications."

And with that variety of work comes a range of clients, including financial institutions, insolvency practitioners, companies and individuals. "You have the opportunity to develop strong relationships with clients over the life of a case and with repeat clients. It's important to keep up with what's going on in your clients' sectors so you can anticipate the issues they might face," she continues. "And although you may have a particular specialism, a commercial litigator should be ready to deal with anything that comes across their desk. The advantage of this is that you develop a broad range of legal skills and are kept on your toes."

The majority of Karla's work has an international dimension. Karla recently acted for the liquidators of an insolvent foreign bank in a high-profile, high-stakes fraud dispute which involved multiple claims

For more firms that work in this practice area, please use the "Training contract regional indexes" starting on p205.

Name: **Karla Sheerin-Griffin**
Firm: **Stephenson Harwood LLP**
Location: **London**
University: **National University of Ireland, Galway**
Undergraduate degree: **BA in legal science and French**

against a Russian businessman and resulted in a favourable judgment for the client. Those proceedings involved multiple hearings: "There were over 20 interim hearings. I was very much involved from the outset of the case, including in the investigation stage, the commencement of proceedings, gathering evidence, instructing experts and preparing for trial. I worked with a very impressive team of solicitors and counsel. It was great to work alongside such talented people."

It's all about the buzz – if you don't get a kick out of the work, it's not worth it, in Karla's view. "It's very intellectually stimulating, helping to find a solution to complex legal issues. The law is constantly evolving, so I have to ensure that I am up to speed on recent judgments and changes in the law." But as she points out, the law does not operate in a vacuum: "You need to know what your client wants to achieve – for example, how will the time and cost involved in pursuing litigation affect their business? Do they need to maintain a relationship with the other side? It's all about combining a legal solution with commercial considerations."

Brexit and technology
Regarding current issues facing the legal industry, Karla says that Brexit remains a subject of much discussion: "There were concerns that it could damage London's position as a litigation hub, but these have calmed to an extent." Karla expects that London will remain a popular forum for litigation given the reputed quality of its courts and the pool of legal talent available. However, she says there remains uncertainty, for example, around the recognition of English jurisdiction clauses by and enforcement of English judgments in other EU member states.

Karla also comments on the increased use of technology in law firms to improve the service delivered to clients, increase efficiency and financial performance, as well as facilitate flexible working: "The traditional ways of working in law firms are changing and there is a growing recognition in the industry of the need to invest in innovative technology to be able to tackle the challenges and make the most of the opportunities that this presents."

Skills to succeed
Intellectual ability is key to being a good litigator. There is a lot to learn and retain. While you also need technical ability to succeed, Karla thinks that is something you build on as you gain experience. "You need to be very organised, resilient and able to deal with the pressure," she adds. "You also have to be prepared to work with other people. I know some fantastic litigators who are introverts, but you must be able to work as part of a team, sharing ideas and working together to come up with a strategy. You also need to be commercially aware and understand what your client is seeking to achieve. And you have to be able to synthesise substantial amounts of information efficiently – in civil fraud it is often about finding the smoking gun in a room full of documents!"

What you shouldn't do is close off your options too early – get as much experience as you can in a variety of areas and remain open-minded. "It can be difficult to stand out, but one way to do that is to gain experience in a range of things, because that then allows you to show a genuine and informed interest in a particular area," says Karla. "You can say you've tried X, Y and Z, and have realised you really like Z for the following reasons. It can also help you to focus on particular firms if you've tried a wide variety of work." She concludes: "When I started out I didn't appreciate the wide variety of specialisms that exist within the main practice areas. I have litigation colleagues who specialise in aviation, property, construction and intellectual property disputes – all of which are very different from my work. So it is possible to find something that you're personally interested in within a broad practice area."

Employment

Employment lawyers work across all areas of employment law, including, for example, handling discrimination, staff restructuring and whistleblowing issues. There has been increased focus on employment law in recent years, due to a combination of new legislation, government policies and employees' increased awareness of their rights. Trainees assist with a wide variety of work, such as the employment aspects of corporate or commercial transactions, preparations for tribunal claims, attending hearings and meetings, and helping to draft documents such as employment contracts or policies.

Grace Malone was attracted to the study of law by the flexibility that it affords later down the line: "I always preferred words to science or maths, and thought that law seemed like a sensible undergraduate degree to do. I wasn't certain I wanted to be a lawyer when I applied for university, but felt that because of its academic nature, a law degree could take you in all sorts of directions." Going to the Bar was never on the radar: "I was swept up into the training contract application process by my second year and really liked the idea of working in a big firm, with lots of colleagues in a supportive environment."

Having secured a training contract at Burges Salmon in her second year, Grace relished the chance to learn more about what daily lawyering really means, in a variety of different departments. "It is quite a big annual intake of trainees, around 20 to 25, and I liked the fact that you were surrounded by people at the same stage as you, forming friendships from the very beginning," Grace reflects. "Also, our six-seat system means that you get to try a large number of different areas within the two years. You are given enough responsibility, without it being overwhelming; there is a real focus on ensuring trainees get lots from the training experience and work out where their skills lie,

rather than more senior lawyers expecting you to be perfect. The firm wants you to get a sense of what lies ahead after qualification."

Grace's second seat was in employment, where she first formed an opinion on what the practice area could offer and whether it might suit her career aspirations: "I enjoyed all my seats and there were aspects of them all that I would have enjoyed if I had qualified there. I was drawn to employment, however, because it is a 'people-based' area. The style of advising is different to other areas – the issues are often very pressing, sensitive or reputational, and there are lots of daily conversations and meetings with clients. I really like the story and human element of it; it is all very tangible and relatable, which I think makes it easier to get your teeth into as a junior lawyer."

Employment work at the firm is a varied mix of contentious and non-contentious work, which keeps things interesting for practitioners. "We do advisory work, such as guiding clients through a restructure or reorganisation, or assisting with tricky grievance or disciplinary scenarios" describes Grace. "We also support our commercial, pensions or corporate teams with transactions that they're working on – for example, the employment elements of an outsourcing deal. On the contentious side, we help to manage clients' tribunal claims, mostly acting for the employer. A claim might be related to whistleblowing or disability or sex discrimination, for example."

Second to none
Both as a trainee and since qualification, Grace has benefited from the professional opportunities that come with going on client secondments: "Last year I was seconded to a business to help with a specific project, a large-scale redundancy. It was really interesting to be based within a projects team because you realise the amount of work that goes on behind the scenes – I had

For more firms that work in this practice area, please use the "Training contract regional indexes" starting on p205.

Name: **Grace Malone**
Firm: **Burges Salmon LLP**
Location: **Bristol**
University: **University of Exeter**
Undergraduate degree: **Law**

good visibility of what it means to implement the advice we give, and an appreciation for the complexities of decision making and administering such a project. Now, when I give advice, I can picture that all going on in the background. What different clients do with our advice, how it is implemented, some of the different business drivers – if you can get a handle on how different businesses operate, then you can advise your clients much better."

Developing the ability to offer timely and strategic advice can be hard for junior lawyers: "One of the most difficult things as a junior lawyer is that there are a lot of grey areas in employment. Often you are giving your view on the best strategic option to get your client to where they want to go and that can be hard before you have a sufficient breadth of experience. It doesn't take long to see similar scenarios and have an idea of what to do though, and there are always more senior lawyers around to ask what their view is."

Employment law is also a very fast-moving area compared to some others, because it is heavily case-law driven, so Grace urges the need to keep updated and on top of trends – many of which appear in the national press: "Because the issues are relatable and interesting, employment law gets a lot of coverage in the press. 'Hot topics' recently have been the calculation of holiday pay, gender pay reporting and a focus on the status of gig economy workers. There are always consultations and case law to keep on top of – you can't rest on your laurels!"

Have you got skills?
Grace reiterates the need to hone your people skills in this very human and emotional field of law: "You have to be personable and able to relate to people; the issues involved are often more sensitive than in other areas of law. You also need

empathy; it's very important to understand what drives individuals. For example, in a tribunal claim if you can understand what is driving both of the parties, there may be a way to resolve things quickly and commercially rather than going through the entire hearing process."

Commerciality is also essential: "Each client has different drivers and appetites for risk – for example, some clients may be unionised, or reputation may be very important to them, and maintaining good employee relations and avoiding criticism will be their primary motivator. Compare that to other businesses where cost may be the ultimate driver. You have to be able to step into your client's shoes and understand what is important to them." This ties in with the need to grasp that being brilliant at law is only one aspect of being a good lawyer: 'It is important to listen' to what your client wants to achieve and connect that to your advice. It's not just an understanding of the legislation; you have to appreciate what that advice will be used for. This helps build strong relationships with your clients."

Grace's top tips centre on the need to find a firm that is a good match with your aspirations. She explains: "In terms of what you can do to make yourself more marketable, you need to show you have taken time to identify which firms might suit you and why, as opposed to just applying to any firm. You want to end up at a firm that suits you, culture and values wise.

And a reassuring final note: "The job is not as difficult or as different to life as a student as you might expect – you're working with people who are there to support you and help you develop, and they recognise that it takes time for you to be confident about what you're doing. You don't need to be a fully formed lawyer on day one – it's a much gentler introduction to the career than that."

Energy

The energy and natural resources sector is an important part of the legal landscape and is currently making more headlines than ever before. It covers, among other things, oil and gas projects, pipelines, refineries, liquefied natural gas, nuclear, renewables, and water and wastewater. Emerging energy initiatives such as biofuels and carbon capture and trading also feature. The key legal issues centre on the development and financing of projects, M&A, disputes and trading, and may be either domestic or international in scope.

It's quite possible that while studying at the University of Edinburgh, Julia Derrick would have come across the work of romantic poet and all-round Scots hero Rabbie Burns. If so, she would be familiar with the idea that "the best-laid schemes o' mice an' men, Gang aft agley" (or 'often go awry', for readers south of the border). Indeed, her own plans for a career in finance moved away from the expected course when she realised that her skills were best suited to a different role.

"Throughout my education and university career, I always thought that I would eventually end up pursuing a career in finance," she recalls. "In my third year at university, I applied for a number of internships at investment banks which involved various psychometric tests and all the feedback that I received was that verbal reasoning was a core strength. That process led me to re-evaluate my aspirations and encouraged me to identify a career that would allow me to leverage my core strengths. To me, law offered the complex, challenging, high-profile international work that had originally attracted me to finance, but was better suited to my skill set."

Put to the test
To test out her theory, Julia applied for a vacation scheme at Ashurst and found that she thoroughly enjoyed her time there. Not only that, but she was offered a training contract on the back of her performance and never looked back; she is now a partner in the firm's global energy team.

She decided to specialise in energy at the end of her training contract; although she had enjoyed all four seats, she found the sheer range involved in energy work intellectually engaging and the industry interesting. "It was a pretty tough decision," she admits, "but my final seat as a trainee was spent working on transactions relating to the energy sector, and specifically the oil and gas sector. I really enjoyed the nature of the work and the legal disciplines I was required to use, and I found the subject matter fascinating."

❝ Our clients really value lawyers who can speak their language and understand the wider trends in the industry and what current market practice is ❞

Julia describes her current workload as "very varied around common themes". It is predominantly project or transaction based, helping clients either buy or sell rights to explore for or produce petroleum, set up joint ventures, develop infrastructure or simply buy or sell oil and gas. In addition, she can find herself involved in negotiations between counterparties, writing reports and guidance for clients, researching points of law, and providing regulatory advice on oil and gas supplies for the UK regime.

Trainees in Ashurst's energy department are encouraged to be as hands on as possible, and to get as broad a range of experience in the different types of transaction which the department is handling. "The type of work trainees get involved in will really depend on the nature and size of the transaction,"

For more firms that work in this practice area, please use the "Training contract regional indexes" starting on p205.

Name: **Julia Derrick**
Firm: **Ashurst LLP**
Location: **London**
University: **University of Edinburgh**
Undergraduate degree: **Geography**

Julia explains. "Current trainees in the team have worked on due diligence in relation to oil drilling in Africa, drafted contracts and attended meetings with clients on several North Sea asset acquisitions, as well as a major nuclear energy project, and helped to close an oil refinery financing deal."

Clarity is key

Since much of the work on the transactional side is contract based, it is vital that those interested in this area can write clearly and concisely, and express themselves fluently to clients when explaining and rationalising the commercial and legal positions set out in the drafted documents. Another key strength is the ability to negotiate effectively and come up with creative solutions to problems that can help the client to navigate any potential problems and actually get the deal inked.

Success in energy is also predicated on keen industry insight, suggests Julia: "It's not really enough just to know about the law and to be a good lawyer. Our clients really value lawyers who can speak their language and understand the wider trends in the industry and what current market practice is. I think for young lawyers looking to break into this area of law, an awareness about what is going on with the oil price and the effect it is having on oil and gas companies is really good basic knowledge to have. It helps you to frame your advice to clients."

Indeed, the oil price crash in late 2014 and ongoing volatility since have had a significant impact on the industry, with different companies affected in different ways; this in turn has had a knock-on effect on law firm workflows. On the M&A front, it has made deals more challenging to close as, for example, parties' price expectations may differ significantly and buyers may need to think in more detail about how they finance any acquisitions.

"While there are a number of assets for sale at the moment, as companies attempt to rationalise their portfolios to focus on their core assets, buyers are being a lot more discerning about the type of assets that they want to buy," says Julia. "When a potential buyer is found, we are seeing negotiations taking much longer than they have historically, with a lot of uncertainty around the completion process once the deal is signed. This has led to some quite interesting trends flowing through in terms of changes to market practice and challenges to traditional ways of dealing with things in sale and purchase documentation."

Building that industry knowledge can be as simple as following the mainstream media, as Julia explains: "One of the things that initially attracted me is that it was and still is a very topical issue. You can't open a newspaper without seeing something about the oil and gas sector. It is one of the cornerstones upon which our way of life depends. We rely on it for heat, light, transport and the manufacture of goods. It's fundamental to our way of life. The other thing that really attracted me is that it is a truly global industry. It exposes you to a lot of different jurisdictions, and to interesting and complex work in those jurisdictions – and then there's a lot of international travel which, of course, helps to keep things interesting!"

Environment

Issues such as climate change and the need for alternative energy sources make environmental laws more important than ever. Environmental regulations seek to limit pollution and to minimise the impact of human activity on the natural world. This sweeping objective means that environmental lawyers are involved in a wide range of matters, from health and safety, risk management, contaminated land, waste, renewable energy and environmental finance; to commercial and property transactions, nuclear law and litigation. Clients can include individuals, community groups, companies of all sizes, local authorities and governments.

Ben Standing's career choices have always been driven by his passions, rather than the potential pay packet. His interest in law was first ignited during his undergraduate years at the University of Birmingham. "I studied labour economics as part of my degree and one of the modules was employment law. I really enjoyed it and decided to study the Graduate Diploma in Law – my interest just kept growing from there," he explains.

After jumping through the qualification hoops with ease, Ben secured a training contract at Browne Jacobson. "It's always quite hectic, being a trainee," he recalls. "You get pulled in all sorts of directions and get on with some teams more than others, but I really enjoyed the experience. It's all about finding your niche and the people you can work with."

That niche turned out to be environmental law, which involves issues that are close to Ben's heart. In fact, Browne Jacobson's prestigious environmental and public planning practice was a key reason that Ben chose to apply to train at the firm. He has not been disappointed – since joining, he has risen through the ranks to represent bodies such as Natural England and has even played a role in the creation of a new Welsh environmental protection body, Natural Resources Wales (NRW). He describes the diversity of the practice area: "A lot of environmental law focuses on property. My team primarily represents public sector clients – such as local councils and environmental bodies – but we also work alongside our colleagues in the property team, whose clients are often in the private sector. We look at environmental issues which come up in relation to land – how they affect planning permission, and sale and purchase agreements when land is sold. We also advise local authorities and private bodies in relation to the contaminated land regime. Another aspect of our work is reviewing environmental reports to look at potential issues that could arise regarding liability and identify relevant clauses which could therefore be required. I personally help to advise public bodies, such as Natural England, on environmental impact assessments and matters concerning sites of special scientific interest. My work on environmental impact assessment in relation to agriculture for the Welsh government sees me travelling all over Wales to present cases in front of planning inspectors."

Ins and outs of judicial review

Public and administrative law is another important element of the practice. Judicial review is central to this area and, as a representative of several public bodies, Ben spends a lot of his time defending clients against judicial review challenges. "Our job is to make sure that the decisions which public bodies enter into are lawfully made and cannot be reversed or quashed," he explains. "The first stage is the permission stage, where someone submits a claim and the defending party then has 21 days to respond by submitting summary grounds of resistance. A decision is then made by the court on whether to grant permission for the claimant to progress the matter; he or she is only allowed to do so if there is an arguable case which

For more firms that work in this practice area, please use the "Training contract regional indexes" starting on p205.

Name: **Ben Standing**
Firm: **Browne Jacobson LLP**
Location: **Nottingham**
University: **University of Birmingham**
Undergraduate degree: **International commerce**

justifies full investigation of the substantive merits. If permission is granted, we move on to the substantive stage. In our practice, often matters don't go to a substantive hearing because we are successful at the permission stage. However, if necessary we will robustly defend our client's decision in court."

When it comes to judicial review, a lot depends on the cards you are dealt initially. "The point at which we become involved has an impact," admits Ben. "If you're instructed when a decision is being made, you look to ensure that all the correct procedures have been followed and that the regulations are being complied with. A common reason for challenge is that the body has not adequately explained in writing its reasons for doing something. Coming up with a reasoned, logical decision and explaining why you have made it is the best way to defend against judicial review. However, if you're instructed after a decision has already been made, you just have to make the best of the situation and try to collect evidence to explain why the body has made its decision. In the worst-case scenario, you have to advise your client that it has made a mistake."

Green at heart
Flying the flag for causes that he cares about is an understandable source of job satisfaction. "I like the feeling of being on the right side, to be honest," says Ben. "I care about green issues and working for these bodies to protect the environment by making people comply with their environmental responsibilities makes me feel that I might be doing some good." Nowhere was this more evident than in Browne Jacobson's role in the formation of NRW: "The firm's property team handled the property aspect of the deal, while our job was to transfer responsibilities from the Countryside Council for Wales, the Environment Agency and the Forestry Commissioners to the new body, which involved amending the relevant

legislation by drafting an order which transferred those powers. I had only just qualified, so the experience stands out as a highlight – it was really rewarding to see what we had written become law."

Looking ahead, Ben is concerned at the amount of holes that remain to be filled in the environmental regime, as well as the possibility of existing protections being eroded. "We're primarily involved in making sure that people comply with the legislation that is there, but there should be more legislation being put in place to protect the environment," he says. "Meanwhile, the decision to leave the European Union is hugely significant, because most of our environmental law – on water, waste, birds and habitats, to name a few – stems from EU directives. I am concerned that some people are looking to unpick the legislative framework concerning the environment and this could have significant negative impacts, especially in relation to biodiversity."

Ben goes on to advise that succeeding in this area of law requires serious dedication. "There aren't many of us environmental lawyers out there, are there?" he muses. "You need to be passionate about what you're doing because, whether you're acting for public bodies or claimants, you won't want to be in this for the money – neither of these types of client have much to spend on legal fees. That said, it's a hard area to get into – there aren't that many firms practising environmental law and I was fortunate enough to join one of them, complete a seat with the team during my training and fill a vacancy when the opportunity arose. When choosing your firm, it would be wise to apply to those which practise a broad range of environmental law, not just the property side, which a lot of firms do. This area of law would be quite difficult to cross into at a later date, I think – you need to get some experience early on."

Family

Family and divorce is very much a people-focused area of law. Family and divorce lawyers deal with diverse legal issues including marriage, civil partnerships and unmarried couples, cohabitation, separation, divorce, financial claims and the now common pre and post nuptial/civil partnership agreements. Work on matters relating to children also form a big part of a family lawyer's daily caseload. Family and divorce lawyers are often litigators, but also negotiate out-of-court settlements. Family law cases often grab the media headlines, particularly when they involve people with high wealth or high-profile personalities. While the role of a family lawyer calls for an astute legal mind, strong communication and pastoral skills are also needed to support clients through often difficult times.

A musical beginning to Anna Ferro's academic career could have seen her focusing on pitch and tempo professionally; but instead, she found herself tapping along to the beat of law's drum: "I did both a bachelor's and master's music degree, and was planning to go back for my doctorate when I gained some work experience as a solicitors' clerk at the firm I'm still with. I enjoyed it so much that I decided to convert to law."

Two years of the Common Professional Exam (now the GDL) and the Law Society Finals (now the LPC) later, and Anna was off to Blaser Mills LLP to do her articles (now the training contract). "Having finished, there was an opportunity to qualify into the family department; I haven't looked back since!" she explains. "I have always worked on a broad range of cases in family law, but now I tend to specialise more in divorce and separation issues, and related financial matters, as well as pre-marital and cohabitation issues and private children matters."

Anna gets a head start on the day by arriving at the office early to go through emails and post, and then getting down to business: "I will then be drafting documents and meeting with clients. I'm also involved with aspects that relate to the firm as a business, including marketing and business development, which regularly takes me into relationship building meetings with third parties, and other, sometimes glamourous events. My days never drag, as there is so much to fit in."

Complex financial and emotional matters
For Anna, every day is tackled in the knowledge that "it is a privilege to help clients to find a way forward from what are often very difficult emotional and practical circumstances". One case stands out in her memory for its speed and international dimensions: "I managed to secure an urgent international freezing order in a divorce case involving offshore assets, followed by a mirror order in the Royal Court of Jersey. It was pretty thrilling!" She also appreciates the "varied selection of circumstances and personalities, which make each day and every case interesting".

Anna reflects on one of her cases: "It raised issues straight from the high-profile *Vince v Wyatt* case, which had a lot of press coverage in 2015. This is essentially where the parties completed their divorce many years ago, but did not formally resolve their financial claims at the time and now issues have arisen which has led to one party bringing a claim. This could see adverse capital adjustments for my client, which might not have occurred had the case been resolved at the time of the divorce."

Empathy required
As in all practice areas, it is essential for family lawyers to have a firm grounding in the relevant statutes and procedures, but Anna makes the point that they also need much more than that: "It is vital to strike a careful

For more firms that work in this practice area, please use the "Training contract regional indexes" starting on p205.

Name: **Anna Ferro**
Firm: **Blaser Mills**
Location: **High Wycombe**
University: **Royal Holloway, University of London**
Undergraduate degree: **Music**

balance between compassion for clients who are often facing huge life changes, sometimes involving the breakdown of their relationships, and good common sense about the way in which the client should proceed practically. You need to be able to combine empathy with the ability to distance yourself from the emotion of a case. That professional distance is key; if you get too involved in the issues, you will not survive. It is also really important to develop good business skills to continue to practise; there is a lot to get involved with at a law firm that is entirely separate from the cases themselves."

In Anna's view, a big challenge facing the profession at the moment is that the fact that legislation has been slow to catch up with the reality of modern family arrangements: "A key issue relates to cohabitee rights – the law is far behind the changes in family relationships, in that where parties choose to cohabit, they currently have very limited rights if their relationships break down. There is also a suggestion that the law on divorce should change to remove the need to assign blame."

As regards divorce finances, Anna hopes that a campaign to clarify the existing regime is successful: "It is currently very complicated, which means that the likely outcome of a case is hard to predict for client and lawyer alike. That can put pressure on parties to settle for commercial and tactical reasons, rather than in the interests of what's right."

Keeping on top of the evolving law, as well as more general professional development, is a daily commitment, says Anna: "You do have to make sure that you undertake a certain amount of training each year, although there have recently been changes to those requirements to allow for greater flexibility in how you go about it. It is also necessary to keep up with changing case law and statutory provisions, as well as the

many precedents and periodicals to read and absorb. You need to make sure that you're doing it every day, and it's very much an ongoing process."

❝ You need to be able to combine empathy with the ability to distance yourself from the emotion of a case ❞

Grab your chances

For budding family lawyers, Anna stresses the importance of work experience and seizing the opportunity to get stuck in: "If you can get a placement, then do it. Anything you can do to get experience – be that at a law firm, at court, or at a local authority – will be valuable. It will give you a good sense of what area of law might be for you and will equip you with relevant skills in advance of your training contract. It also gives you a feel for what you need to do in terms of keeping up to date with the news and legal press. That will help with your understanding of the law, but also of the business world." And while there, throw yourself into the experience wholeheartedly she advises: "Be ready to work very hard and to promote yourself – make yourself an asset to your firm. As the saying goes, the more you put into it, the more you will get out!"

Human rights

Human rights law has long been a popular choice for students and practitioners, with universities increasingly offering human rights modules as part of their law degrees, and ever more firms and chambers boasting specialisms in the field. It covers a wide range of legal matters, but broadly refers to the fundamental rights and freedoms set out in the Human Rights Act 1998, which made the European Convention on Human Rights (ECHR) directly enforceable in the UK courts.

Jocelyn Cockburn charts her progress from commercial trainee to human rights/civil liberties partner: "I did my training contract at City firm Druces & Attlee, but I wasn't gripped by the work and, unsure about whether the law was really for me, I went travelling. That period cemented the idea that I wanted to do something in the human rights field, so I came back and volunteered at Amnesty for a year and then worked on the land mines campaign, before coming back to the law in 1999." She spent time at two other human rights firms before joining Hodge Jones & Allen in 2004.

Fighting the good fight

Today, Jocelyn's expertise is in two of the main protections provided by the Human Rights Act, namely Article 2 (the right to life) and Article 3 (the right to freedom from torture and inhuman or degrading treatment), as well the occasional Article 8 or Article 14 case (rights to a private life and freedom from discrimination, respectively). "One of my main interests is in the state's obligation to protect vulnerable people in society where there is a real and immediate risk to life," she explains. "A lot of my work centres on the prison and police context, representing the families of those who have died in custody. For example, I've got two cases at the moment where a detainee has died during police restraint; the issues are those of whether the practices deployed were safe, but also give rise to questions of racial stereotyping by the police."

She notes that since austerity began in 2008, prison conditions have deteriorated, with more deaths in custody and more people with serious mental health issues detained. "There has also been an increase in the amount of private providers carrying out functions that are the state's responsibility. The concern is that while private companies are subject to human rights laws, there is not the same culture of human rights protections as in the public sector and they may in fact be in direct conflict with those companies' profit drives. There is also concern that safety is not sufficiently high up on their list of priorities."

Actions relating to soldiers' deaths during the Iraq War also feature in Jocelyn's caseload, including the ongoing Snatch Land Rover Case: "This is to do with allegations that during the war three soldiers were killed because the army vehicles were insufficiently safe to protect against the types of insurgency deployed. The case went through the High Court, the Court of Appeal and finally to the Supreme Court in 2013, when the court ruled on the state's legal obligations to protect soldiers on the battlefield. The legal issues involved first whether the death of a soldier outside the geographical boundaries of the United Kingdom still come within the UK jurisdiction for the purposes of the ECHR, and second whether there was a breach of the soldier's right to life by the ministry of defence, or even whether there was a legal obligation owed at all. I meet a lot of families who've lost a loved one and who are desperate for help, particularly because they've not always been treated very well. I like to show them that there are people who will listen and take them seriously."

This topical and newsworthy subject matter is one of the main drivers for Jocelyn: "I enjoy current affairs and politics, and naturally I see events though a human rights perspective". "I can choose to work on things that I find motivating. One big one for me at the moment is formulating a case on behalf of individuals

For more firms that work in this practice area, please use the "Training contract regional indexes" starting on p205.

Name: **Jocelyn Cockburn**
Firm: **Hodge Jones & Allen LLP**
Location: **London**
University: **University of Newcastle**
Undergraduate degree: **History**

asserting their right to breathe clean air and the duty of the state to take reasonable steps to immediately reduce pollution caused by traffic. There is evidence that in London alone, around 9,500 people die from pollution every year – many of those are society's most vulnerable, including children. It is a scandal and the United Kingdom is currently in breach of safe legal limits as required by the European Union. I am personally affected by it and this is why I am trying to use the law creatively to tackle these huge issues."

Legal aid and Brexit

The seismic shift in the legal aid landscape has had a dramatic impact on the way that Jocelyn's cases are funded and which of them are viable. "Eight years ago, most of my cases were covered by legal aid – now, it's only about half," she reflects. "The rest are 'no win, no fee' conditional fee agreements, which is not the best way to run these types of public interest case. For example, you need 'after the event' insurance to protect clients against a costs award, and insurers simply aren't motivated to insure a case where the legal landscape is uncertain. Fewer cases than ever qualify for legal aid – you may have a viable judicial review challenge to a decision, but you won't be able to run it if the client is not eligible for legal aid. Many of our clients are not motivated primarily by a desire for compensation; it is about righting a wrong. Recently I was heartened to hear the chief coroner talking about giving "equality of arms" in terms of access to funding for families at inquest where they are up against the state, but whether it will happen under this government is another matter."

Ironically, post-referendum, Jocelyn feels that there may be some good news on the human rights front: "Previously, Theresa May was vehemently against the Human Rights Act and was all for withdrawing the United Kingdom from the European Court of Human Rights, so Brexit may have given us a reprieve! The legal complexity of separating ourselves from the European Union is big enough without adding to that disentangling our case law and legal system from the ECHR. This is not to say that the government won't try to repeal the Human Rights Act and introduce a bill of rights, but there are no details of what that may look like at this stage." Worth noting is that one possible new avenue of work for human rights lawyers post-Brexit may relate to the dangers of the removal of rights and protections without parliamentary scrutiny.

Realism required

A lot of students are drawn to human rights by a romanticised view of what it means: "Students are naturally quite idealistic, so it makes sense that many are attracted to this type of work. But it's all about whether you have the necessary commitment – you're giving up a potentially much higher salary, but on the flipside, there is so much of interest in this work."

So, what are the attributes of a good human rights lawyer? "You need to have a strong and persistent character, and enjoy the fight; you need to be somebody who is willing to take on the big guys, whether that is government or big business. It helps to be tenacious and committed to what human rights and civil liberties stand for. It also helps to be good with people; lots of our clients have difficult stories to tell so being a good communicator and listener is a real skill."

If you think that sounds like you, then taking opportunities to find out more is essential, including going to relevant talks and absorbing some of the mountain of information that is accessible online. Jocelyn also takes a pragmatic approach to the question of work experience: "While voluntary work experience with organisations such as Liberty, INQUEST or Justice is useful, I know that not everyone can afford to do that. I suspect that more and more graduates are working as paralegals before getting a training contact and it's a great way to learn more, in a paid job."

Immigration

Immigration lawyers deal with all legal matters relating to immigration and nationality. The work ranges from asylum and human rights claims through applications by family members and students to how businesses can secure immigration status for their employees. There is a significant and increasing EU law element, and many cases raise important human rights issues. The law is rapidly developing in terms of both statute law and jurisprudence, and procedural timeframes are tight. There is a good deal of overlap with employment, tax, social welfare, mental health, prison law, criminal law and civil actions.

Keen to keep her career options open when deciding what to study, Andrea Beveney opted for the versatility of a law degree: "I didn't know if I wanted to be a lawyer when I started university, but I felt that a law degree would stand me in good stead for whatever profession I chose to pursue later," she explains. "Over the course of the degree I changed my mind, as I found that I was enjoying particular subjects such as employment law and criminal law a lot more than I expected."

Off the beaten track
Although Andrea eventually trained at magic circle firm Linklaters, her journey there was not the well-trodden route from university to Legal Practice Course (LPC) to training contract: "I think I'm a good example of the different ways to get into the law. As I mentioned, I enjoyed employment law and criminal law, so I always envisaged that I would end up in a high-street firm. With many high-street firms, it is not necessary to apply until you have finished the LPC; but while I was completing the course I did some work experience at a high-street firm and I didn't like it at all. I had to think again about what I really wanted to do. At that stage it was too late to apply to the big firms, as I didn't want

to go through a frustrating period of making lots of applications and receiving rejections when I needed a job fairly quickly, which is why I made the decision to apply for a job as a tax consultant, where I could still use the legal skills that I had gained. I applied to the 'big four' accountancy firms, which favoured law graduates. I joined KPMG as a tax consultant, moved from Birmingham to London, made new friends and took my tax exams. Later, Linklaters was recruiting share scheme lawyers and was specifically looking for LPC graduates with tax experience. The role was perfect for me and my previous experience meant that the length of my training contract was reduced to just one year."

Sometime after qualifying, Andrea moved on from Linklaters to continue working in share schemes at Ernst & Young, but really she was ready for a change. "One of the downsides to early specialisation is that it can be quite difficult to move onto something else and I was at the stage where I wanted to do something new," she explains. "I applied to be a tax lawyer at HMRC, a role which I thought suited my experience, and fortunately was successful; so that's how I joined the Government Legal Service (GLS). One of the great things about GLS is that is possible to move into different areas of law every three years or so, and I moved into employment. Later my whole team was moved from HMRC into the Government Legal Department, which is where I began to practise immigration law."

Judicial review
Now an experienced immigration practitioner, Andrea is a mini-team leader of 10 within the government's wider team of around 200 immigration lawyers and support staff. Most of the cases that she works on concern judicial review. "Judicial review is often the only way that people can challenge immigration decisions, as while there is an appeals process in place, some Home Office decisions don't carry a right to appeal," she explains. "We

For more firms that work in this practice area, please use the "Training contract regional indexes" starting on p205.

Name: **Andrea Beveney**
Firm: **Government Legal Service**
Location: **London**
University: **Nottingham Trent University**
Undergraduate degree: **Law**

represent the Home Office and provide litigation services in response to claims for judicial review that are made against Home Office decisions. Cases vary from people who have not been granted leave to enter the country; to people who are already in the United Kingdom who have been refused variations to or further leave to remain; to people who have requested leave to remain as the spouses of partners who are, for example, EEA nationals. In other cases there is a judicial review because the claimant considers that the Home Office has taken too long to make a decision. The work totally varies on a day-to-day basis. We handle cases in their entirety, from the initial response to a request for judicial review to the negotiation of some form of settlement where we accept that the Home Office's decision was not the right one. Some cases go all the way to the Supreme Court."

Government policy must be taken into account, but Andrea and her team still assess each case individually. "The Home Office makes decisions in line with government policy, but this does not mean that our position is to defend every decision regardless of the merits of the individual case – all decisions are looked at on a case-by-case basis to determine whether the home secretary's decision was rational and lawful," she explains. "For example, in some cases we may find that certain evidence was not taken into consideration, which means that the decision has to be reconsidered."

Deportation laws

The highlight of Andrea's career thus far has been working on the high-profile case of Kevin Kiarie and Courtney Byndloss, who were the first to challenge the government's so-called 'deport first, appeal later' rule for foreign nationals who have committed serious criminal offences. "The home secretary has the right to deport people who were not originally British citizens in cases where they have been convicted of a criminal offence

serious enough to incur prison sentence of at least 12 months," she explains. "Previously, offenders were able to challenge their deportation on the basis of their human rights, among other reasons, with the appeal taking place in the United Kingdom, thus delaying deportation. The Immigration Act 2014 gave the home secretary the ability to determine – based on information provided by the person who is due to be deported – whether she considered any human rights appeal made in those circumstances would be prejudiced if it took place outside the country. The case I worked on was a challenge to the home secretary's ability to make decisions in that way. It was dealt with on an expedited timetable for the Court of Appeal to hear it as soon as possible, as other similar challenges were stayed behind it due to it being the first case testing this new power. We had two months to prepare and worked closely with advisory lawyers and litigators, as well as policy clients and other stakeholders. The advocate general for Scotland represented the Home Office in court and we were successful. The case actually demonstrated how different parts of the government can work really well together."

Looking forward to the medium term, Andrea and her colleagues will continue to be very busy: "The Immigration Act 2016 has come into force and clauses from that are currently being implemented. Brexit is also going to have a massive impact, with the right to remain of EU nationals currently uncertain."

Andrea concludes that "the things that I enjoy about this job are also sometimes the things that I don't enjoy. I enjoy the fact that each day is different and I often don't know what is going to happen when I arrive in the morning – it keeps things really interesting, even though sometimes this means having to rethink my day. If you are robust and enjoy unpredictability, you might just make a good immigration lawyer yourself."

Insurance

Insurance (and reinsurance – the insurance of insurers) is an integral part of commercial activity throughout the world. The insurance practices of top-end firms advise on a range of areas, including coverage disputes, investment management, documentation, mergers and acquisitions of insurers, and the transfer of books and business between insurers. Regulatory law governs matters such as the establishment and regulation of insurance companies throughout the world. Clients include insurers, reinsurers and UK insurance institutions, as well as major insured companies and their captive insurers.

Stephanie Castell's journey into the legal profession began at the University of Kent, where she gained her law degree; and continued at The University (then College) of Law for the Legal Practice Course stage. She joined BLM, well known for its status as a leader in the field of insurance law, as a trainee in the Southampton office in 2010, where her experiences during the training contract proved to be ideal preparation for her future practice: "I spent one of my seats on secondment at the Association of British Insurers (ABI), which was a very interesting and beneficial experience, seeing bills being written and presented through Parliament and particularly as many of the firm's customers work with the ABI on current topical issues."

Now a partner at the firm, Stephanie is part of the catastrophic injury team, where she acts on behalf of insurers defending high-value claims brought against them or their insured's involving serious injuries. "My caseload involves defending claims for traumatic brain and spinal injuries as well as amputation cases, with most claims valued above £1 million," she explains.

In addition to the kinds of claim already described, Stephanie has worked on a number of complex cerebral palsy cases where there is dispute as to whether injuries may have been caused by, for example, a road traffic accident, or an unexplained and unregistered insult to the foetus en ventre sa mere (in the womb).

Complex investigations

Such serious issues require sensitivity and the opinions of medical experts – and sometimes those in other fields, as well – to establish the facts and arrive at an appropriate level of damages. "Some cases can take years to run from start to finish given the complexity of the medical problems and investigations needed," she explains. "Part of my role is to investigate liability and determine fault, which may involve analysing an accident scenario, conducting interviews and considering expert reconstruction evidence. The next stage is to consider quantum, which is the value of the injuries as set out by the courts and the compensation that should be paid to put the claimant back in the position they would have been in pre-accident. These valuations are based on medical evidence, so in the case of a traumatic brain injury with ongoing effects, we would usually instruct a neurologist who will not only comment on the severity of the injury, but also any risk of post traumatic epilepsy and any effect on life expectancy. There is often an array of evidence to get through and experts to consult." Clearly, solicitors who work on cases involving catastrophic injury can foster very different relationships with the solicitors on the opposing side than might be the case with solicitors in other practice areas, as the severity of the injuries involved in such cases requires, more often than not, a collaborative approach to securing the right level of damages.

One of the most appealing aspects of the role is the regular opportunity to consult

For more firms that work in this practice area, please use the "Training contract regional indexes" starting on p205.

Name: **Stephanie Castell**
Firm: **BLM**
Location: **Southampton**
University: **University of Kent**
Undergraduate degree: **Law**

with experts who are frequently leaders in their fields. "The same applies on the purely legal side," she adds. "I instruct top QCs and work with excellent solicitors. The variety of professionals that I work with is another attraction of the role." But an interesting, high-value caseload is not without its pressures: "The workload is not for the faint hearted, dealing with complex medical terminology and conditions, while balancing court-imposed time limits to factor in with many other cases as part of one's caseload; it can be demanding."

ᏝᏝ The workload is not for the faint hearted, dealing with complex medical terminology and conditions, while balancing court-imposed time limits ᏝᏝ

As for highlights in Stephanie's career so far, becoming a partner would be a tough one to surmount: "I have helped to build a strong catastrophic injury team in the Southampton office and have responsibility not only to conduct my own caseload, but also to train and develop the more inexperienced members of the team."

Unknown territory

Stephanie comments on the recent change to the discount rate causing concern in the insurance industry, which has sparked wide debate as to how such a rate should be set in the future: "We are still very much in unknown territory. Such uncertainties, and the status of the industry, mean that there is an onus on solicitors' firms to continue adapting to meet the challenges of an environment that is as competitive as ever where you are judged not only on your ability to carry out the work, but what 'extras' you can bring to the table."

Finally, Stephanie has the following advice for those aspiring to join the solicitors' profession themselves. "A strong academic record and the ability to manage complex information to arrive at good solutions is essential, but there is much more to being a solicitor than legal expertise – you need a much wider skill set. Excellent interpersonal and communication skills are also essential in addition to prioritising your workload and the ability to adapt and understand evidence in an array of often unfamiliar fields of expertise."

Intellectual property

IP work can be divided into two main areas: so-called 'hard' and 'soft' intellectual property. 'Hard' intellectual property generally relates to registered IP rights such as patents, while 'soft' intellectual property includes registered trademarks and registered designs, copyright, unregistered design rights, database rights, trade secrets, confidential information and passing off. IP lawyers advise on issues ranging from commercial exploitation to infringement disputes, and agreements that deal either exclusively with IP or with IP rights in the wider context of larger commercial transactions. Many lawyers specialise in either contentious or non-contentious IP work.

As is the case for many IP lawyers, Nadine Bleach took her undergraduate background in the sciences and converted it into a career in law: "I wanted to use my physics degree, but not necessarily in a purely scientific field. IP law, which requires the application of technical understanding to a legal framework, seemed like a sound option. Although it was intellectual property that drew me in, looking at many different areas of law made me realise that even without the direct use of science, there are a lot of transferable skills, including problem-solving and analysis, and the ability to structure and work through issues in a logical way."

Patently clear

Nadine trained at Bristows, enjoying among other things the fact that she was able to undertake six seats, which offered the chance to try a variety of departments and make an informed choice at the point of qualification. That led her to join their market-leading IP department in 2014. "At Bristows there is a split between transactional and litigious intellectual property; I'm in the litigation department, specialising in patents," she explains. "I work on disputes in all kinds of scientific area, but I am drawn more to the technological areas – such as telecoms, engineering and mechanics.

It is a mix of advising clients who can be at various stages of the dispute process, and running litigation at court."

Nadine was a part of one of the most high-profile patent cases of recent years, *Unwired Planet v Huawei, Samsung & others*, acting for Samsung: "It was my first telecoms case at Bristows and I was involved from the very beginning and throughout the life cycle of the case. Piecing it all together, working on the high-level strategy as well as getting to grips with the technical detail and then attending court and watching it all unfold – it was very interesting and exciting."

Day to day, what you will find yourself doing depends largely on the type of matter you are involved in and, if it is a court case, the stage the trial has reached, as Nadine explains: "At the beginning of a trial, you're getting into the subject matter, working with the client to understand what the case is all about, including any products, features of the market and the issues in dispute. You need to understand things from the client's perspective, including their commercial goals. The focus then turns to strategy, including finding and working with experts in the particular field. Cases often feel fast-moving and before you know it you are in the nitty gritty of trial preparation, working with barristers on the strategy for presenting the case to the court."

One of the most interesting things about the job is the opportunity to work with and meet a huge variety of people: "Clients, barristers, experts; they all have a role to play in preparing patent cases for court. Much of it is often understanding complicated technical information; despite having a scientific background, we will work with experts who know these areas in incredible detail. I love working with people who are the best in their fields; you learn about some very interesting things, which you wouldn't otherwise have access to. You also become something of a

For more firms that work in this practice area, please use the "Training contract regional indexes" starting on p205.

Name: **Nadine Bleach**
Firm: **Bristows**
Location: **London**
University: **Imperial College London**
Undergraduate degree: **Physics**

mini-expert in each area as you go from case to case. For example, I might move from telecoms to medical devices to product packaging!"

The unpredictability of hours and workload is one of the few disadvantages to this exciting career: "Especially coming up to deadlines, you don't always know in advance how busy you're going to be. Things come up when you least expect them to and that can be tough. But I like that we are often working in teams – working things through together. As a junior lawyer, that's a great way to learn."

Nadine explains the significance of the much-anticipated 2018 launch of the Unified Patent Court (UPC): "For example, rather than having to launch a patent action in each country of infringement, under the UPC it will be possible to bring a single action, provided the countries in which infringement is alleged are part of the UPC. A similar principle applies for invalidating patents. It will be quite different to the current UK system, including different rules of procedure and involving judges from all over Europe. While Brexit certainly muddied the waters, the plan is still for the UPC to open in early 2018 and for the United Kingdom to be part of the system. What is less certain is the United Kingdom's longer term participation."

There is also a concern among some patent lawyers that the United Kingdom may lose some work as a result of the UPC because all European lawyers will be competing for the same work. However, there remains confidence in the ability to win work and there is also the prospect of work flowing in from across the Atlantic: "There has been a change in the United States in the rules as to where patent infringement proceedings can be brought. This restricts a patentee's ability to bring cases in the most patentee-friendly jurisdictions in the United States, such as the Eastern District of Texas. This may drive more work in the direction of the future UPC, where the patentee will have more options as to where it can bring its claims. In

fact the UPC could well cause a global shift in litigation from the United States to Europe."

Skills and challenges
Nadine reflects on some of the most important skills associated with a successful career in IP law. "Teamwork is a huge part; the more experienced I get, the more I realise its importance, in terms of working more efficiently and making me a better lawyer," she says. "You need an eye for detail – that's very important. The entire strategy in a case can change on the smallest of details. It's also essential to be logical and not jump to conclusions and do things in a methodical way. You also need to be able to look at what the client wants and needs, their commercial goals, as well as the technical case, as it all feeds into a cohesive whole. This is both challenging and enjoyable – I feel fulfilled when I've manged to put together what can be a very complicated puzzle. I enjoy this mental challenge."

A challenge ahead of would-be lawyers is finding the firm that is the best fit for them. Nadine has a few suggestions on how to go about doing that: "Do your research to work out what firms do and specialise in. All firms are different, they are different sizes, working in different ways with different types of client; so you need to identify what is best for you. Try to understand about a firm before you apply, so that you can make a targeted application." The best way of doing that is to get out there and talk to people: "Go to open days and law fairs; they're really helpful to get insight into a range of firms. I realised that I wanted to work here at Bristows when I did the vacation scheme – I really liked the people and the work I was exposed to. Understanding a firm's culture and type of work is best done through speaking to people first hand, especially trainees but also more senior lawyers, who can offer insight into life at the firm once qualified. If you like what you hear, then it's a good indicator that the firm will suit you too."

Islamic finance

The term 'Islamic finance' refers to a system of banking that is consistent with *Sharia* law. In particular, interest is prohibited, as is investing in businesses considered unlawful, such as those which trade in pork or alcohol. Although Islamic finance was initially important predominantly to commercial firms with interests in the oil-rich countries of the Middle East, it is now a practice area in every major international firm. Banks, financial institutions, sovereigns and corporates worldwide still take a great interest in traditional Islamic finance markets such as Malaysia, the United Arab Emirates and Saudi Arabia, but there are also significant Islamic financial centres in London, Hong Kong and Singapore. This, combined with the growth of Islamic finance throughout Asia and Africa, is leading to an increased need for lawyers who understand Islamic finance.

Farmida Bi was initially drawn to the law by the prospect of "going out there and righting wrongs and helping people" – a lofty ideal, and not uncommon when the notion of becoming a lawyer is dreamed up in childhood. It took a law degree and a few stints of work experience to discover that in fact, she wanted to be an entirely different type of lawyer: "I did a vacation scheme at Clifford Chance in my second year. I loved the international nature of the work, and the informality when compared to the chambers at which I'd done mini-pupillages." Another reason for turning down the Bar was financial: "At that time, you generally had to fund your way through Bar school and pupillage, whereas the big law firms paid for law school, a maintenance grant and your training. For me, the financial imperatives were decisive."

Farmida studied her finals (now the LPC) at The College of Law (now The University of Law) in Guildford and went on to do her articles (now the training contract) at Clifford Chance. She recalls the time fondly: "We had about 80 people in our intake, so there were lots of us in the same position. It was a well-organised programme and you got a real sense of the different options available to you. I also spent six months in Singapore, which I loved."

> **❝ The workload is not for the faint hearted, dealing with complex medical terminology and conditions, while balancing court-imposed time limits ❞**

Leader in the field

Leaving Clifford Chance when she was four years' qualified, and after a brief spell in-house at JP Morgan, Farmida moved to US firm Cleary Gottlieb and qualified at the New York Bar. That was, she enthuses, "a wonderful experience; I had a much broader range of work than before, with a huge amount of responsibility – it was exhilarating". She then became a partner at Denton Wilde Sapte (now Dentons), which is where, as part of the capital markets team, she first encountered Islamic finance; in 2008 she joined Norton Rose (now Norton Rose Fulbright) as a partner, where she is European head of Islamic finance. She is the only woman ranked for Islamic finance in *Chambers UK* and has also added to her trophy cabinet by scooping 'Best in Banking and Finance' at the European Women in Business Law Awards in 2011 and 2013.

Farmida's practice is primarily focused on capital markets and she explains where Islamic finance fits into that: "Islamic finance can be used for all sorts of deals – be that financing an aeroplane, constructing a building or going out into the markets and raising money – while fulfilling the requirements of *Sharia* law, which includes a prohibition on the charging of interest."

For more firms that work in this practice area, please use the "Training contract regional indexes" starting on p205.

Name: **Farmida Bi**
Firm: **Norton Rose Fulbright**
Location: **London**
University: **University of Cambridge**
Undergraduate degree: **Law**

Change is afoot

She describes the changing nature of Islamic finance: "For us as a firm, and for me personally, Islamic finance has become quite specialised. Three or four years ago, if you were an Islamic finance lawyer, you could work on a fund one day, a property acquisition the next and a *sukuk* (a *Sharia*-compliant bond issue) on the third. Nowadays, it is more common to specialise in a particular area – such as capital markets – and you have to work on that in both a conventional and an Islamic way. Some clients can switch from one option to the other – they might start out with a conventional deal and then find an investor that wants it to be sharia compliant, so it changes, and vice versa." Farmida's advice to those interested in Islamic finance is to think instead about becoming a lawyer who can work in both a conventional and an Islamic speciality: "The skills you will be offering are those of a lawyer. Our job is to structure a transaction which satisfies the client's commercial needs and meets the requirements of the *Sharia*, as evidenced by a fatwa provided by an Islamic scholar. We have to understand that we are not the scholars and we have been employed for our legal skills rather than our religious beliefs."

As a partner, Farmida's day is a mix of client work and general firm-related matters: "On any given day, I could be meeting clients, reviewing the work of associates in the team, structuring a new deal and marketing the firm, as well as dealing with internal administrative issues." There is also some travel – particularly to the Middle East, although not exclusively: "We also have a lot of clients in Europe who are interested in Islamic finance and potentially looking to do deals which are sharia compliant."

Ground-breaking work

A professional highlight for Farmida was working on the first UK corporate *sukuk* for IIT: "It was a small deal, but the fact that it was the first of its kind made it interesting.

By contrast, a few years ago I worked on one of the biggest deals in the market – the $3.5 billion Dubai Ports acquisition. That really changed the market. Most of the deals I work on have an average lifespan of around three months, so you work on something, it comes to market and you move on to the next one. That's satisfying."

For those keen to find out more, Farmida recommends starting with the press, such as the *Financial Times* and the *Economist*, to "get a general idea of what's happening in the world and with Islamic finance in particular, as it gets significant coverage". A number of textbooks are also available. And a familiarity with Islam itself will help: "If you speak Arabic or have an understanding of the principles of Islam, it makes a big difference. Having said that, there are plenty of successful people in the industry who are not Arabic speakers or Muslims; but an interest in the religion and the culture definitely helps."

Finally, Farmida stresses the importance of experience – and not just of the legal variety: "Getting a training contract now seems more difficult, so it's important to be an interesting and engaged person. Legal work experience gives you an advantage, but so can other experience. I interviewed a solicitor recently who'd taken a couple of years off to manage a jazz band. The skills she had picked up, such as managing a business, researching the market and meeting client needs, were all relevant for a successful lawyer. She had also done something she was interested in. I think that people can be narrowly CV-focused these days; general life experience and doing things you're interested in will also help you to be a more attractive candidate as you try to build a career."

Personal injury

Personal injury (PI) law falls under the law of tort. It involves civil law cases brought to obtain compensation for injuries sustained, to restore the injured person to the position he or she would have been in had the injury not happened. The subject matter varies considerably and can range from controversial, high-profile disasters to road traffic accidents to health and safety cases. A related specialised practice area of PI law is clinical negligence, which involves injuries suffered during medical procedures.

Although he can't pinpoint exactly why, law was always where Matt Bacon imagined himself ending up: "I studied it at A level and at university; I just never wanted to do anything else. I've always been interested in litigation – I like putting together arguments to see how they play out. I also have some family members in law, so having spoken to them and others, it sounded even more like something I would enjoy."

Matt secured his training contract at what was then Henmans (although the firm announced its merger with Freeths just a few days later). He benefited from having spent time paralegalling elsewhere, which meant that he was able to knock six months off his training contract as 'time to count', and went on to qualify into the defendant personal injury team. "I only do defendant work, and we mainly receive our instructions from insurers or corporate clients that have large self-insured elements of their business", Matt explains. "I specialise in employers' liability, covering any accident that occurs at work, public liability and product liability. I'm also involved with defending health and safety prosecutions – so those companies that are prosecuted by the Health and Safety Executive as a result of a one-off accident or breaches in relation to health and safety in general."

As a trainee, Matt enjoyed great exposure to work of this nature and he still works closely with his former supervisor: "Now I have my own caseload, which I run from start to finish, and which involves thinking of my own tactics. It allows me to be more independent with the way I deal with cases. On top of that, I help my supervisor with his cases. Things do ramp up in terms of responsibility when you qualify, but you can always run tactics past your supervisor and there is continued support."

Tactical advantage

Matt recalls as a highlight his first experience of a case discontinuance – "we presented evidence in defence and the claimant discontinued the claim" – but generally speaking, it is the process of working through a PI matter that provides the everyday satisfaction: "I enjoy when you get a case in and you're deciding on tactics and formulating the best arguments." He makes the point that sometimes, the best way forward is not to defend a claim, especially if there is little chance of success and it may be better for the client simply to take it on the chin: "Most clients just want you to be open and honest with your advice; if there isn't a case to defend, they don't want to waste money on defending it. Economics plays a big part in what we do and you have to be commercially minded, putting pragmatic business interests first."

Not unique to PI lawyers, but certainly something with particular resonance to them, the profession is keeping a close eye on changes relating to costs, particularly those of the claimant. "There was a change in legislation a few years ago – and there are others in the pipeline – to make most personal injury claims up to £25,000 subject to fixed costs, so as the lawyer, you would receive a fixed amount as opposed to an hourly fee," Matt explains. There is also the small claims track for low-value claims,

For more firms that work in this practice area, please use the "Training contract regional indexes" starting on p205.

Name: **Matt Bacon**
Firm: **Freeths LLP**
Location: **Oxford**
University: **University of Reading**
Undergraduate degree: **Law**

where you can't usually recover the costs of instructing a lawyer. The government is looking at increasing the claim limit for that from £1,000."

More generally, lawyers must keep up with clients' evolving needs and expectations – particularly as these relate to the use of technology – in order to maintain a successful practice: "Especially in light of the changeable economy, clients expect you to be doing the work on the most cost-efficient basis, using all the tech that is available. Every firm has to keep abreast of that now."

> **❝ Being commercial is something to remember; you have to understand your clients' businesses, establish what they're looking for and tailor your advice to their particular needs ❞**

Keep cool
Something else that clients want from their legal adviser is the ability to stay both cool under pressure and commercially attuned, as Matt notes: "Given the often very tight timescales, and as you normally have several cases going on at once, you have to remain calm and deal with them all as efficiently as you can. Being commercial is something to remember; you have to understand your clients' businesses, establish what they're looking for and tailor your advice to their particular needs. When you're dealing with insurers, who are very knowledgeable about the law because they handle it every day, your advice has to be pitched at someone who is an experienced user of the legal profession. Conversely, if it's an individual who is not familiar with the law or the system, you have to adjust your advice to that."

In order to stand out from the hordes of other would-be lawyers, Matt suggests talking to those already in the profession as a way to learn more and to establish whether it's right for you: "It's very important to get yourself out there, so do some work experience and try to meet as many people as possible. Law fairs are another important way of gaining exposure to firm reps, so that when you come to apply, you're not doing so from a completely blank background. Firms have so many people applying, it's important you have something that separates you from the pack."

While you shouldn't be put off by the levels of competition, you also have to be realistic about your chances: "One thing that didn't really strike me until I was through the process is how competitive it is and how many people are going for each vacancy; I didn't get my training contract until after law school and it was a real eye-opener to see how many of us there didn't have training contracts. I wouldn't change the way I did it, but it is very competitive and you have to put yourself out there."

Private client

A private client solicitor looks after the affairs of individual clients and trustees, planning and managing all aspects of their finances, including wills and probate, onshore and offshore trusts, and tax matters. Private client lawyers also handle a wide range of charity work, advising on specific legal issues as well as on commercial and property matters that affect charitable organisations and the establishment of charities. Private client work is booming and, increasingly, multi-jurisdictional issues are becoming more important for private client lawyers as a result of acting for clients who are based outside the United Kingdom or who own assets in various countries throughout the world.

The legal profession was of early interest to Tom Lawrence with his father practising as a local solicitor. After completing his law degree at the University of Hull, Tom returned to his home city of Norwich to train as a solicitor, only briefly considering the Bar as an option. "At the time I was thinking that I might want to follow a career in the law, direct access to barristers was not available and I knew that I wanted to be involved with clients from an early stage," he recalls. "And I'm happy to admit that standing up on my feet all day in court was not something that really appealed to me!"

Tom trained at Norwich firm Leathes Prior starting in 2003. "It was a really interesting two years and I learnt a lot – there were plenty of opportunities to take on responsibilities which I enjoyed greatly," he explains. "It was a supportive environment, with good quality work."

After qualifying, Tom continued on at Leathes Prior for nearly two years before being given an opportunity at another local firm to progress his career, where he stayed for five years and in that time was appointed as one of its partners and head of the private client, tax and trusts team. Tom was then approached to join Howes Percival as a director, where he has been ever since.

Now a partner of the firm's estates team, Tom's specialises in advising the firm's non-landed private clients. "These are primarily business and entrepreneurial clients who own small to medium-sized enterprises," he explains. "My clients range across a number of sectors, including manufacturing, technology and professional services."

The work can be split broadly into two separate areas: "The first centres on estate and succession planning using wills, trusts and lifetime gifting, together with providing related tax advice. The other area of work relates to estates and probate administration and powers of attorney. This type of work can often be quite sensitive and emotions can run extremely high, which is understandable – over the years I have managed a number of estates disputes where relations between executors and beneficiaries have become quite fractious."

Day to day, the role is naturally very people focused. "A large proportion of my time is spent in meeting clients, their families and other professional advisers," Tom explains. "Part of my work includes report writing, liaising and connecting the various strands of advice received so as to provide holistic and understandable solutions for clients."

And it is the human element – forming and maintaining long-term working relationships with clients – which initially attracted Tom to this area of work: "I like meeting and understanding people, and, if it's not trite to say so – trying to make a positive difference to them and their families. My working relationships with clients often continue for many years through generations, which is rewarding. You do really get to

For more firms that work in this practice area, please use the "Training contract regional indexes" starting on p205.

Name: **Tom Lawrence**
Firm: **Howes Percival LLP**
Location: **Norwich**
University: **University of Hull**
Undergraduate degree: **Law**

know people and what is important to them and occasionally I receive calls from clients asking me about issues that are entirely unrelated to the law. I take the view that the wider my understanding of their circumstances, the better informed I am for providing advice."

❝ My working relationships with clients often continue for many years through generations, which is rewarding ❞

A particular highlight of Tom's career so far reinforced the value of making sure you 'know your subject': "I was approached a few years ago by a beneficiary of a property left to her by will. Unfortunately, the property had been sold before the deceased died. The beneficiary had been advised by a number of other solicitors that the gift in the will simply failed. However, when the beneficiary approached me, through our discussions, I was able to find out that the deceased had in fact lost mental capacity some time before the property was sold and due to some quite rarely used legislation, the gift to the beneficiary did not lapse but instead took effect as a gift over the remaining net proceeds of sale. After a short exchange of letters with the solicitors dealing with the estate to assert the client's rights in this case, a substantial cheque was received in satisfaction of my client's interest."

Assessing the future for the legal profession, Tom is keen to emphasise the need for solicitors to continue modernising: "Historically solicitors' firms have been slow to react and move with the times, and there have been a number of new entrants to the legal market that are providing competition which we must take seriously. We have to

learn to be more creative and outward facing, and ask ourselves challenging questions about the ways in which our clients want us to deliver services now and in the future. Improvements in technology year on year mean that we need to make sure we keep ahead in service delivery and pricing of our work is critical. Communicating clearly to our clients our charges and the value we are delivering for our costs is fundamental. All of these challenges are positive as they keep us sharp and focused, and they reinforce that we must always look to move forward."

While it's important to have sound legal knowledge, becoming a successful solicitor requires a wide skill set: "You need to be focused and driven, while also having the confidence to tackle difficult and often sensitive issues. It is important to be a self-starter and have first-class interpersonal skills because if you cannot explain the issues to the client, you cannot expect they will understand them. Sadly, you will never have all of the answers all of the time – just know where to find them!"

Restructuring and insolvency

Restructuring and insolvency lawyers are called in when a company, individual or other organisation is in financial difficulties and is facing possible liquidation, administration or bankruptcy. In such situations, restructuring and insolvency lawyers work to advise the organisation's management and other stakeholders on what to do next, which could be filing for administration or a distressed merger. A restructuring and insolvency lawyer's work is also to advise organisations that have not yet become insolvent on how to avoid such a situation and formulate contingency plans. In addition, restructuring and insolvency lawyers will also advise an organisations' creditors where their borrower is facing financial problems.

When studying and training to be a lawyer in her native Australia, Hanh Nguyen may not have imagined that she would be a partner, specialising in restructuring and insolvency, in a respected City firm a decade later. However, she had always been open to wherever her legal career might take her: "I always wanted to keep my options open, which is why I did a double degree. However, towards the end of the degree when I was looking for part-time work, I was drawn to legal secretary roles and having secured one, realised that the practical element of law really resonated with me."

After qualification in 2004, Hanh spent seven years at a boutique general practice firm in Sydney, before sitting the Qualified Lawyers Transfer Test and coming to the United Kingdom. She spent time at both Teacher Stern LLP and Salans LLP, where she first explored corporate and personal insolvency work, coinciding as it did with the global recession. She then joined Speechly Bircham LLP (which merged with Charles Russell LLP in 2014 to form Charles Russell Speechlys LLP), for what was supposed to be a six-month contract: "Seven years on, I'm still here – and now a partner!"

Cradle to grave

Hanh explains the way in which the firm occupies a unique place in terms of restructuring and insolvency work, aiming to be a one-stop-shop for clients. "We do both contentious and non-contentious work, so consider our role to be from cradle to grave," she explains. "Stage one is where a company or individual is in financial difficulties and our client – for example, the company's board of directors, shareholders or bank – gets us involved to see if we can restructure or rescue the company, to avoid it going into an insolvency process. In that case, you're looking at ways to avoid the company being wound up or placed into another insolvency process, such as via restructuring its debt or minimising its liabilities. In those cases we work closely with our corporate finance and banking colleagues to see what can be done."

Stage two is when the company moves officially into the relevant insolvency process, and Hanh and her colleagues find themselves usually acting for the office holder that has been appointed as the agent of the company, namely, an insolvency practitioner – for example, Deloitte, KPMG, Duff & Phelps or Grant Thornton: "Our role then is to advise on whatever needs doing, such as selling the business or making employees redundant – whatever needs to be done in order to realise assets for the company's creditors."

The third and final stage can involve pursuing delinquent directors or others who may carry fault for the failure of the company: "The situation may involve fraudulent or questionable conduct by directors, such as stripping the company of assets before it was wound up. We then issue court proceedings to recover assets that rightfully belong to the company. Again, the main objective is to achieve a result for the creditors."

For more firms that work in this practice area, please use the "Training contract regional indexes" starting on p205.

Name: **Hanh Nguyen**
Firm: **Charles Russell Speechlys LLP**
Location: **London**
University: **University of Sydney**
Undergraduate degree: **Commerce and law**

Variety is the spice

This full-service offering means work is never dull and the chance to work internally with many of the firm's different teams is a key feature of her practice: "No two days are the same. I work with our corporate finance, employment, banking and private client colleagues, which keeps thing interesting. I'm not an expert in any of these areas, I have to be aware of them and liaise with colleagues accordingly. Compared to other firms that might just do contentious or non-contentious work, we have always thought it was useful to have both skill sets, even though my preference is probably for the advisory and transaction work."

There is also satisfaction to be derived from the variety of clients that Hanh deals with on a daily basis: "It ranges from fellow professionals in accountancy firms to personnel at all manner of different companies. It's good not to get too entrenched with one type of client."

Hanh reflects on some of the challenges that come with being made partner: "It requires a different skill set, namely learning to manage people, supervise and delegate. It's assumed that you're technically sound and competent by this point in your career, but there are new people skills that you can only really learn on the job. Business development and marketing is also part of it – and again, not something that you're taught at uni! Developing long-term relationships with clients is a real skill. Still, I welcome the challenge – BD is encouraged by the firm from a very junior stage, especially developing networks among your peer group, both within and outside of the firm."

There is also real satisfaction from working on matters that non-lawyers can understand. "I like it when I'm involved with something that's in the press or quite high profile, such as the Borders or East Retail insolvencies.

They may not be billion-pound-deals, but it's nice to have some spark of recognition from people, in terms of them understanding what I do. I worked on a case that involved a power plate manufacturer, which friends I talked to found relatable! I also find that friends use me as a sounding board if they want advice about investing; I can offer a different perspective that has been gained by working in restructuring and insolvency, even though sometimes it is all a bit doom and gloom!"

As you might expect, the spectre of Brexit looms large on the horizon, as Hanh describes: "There is a lot of uncertainty ahead. All law firms and accountants can do briefings about what might happen, but who really knows? There might be a decline in investment, fewer exports and imports, but it's all speculation. The key issues facing our area of law and the profession generally will be founded in the outcome of the Brexit negotiations and where that takes us."

Sage advice

Hanh's top tips to would-be lawyers include the need to "research firms well; don't just apply to the top five firms just for the sake of it or because everyone else is." She cites client interaction or being part of a team as two potential motivators and, more broadly, a need to think about what you really want out of your career: "It's a long-term commitment and you have to be certain it's right for you. What are your strengths and are they something that you can apply to a particular practice area or way of working? One example – if the idea of advocacy makes you want to jump out of bed, then life as a barrister could be for you. If it fills you with dread, then it's probably not! Working culture and environment are also important. Listen to what others have to say about the firms you're interested in – it's not just the quality of work, but also the quality of colleagues; a good environment and sound career progression may become more important than massive deals."

Shipping

Shipping law is one of the oldest and most developed branches of commercial law. It falls into two areas: contentious and non-contentious. On the contentious side, 'dry' shipping involves contractual issues such as bill of lading and charterparty disputes, whereas 'wet' shipping tends to involve issues of tort and insurance law (eg, collisions). Non-contentious work includes ship finance (eg, lending and security) and the drafting of commercial agreements (eg, charters and shipbuilding contracts). Whereas the shipping industry is by its nature international, London remains the pre-eminent venue for dispute resolution and marine insurance, and English law is the legal system of choice.

An upbringing split between the seaside town of Brighton and the Caribbean capital of Kingston, Jamaica gave Ceri Done a life-long love of all things aquatic. A keen sailor as a teenager, he initially planned to study marine biology at the University of Plymouth to keep close to the water. Unfortunately, those plans ran aground and after an A-level resit year, he changed tack from science to business. After further considering the maritime section of the UCAS handbook, he settled on a course in maritime business at Plymouth and added on maritime law as an option out of interest.

Ceri's interest in maritime law was indeed piqued and at the end of his second year he undertook a week's work experience at the Plymouth office of Davies Johnson & Co, which helped to cement that interest. On graduating from Plymouth, he was awarded the maritime law prize and then undertook a further three years of study, reading for an undergraduate degree in law at University College London. To give himself the best chance of securing a training contract with a maritime firm and to gain some valuable experience, he then spent a year and a half with a niche professional indemnity insurer before moving to a leading maritime insurer, where he remained for the next few years.

It was during his time at the latter insurer that he came to know Thomas Cooper (then Thomas Cooper & Stibbard) and in September 2007 he joined as a trainee, qualifying in 2009 and becoming partner in 2014: "It perhaps took me slightly longer than my contemporaries to secure a training contract in my chosen area and I did so via a somewhat circuitous route. However, the experience I gained from working in the maritime insurance sector stood me in good stead. When I joined Thomas Cooper as a trainee, I had both academic and industry experience of their core practice area, which definitely gave me a head start and helped me get on both as a trainee and as a junior solicitor post qualification."

> ** Shipping is a fast-paced and technically complex area of law, where your advice can have a bearing on operational and commercial decisions taken by clients in real time **

Industry insight
Today, Ceri's work predominantly revolves around litigation, with a focus on dry shipping contractual disputes arising under charterparty contracts and bills of lading. However, as the firm has a broad contentious practice, he also works in wet shipping, is a member of the firm's emergency response team taking evidence on casualties around the world, and is involved in yacht disputes, sale of goods disputes and international arbitration work.

"One of the great things about shipping is that you can be involved at the genesis of a dispute. Shipping is a fast-paced and technically complex area of law, where your

For more firms that work in this practice area, please use the "Training contract regional indexes" starting on p205.

Name: **Ceri Done**
Firm: **Thomas Cooper LLP**
Location: **London**
University: **University of Plymouth/University College London**
Undergraduate degree: **Maritime business and maritime law/Law**

advice can have a bearing on operational and commercial decisions taken by clients in real time. You therefore need to think fast and to think a few moves ahead, bearing in mind the underlying commercial relationship and the business reasons that brought the parties together in the first place."

Ceri elaborates. "In the context of a casualty, for instance a ship fire, we will be involved from the outset, meaning that I have on occasion found myself on board ships that are still smoking. My task is to find out what happened and how the ship and crew responded. I will typically take an expert with me and will take witness statements from the crew – those statements could be used in litigation years later, so at this stage we still have to give thought to the case the client will potentially bring or face in litigation and the arguments that might be run. That can be quite a challenge, but when gathering evidence we work as a team, with the result that those on the ground are assisted by other members of the Thomas Cooper team back in the office."

Responsibility and initiative
As trainees at Thomas Cooper, prospective lawyers won't be sent out to smoking ships, but they will be expected to roll up their sleeves and get stuck into the work of the firm. Taking responsibility at an early stage is encouraged, as is showing initiative in the conduct of a matter, while working under the close supervision of a partner.

They will also soon discover something else that Ceri enjoys about the area: although there is plenty of law involved, other skills and strengths are also required – not least the ability to digest a lot of technical information and understand the bearing it might have on the client's case as a matter of law: "For instance, if we are instructed on a case where the ship's main engine has broken down, we need to have a

working understanding of the engineering or science involved, helped by the input and guidance of a relevant expert. We then need to consider how the technical or scientific aspects affect the client's case as a matter of law and develop the evidence as appropriate. With this in mind, in addition to the usual trainee tasks of research and drafting, trainees will also be involved in liaising with witnesses, experts and, if the matter develops, counsel. They might also continue working on cases as they move seats and so there is the possibility of seeing a matter through from start to finish."

Those keen to steal a march on the competition and give themselves an advantage when applying for a training contract could do a lot worse than to follow Ceri's lead and spend some time gaining experience within the shipping industry itself. As a starting point, candidates should have an awareness of the industry and the role it plays in international trade, which can be developed by reading the trade press or the business sections of the broadsheets, as more and more shipping stories appear in the mainstream media: "Being able to see and understand how the wider global economy affects the sector is important as that will aid your understanding of at least some of the commercial issues affecting the clients' business."

Sport

Sports law involves the legal issues at play in the worlds of both amateur and professional sport. It overlaps employment, contract, competition and tort law. Defamation, intellectual property and privacy are also integral to sports law.

Emma Mason's journey to life as a lawyer began in the demanding world of international sport – badminton, to be precise. She describes how she converted what she loved about being a professional athlete into a legal career: "I played badminton for Scotland until I retired in 2011, a year after appearing at the Commonwealth Games. I was also the chair of the Athletes' Commission for the Badminton World Federation (BWF), which is the sport's regulatory and governing body at a global level. I had been elected by my peers for a four-year term to represent them on the BWF Council, the highest decision-making body within the BWF. At a similar time, I came to the conclusion that chemistry (which I was studying at the time) wasn't something that I wanted to pursue as a career; although I enjoyed the analytical side of it, I felt that working underground in a lab didn't suit my personality! I loved representing the athletes and making a difference within the industry. During a period of injury and illness, I thought about how I could take the experiences that I'd had in sport and my passion for representing people and make use of them in a new career. It was then that I came across law."

It was a solicitor's, rather than a barrister's, life that attracted Emma: "As an athlete, I had worked for myself for the best part of eight years; the pressure of supporting yourself financially can be a real challenge, particularly when funding and sponsorship monies are almost solely dependent on performance and meeting performance targets, and I was looking for more certainty and structure in my career. Having said that, I do really enjoy public speaking and representing people, but there are still opportunities to do both as a solicitor."

A training contract at Squire Patton Boggs beckoned, in what Emma felt was a particularly good match between firm and trainee. "I don't think I could have found a firm that was more supportive of my background and passions," she suggests. "For example, I still hold a number of positions in international sports politics and the firm is very supportive of that. It's also great that trainees here spend time in six seats, which means that they get a greater range of experience than if they were at most other law firms, which tend to offer the traditional four seats. There is also plenty of opportunity for secondment; I went to a Premier League football club for eight months, which was fantastic and couldn't have been a better choice or fit for me."

Game of two halves

Now qualified as a disputes and regulatory lawyer within the firm's sports and entertainment group, Emma enjoys a mix of contentious and non-contentious work. She describes some of the matters that this entails: "I might be involved with arbitration or dispute resolution proceedings within a sport's governing body – many governing bodies have their own dispute resolution rules – or an appeal to the Court of Arbitration for Sport in Lausanne. The majority of our clients tend to be international federations, national governing bodies, Premier League and EFL clubs, as well as players and/or their agents."

That variety is what keeps things interesting: "The days are never the same. I was working on a really fascinating case yesterday – even though it was a Sunday – whereas on Friday I was less busy, so I wrote an article and worked on business development. I might be out at a client meeting, in the office working on technical arguments, writing something for our sports blog, Sports Shorts, or public speaking. The good thing about sports law is that everyone is incredibly passionate about the industry."

For more firms that work in this practice area, please use the "Training contract regional indexes" starting on p205.

Name: **Emma Mason**
Firm: **Squire Patton Boggs (UK) LLP**
Location: **London**
University: **University of Glasgow**
Undergraduate degree: **Chemistry**

As you might imagine for someone with a love of sport, two secondments to football clubs have been career highlights for Emma – the first as a trainee to a Premier League club and the second as a qualified lawyer to an EFL club. She says: "I absolutely loved the experience of working for a football club. Another football-related highlight was when I was a trainee in our corporate team, acting on the sale of my dad's favourite football team. I couldn't talk about it until the deal went through, but the moment it went public, I told him straightaway!"

Having had prior experience of an industry keen to embrace digital technologies and new media, Emma would like to see the legal industry as a whole adopt a more innovative approach: "I feel that the profession doesn't yet use new technologies to maximise its efficiency. I'm aware that the profession has many important procedures and protections for clients that shouldn't be compromised. However, if we don't modernise, at least on the administration side, we may risk losing clients who are, after all, constantly looking for ways in which technology can improve their business. We need to make sure that we communicate with them on their level."

In terms of a shifting landscape, Emma also notes the significant increase in regulation and legalisation of sport and a commensurate appetite from regulators to enforce their rules. "Over the past 20 years, sport has become much more commercial and professional, and it's not just footballers who can earn a good living," she observes. "As more money is involved, sponsors and investors, including the public, demand higher standards and greater accountability. This has, to a certain extent, been catalysed by failures within some high-profile institutions, including recent corruption scandals, which in some ways has been good in that it has forced change. Our clients must ensure that they comply with everything."

Hone your skills

Over and above the absolutely essential need for solid legal expertise, Emma thinks that there are a couple of other key skills you need to succeed in this field: "You must be able to communicate – especially within sport, as your typical client will likely be an exceptionally busy person who is passionate about their business and working within the all-encompassing sport bubble. If you can't communicate with them or understand their business and the pressures they're under, you won't have the same connection that you could have." And it goes without saying that it helps to be passionate about sport: "You don't have to have been a professional sportsperson – I don't want to put anyone off! You just need to have sufficient interest so that your clients feel that you have a mutual understanding about what's important. You also need to know that this isn't a job, it's a lifestyle. I went from one all-consuming lifestyle to another, and it works for me, but some may be unprepared for that."

Finally, Emma urges those considering a legal career to have a good, hard think about what they want from it: "This is a long career and you have to choose a job and firm that aligns with your own personal brand and what matters to you. I had a training contract offer at a magic circle firm, which I chose not to accept because I knew that it wasn't the right environment for me. Don't be swayed by money or reputation; that is likely to come back to haunt you further down the line."

Part of the process of figuring out what is right for you is gaining experience: "Take every opportunity that you come across, especially in the early years – soak it all up. Have faith in yourself – don't be afraid to put yourself forward for things. In my badminton days, you had to fight hard to earn your position in the top squad, so everyone – trainees included – should push themselves forward."

Technology, media and telecommunications

Technology, media and telecommunications (TMT) is one of the fastest-developing sectors of the legal market. The constant evolution of technology pushes legal boundaries and begs for the provision of innovative legal advice. In advising their clients, TMT lawyers are required not only to apply black letter law, but also to take into account market developments, regulatory considerations, and commercial and technical issues. Outsourcing continues to be a particularly hot topic.

It is probably a stretch to describe his decision to become a lawyer as a Damascene conversion, but physics graduate Mark Watts's entry into the profession was certainly sudden. "When I was starting out in my career around 1991, Bristows ran a now-legendary job advert in *New Scientist*, which didn't say anything – not even the firm's name – except to pose the question, 'Have you ever thought about becoming a lawyer?' with a phone number underneath," he recalls. "Like many of the lawyers who joined Bristows at that time, I was a *New Scientist* reader and I saw the ad and called the number – the next thing I knew, I had a training contract. Perhaps I should have also explored the Bar, but the way I joined the profession – by responding to that ad – meant that this never came into it."

Historically, Bristows has always attracted a very healthy proportion of lawyers with science and engineering backgrounds, as well as prior expertise in other fields besides law more generally. Mark enjoyed the new environment he found himself in: "It was a lot more sociable than my PhD! I had a gang of physics mates, but it also wasn't unusual for me to spend long nights on my own in the laboratory. One of the reasons I was interested in changing to the legal profession was that the work is more based around people."

Data privacy

After qualifying, Mark left Bristows for a spell in an in-house legal department, but returned to the firm in 2003. Since then, he has been able to develop highly specialist know-how. "I would still describe myself as a commercial IT lawyer and I used to have a very broad practice," he explains. "I handled outsourcing, online and data matters – anything to do with computers, really. As the group has become more successful, with lots of work coming in, we have been able to expand the department, which now has five partners. This has enabled me to specialise further, so these days most of my work is to do with data privacy."

Clearly, data privacy is a huge issue and looks set to remain a defining one of the first half of the 21st century. The range of matters that Mark advises on therefore directly affect how business, politics and society work. "We advise big technology companies – particularly online providers such as Google, Twitter and Spotify – on how to comply with the law. This may sound obvious, but for the companies that I have described, it can mean advising them on their product development," he explains. "This is where having a 'techy' background comes in handy, as you wouldn't be able to advise some of these companies without knowing, say, what an API or a cookie is. Sometimes to help our clients, we have to sit down with their engineers and brainstorm how the product should be developed so that it both does what they want and sufficiently meets the legal requirements."

Mark identifies two other broad categories into which to divide his work. "Another aspect of our practice involves advising big multinationals that may operate in hundreds of different countries. Some countries have similar laws in this area, while others have none at all. It is complicated to say the least, so we work with those multinationals

For more firms that work in this practice area, please use the "Training contract regional indexes" starting on p205.

Name: **Mark Watts**
Firm: **Bristows LLP**
Location: **London**
University: **University of Oxford**
Undergraduate degree: **Physics**

to ensure that they comply with the law everywhere that they do business in a way that is consistent and that doesn't drive everyone crazy by trying to match every particular legal requirement in every country."

The final area is a form of litigation. "Data privacy is a regulatory area of law, which means that there are regulators – data protection authorities – which have the task of enforcing the law and which will therefore try to fine organisations which are not meeting those requirements," he explains. "If a big client has a data breach – and if you watch the news, you will know that these do happen – we will typically be involved in helping to defend the client from enforcement action."

Ground-breaking cases

Mark has already been involved in two defining data privacy cases. "Some of the team here worked on the *Google v Costella* 'right to be forgotten' case, a historic case that was amazing to be a part of, really," he reflects. "But perhaps the biggest high point of my career was the *Google Street View* case in 2010, a vast piece of international litigation involving all of Europe, the United States, Korea – it was incredible. I spoke to the client every day for three or four hours, for about nine months straight. It was the most intense period of work that I have experienced and the case still probably remains one of the biggest privacy cases that there has ever been."

One of the biggest challenges of the job is managing the tension between the law and the practical reality of constantly advancing mass-market technology. "The law as it stands today was written in the mid-1990s, when there was the Internet, but no worldwide web, apps, social media, big data or cloud computing," explains Mark. "All of these things have become a fact of life for most organisations, but the law overseeing them was made when they were not yet invented. From May 2018, a new data protection law – the General Data

Protection Regulation (GDPR) – will replace the old one. The GDPR was written to be more relevant to modern technology, but unfortunately it is in many ways worse, in my opinion, because it is just not reflective of modern life, where information exchanges are going on every second, all over the world."

Complete package

Nonetheless, there is nothing else that Mark would rather be doing: "It is a really interesting – almost perfect – intersection of things that I find interesting. There is a lot of technology involved, as well as a lot of law because I'm involved in the regulatory side of things. It might sound obvious to say that the job involves a lot of law, but that is actually not the case in other areas of IT law. There is also a big commercial aspect to the role, as well as a human rights dimension in the right to privacy. Plus I work with great people – the technology clients I work with tend to attract the kind of people who are easy to get on with."

Looking at the commercial side of the solicitors' profession more widely, Mark expresses concern at the long-hours cultures evident at some firms: "Many law firms make people work too hard, creating an 'hours culture' that can be just brutal. The danger for the profession is that careers at those law firms become unsustainable, where lawyers will work like that for a couple of years before getting out. It's not a healthy norm for the profession."

And those interested in becoming technology lawyers should bear in mind the following advice: "To be a good privacy lawyer or IT lawyer, you need an interest in technology and a level of curiosity and inquisitiveness. You also need to be pragmatic and able to get on with people. It is not the case that lawyers sit in their offices and the work just comes in – it's all about networks and meeting people. And far from being a downside, if you like meeting and working with people, it is a great career to be in."

Training contract directory

How to use the training contract regional indexes and directory

Solicitors' regional indexes

These tables are designed to allow you to shortlist firms by particular criteria. Further information about each firm is contained within the training contract directory.

The tables detail:
- the number of annual vacancies at the firm (unless a particular year has been specified);
- the number of partners (which generally includes equity and salaried partners) and total staff;
- whether work placement schemes are available; and
- up to five general practice and 19 specialisation work areas.

Firms that claim to have an office in a particular region are listed from A to Z in the appropriate regional table.

For the purposes of the indexes we have used the 10 standard economic planning regions of Great Britain (not including Scotland), and London is dealt with separately. There is also a table for the Channel Islands and the Isle of Man, and an international table.

Please note, the following abbreviations have been used for the specialisation work areas:
- 'Banking' refers to Banking and finance;
- 'Property' refers to Commercial property; and
- 'Comp/comm' refers to Company/commercial.

It should be noted that the information has been provided by the firms themselves and has generally not been verified by us. We do not, therefore, claim that the information is fully accurate and comprehensive, only that it can be used as a starting point for shortlisting appropriate firms. Furthermore, although we have attempted to contact every firm that is authorised to provide training contracts, not all firms that take trainees have supplied their details.

Training contract directory

The directory contains contact information and a brief practice description for all firms that are authorised to offer training contracts by the SRA and have supplied us with their details. It is therefore an essential reference guide to firms that offer work placement schemes, training contracts and funding.

The basic entry includes the firm's application address (not necessarily its main office), telephone number, email address, the applications contact and a brief description of the firm, together with the number of vacancies per year (unless a particular year is specified), the number of current trainees, partners and total staff, and whether the firm offers work placement schemes. Firms with a more detailed directory entry appear in bold in the regional indexes.

Every effort has been made to collate accurate information from all firms that are authorised to provide training contracts and we are confident that the directory is the most comprehensive of its kind. However, as TCPH is published in October and firms may change their information at any point, we recommend that you double check key information on firms' own websites. Deadlines can also be checked on www.LawCareers.Net.

These resources should be used in conjunction with the section on law firm practice areas, which features in-depth interviews with numerous solicitors who are keen to pass on their advice about making it in the legal profession.

Training contract regional indexes

Channel Islands

	Vacancies	Partners	Total staff	Work placement	Corporate/ commercial	General commercial	Niche	General practice	High street/ legal aid
Cains Advocates Limited	2	9	50	✔	•	•	•		
Collas Crill	3(18)	33	183		•			•	

East Anglia

	Vacancies	Partners	Total staff	Work placement	Corporate/ commercial	General commercial	Niche	General practice	High street/ legal aid
Accutrainee	Varies				•	•	•	•	
Adlams LLP	0	4	23	✔				•	•
Ashtons Legal	4(19)	30	300	✔	•	•	•	•	
Barker Gotelee	0	8	54					•	
Birkett Long LLP	0	24	175	✔	•	•		•	
Birketts LLP	7	59	504	✔	•				
Buckles Solicitors LLP	2	14	100		•	•		•	
Chamberlins	0	5	32					•	•
Chelmsford Borough Council	0		16				•		
Cozens-Hardy LLP	1(18)	13	70			•		•	
Crown Prosecution Service	1(18)		5974				•		
Cunningtons	Varies	9	60	✔				•	•
Edmondson Hall	0	3	20	✔		•	•		
Ellisons	1(19)	17	160					•	
England & Co	0	6	25					•	•
Eversheds Sutherland (International) LLP	50	395	3215	✔	•	•			
Fisher Jones Greenwood Solicitors	0	21	143		•	•	•	•	•
Fosters	0	13	130					•	•
Goody Burrett LLP	1(19)	4	30	✔	•			•	•
Gotelee	0	20	127		•			•	
Greenwoods Solicitors LLP	3	8	100	✔	•	•			
Gross & Co	0	5	28		•	•	•	•	
Hayes + Storr	2	13	105		•	•			
Her Majesty's Courts & Tribunals Service	0		1200					•	
Hewitsons LLP	15	46	243	✔	•	•	•	•	
Hilliers HRW	0	2	32		•	•			
Holmes & Hills	0	6	95		•	•			
Hood Vores & Allwood	0	5	25					•	
Howes Percival LLP	8	43	229	✔	•	•			
Hunt and Coombs Solicitors	2	8	85			•		•	•
Irena Spence & Co	1	4	24	✔				•	•

Banking	Comp/comm	Competition	Construction	Corporate tax	Crime	Dispute resolution	Employment	Environment	Family	Human rights	Insurance	IP	Personal injury	Private client	Property	Shipping	Sport	TMT
•	•					•	•				•	•		•	•	•		•
•	•			•		•	•				•	•		•	•			•

Banking	Comp/comm	Competition	Construction	Corporate tax	Crime	Dispute resolution	Employment	Environment	Family	Human rights	Insurance	IP	Personal injury	Private client	Property	Shipping	Sport	TMT
•	•	•	•	•		•	•	•	•		•	•	•	•	•	•	•	•
	•						•		•				•	•	•			
	•		•	•		•	•	•	•				•	•	•		•	•
•	•					•		•	•					•				
•	•	•	•	•		•	•	•	•	•		•	•	•	•		•	•
•	•	•	•	•	•	•	•	•	•			•		•	•	•		•
	•		•			•	•		•			•	•	•	•		•	•
	•					•	•		•				•	•	•			
	•					•	•		•				•	•	•			
					•													
	•					•	•		•				•	•	•			
	•					•	•		•		•		•	•	•		•	
	•					•	•		•				•	•	•			
	•					•	•		•					•	•			
•	•	•	•	•		•	•	•			•	•	•	•	•	•	•	•
	•				•	•	•		•	•			•	•	•			•
	•			•		•	•		•				•	•	•			
	•					•	•		•				•	•	•			
	•			•	•	•	•		•				•	•	•			
•	•	•	•	•		•	•	•					•	•	•		•	•
	•								•					•	•			
	•					•	•		•			•	•	•	•			
•	•	•	•	•		•	•	•				•	•	•	•		•	•
	•		•	•		•	•		•				•	•	•			
	•		•			•	•	•	•				•	•	•			
	•					•	•						•	•	•			
•	•	•	•	•		•	•	•	•			•	•	•	•		•	•
	•	•			•	•	•	•	•	•		•	•	•	•			•
						•	•						•	•	•			

	Vacancies	Partners	Total staff	Work placement	Corporate/ commercial	General commercial	Niche	General practice	High street/ legal aid
Irwin Mitchell	45	269	2700	✔	•	•		•	
Jeremy Roberts & Co	1	1	8	✔				•	
Kennedys	16	245	1700	✔	•	•			
Lawtons Solicitors	2(18)	2	25						•
Leathes Prior	1-4	13	100	✔	•	•	•	•	
Malletts	1	3	30	✔	•			•	•
Metcalfe Copeman & Pettefar	1(18)	15	120			•	•	•	•
Mills & Reeve LLP	18	117	800	✔	•	•			
Morgan Jones & Pett	0	3	23					•	
Nockolds	3(19)	13	140	✔	•	•		•	
Palmers	0	8	90	✔	•	•		•	
Park Woodfine Heald Mellows LLP	0	7	60			•		•	•
Paul Robinson Solicitors LLP	1	9	85		•			•	•
Penningtons Manches LLP	12-14	110	600	✔	•	•		•	
Plexus Law	0	117	1800				•		
Prettys	3-4	6	75	✔	•	•	•	•	
Ronaldsons	1	1	10				•		•
Roythornes Solicitors	6(19)	26	187	✔	•	•	•	•	
The Sethi Partnership Solicitors	1	3	25	✔	•	•		•	
Shoosmiths	20	175	1550	✔	•	•	•	•	
Steeles Law LLP	1-3	8	80	✔	•	•	•	•	
Stone King	4	33	197	✔	•	•	•	•	
Taylor Vinters LLP	6	26	170	✔	•	•	•	•	
Tees Law	3	20	240	✔				•	
Terrells LLP	1	2	18						•
Thompson Smith and Puxon	Poss	11	75		•	•	•	•	
Thomson Webb & Corfield	1(18)	9	39		•			•	
Tollers Solicitors	4	19	138		•	•		•	
Ward Gethin Archer	1(19)	16	149		•	•		•	
Watson Legal	1(18)	1	2	✔				•	
Wilkinson & Butler	0	4	20					•	•
Woodfines LLP	3(19)	20	152	✔	•	•		•	

Banking	Comp/comm	Competition	Construction	Corporate tax	Crime	Dispute resolution	Employment	Environment	Family	Human rights	Insurance	IP	Personal injury	Private client	Property	Shipping	Sport	TMT
•	•	•	•	•	•	•	•	•	•	•	•	•	•	•	•			•
					•		•		•					•				
•	•		•			•	•	•			•	•	•		•	•	•	
					•													
•	•		•		•	•	•		•	•			•	•	•		•	
	•				•	•			•					•			•	
	•				•	•	•		•				•	•	•			
•	•	•	•	•		•	•	•	•			•	•	•	•		•	•
									•					•				
	•					•	•		•				•	•	•	•		•
	•		•	•	•	•	•		•				•	•	•			•
	•	•	•			•			•				•	•	•			
	•				•	•			•				•	•	•			
•	•		•	•		•			•				•	•	•		•	•
		•				•					•		•					
	•	•	•	•		•	•	•	•			•		•	•	•	•	•
									•					•				
	•		•	•		•	•	•	•				•	•	•			
	•				•	•	•		•				•	•	•			•
•	•	•	•	•		•	•	•	•			•	•	•	•	•	•	•
•	•	•	•	•		•	•	•	•		•	•	•	•			•	•
	•		•			•	•		•			•		•	•			•
	•	•		•		•	•	•	•			•	•	•	•			•
	•					•	•	•	•		•	•	•	•	•			
									•				•	•				
	•		•			•	•		•				•	•	•			
	•				•	•	•		•					•	•			
•	•	•	•			•	•		•				•	•	•			
	•				•	•	•	•	•				•	•	•			
						•	•		•					•	•			
			•															
	•	•	•		•	•	•	•	•				•	•	•			•

East Midlands

	Vacancies	Partners	Total staff	Work placement	Corporate/ commercial	General commercial	Niche	General practice	High street/ legal aid
Accutrainee	Varies				•	•	•	•	
Actons	2[19]	15	70		•	•		•	
Atteys Solicitors	2	3	48	✔	•				•
Banner Jones	0	10	90					•	•
Beetenson & Gibbon Solicitors	0	5	30					•	•
Bhatia Best	0	11	128					•	•
BHW Solicitors	2-4[19]	8	50	✔				•	
Bilton Hammond	0	6	35	✔				•	•
Bird & Co Solicitors LLP	0	4	50					•	
BLM	25	210	1700	✔		•			
Bray & Bray	1	12	95					•	
Bridge McFarland	2[18]	25	167	✔	•	•		•	•
Browne Jacobson LLP	20	115	964	✔	•	•	•		
Bryan and Armstrong	0	4	21					•	•
Buckles Solicitors LLP	2	14	100		•	•		•	
Burton & Burton Solicitors Ltd	0-1	4	20					•	•
Burton & Co LLP	0	5	40	✔	•	•		•	
Cartwright King	0	26	280					•	•
Cocks Lloyd	0	10	50		•			•	•
Crown Prosecution Service	1[18]		5974				•		
Emery Johnson Astills	0	5	45	✔			•	•	•
Eversheds Sutherland (International) LLP	50	395	3215	✔	•	•			
Fishers	0	5	38		•	•	•	•	
Franklins Solicitors LLP	0	14	100	✔	•	•		•	
Fraser Brown	0	16	93		•	•		•	
Freeths LLP	20	135	750		•	•		•	
Gateley Plc	14	150	802	✔	•	•			
Geldards LLP	6[19]	57	352		•	•	•		
Greenwoods Solicitors LLP	3	8	100	✔	•	•			
Hatton	1-2	1	6	✔			•		
Her Majesty's Courts & Tribunals Service	0		1200					•	
Hewitsons LLP	15	46	243	✔	•	•	•	•	
Howes Percival LLP	8	43	229	✔	•	•			
HSR Law	0	7	42		•	•		•	•
Jeremy Roberts & Co	1	1	8	✔				•	
JH Powell & Co	0	6	20		•	•		•	
Johar & Co	1	2	25					•	•
The Johnson Partnership	1-2	13	110	✔			•		
Langleys Solicitors LLP	5	34	340	✔	•	•		•	•
M & S Solicitors Limited	0	3	10		•		•		
Marrons	1	7	30				•		

Banking	Comp/comm	Competition	Construction	Corporate tax	Crime	Dispute resolution	Employment	Environment	Family	Human rights	Insurance	IP	Personal injury	Private client	Property	Shipping	Sport	TMT
•	•	•	•	•		•	•	•	•			•	•	•	•	•	•	•
	•					•	•		•		•		•	•	•			
	•					•	•						•	•	•			
	•				•	•	•		•				•	•	•			
							•						•		•			
					•				•	•			•	•	•			
	•					•	•		•				•	•	•			•
					•				•					•	•			
	•					•	•		•				•	•	•			
			•			•	•	•	•		•		•		•		•	
	•		•		•	•	•		•				•	•	•			
	•		•	•		•	•		•				•	•	•		•	
•	•	•	•	•		•	•	•	•		•		•	•	•		•	•
	•					•	•		•				•	•	•			
	•		•			•	•		•				•	•	•		•	•
	•					•	•		•				•	•	•			
	•				•	•	•		•	•			•	•	•			
						•	•	•	•					•				
	•					•	•	•	•				•	•	•			
					•										•			
					•				•				•		•			
•	•	•	•	•		•	•	•			•	•		•	•	•	•	•
	•		•			•	•	•	•		•		•	•	•			
	•					•	•		•				•	•	•			•
•	•		•			•	•		•			•	•	•	•			
•	•	•	•	•		•	•	•	•	•	•	•	•	•	•		•	•
•	•	•	•	•		•	•	•	•			•	•	•	•	•	•	•
•	•		•	•		•	•		•		•	•	•	•	•		•	•
•	•	•	•	•		•	•		•			•	•	•	•		•	•
•	•		•	•	•	•	•	•	•	•	•		•	•	•			
•	•	•	•	•		•	•	•				•		•	•		•	•
•	•	•	•	•		•	•	•	•			•	•	•	•		•	•
	•					•	•		•				•	•	•			
					•		•		•				•					
	•		•			•	•		•				•		•	•		•
					•	•	•		•	•			•	•	•			
					•													
•	•		•	•		•	•		•		•	•	•	•	•			
	•					•	•						•		•	•	•	
	•					•		•							•			

	Vacancies	Partners	Total staff	Work placement	Corporate/ commercial	General commercial	Niche	General practice	High street/ legal aid
Matrix Solicitors	0	1	7	✔	•		•		
Moosa-Duke Solicitors	1(18)	2	11	✔			•		
Nelsons	0	48	193		•	•		•	•
Oldham Marsh Page Flavell	Poss	3	30					•	•
Paragon Law Limited	0	2	30	✔	•		•		•
Park Woodfine Heald Mellows LLP	0	7	60			•		•	•
Phillips	0-1	2	9						•
QualitySolicitors Davisons	0	7	150					•	
Robinsons	0	7	61		•	•		•	
Roythornes Solicitors	6(19)	26	187	✔	•	•	•	•	
Shacklocks LLP	2-4(18)	7	35					•	
Shakespeare Martineau LLP	10	130	850		•				
Sharp Young & Pearce	0-1	10	65					•	
Shoosmiths	20	175	1550	✔	•	•	•	•	
Sills & Betteridge LLP	2(19)	43	265	✔	•	•		•	•
Slater & Gordon (UK) LLP	53	86	3500			•		•	
Smith Partnership	4	28	250		•	•	•	•	•
Spearing Waite LLP	2-4(19)	21	98		•	•		•	
Talbot & Co	1	1	20	✔	•	•		•	
Tallents Solicitors	0	5	51					•	•
Taylor Rose TTKW	1-2	13	250		•	•	•	•	
Thaliwal & Co Solicitors	0	1	11	✔			•		
Thompsons Solicitors	0	50	888				•		
Tinn Criddle & Co	0	4	10					•	
Tollers Solicitors	4	19	138		•	•		•	
Vincent Sykes	0	1	6			•		•	
Vincent Sykes & Higham LLP	0	4	26					•	
Weightmans LLP	Up to 18	187	1306	✔	•	•	•		
Wilson Browne Solicitors	0	16	118		•			•	
Woodfines LLP	3(19)	20	152	✔	•	•		•	
Young & Pearce	1	8	33	✔		•	•	•	•

Banking	Comp/comm	Competition	Construction	Corporate tax	Crime	Dispute resolution	Employment	Environment	Family	Human rights	Insurance	IP	Personal injury	Private client	Property	Shipping	Sport	TMT
	•					•		•				•	•	•	•			
•	•	•	•	•		•	•		•	•	•	•	•	•	•		•	•
					•		•		•					•	•			
														•				
	•	•	•			•	•		•				•	•	•			
					•				•									
						•	•		•				•	•	•			
	•	•				•	•		•			•	•	•	•			•
	•		•	•		•	•	•	•				•	•	•			
	•					•	•		•				•	•	•			
•	•	•	•	•		•	•	•	•		•	•	•	•	•			•
	•					•	•		•				•	•	•			
•	•	•	•			•	•	•	•		•	•	•	•	•	•	•	•
•	•			•	•	•	•	•	•			•	•	•	•			
			•		•	•	•		•			•	•	•	•			•
	•		•	•	•	•	•		•	•		•	•	•	•		•	
•	•	•	•			•	•		•			•	•	•	•		•	•
	•					•	•		•				•	•	•			
		•			•	•	•		•				•	•	•			
•	•					•							•	•				
					•		•						•					
	•													•				
•	•	•	•			•	•		•			•	•	•	•			
	•						•		•			•	•	•	•			
	•							•				•	•	•	•			
•	•	•	•	•	•	•	•	•	•		•	•	•	•	•	•	•	•
	•					•	•		•			•	•	•	•			
	•	•	•		•	•	•	•	•			•	•	•	•			•
	•				•	•	•		•				•	•	•			•

	Vacancies	Partners	Total staff	Work placement	Corporate/ commercial	General commercial	Niche	General practice	High street/ legal aid
Addleshaw Goddard	37	240	1500	✔	•				
Allen & Overy LLP		530	5300	✔	•				
Anglo-Thai Legal (ATL)	Varies	1	5	✔			•	•	
Arnold & Porter Kaye Scholer LLP	2	28	126	✔	•	•	•		
Ashurst LLP	40-45	400	3100	✔	•				
Baker McKenzie	30	90	891	✔	•				
Beale & Company Solicitors LLP	5-6[19]	23	120		•	•	•		
Berwin Leighton Paisner	40	200	1417	✔	•	•			
Bird & Bird	18	298	3000	✔	•				
Brown Rudnick LLP	3[18]	29	100		•				
Cains Advocates Limited	2	9	50	✔	•	•	•		
Charles Russell Speechlys	24	148	1001	✔	•	•		•	
Cleary Gottlieb Steen & Hamilton LLP	15-20	193	2500	✔	•				
Clifford Chance	Up to 80	567	6021	✔	•	•			
Clyde & Co LLP	45-50	375	3600	✔	•	•			
CMS Cameron McKenna Nabarro Olswang LLP	65	1000	7500	✔	•	•			
Collyer Bristow LLP	4-5[19]	30	138	✔	•	•		•	
Covington & Burling LLP	8	283		✔	•	•	•	•	
Curtis Mallet-Prevost Colt & Mosle LLP	0	4	14		•				
DAC Beachcroft	13[19]	240	2300	✔	•	•		•	
Davis Polk & Wardwell London LLP	Approx 4	10	90	✔	•				
Debevoise & Plimpton LLP	8-10	19	215	✔	•			•	
Dechert LLP	10	312	2295	✔	•				
DLA Piper UK LLP	Up to 70	1300	8500	✔	•				
Dorsey	2	14	45		•				
Eversheds Sutherland (International) LLP	50	395	3215	✔	•	•			
Faegre Baker Daniels LLP	2	7	40	✔	•	•			
Fieldfisher	18	223	986	✔	•	•			
Freshfields Bruckhaus Deringer LLP	80	391	4960	✔	•				
Gateley Plc	14	150	802	✔	•	•			
Gide Loyrette Nouel LLP	4	6	42				•		
Greenberg Traurig LLP	4+[18]	25	105	✔	•				
Herbert Smith Freehills LLP	60	476	4965	✔	•				
HFW	15	161	840	✔	•	•	•		
Hill Dickinson LLP	14	132	1000	✔	•	•	•		
Ince & Co LLP	10	100	550	✔	•		•		
Jones Day	20	60	350	✔	•				
K&L Gates LLP	TBD	55	244	✔	•	•			
Kennedys	16	245	1700	✔	•	•			
Kirkland & Ellis International LLP	10	850	3811	✔	•				

Banking	Comp/comm	Competition	Construction	Corporate tax	Crime	Dispute resolution	Employment	Environment	Family	Human rights	Insurance	IP	Personal injury	Private client	Property	Shipping	Sport	TMT
•	•	•	•	•		•	•	•			•	•		•	•		•	•
•	•	•	•	•		•	•	•			•	•			•			•
	•	•		•	•	•	•		•	•		•	•	•	•			
•	•	•		•	•	•	•					•	•		•			•
•	•	•		•		•	•				•	•			•			•
•	•	•	•	•		•	•	•			•	•		•	•			•
	•	•		•		•	•	•			•	•			•			•
•	•	•	•	•		•	•	•			•	•		•	•	•	•	•
•	•	•	•	•		•	•	•			•	•			•		•	•
•	•			•	•	•					•	•						
•	•					•	•				•	•		•	•	•		•
•	•	•	•	•		•	•	•	•		•	•		•	•		•	•
•	•	•		•		•	•				•	•						•
•	•	•	•	•		•	•	•			•	•		•	•	•		•
•	•	•	•	•		•	•	•			•	•	•		•	•		•
•	•	•	•	•		•	•	•			•	•			•		•	•
•	•	•		•		•	•		•		•	•		•	•		•	•
•	•	•		•		•	•				•	•			•		•	•
•	•					•						•						
•	•	•	•	•		•	•	•			•	•	•		•			•
•	•	•	•	•		•	•				•				•			
•	•	•	•	•		•					•							•
•	•	•	•	•		•	•				•	•			•			•
•	•	•		•		•	•					•		•	•			•
•	•	•	•	•		•	•	•			•	•		•	•	•	•	•
	•	•		•		•						•			•			•
•	•	•	•	•		•	•	•			•	•		•	•	•	•	•
•	•	•		•		•	•					•			•			•
•	•	•	•	•		•	•				•	•	•	•	•		•	•
•	•	•	•	•		•	•	•			•	•			•	•	•	•
•	•	•	•	•		•	•	•	•			•		•	•	•	•	•
•				•		•									•			
•	•	•		•		•	•	•				•			•			•
•	•	•	•	•		•	•	•			•	•		•	•			•
•	•	•	•			•	•	•			•		•		•		•	
•	•	•	•	•	•	•	•	•	•		•	•	•	•	•	•	•	•
	•	•				•					•					•		
•	•	•	•	•		•	•	•			•	•			•			•
•	•	•	•	•	•	•	•	•			•	•			•		•	•
•	•	•		•		•	•	•			•	•	•		•		•	
•	•	•		•		•						•						

	Vacancies	Partners	Total staff	Work placement	Corporate/commercial	General commercial	Niche	General practice	High street/legal aid
Latham & Watkins	24	75	530	✔	•				
Lewis Silkin	Up to 6	59	343	✔	•	•			
Linklaters LLP	110	450	5200	✔	•				
Magrath LLP	2[18]	8	65		•	•	•		
Malik Legal Solicitors Ltd	4	3	14	✔			•		
Mayer Brown International LLP	15	86	460	✔	•	•			
McGuireWoods London LLP	1	15	61					•	
Milbank Tweed Hadley & McCloy	5	23	165	✔	•				
Morgan, Lewis & Bockius UK LLP	6-8	34	100	✔	•	•			
Norton Rose Fulbright	Up to 45	1180	7100	✔	•	•			
Obaseki	1[19]	3	11	✔		•		•	
O'Melveny	Up to 3	7	50	✔	•				
Orrick, Herrington & Sutcliffe (UK) LLP	6-8	30	160		•				
Osborne Clarke LLP	20	213	1370	✔	•	•	•		
Paragon Law Limited	0	2	30	✔	•			•	•
Paul Hastings	6	27	150	✔	•				
Pinsent Masons LLP	72	420	3000	✔	•	•			
Reed Smith	25	681	3232	✔	•				
RPC	12	81	760	✔	•	•			
Shearman & Sterling (London) LLP	Approx 17	35	300	✔	•				
Sidley Austin LLP	12	43	260	✔	•				
Simmons & Simmons LLP	30	250	1600	✔	•	•			
Skadden, Arps, Slate, Meagher & Flom (UK) LLP	Approx 10	31	235	✔	•				
Slaughter and May	80	115	1100	✔	•	•			
Squire Patton Boggs (UK) LLP	25	500	2600	✔	•	•			
Stephenson Harwood LLP	18	150	900	✔	•				
Sullivan & Cromwell LLP	4-6	21	154	✔	•				
Systech Solicitors Limited	0		25				•		
Taylor Vinters LLP	6	26	170	✔	•	•		•	•
Taylor Wessing	20	400	1800	✔	•	•			
Thomas Cooper LLP	Up to 3	28	103		•			•	
TLT LLP	Up to 15	115	1020	✔	•	•		•	•
Travers Smith LLP	25	77	604	✔	•	•			
Trowers & Hamlins LLP	23	161	903	✔	•				
Vinson & Elkins RLLP	4	15	79	✔	•				
Watson Farley & Williams LLP	18	155	850	✔	•	•			
Weil, Gotshal & Manges (London) LLP	15	33	297	✔	•				
White & Case LLP	50	101	828	✔	•				
Withers LLP	11	167	1000	✔	•		•	•	

Banking	Comp/comm	Competition	Construction	Corporate tax	Crime	Dispute resolution	Employment	Environment	Family	Human rights	Insurance	IP	Personal injury	Private client	Property	Shipping	Sport	TMT
•	•	•		•		•	•	•				•			•			•
	•		•	•		•	•					•			•		•	•
•	•	•	•	•		•	•	•			•	•			•			•
	•					•	•											
	•				•	•			•	•			•	•				
•	•	•	•	•		•	•	•			•	•			•			•
•	•	•		•		•	•	•				•		•	•			
•	•	•		•		•	•					•			•		•	
•	•	•		•		•	•					•						•
•	•	•	•	•		•	•	•				•			•	•		•
			•			•			•						•			
•	•			•		•	•								•			•
•	•	•		•		•	•					•			•			
•	•	•	•	•		•	•	•				•		•				•
														•				
•	•			•		•	•								•			•
•	•	•	•	•		•	•	•			•	•			•	•	•	•
•	•	•	•	•		•	•	•			•	•			•	•		•
•	•	•	•	•		•	•				•	•	•		•			•
•	•	•	•	•		•	•	•				•			•			•
•	•	•		•		•	•				•	•			•			•
•	•	•		•		•	•	•			•	•			•			•
•	•	•		•		•						•						
•	•	•	•	•		•	•	•			•				•		•	•
•	•	•	•	•	•	•	•	•		•	•	•		•	•	•	•	•
•	•	•	•	•		•	•				•	•			•	•		•
•	•	•		•		•	•											
		•				•												
	•	•		•		•	•	•	•			•		•	•			•
•	•	•	•	•		•	•	•			•	•		•	•	•	•	•
•	•	•				•	•				•		•	•		•	•	
•	•	•	•	•		•	•	•	•			•		•	•			•
•	•	•	•	•		•	•	•		•	•	•			•	•	•	•
•	•		•	•		•	•							•	•			
•	•		•	•		•	•											•
•	•	•	•	•		•	•					•			•	•		
•	•	•		•		•	•				•	•			•			•
•	•	•	•	•		•	•					•		•	•			•
•	•	•	•	•		•	•	•	•			•			•	•	•	•

London

	Vacancies	Partners	Total staff	Work placement	Corporate/ commercial	General commercial	Niche	General practice	High street/ legal aid
Abrahams Dresden LLP	2(18)	3	26		•	•	•	•	
ACA Law Ltd	Varies	1	24	✔					•
Accutrainee	Varies				•	•	•	•	
Addleshaw Goddard	37	240	1500	✔	•				
Ahmed & Co	0	2	15						•
Akin Gump Strauss Hauer & Feld	4	37	170	✔	•				
Akin Palmer LLP	1-2	4	10			•			
Allen & Overy LLP		530	5300	✔	•				
Alpha Lexis Law Firm	0	2	8					•	
Anthony Gold Solicitors	3(19)	32	160			•		•	•
Anthony Louca Solicitors	1	3	7				•		•
AP Law Solicitors Ltd	0	2	50	✔	•		•	•	•
AP Solicitors	2	2	6					•	
Arbis Sutherland LLP	1-2	5	18				•		
Archon Solicitors Limited	0	5	19				•		
Arlingtons Sharmas Solicitors	Poss	2	14	✔	•	•		•	
Arnold & Porter Kaye Scholer LLP	2	28	126	✔	•	•	•		
Aschfords Law	1	3	5	✔				•	
Ashfords	9	74	540	✔	•	•		•	
Ashurst LLP	40-45	400	3100	✔	•				
Aston Clark Solicitors	0	3	12					•	•
Atkins Hope	0	4	35	✔				•	•
Avadis & Co Solicitors	1	1	5	✔				•	•
Avery Emerson	2	1	6	✔				•	
Baker McKenzie	30	90	891	✔	•				
Bargate Murray	0	3	11		•		•		
Baron Grey	0	1	9	✔		•		•	
Batchelors	0	14	55			•			
Bates Wells Braithwaite	6	38	248	✔	•	•	•		
Beale & Company Solicitors LLP	5-6(19)	23	120		•	•	•		
Berwin Leighton Paisner	40	200	1417	✔	•	•			
Bevan Brittan LLP	9	58	403	✔	•	•			
Bhatt Murphy	0	2	33	✔			•		
Bhogal Partners Solicitors	1	3	19	✔	•	•		•	
Bindmans LLP	0	14	114					•	•
Bircham Dyson Bell LLP	5	47	280	✔	•	•		•	
Bird & Bird	18	298	3000	✔	•				
Bishop & Sewell LLP	0	9	54		•	•		•	
Blake Morgan LLP	18	101	1000	✔	•	•	•	•	
Blandy & Blandy LLP	2-3	20	104	✔	•	•		•	
Blaser Mills	4	22	125		•	•		•	

Banking	Comp/comm	Competition	Construction	Corporate tax	Crime	Dispute resolution	Employment	Environment	Family	Human rights	Insurance	IP	Personal injury	Private client	Property	Shipping	Sport	TMT
	•					•	•								•			
					•				•	•								
•	•	•	•	•		•	•	•	•		•	•	•	•	•	•	•	•
•	•	•	•	•		•	•	•			•	•			•		•	•
			•															
•	•	•	•	•		•												•
	•					•	•		•				•		•			
•	•	•	•	•		•	•	•			•	•			•			•
	•					•	•		•					•	•			
	•		•	•		•	•		•	•		•	•	•	•			
						•			•					•	•			
	•				•				•					•	•			
									•						•			
•	•	•				•					•					•		
							•											
•	•		•			•	•					•	•	•	•			•
•	•	•		•	•	•	•		•			•	•	•	•		•	•
					•				•									
•	•	•	•	•	•	•	•	•	•		•	•	•	•	•	•	•	•
•	•	•		•		•	•				•	•			•			•
					•													
						•	•		•				•	•				
						•	•		•				•	•				
	•					•	•		•					•	•			
•	•	•	•	•		•	•	•			•	•			•	•		•
•	•					•	•					•			•	•		
	•					•	•		•					•	•			
	•		•			•	•						•		•			
•	•	•		•		•	•	•		•		•			•		•	•
	•		•			•	•	•			•	•			•			•
•	•	•	•	•		•	•	•	•			•	•			•	•	•
	•	•	•			•	•	•	•				•	•				•
										•								
	•			•		•	•		•		•	•	•	•	•			
				•			•	•	•	•			•	•				
•	•	•	•	•		•	•	•	•			•		•	•			
•	•	•	•	•		•	•		•			•			•		•	•
	•		•			•	•		•			•		•	•			
•	•	•	•	•		•	•	•	•		•	•	•	•	•	•		•
	•	•		•		•	•		•			•		•	•		•	•
	•				•	•	•		•				•	•	•			

	Vacancies	Partners	Total staff	Work placement	Corporate/ commercial	General commercial	Niche	General practice	High street/ legal aid
BLM	25	210	1700	✔		•			
Bolt Burdon	0	5	70			•		•	
Bond Dickinson	30	123	1200	✔	•	•			
Bonnett Son & Turner LLP	0	3	30					•	
Boodle Hatfield LLP	4	34	150	✔	•	•	•		
Bristows LLP	10	40	275	✔	•				
Bross Bennett	0	5	20	✔			•		
Brown Rudnick LLP	3(18)	29	100		•				
Browne Jacobson LLP	20	115	964	✔	•	•	•		
Bryan Cave	0	15	80	✔	•				
Burges Salmon LLP	30	87	750	✔	•	•		•	
BWF Solicitors	2	2	5					•	
Cains Advocates Limited	2	9	50	✔	•	•	•		
Campbell Chambers	0	2	10					•	•
Campbell-Taylor Solicitors	0	1	10	✔			•		•
Cannings Connolly Solicitors	1(19)	7	25		•				
Carpenter & Co	0-1	3	25					•	•
Cartwright King	0	26	280					•	•
Chadbourne & Parke (London) LLP	1	15	73		•				
Charles Russell Speechlys	24	148	1001	✔	•	•		•	
Chhokar & Co	1	3	11					•	
Clarke Willmott LLP	TBC	73	410		•	•		•	
Clarkslegal LLP	2	13	70			•			
Clarkson Wright & Jakes Ltd	0	15	77		•	•		•	
Cleary Gottlieb Steen & Hamilton LLP	15-20	193	2500	✔	•				
Clifford Chance	Up to 80	567	6021	✔	•	•			
Clifford Harris & Co	0	2	8		•	•			
Clintons	2	21	75			•	•		
Clyde & Co LLP	45-50	375	3600	✔	•	•			
CMS Cameron McKenna Nabarro Olswang LLP	65	1000	7500	✔	•	•			
Cohen Davis Solicitors	3(18)	1	4	✔			•		
Collyer Bristow LLP	4-5(19)	30	138	✔	•	•		•	
Community Law Clinic Solicitors	0	1	24					•	•
Cooley (UK) LLP	4	27	145	✔	•	•			
Covington & Burling LLP	8	283		✔	•	•	•	•	
Cripps LLP	10	51	350	✔	•	•		•	
Crown Prosecution Service	1(18)		5974				•		
Cunningtons	Varies	9	60	✔				•	•
Curtis Mallet-Prevost Colt & Mosle LLP	0	4	14		•				
Curwens LLP	2(18)	15	90					•	

Banking	Comp/comm	Competition	Construction	Corporate tax	Crime	Dispute resolution	Employment	Environment	Family	Human rights	Insurance	IP	Personal injury	Private client	Property	Shipping	Sport	TMT
			•			•	•	•	•		•		•			•		•
	•					•	•		•					•	•			
•	•	•	•	•		•		•			•	•		•	•	•		•
							•						•	•	•			
	•		•	•		•			•					•	•			
•	•	•		•		•	•					•			•			•
									•									
•	•			•	•	•						•						
•	•	•	•	•		•	•	•			•	•	•	•	•		•	•
•	•	•		•		•								•	•			
•	•	•	•	•		•	•	•	•		•	•		•	•		•	•
									•				•	•				
•	•					•	•				•	•	•	•	•	•		•
					•				•									
										•				•				
	•					•									•			
							•		•				•	•	•			
					•	•	•	•	•						•			
	•		•			•					•							
•	•	•	•	•		•	•	•	•		•	•		•	•		•	•
	•								•	•				•	•			
•	•	•	•	•		•	•	•	•		•	•	•	•	•		•	•
•	•	•	•			•	•	•				•		•	•			•
•	•		•			•	•		•			•	•	•	•			•
•	•	•		•		•	•					•						•
•	•	•	•	•		•	•	•			•	•		•	•	•		•
•	•					•	•		•			•		•	•			
	•					•	•		•			•		•	•		•	•
•	•	•	•	•		•	•	•			•	•	•		•	•		•
•	•	•	•	•		•	•	•			•	•		•			•	•
												•						•
•	•	•	•			•	•					•		•	•			•
							•		•					•				
•	•	•		•		•	•				•	•						•
•	•	•		•		•	•				•	•			•		•	•
	•			•		•	•		•				•	•	•			•
					•													
	•					•	•		•				•	•	•			
•	•					•												
	•	•				•	•		•				•	•	•			

	Vacancies	Partners	Total staff	Work placement	Corporate/ commercial	General commercial	Niche	General practice	High street/ legal aid
Curzon Green Solicitors	2(18)	3	22	✔				•	
DAC Beachcroft	13(19)	240	2300	✔	•	•		•	
Darlingtons	1	6	42	✔	•			•	
David Phillips & Partners	0	15	75	✔			•	•	•
Davies and Partners	1(18)	12	170		•	•		•	
Davis & Co	1	1	2				•		
Davis Polk & Wardwell London LLP	Approx 4	10	90	✔	•				
Dawson Cornwell	1(19)	11	34	✔			•		
Daybells LLP	1(19)	3	10	✔				•	
Dean Manson LLP – Solicitors	4	2	10	✔				•	
Debevoise & Plimpton LLP	8-10	19	215	✔	•			•	
Debidins	0	2	4					•	
Dechert LLP	10	312	2295	✔	•				
Devonshires Solicitors	6(19)	34	230		•		•		
DH Law Solicitors Ltd	0	1	10	✔					•
DLA Piper UK LLP	Up to 70	1300	8500	✔	•				
DMH Stallard LLP	0	59	259	✔	•	•		•	
Dorsey	2	14	45		•				
Dowse & Co	0	3	14						•
Druces LLP	2	20	78	✔	•	•			
Duncan Lewis Solicitors Ltd	100	33	421	✔	•				•
DWF LLP	40	329	2600	✔	•	•			
Edwards Duthie	0	12	85		•	•		•	•
Edwin Coe LLP	4	38	160	✔	•	•	•	•	
Elborne Mitchell LLP	2	9	33				•		
EMW Law LLP	5	34	172		•				
Everatt's Solicitors	1	1	6		•	•		•	
Eversheds Sutherland (International) LLP	50	395	3215	✔	•	•			
Everys	0	10	100		•	•		•	•
Ewings & Co	0	3	30					•	•
Faegre Baker Daniels LLP	2	7	40	✔	•	•			
Faradays Solicitors	Varies	4	20	✔				•	•
Farrer & Co LLP	10	73	415	✔	•	•	•	•	
Fellowes Solicitors LLP	1	4	14	✔				•	•
Fentons	0	24	210					•	•
Fieldfisher	18	223	986	✔	•	•			
Fisher Jones Greenwood Solicitors	0	21	143		•	•	•	•	•
Fisher Meredith	2(19)	11	41					•	
Fladgate LLP	6	75	265		•	•			
Fletcher Dervish	0	1	20					•	•
Forsters LLP	7-9	52	390	✔			•		

Banking	Comp/comm	Competition	Construction	Corporate tax	Crime	Dispute resolution	Employment	Environment	Family	Human rights	Insurance	IP	Personal injury	Private client	Property	Shipping	Sport	TMT
	•		•			•	•		•				•		•			
•	•	•	•	•		•	•	•			•	•	•		•			•
	•		•			•	•		•				•	•	•			
					•		•						•	•				
	•		•			•	•	•	•			•	•	•	•			•
						•					•					•		
•	•	•		•														
							•							•				
	•					•	•		•			•		•	•			
										•								
•	•	•	•	•		•	•				•							•
						•	•		•					•	•			
•	•	•	•			•	•					•			•			
•	•		•			•	•					•	•	•	•		•	•
						•	•			•			•	•				
•	•	•	•	•		•	•				•	•	•		•		•	•
•	•		•			•	•	•	•		•	•	•	•	•			•
	•			•		•						•	•		•			•
			•			•	•	•	•	•			•		•			
•	•		•	•		•	•				•	•		•	•			
					•						•		•	•	•			
•	•	•	•	•		•	•				•	•	•	•	•	•		
					•		•		•				•	•	•			
•	•	•	•	•		•	•	•			•	•	•	•	•		•	•
	•						•				•					•		
•	•		•			•	•						•		•			•
	•					•	•		•				•	•	•			
•	•	•	•	•		•	•	•			•	•	•	•	•		•	•
	•					•	•		•	•		•	•	•	•			
					•				•					•	•			
•	•	•				•	•					•			•			•
			•				•		•				•	•				
•	•		•	•		•	•		•			•		•	•		•	•
					•				•					•	•			
												•						
•	•	•	•	•		•	•				•	•	•	•	•		•	•
	•				•	•	•		•	•		•	•	•	•			•
	•					•	•		•	•								
•	•	•	•	•		•	•	•	•		•	•		•	•		•	•
					•	•	•		•					•	•			
•	•		•	•		•	•		•					•	•			

	Vacancies	Partners	Total staff	Work placement	Corporate/ commercial	General commercial	Niche	General practice	High street/ legal aid
Fox Williams LLP	3(19)	32	112		•	•	•	•	
Frank Brazell & Partners	0	3	28						•
Freeths LLP	20	135	750		•	•		•	
Freshfields Bruckhaus Deringer LLP	80	391	4960	✔	•				
Fried, Frank, Harris, Shriver & Jacobson (London) LLP	2	14	99		•				
Galbraith Branley	1	1	15						•
Gateley Plc	14	150	802	✔	•	•			
Geldards LLP	6(19)	57	352		•	•	•		
Gibson Dunn & Crutcher LLP	8	26	130	✔	•				
Gide Loyrette Nouel LLP	4	6	42				•		
Gill & Co	1	2	14					•	•
Glovers Solicitors LLP	2(19)	11	38			•			
Goodman Derrick LLP	3	32	102		•	•	•	•	
Goodman Ray	0	5	20				•		•
Gordon Dadds LLP	6(19)	39	236		•	•		•	
Government Legal	40		2000						
Gowling WLG (UK) LLP	25	593	3171	✔	•	•	•		
Greenberg Traurig LLP	4+(18)	25	105	✔	•				
Greenhouse Stirton & Co	0	2	3	✔					•
Greenwoods Solicitors LLP	3	8	100	✔	•	•			
Gregory Abrams Davidson LLP	0	9	78	✔				•	
Gregory Rowcliffe Milners	1	13	55					•	
Guile Nicholas Solicitors	0	5	30	✔				•	•
Hanne & Co	3(18)	10	57					•	
Harbottle & Lewis LLP	6	42	186		•	•	•		
Harper & Odell	TBC	2	5			•			
Harris Waters & Co	1	2	11	✔	•	•		•	•
Hempsons	3	46	300				•		
Her Majesty's Courts & Tribunals Service	0		1200					•	
Herbert Smith Freehills LLP	60	476	4965	✔	•				
Hewitsons LLP	15	46	243	✔	•	•	•	•	
Hextalls Ltd	0	8	30				•		
HFW	15	161	840	✔	•	•	•		
Hill Dickinson LLP	14	132	1000	✔	•	•	•		
Hilliers HRW	0	2	32		•	•			
Hine Solicitors	10	8	180					•	•
HKH Kenwright & Cox	0	2	19	✔	•			•	
Hodders	0	5	65		•	•		•	•
Hodge Jones & Allen LLP	7(19)	41	210				•		•
Hogan Lovells	60	800	5000	✔	•				

Banking	Comp/comm	Competition	Construction	Corporate tax	Crime	Dispute resolution	Employment	Environment	Family	Human rights	Insurance	IP	Personal injury	Private client	Property	Shipping	Sport	TMT
•	•	•		•		•	•				•	•		•	•			•
					•				•					•				
•	•	•	•	•		•	•	•	•	•	•	•	•	•	•		•	•
•	•	•	•	•		•	•	•			•	•			•			•
•		•		•		•												
					•				•					•				
•	•	•	•	•		•	•		•			•		•	•	•	•	•
•	•		•	•		•	•		•		•	•	•	•	•		•	•
•	•	•		•		•	•	•			•	•			•			•
•			•			•									•			
					•	•			•					•	•			
•		•				•	•								•			
•	•	•	•	•		•	•		•		•	•		•	•		•	•
									•									
•	•	•	•	•		•	•		•		•	•	•	•	•		•	•
•	•	•		•			•	•		•	•	•		•	•	•	•	•
•	•	•	•	•		•	•	•			•	•		•	•	•	•	•
•	•	•		•		•	•	•				•			•			•
														•				
•	•	•	•	•		•	•	•			•	•		•	•		•	•
	•					•	•		•				•	•	•			•
	•	•				•	•		•		•	•		•	•		•	•
							•		•					•				
	•				•	•	•		•					•	•			
	•					•	•		•			•	•		•		•	•
							•						•		•			
	•					•	•		•					•	•			
	•	•			•	•	•					•		•	•			
•	•	•	•	•		•	•	•			•	•		•	•			•
•	•	•	•	•		•	•	•				•		•	•		•	•
•			•			•		•			•	•	•			•	•	
•	•	•	•			•	•	•				•	•		•			
•	•	•	•	•	•	•	•	•	•		•	•		•	•	•	•	•
	•		•	•		•	•		•			•	•	•	•			
					•		•		•					•	•			
					•	•	•		•			•		•	•			•
	•					•	•		•					•	•			
					•	•	•		•	•			•	•				
•	•	•		•		•	•	•			•	•			•			•

	Vacancies	Partners	Total staff	Work placement	Corporate/ commercial	General commercial	Niche	General practice	High street/ legal aid
Horwich Farrelly	15	35	730	✔			•		
Howard Kennedy	10[19]	53	350					•	
Howell Jones LLP	0	14	75					•	
Hugh James	10	62	690	✔	•	•	•	•	•
Humphries Kirk LLP	1[19]	20	180	✔				•	
Hunters	1-2	28	71	✔				•	
IBB Solicitors	4	28	191		•	•		•	•
Ikie Solicitors LLP	0	2	5					•	
Ince & Co LLP	10	100	550	✔	•		•		
Irwin Mitchell	45	269	2700	✔	•	•		•	
Jay Vadher & Co	1	3	8			•		•	•
Jeffrey Green Russell Limited	2	21	76		•				
Joelson JD LLP	4[18]	14	80		•	•	•		
John Chapman and Co	0	4	22					•	•
Johns & Saggar LLP	0	2	13	✔	•			•	
Jones Day	20	60	350	✔	•				
Joseph Hill & Co	4[18]	2	13	✔				•	•
Joves Solicitors	0		3	✔				•	
K&L Gates LLP	TBD	55	244	✔	•	•			
Kaim Todner Solicitors Ltd	0	8	70					•	•
KC Law Chambers Solicitors	2[18]	2	5	✔				•	
Kennard Wells Solicitors	1	5	35					•	•
Kennedys	16	245	1700	✔	•	•			
Kingsley Napley LLP	6[19]	52	352	✔				•	
Kirkland & Ellis International LLP	10	850	3811	✔	•				
Kotecha & Co	0	2	5	✔		•		•	
Laderman and Co	Poss	2	13		•	•		•	
Latham & Watkins	24	75	530	✔	•				
Laytons Solicitors LLP	6	29	118	✔	•	•			
Lee Bolton Monier-Williams	2	8	45	✔		•	•	•	
Leigh Day	8-10[19]	44	395				•		•
Lester Aldridge LLP	8	42	309	✔	•	•	•	•	
Lewis Silkin	Up to 6	59	343	✔	•	•			
Linklaters LLP	110	450	5200	✔	•				
London Solicitors LLP	2	2	10	✔				•	
Luqmani Thompson & Partners	0	5	9				•		•
Lyons Davidson	4-6	36	1200		•	•		•	
M Olubi Solicitors	4	1	7	✔				•	
Macfarlanes LLP	Up to 30	87	691	✔	•				
MacRae & Co LLP	0	3	7				•		
Magrath LLP	2[18]	8	65		•	•	•		

Banking	Comp/comm	Competition	Construction	Corporate tax	Crime	Dispute resolution	Employment	Environment	Family	Human rights	Insurance	IP	Personal injury	Private client	Property	Shipping	Sport	TMT
						•							•					
•	•		•	•		•	•		•	•		•	•	•	•		•	
	•						•		•				•		•			
•	•		•			•	•	•	•		•	•	•	•	•		•	•
	•	•				•	•		•			•		•	•			
	•					•	•		•					•	•			
•	•		•		•	•	•		•		•	•	•	•	•			
					•		•		•				•	•				
	•	•				•					•					•		
•	•	•	•	•	•	•	•	•	•	•	•	•	•	•	•			•
	•					•			•				•	•	•			
•	•		•	•		•	•		•			•		•	•		•	•
	•	•		•		•	•					•		•	•			•
									•				•					
	•					•	•		•			•		•	•		•	
•	•	•	•	•	•	•	•	•			•	•		•				•
					•									•				
							•		•									
•	•	•	•	•	•	•	•	•			•	•			•		•	•
					•				•									
						•	•		•			•	•	•				
					•		•		•			•	•	•				
•	•		•			•	•	•			•	•		•	•	•	•	
•	•		•	•	•	•	•		•			•	•	•	•		•	•
•	•	•		•		•						•						
									•			•		•				
	•					•	•		•				•		•			
•	•	•		•		•	•	•				•		•				•
•	•	•	•	•		•	•	•	•			•	•	•				•
	•					•	•					•	•	•	•			•
						•	•		•			•		•				
										•								
	•					•	•	•	•		•		•	•	•			
				•		•	•		•									
•	•	•	•	•		•	•	•			•	•		•	•		•	•
•	•	•	•			•	•	•				•		•				•
	•					•	•							•				•

	Vacancies	Partners	Total staff	Work placement	Corporate/ commercial	General commercial	Niche	General practice	High street/ legal aid
Makka Solicitors Ltd	1	3	8	✔				•	•
Makwana Solicitors	1	1	2	✔				•	
Malik & Malik	1	2	15	✔				•	•
Malletts	1	3	30	✔	•		•		•
Maples Teesdale LLP	3(19)	18	68				•		
Marriott Harrison LLP	2-3(19)	18	52	✔	•	•	•		
Martin Murray & Associates	0	9	70					•	•
Martin Shepherd Solicitors LLP	0	6	34					•	
Maurice Turnor Gardner LLP	1-2(19)	10	38	✔			•		
Mayer Brown International LLP	15	86	460	✔	•	•			
McDermott Will & Emery UK LLP	2	581	1072	✔	•	•			
McGuireWoods London LLP	1	15	61					•	
McMillan Williams Solicitors	Varies	60	400	✔	•	•	•	•	•
Memery Crystal LLP	4	27	120		•	•	•		
Michelmores LLP	8	64	450	✔	•	•		•	
Milbank Tweed Hadley & McCloy	5	23	165	✔	•				
Miller Evans & Co	0	2	9					•	
Mills & Reeve LLP	18	117	800	✔	•	•			
Mills Chody LLP	1-2	5	20					•	
Minster Law Solicitors	5		830	✔			•	•	
Mishcon de Reya LLP	12-15	115	772	✔	•	•			
Monro Wright & Wasbrough LLP	2(19)	9	35				•		
Moore Blatch LLP	3(19)	42	270					•	
Morgan, Lewis & Bockius UK LLP	6-8	34	100	✔	•	•			
Morrison & Foerster (UK) LLP	5(18)	19	85	✔	•				
Moss & Co	1(18)	2	10	✔					•
Nandy & Co	0							•	
Nockolds	3(19)	13	140	✔	•	•		•	
Norton Rose Fulbright	Up to 45	1180	7100	✔	•	•			
Obaseki	1(19)	3	11	✔		•		•	
O'Melveny	Up to 3	7	50	✔	•				
Orrick, Herrington & Sutcliffe (UK) LLP	6-8	30	160		•				
Osborne Clarke LLP	20	213	1370	✔	•	•	•		
Osbornes Solicitors LLP	4	18	108	✔				•	•
Osmond & Osmond	1(18)	2	8	✔	•	•		•	
Oury Clark	1	6	22		•	•	•		
Ozoran Turkan	2(18)	2	10	✔			•	•	
Paragon Law Limited	0	2	30	✔	•		•		•
Paul Hastings	6	27	150	✔	•				
Payne Hicks Beach	3	30	146					•	
Peacock & Co	1	8	30					•	

Banking	Comp/comm	Competition	Construction	Corporate tax	Crime	Dispute resolution	Employment	Environment	Family	Human rights	Insurance	IP	Personal injury	Private client	Property	Shipping	Sport	TMT
						•			•						•			
					•	•			•									
					•				•					•				
	•				•	•			•								•	
•	•		•			•									•			
•	•					•	•					•			•		•	•
					•				•									
	•					•			•					•	•			
														•	•			
•	•	•	•	•		•	•	•			•	•			•			•
				•		•	•							•				
•	•	•		•		•	•	•				•		•	•			
	•	•	•	•	•	•	•		•	•			•	•	•			•
•	•		•	•		•	•				•	•			•		•	
•	•	•	•	•		•	•	•	•		•	•			•			•
•	•	•	•	•		•	•					•			•	•		•
														•	•			
•	•	•	•	•		•	•	•	•		•	•		•	•		•	•
	•					•			•				•	•	•			
						•							•	•	•			
•	•	•	•			•	•	•	•			•		•	•		•	•
	•					•			•					•	•			
	•		•			•	•	•	•		•	•		•	•			
•	•	•		•		•	•					•						•
•				•		•	•					•						•
					•					•								
									•	•								
	•					•	•		•				•	•	•		•	
•	•	•	•	•		•	•	•			•	•			•	•		•
					•	•	•		•						•			
•	•		•			•												
•	•	•		•		•	•					•			•			
•	•	•	•	•		•	•	•				•		•	•			•
						•			•				•	•	•			
	•					•	•		•					•	•			
	•					•	•					•			•			
		•			•				•					•				
														•				
•	•			•		•	•								•			•
	•		•			•	•		•			•		•	•		•	•
	•						•		•					•	•			

	Vacancies	Partners	Total staff	Work placement	Corporate/ commercial	General commercial	Niche	General practice	High street/ legal aid
Pemberton Greenish LLP	0	16	87		•	•	•		
Penningtons Manches LLP	12-14	110	600	✔	•	•		•	
Peter Brown & Co Solicitors LLP	1	6	20		•	•		•	
Peters & Peters	2	10	75	✔			•		
Philcox Gray Ltd	0		18	✔					•
Pinsent Masons LLP	72	420	3000	✔	•	•			
Pitmans LLP	8	40	210		•	•	•	•	
Plexus Law	0	117	1800				•		
Portner	1	4	29			•	•	•	
Pothecary Witham Weld	1(18)	4	28				•		
Powell & Co	0	2	14				•		•
Powell Spencer & Partners	0	2	44						•
PwC	25	35	320	✔	•				
QualitySolicitors Mirza	2	4	18	✔				•	•
RadcliffesLeBrasseur	4	40	170		•	•	•		
Rai Solicitors	0		3	✔				•	
Raj Law Solicitors	0	2	8					•	•
Ratna & Co	Poss	2	7					•	•
Rawal & Co	0	1	7	✔				•	•
Reed Smith	25	681	3232	✔	•				
Rest Harrow & Co Solicitors	0	2	3	✔				•	
Reynolds Colman Bradley LLP	1	3	22	✔			•		
Rippon Patel & French LLP	1	2	6	✔			•	•	
Ronald Fletcher Baker LLP	3	9	40			•			
Rooks Rider	0	7	37		•	•	•		
Ropes & Gray International LLP	5-7	30	214	✔	•	•			
Rosenblatt	0	22	80		•				
Rosling King LLP	4(19)	13	85		•				
Royds Withy King	12	64	470	✔	•	•		•	•
RPC	12	81	760	✔	•	•			
Russell-Cooke Solicitors	9	61	385		•	•		•	•
SB Solicitors	0	2	4					•	
Schillings International	0	9	62		•	•	•		
Seddons	2	32	116		•	•		•	
Sentinel Solicitors	2(18)	3	6	✔				•	•
The Sethi Partnership Solicitors	1	3	25	✔	•	•		•	
Shakespeare Martineau LLP	10	130	850		•				
Shearman & Sterling (London) LLP	Approx 17	35	300	✔	•				
Sheikh & Co	2	3	35	✔				•	•
Sherrards Solicitors LLP	1	15	90		•	•	•		
Shranks	0	2	9			•	•		

Banking	Comp/comm	Competition	Construction	Corporate tax	Crime	Dispute resolution	Employment	Environment	Family	Human rights	Insurance	IP	Personal injury	Private client	Property	Shipping	Sport	TMT
	•		•			•								•	•			
•	•		•	•		•	•		•			•	•	•	•		•	•
	•														•			
		•			•	•												
									•									
•	•	•	•	•		•	•	•			•	•			•	•	•	•
•	•		•			•	•	•	•		•	•	•	•	•			•
		•				•					•		•					
		•				•	•							•	•			
	•					•								•	•			
									•					•				
					•				•					•				
•	•	•		•		•	•					•		•	•			
									•				•	•				
•	•	•		•	•	•	•	•	•		•	•	•		•		•	•
							•		•				•					
						•		•						•				
							•		•						•			
					•	•			•					•				
•	•	•	•	•		•	•	•			•	•			•	•		•
						•	•		•					•				
		•				•					•							
																		•
	•					•			•					•				
	•				•	•	•		•			•	•		•			•
•	•	•	•	•		•	•	•		•		•		•	•			•
•		•		•		•							•		•			
•	•		•	•		•	•					•	•		•			•
•	•		•			•	•	•			•	•	•		•		•	•
•	•	•	•	•		•	•		•			•	•	•	•		•	•
•	•	•	•	•		•	•				•	•	•		•			•
•	•		•	•	•	•	•	•	•			•	•	•	•		•	•
							•					•	•	•				
						•			•			•		•	•			•
	•					•	•		•			•	•	•	•			
									•	•								
	•				•	•	•		•				•	•	•			•
•	•	•	•	•		•	•	•	•		•	•	•		•			•
•	•	•	•	•		•	•	•							•			•
					•	•			•						•			
•	•					•	•						•		•	•		•
	•					•	•							•	•	•		

	Vacancies	Partners	Total staff	Work placement	Corporate/ commercial	General commercial	Niche	General practice	High street/ legal aid
Sidley Austin LLP	12	43	260	✔	•				
Simkins LLP	2	20	45	✔	•	•	•		
Simmons & Simmons LLP	30	250	1600	✔	•	•			
Skadden, Arps, Slate, Meagher & Flom (UK) LLP	Approx 10	31	235	✔	•				
Slater & Gordon (UK) LLP	53	86	3500			•		•	
Slater Gordon Solutions Legal Ltd	1	5	1150				•		
Slaughter and May	80	115	1100	✔	•	•			
Sonn Macmillan Walker	2(19)	3	25	✔					•
Sookias & Sookias	0	4	20			•			
Spence & Horne	0	1	4	✔				•	•
Squire Patton Boggs (UK) LLP	25	500	2600	✔	•	•			
Sri Kanth & Co	2	2	11	✔				•	
Steeles Law LLP	1-3	8	80	✔	•	•	•	•	
Stephenson Harwood LLP	18	150	900	✔	•				
Stone King	4	33	197	✔	•	•	•	•	
Stone Rowe Brewer	1-2	5	50		•	•		•	
Stowe Family Law LLP	Varies	20	60	✔			•		
STS Solicitors	2	1	5	✔		•		•	
Stuart Miller Solicitors	2(18)	2	32	✔					•
Sullivan & Cromwell LLP	4-6	21	154	✔	•				
Sweetman Burke & Sinker	Poss	3	16	✔				•	•
Systech Solicitors Limited	0		25				•		
Taylor Rose TTKW	1-2	13	250		•	•	•		
Taylor Vinters LLP	6	26	170	✔	•	•	•		
Taylor Wessing	20	400	1800	✔	•	•			
Teacher Stern LLP	4	31	121	✔	•	•	•		
Thomas Cooper LLP	Up to 3	28	103		•		•		
Thompsons Solicitors	0	50	888				•		
Thrings	10(19)	60	337		•	•	•	•	
Tim Johnson / Law	0	1	4	✔			•		
Tinklin Springall	2(18)	7	50					•	
TLT LLP	Up to 15	115	1020	✔	•	•	•	•	
Travers Smith LLP	25	77	604	✔	•	•			
Trowers & Hamlins LLP	23	161	903	✔	•				
TV Edwards Solicitors	0	13	120	✔				•	•
TWM Solicitors LLP	0	32	200		•	•		•	
Veale Wasbrough Vizards LLP	8-10	72	411	✔	•	•	•	•	
Vinson & Elkins RLLP	4	15	79	✔	•				
Vyman Solicitors Ltd	2	4	24	✔		•			•
W H Matthews & Co	0	12	49					•	

Banking	Comp/comm	Competition	Construction	Corporate tax	Crime	Dispute resolution	Employment	Environment	Family	Human rights	Insurance	IP	Personal injury	Private client	Property	Shipping	Sport	TMT
•	•	•		•		•	•				•	•			•			•
	•					•	•					•			•		•	•
•	•	•		•		•	•	•			•	•			•			•
•	•	•		•		•						•						
			•		•	•	•		•			•	•	•	•			•
													•					
•	•	•	•	•		•	•	•			•	•			•		•	•
					•													
	•					•									•			
							•		•					•	•			
•	•	•	•	•	•	•	•	•		•	•	•		•	•	•	•	•
							•							•	•			
•	•	•	•	•		•	•	•			•	•		•	•		•	•
•	•	•	•	•		•	•	•			•	•		•	•	•		•
	•			•		•	•		•			•		•	•			•
	•					•	•		•				•	•	•			
									•					•				
						•			•					•				
					•									•				
•	•	•		•										•				
				•					•					•				
		•				•												
•	•					•								•	•			
	•	•		•		•	•	•	•			•		•	•			•
•	•	•	•	•		•	•	•			•	•		•	•	•	•	•
•	•	•	•	•		•	•					•		•	•		•	•
•	•	•				•	•				•		•	•		•	•	
					•		•							•				
•	•	•	•	•		•	•	•	•		•	•	•	•	•	•	•	•
							•											
	•					•	•		•					•	•			
•	•	•	•	•		•	•	•	•			•		•	•	•		•
•	•	•	•	•		•	•	•		•	•	•				•	•	•
•		•		•		•	•							•	•			
						•	•		•	•			•	•				
	•		•			•	•		•					•	•			
•	•	•	•	•		•	•	•	•			•		•	•			•
•	•		•	•		•	•											•
•					•	•									•			
	•		•		•	•	•		•				•	•	•			

	Vacancies	Partners	Total staff	Work placement	Corporate/ commercial	General commercial	Niche	General practice	High street/ legal aid
Wainwright & Cummins	0	4	35	✔					•
Wallace LLP	0	18	60		•	•			
Walter Wilson Richmond	0	1	7	✔				•	•
Watson Burton LLP	3(19)	14	110	✔	•				
Watson Farley & Williams LLP	18	155	850	✔	•	•			
Wedlake Bell LLP	6	59	250	✔	•	•			
Weightmans LLP	Up to 18	187	1306	✔	•	•	•		
Weil, Gotshal & Manges (London) LLP	15	33	297	✔	•				
Wellers Law Group LLP	1(19)	3	85		•	•		•	
White & Case LLP	50	101	828	✔	•				
Whitehead Monckton	Varies(19)	10	118					•	
Whitworth & Green Solicitors Ltd	4	2	16	✔	•	•		•	•
Wilson Solicitors LLP	5	12	70						•
Wilsons Solicitors LLP	4	29	157	✔	•	•	•	•	
Winckworth Sherwood LLP	8	58	328	✔			•		
Winston & Strawn London LLP	4	16	58	✔	•	•			
Withers LLP	11	167	1000	✔	•	•	•	•	
WLL Solicitors	2	1	7	✔			•		

North

	Vacancies	Partners	Total staff	Work placement	Corporate/ commercial	General commercial	Niche	General practice	High street/ legal aid
Accutrainee	Varies				•	•	•	•	
Anglo-Thai Legal (ATL)	Varies	1	5	✔			•	•	
Ben Hoare Bell LLP	0	8	75					•	•
Bevan Brittan LLP	8	51	292	✔	•	•			
BHP Law	0	10	125		•			•	
BLM	25	210	1700	✔		•			
Bond Dickinson	30	123	1200	✔	•	•			
Cartmell Shepherd	2	7	90	✔				•	
Cartwright King	0	26	280					•	•
Crown Prosecution Service	1(18)		5974				•		
Darlington Borough Council	0		19					•	
David Gray Solicitors LLP	1(18)	9	67	✔				•	•
Davies Johnson	0		26				•		
DMA Law	0	5	34					•	
DWF LLP	40	329	2600	✔	•	•			
The Endeavour Partnership LLP	3	8	50	✔	•	•			

Banking	Comp/comm	Competition	Construction	Corporate tax	Crime	Dispute resolution	Employment	Environment	Family	Human rights	Insurance	IP	Personal injury	Private client	Property	Shipping	Sport	TMT
					•		•		•									
	•					•						•		•	•		•	•
						•	•		•						•			
•	•		•	•		•	•	•			•	•			•			•
•	•	•	•	•		•	•					•			•	•		
•	•	•	•	•		•	•		•			•		•	•			•
•	•	•	•	•	•	•	•	•	•		•	•	•	•	•	•	•	•
•	•	•	•			•	•				•	•			•			•
	•					•	•	•	•			•	•	•	•			
•	•	•	•	•		•	•		•			•		•	•			•
	•		•			•	•		•			•		•	•			
	•				•	•	•		•				•					
					•				•	•								
	•	•	•			•	•		•			•		•	•			
•	•		•	•		•	•	•	•			•		•	•			•
•	•	•				•									•			
•	•	•	•	•		•	•	•	•			•		•	•	•	•	•
						•												

Banking	Comp/comm	Competition	Construction	Corporate tax	Crime	Dispute resolution	Employment	Environment	Family	Human rights	Insurance	IP	Personal injury	Private client	Property	Shipping	Sport	TMT
•	•	•	•	•		•	•	•	•		•	•	•	•	•	•	•	•
	•		•		•	•	•		•	•		•	•	•	•			
					•				•	•				•				
	•	•	•			•	•	•				•	•		•			•
•	•			•	•	•	•		•			•	•	•	•			•
		•				•	•		•		•	•				•		•
•	•	•	•	•		•			•		•	•		•	•	•		•
	•					•	•		•				•	•	•			
					•		•	•	•						•			
					•													
					•	•			•					•	•			
						•					•		•			•		
					•				•						•			
•	•	•	•	•		•	•	•	•			•	•	•	•	•		•
•	•		•			•						•			•			•

	Vacancies	Partners	Total staff	Work placement	Corporate/commercial	General commercial	Niche	General practice	High street/legal aid
Eversheds Sutherland (International) LLP	50	395	3215	✔	•	•			
Freeman Johnson	1	8	45	✔				•	•
Hay & Kilner Law Firm	3	24	82	✔	•	•		•	
Hempsons	3	46	300				•		
Her Majesty's Courts & Tribunals Service	0		1200					•	
Hethertons LLP Solicitors	0	3	31					•	•
Hewitts	0	13	103					•	•
Horwich Farrelly	15	35	730	✔			•		
Irwin Mitchell	45	269	2700	✔	•	•		•	
Jacksons Law Firm	2	11	70		•	•		•	
K J Commons & Co	Poss	2	55					•	•
Latimer Hinks	Poss	9	51					•	
Meikles	1(19)	9	52	✔				•	•
Mills & Co Solicitors Limited	1	12	33	✔			•		
Mincoffs Solicitors LLP	1(19)	9	70	✔	•				
Mortons	0	6	35					•	
Muckle LLP	3-5	30	137	✔	•				
Plexus Law	0	117	1800				•		
Punch Robson	1-2(18)	7	53	✔	•	•	•	•	•
QualitySolicitors Lawson & Thompson	0	6	30					•	•
Samuel Phillips Law Firm	1	4	44	✔		•	•	•	
Short Richardson & Forth LLP	1	8	23			•			
Sintons LLP	0	26	200	✔	•	•			
Slater & Gordon (UK) LLP	53	86	3500			•		•	
Stone King	4	33	197	✔	•	•	•	•	
Stowe Family Law LLP	Varies	20	60	✔			•		
Thompsons Solicitors	0	50	888				•		
Tilly Bailey & Irvine LLP	TBC(18)	13	146		•	•		•	•
TLT LLP	Up to 15	115	1020	✔	•	•	•	•	
TMJ Legal Services Ltd	Poss	3	35	✔				•	•
Ward Hadaway	10	85	450	✔	•	•			
Watson Burton LLP	3(19)	14	110	✔	•				
Weightmans LLP	Up to 18	187	1306	✔	•	•	•		

Banking	Comp/comm	Competition	Construction	Corporate tax	Crime	Dispute resolution	Employment	Environment	Family	Human rights	Insurance	IP	Personal injury	Private client	Property	Shipping	Sport	TMT
•	•	•	•	•		•	•	•			•	•		•	•	•	•	•
	•				•	•	•		•					•	•	•		
•	•					•	•	•			•			•	•	•		•
	•		•		•	•	•						•		•	•		
						•	•		•				•	•	•			
	•		•		•	•	•		•				•	•	•			
						•							•					
•	•	•	•	•	•	•	•	•	•	•	•	•	•	•	•			•
	•	•	•		•	•	•	•	•				•	•	•			•
			•			•			•				•	•	•			
	•					•	•	•	•				•	•	•			•
			•			•			•				•	•				
																•		
•	•			•		•	•		•				•		•	•		•
									•				•					
•	•		•			•	•		•				•	•	•	•	•	•
		•				•					•		•					
	•					•	•		•				•	•	•			
					•	•	•		•				•	•	•			
	•					•	•		•				•	•				
•	•		•			•	•	•	•				•	•	•		•	•
					•	•	•		•				•	•	•			•
	•			•		•	•		•				•	•	•			•
									•				•					
					•		•		•				•	•	•			
	•		•		•	•	•		•				•	•	•			
•	•	•	•	•		•	•	•	•				•		•	•		•
						•	•		•				•	•				
•	•	•	•	•		•	•	•	•		•	•	•	•	•		•	•
•	•		•	•		•	•	•			•	•			•			•
•	•	•	•	•	•	•	•	•	•		•	•	•	•	•	•	•	•

Northwest

	Vacancies	Partners	Total staff	Work placement	Corporate/ commercial	General commercial	Niche	General practice	High street/ legal aid
Aaron and Partners	0	24	124		•	•	•		
Accutrainee	Varies				•	•	•	•	
Addleshaw Goddard	37	240	1500	✔	•				
Alfred Newton Solicitors	0	4	25					•	•
Allington Hughes Law	1(19)	14	75					•	•
ALP LAW LLP	Poss	4	90				•		
Amicus Solicitors LLP	1	2	7	✔				•	
Ams Solicitors Limited	2	2	16	✔		•		•	
Antony Hodari & Co	0	6	110					•	
Arnold Greenwood Solicitors Ltd	0	4	16					•	
Barnetts	2	6	135					•	
Berg	2(19)	7	50	✔	•	•			
Bermans	1(18)	12	70		•		•		
Berry & Berry	1	8	52		•	•		•	•
Berwin Leighton Paisner	40	200	1417	✔	•	•			
Birchall Blackburn Law	0	21	240		•				•
Blackhurst Swainson Goodier LLP t/a BSG Solicitors	1	6	22		•	•		•	•
BLM	25	210	1700	✔		•			
Bott & Company Solicitors LTD	0	3	102					•	
Bowcock Cuerden LLP	1	3	28			•	•		
Brabners LLP	6	64	356		•	•			
Brian Koffman & Co	0	1	2				•		
Brighouse Wolff	1	10	80					•	
Browne Jacobson LLP	20	115	964	✔	•	•	•		
Burnetts	2	10	126					•	
Butcher & Barlow LLP	2(19)	24	139					•	
Camps	0	5	170	✔			•		
Canter Levin & Berg	1-2	10	91	✔				•	•
Cartmell Shepherd	2	7	90	✔				•	
CFG Law (part of the client first group)	4	1	75	✔				•	
Chenery Maher	0	2	11				•		
Clyde & Co LLP	45-50	375	3600	✔	•	•			
CMS Cameron McKenna Nabarro Olswang LLP	65	1000	7500	✔	•	•			
Colemans-ctts t/a Simpson Millar	0	12	200		•			•	
Crown Prosecution Service	1(18)		5974				•		
Cumbria Law Centre	0		13				•		•
Curtis Law Solicitors LLP	8	4	115	✔				•	
DAC Beachcroft	13(19)	240	2300	✔	•	•		•	
Darbys Solicitors LLP	4	38	219	✔	•	•	•	•	•

Banking	Comp/comm	Competition	Construction	Corporate tax	Crime	Dispute resolution	Employment	Environment	Family	Human rights	Insurance	IP	Personal injury	Private client	Property	Shipping	Sport	TMT
●	●	●	●			●	●	●	●			●		●	●		●	●
●	●	●	●	●		●	●	●	●		●	●	●	●	●	●	●	●
●	●	●	●	●		●	●	●			●	●		●	●		●	●
	●						●		●				●	●	●			
	●				●	●	●		●				●	●	●			
													●					
													●					
									●				●	●	●			
													●					
						●	●		●					●	●			
	●					●							●	●	●			
●	●		●			●	●								●			●
●	●		●			●	●				●			●	●		●	●
	●				●	●	●		●				●	●	●			
●	●	●	●	●		●	●	●			●	●	●	●	●	●	●	●
	●				●	●			●	●			●	●	●			
	●					●	●	●	●			●	●	●	●		●	
			●			●	●	●			●		●			●		●
													●					
	●					●			●				●	●	●			
●	●	●	●	●		●	●	●	●		●	●	●	●	●		●	●
					●													
					●				●				●	●	●			
●	●	●	●	●		●	●	●			●	●	●	●	●		●	●
●	●		●			●	●		●			●	●	●	●			●
	●		●			●	●		●				●	●	●			
													●					
					●	●	●		●				●	●				
	●					●	●		●				●	●	●			
													●					
							●		●					●	●			
●	●	●	●	●		●	●	●			●	●	●		●	●		●
●	●	●	●	●		●	●	●			●	●			●		●	●
	●		●			●	●						●		●			
				●														
							●			●								
	●								●				●	●				
●	●	●	●	●		●	●	●			●	●	●		●			●
	●		●		●	●	●	●	●				●	●	●			●

	Vacancies	Partners	Total staff	Work placement	Corporate/ commercial	General commercial	Niche	General practice	High street/ legal aid
David Phillips & Partners	0	15	75	✔			•	•	•
Davis Blank Furniss	2	10	60		•	•	•	•	
Dean Solicitors	0	2	9					•	
Denby & Co	1	5	26			•	•	•	•
Derek B Forrest Solicitors	1	2	8					•	
DLA Piper UK LLP	Up to 70	1300	8500	✔	•				
Donald Race & Newton	0	6	47	✔				•	•
Duncan Gibbins Solicitors	2	2	34				•		
DWF LLP	40	329	2600	✔	•	•			
Eb Legal	1	1	5	✔			•		
Eversheds Sutherland (International) LLP	50	395	3215	✔	•	•			
Express Solicitors	5	15	185	✔			•		
Farleys Solicitors LLP	2(18)	12	170		•	•		•	•
Fentons	0	24	210					•	•
Fieldfisher	18	223	986	✔	•	•			
Fieldings Porter	3-4	11	76		•	•		•	•
Forbes Solicitors	4	44	320	✔	•	•	•	•	•
Forresters Solicitors Limited	0	2	15						•
Freeths LLP	20	135	750		•	•		•	
Gateley Plc	14	150	802	✔	•	•			
GHP Legal	0	10	87	✔				•	•
Glaisyers Solicitors LLP	0	11	85	✔	•	•		•	
GLP Solicitors	0-1	4	9					•	•
Government Legal	40		2000						
Gregory Abrams Davidson LLP	0	9	78	✔				•	
Hall Smith Whittingham	0	5	40					•	
Hempsons	3	46	300				•		
Henry's Solicitors Limited	1		25	✔				•	
Her Majesty's Courts & Tribunals Service	0		1200					•	
Hibberts LLP	1(18)	7	96	✔		•		•	•
Hill Dickinson LLP	14	132	1000	✔	•	•	•		
Hillyer McKeown LLP	1	12	80		•	•	•	•	
Horwich Farrelly	15	35	730	✔		•			
Howarth Goodman	Poss	2	11	✔	•	•			
Howes Percival LLP	8	43	229	✔	•	•			
Inghams	Poss	7	43	✔		•		•	•
Irwin Mitchell	45	269	2700	✔	•	•		•	
Jackson Lees Group	0	5	100					•	
James Murray Solicitors	0	4	68					•	•
JMW Solicitors	Approx 10	35	380		•	•	•	•	
JWK Solicitors	0	5	34					•	•

Banking	Comp/comm	Competition	Construction	Corporate tax	Crime	Dispute resolution	Employment	Environment	Family	Human rights	Insurance	IP	Personal injury	Private client	Property	Shipping	Sport	TMT
					•				•				•	•				
•	•	•	•			•	•		•		•	•	•	•	•		•	•
													•					
	•				•	•	•		•				•	•	•			
	•				•		•		•				•	•				
•	•	•	•	•		•	•	•			•	•			•	•	•	•
						•	•	•	•				•		•			
													•	•				
•	•	•	•	•		•	•	•	•		•	•	•	•	•	•		•
						•							•					
•	•	•	•	•		•	•	•			•	•	•	•	•	•	•	•
													•					
	•				•				•				•	•			•	
•	•	•	•	•		•	•				•	•	•	•	•		•	•
	•				•	•	•		•		•	•	•	•			•	•
	•	•	•	•	•	•	•	•	•		•	•	•	•			•	•
						•			•				•	•				
•	•	•	•	•		•	•	•	•	•	•	•	•	•	•		•	•
•	•	•	•	•		•	•	•	•			•	•	•	•	•	•	•
	•			•	•	•	•		•				•	•	•			
•						•	•				•	•	•	•				
									•				•					
•	•	•		•			•	•		•		•	•	•	•	•	•	•
	•						•		•				•	•	•			•
	•					•	•		•				•	•	•			
	•		•		•	•	•		•			•	•	•				
						•			•				•					
	•					•	•		•					•	•			
•	•	•	•	•	•	•	•	•	•		•	•	•	•	•	•	•	•
	•		•			•	•		•		•	•	•	•			•	•
						•							•					
	•		•			•									•			
•	•	•	•	•		•	•	•	•			•	•	•	•		•	•
	•					•			•				•	•	•			
•	•	•	•	•	•	•	•	•	•		•	•	•	•				•
	•		•			•	•		•				•	•	•			
					•				•				•					
	•				•	•	•		•			•	•	•	•		•	•

	Vacancies	Partners	Total staff	Work placement	Corporate/ commercial	General commercial	Niche	General practice	High street/ legal aid
The Keith Jones Partnership	0	3	15	✔		•	•		
Kennedys	16	245	1700	✔	•	•			
Kirwans	0	5	80			•		•	•
Kuit Steinart Levy	6	35	185	✔	•	•	•	•	
Land Law LLP	0	6	46			•			
Latimer Lee	0			✔		•			
Laytons Solicitors LLP	6	29	118	✔	•	•			
Leigh Day	8-10[19]	44	395				•		•
Malik Legal Solicitors Ltd	4	3	14	✔		•			
McHale & Company	1	5	40		•	•		•	•
Middleton Solicitors	1[18]	3	25	✔		•		•	
Middleweeks	0	2	19	✔			•		•
Milburns Solicitors Limited	1[18]	8	50	✔				•	•
Mills & Reeve LLP	18	117	800	✔	•	•			
Milne Moser	0	6	27					•	
MLP Law LLP	3[19]	6	22	✔	•	•	•	•	
Mohammed & Co	0	1	13	✔				•	•
Myerson Solicitors LLP	0	19	81	✔	•	•	•		
Napthens	2-4[19]	27	227					•	
Nexus Solicitors	0	9	45		•	•			
Oglethorpe Sturton & Gillibrand	1-2	8	46			•		•	
O'Neill Patient Solicitors LLP	0	10	240				•		
Pearson Hinchliffe LLP	2[18]	8	49		•	•		•	•
Pinsent Masons LLP	72	420	3000	✔	•	•			
Plexus Law	0	117	1800				•		
QualitySolicitors Jackson Canter	1	10	190					•	•
QualitySolicitors Turnerlaw	0	3	25					•	
Ralli	0	6	55		•	•	•		
Ratcliffe & Bibby Solicitors	0	5	45	✔				•	•
Robert Lizar	Poss	6	22						•
Robert Meaton and Co Solicitors	1	2	13			•		•	
Roberts Jackson Solicitors	6	9	220	✔			•		
The Roland Partnership	0	2	20					•	•
Russell & Russell	4	22	200					•	•
SAS Daniels LLP	4[19]	20	150	✔	•	•	•	•	
Savas & Savage Solicitors Limited	3	4	25	✔				•	
Shoosmiths	20	175	1550	✔	•	•	•	•	
Silverbeck Rymer	0-3	7	218				•		
Silverdale Solicitors	0	4	25	✔	•	•		•	
Slater & Gordon (UK) LLP	53	86	3500			•	•		
Slater Gordon Solutions Legal Ltd	1	5	1150				•		

Banking	Comp/comm	Competition	Construction	Corporate tax	Crime	Dispute resolution	Employment	Environment	Family	Human rights	Insurance	IP	Personal injury	Private client	Property	Shipping	Sport	TMT
						•												
•	•		•			•	•	•			•		•		•	•	•	
			•			•	•				•		•	•	•			
•	•	•	•	•		•	•				•		•		•		•	•
															•			
	•					•	•		•	•			•	•	•	•		
•	•	•	•	•		•	•	•	•				•	•	•			•
							•	•		•			•					
	•				•	•			•	•			•	•				
	•		•		•	•			•				•	•	•		•	
•	•					•	•		•				•	•			•	
					•													•
	•					•			•				•	•	•			
•	•	•	•	•		•	•	•	•		•	•	•				•	•
	•			•		•			•				•	•	•			
	•					•	•		•			•		•	•			•
			•			•	•						•	•	•			
•	•	•		•		•	•	•	•			•		•	•			•
	•		•	•		•	•	•	•			•	•	•				
	•					•	•				•	•	•				•	•
	•					•	•	•	•				•	•	•			
•	•								•						•	•	•	
	•		•			•							•	•	•			
•	•	•	•	•		•	•	•			•	•			•	•	•	•
		•				•					•		•					
	•		•		•	•	•		•	•		•	•	•	•			
					•				•				•	•				
	•		•		•	•	•				•	•	•	•			•	•
	•					•	•		•				•	•	•			
			•				•	•					•					
	•					•	•		•				•	•	•			
													•					
													•					
			•				•		•				•	•	•			
	•		•			•	•		•			•	•	•	•			
	•						•						•	•	•			
•	•	•	•	•		•	•	•	•		•	•	•	•	•	•	•	•
													•	•				
	•				•	•	•		•				•	•	•			
			•		•	•	•		•			•	•	•	•			•

	Vacancies	Partners	Total staff	Work placement	Corporate/ commercial	General commercial	Niche	General practice	High street/ legal aid
Southerns	0	6	63					•	•
Squire Patton Boggs (UK) LLP	25	500	2600	✔	•	•			
Stephensons	5	26	325	✔	•	•		•	•
Storrar Cowdry	0	7	24					•	
Stowe Family Law LLP	Varies	20	60	✔			•		
Systech Solicitors Limited	0		25				•		
Temple Heelis LLP	0	6	30					•	
Thompsons Solicitors	0	50	888				•		
TLT LLP	Up to 15	115	1020	✔	•	•	•	•	
TMJ Law Solicitors	2	2	12	✔		•			
Tranters	4	6	100	✔					•
Trowers & Hamlins LLP	23	161	903	✔	•				
Ward Hadaway	10	85	450	✔	•	•			
Weightmans LLP	Up to 18	187	1306	✔	•	•	•		
WH Darbyshire & Son	0	5	13			•		•	•
Whitworth & Green Solicitors Ltd	4	2	16	✔	•	•		•	•
Winckworth Sherwood LLP	8	58	328	✔			•		
Wrigley Claydon	1	5	26					•	•

Scotland

	Vacancies	Partners	Total staff	Work placement	Corporate/ commercial	General commercial	Niche	General practice	High street/ legal aid
Addleshaw Goddard	37	240	1500	✔	•				
BLM	25	210	1700	✔		•			
Bond Dickinson	30	123	1200	✔	•	•			
Clyde & Co LLP	45-50	375	3600	✔	•	•			
CMS Cameron McKenna Nabarro Olswang LLP	65	1000	7500	✔	•	•			
Corries Solicitors Ltd	0	2	47				•		
DLA Piper UK LLP	Up to 70	1300	8500	✔	•				
DWF LLP	40	329	2600	✔	•	•			
Eversheds Sutherland (International) LLP	50	395	3215	✔	•	•			
Irwin Mitchell	45	269	2700	✔	•	•		•	
Pinsent Masons LLP	72	420	3000	✔	•	•			
Shoosmiths	20	175	1550	✔	•	•	•	•	
Slater & Gordon (UK) LLP	53	86	3500			•		•	
TLT LLP	Up to 15	115	1020	✔	•	•	•	•	
Weightmans LLP	Up to 18	187	1306	✔	•	•	•		

Banking	Comp/comm	Competition	Construction	Corporate tax	Crime	Dispute resolution	Employment	Environment	Family	Human rights	Insurance	IP	Personal injury	Private client	Property	Shipping	Sport	TMT
	•				•	•	•		•				•	•	•			
•	•	•	•	•	•	•	•	•		•	•	•		•	•	•	•	•
	•		•		•	•	•	•	•				•	•	•			
	•						•		•				•	•	•			
									•					•				
			•			•												
	•					•	•		•				•	•	•			
					•								•					
•	•	•	•	•		•	•	•	•			•		•	•	•		•
	•					•	•		•					•	•			
					•								•					
•	•		•			•	•		•					•	•			
•	•	•	•	•		•	•	•	•		•	•		•	•		•	•
•	•	•	•	•	•	•	•	•	•		•	•	•	•	•	•	•	•
					•				•				•	•	•			
	•		•			•	•		•				•					
•	•		•	•		•	•	•	•		•			•	•			•
	•					•	•		•				•	•	•			•

Banking	Comp/comm	Competition	Construction	Corporate tax	Crime	Dispute resolution	Employment	Environment	Family	Human rights	Insurance	IP	Personal injury	Private client	Property	Shipping	Sport	TMT
•	•	•	•	•		•	•	•			•	•		•	•		•	•
			•			•	•	•	•		•		•			•		•
•	•	•	•	•		•	•	•			•	•		•	•		•	•
•	•	•	•	•		•	•	•			•	•						•
•	•	•	•	•		•	•	•			•	•			•		•	•
											•		•	•				
•	•	•	•	•		•	•	•			•	•		•	•		•	•
•	•	•	•	•		•	•	•	•		•	•	•	•	•		•	•
•	•	•	•	•		•	•	•			•	•		•	•		•	•
•	•	•	•	•	•	•	•	•	•	•	•	•	•	•	•		•	•
•	•	•	•	•		•	•	•	•		•	•		•	•	•	•	•
•	•	•	•	•		•	•	•			•	•		•	•		•	•
		•			•	•	•		•				•	•	•			•
•	•	•	•	•		•	•	•			•			•	•	•		•
•	•	•	•	•	•	•	•	•	•		•	•	•	•	•	•	•	•

	Vacancies	Partners	Total staff	Work placement	Corporate/ commercial	General commercial	Niche	General practice	High street/ legal aid
Accutrainee	Varies				•	•	•	•	
Alan Simpson & Co	0-1	1	12					•	
Allan Janes	1	5	20	✔	•				
Antony Clapp Solicitors	0	2	13				•		
asb law LLP	2(18)	17	134	✔	•	•		•	
Aston Bond	1	3	20	✔	•	•			
Atkins Hope	0	4	35	✔				•	•
B P Collins LLP	3-4(18)	16	105	✔	•	•		•	
Barlow Robbins LLP	4	18	150		•			•	
Basingstoke & Deane Borough Council	1-2	1	20				•		
Bastian Lloyd Morris LLP	0	3	14	✔					•
Batchelors	0	14	55			•			
Berry & Lamberts Solicitors	1(18)	12	80					•	•
BG Group Plc	1		100				•		
Bhogal Partners Solicitors	1	3	19	✔	•	•			
Birkett Long LLP	0	24	175	✔	•	•		•	
Blake Morgan LLP	18	101	1000	✔	•	•	•	•	
Blandy & Blandy LLP	2-3	20	104	✔	•	•		•	
Blaser Mills	4	22	125		•	•		•	•
BLM	25	210	1700	✔		•			
Bond Dickinson	30	123	1200	✔	•	•			
Boodle Hatfield LLP	4	34	150	✔	•	•	•		
Bosley & Co	1	3	13	✔				•	•
Boyes Turner	3	23	160	✔	•	•	•	•	
Brachers LLP	2(19)	23	180	✔	•				
Bramsdon & Childs	1	5	34			•		•	•
Breeze & Wyles Solicitors Ltd	4(18)	9	180		•			•	
Brignalls Balderston Warren	0	13	57					•	
Brooks & Partners	0	1	24		•	•		•	
BTMK Solicitors LLP	2(18)	10	70	✔	•	•	•	•	
Buss Murton Law LLP	1(19)	9	80					•	
Carpenter & Co	0-1	3	25					•	•
Carter Bells LLP	0	7	25					•	
Charles Russell Speechlys	24	148	1001	✔	•	•			
Chatham Chambers Solicitors	1	2	6	✔		•	•	•	
Churchers Bolitho Way	0	7	22	✔	•	•	•	•	•
Clarke Kiernan	1(18)	2	27						•
Clarke Willmott LLP	TBC	73	410		•	•			
Clarkslegal LLP	2	13	70			•			
Clarkson Wright & Jakes Ltd	0	15	77		•	•		•	
Clifton Ingram LLP	1	12	70			•		•	

Banking	Comp/comm	Competition	Construction	Corporate tax	Crime	Dispute resolution	Employment	Environment	Family	Human rights	Insurance	IP	Personal injury	Private client	Property	Shipping	Sport	TMT
•	•	•	•	•		•	•	•	•		•	•	•	•	•	•	•	•
	•						•		•				•		•			
	•		•			•	•						•	•	•			•
									•									
•	•	•	•	•		•	•	•	•			•	•	•	•		•	•
	•		•			•	•					•		•				•
							•		•				•	•				
•	•	•	•	•		•	•	•				•		•	•			•
	•					•	•		•			•	•	•	•			•
		•	•		•	•	•	•				•			•		•	•
					•				•	•								
	•		•			•	•		•				•		•	•		
	•				•	•	•		•	•				•	•			
	•		•			•			•							•		
	•				•	•	•		•		•	•	•	•	•			
•	•	•	•	•		•	•	•	•	•	•	•	•	•	•		•	•
•	•	•	•	•		•	•		•			•	•	•	•	•		•
	•	•		•		•	•	•	•			•		•	•		•	•
	•				•	•	•		•				•	•	•			•
		•				•	•	•	•		•				•			•
•	•	•	•	•		•		•			•	•		•	•	•		•
	•		•	•					•					•	•			
					•		•		•				•	•	•			
•	•	•	•	•		•	•		•			•	•	•	•			•
•	•		•	•		•	•	•	•				•	•	•			
						•	•		•				•	•	•			
	•					•			•			•		•	•			
	•				•	•	•		•				•	•	•			
	•		•			•	•		•			•		•	•			
	•					•	•		•			•	•	•	•			
	•	•	•	•		•	•		•	•		•		•	•			
						•	•		•				•	•	•			
	•					•			•				•	•	•			
•	•	•	•	•		•	•	•	•		•	•	•	•	•		•	•
						•	•		•				•	•	•			
	•	•				•			•			•	•	•			•	•
					•		•		•	•			•					
•	•	•	•	•		•	•	•	•		•	•	•	•	•		•	•
•	•	•	•			•	•	•				•		•	•			•
•	•		•			•	•		•			•	•	•	•			•
	•					•	•		•			•		•	•			•

	Vacancies	Partners	Total staff	Work placement	Corporate/ commercial	General commercial	Niche	General practice	High street/ legal aid
Clyde & Co LLP	45-50	375	3600	✔	•	•			
Coffin Mew LLP	4	16	137		•	•	•	•	
Colemans-ctts t/a Simpson Millar	0	12	200		•			•	
Collins Solicitors	0	5	24				•		•
Cowans Solicitors LLP	0	2	25					•	•
Cripps LLP	10	51	350	✔	•	•		•	
Crown Prosecution Service	1(18)		5974				•		
Cunningtons	Varies	9	60	✔				•	•
Curwens LLP	2(18)	15	90					•	
Curzon Green Solicitors	2(18)	3	22	✔					
DAC Beachcroft	13(19)	240	2300	✔	•	•			
Dakers Marriott Solicitors	0	3	12			•			
Darbys Solicitors LLP	4	38	219	✔	•	•	•	•	•
Darlingtons	1	6	42	✔	•			•	
David Phillips & Partners	0	15	75	✔			•	•	•
Dawson Hart	0	7	42					•	
Dean Wilson LLP	2(19)	13	69		•	•		•	
Debenhams Ottaway LLP	0	12	120					•	
Dexter Montague LLP	1(19)	4	24	✔				•	•
DMH Stallard LLP	0	59	259	✔	•	•		•	
Drysdales Solicitors LLP	1	3	20					•	
DW Law	1	2	8	✔					•
East Hampshire District Council	0		7						
Edwards Duthie	0	12	85		•	•		•	•
EMD Law LLP	0	3	13					•	
EMW Law LLP	5	34	172		•				
Eric Robinson Solicitors	2	9	140					•	
Essex Legal Services	0		120						
Fearon & Co	0	1	6				•		
Field Seymour Parkes	3	20	110	✔	•	•		•	
Fitz Solicitors	0	1	5		•	•		•	
Frances Lindsay & Co	0-1	1	5				•		
Franklins Solicitors LLP	0	14	100	✔	•	•		•	
Furley Page LLP	2	18	150	✔	•			•	
Gaby Hardwicke	2(19)	20	150		•	•		•	
Garden House Solicitors	1(18)	1	12					•	
GC Solicitors	0	2	17					•	•
Gepp & Sons Solicitors LLP	2(18)	17	85					•	
Gill Turner Tucker	0	4	27			•		•	•
Girlings	2(19)	12	81		•	•		•	
Glanvilles	1	12	100		•	•		•	•

Banking	Comp/comm	Competition	Construction	Corporate tax	Crime	Dispute resolution	Employment	Environment	Family	Human rights	Insurance	IP	Personal injury	Private client	Property	Shipping	Sport	TMT
•	•	•	•	•		•	•	•			•	•	•		•	•		•
•	•	•	•			•	•		•				•	•	•			•
	•					•	•						•		•			
								•	•				•	•				
					•				•									
	•		•	•		•	•		•				•	•	•			•
					•													
	•					•	•		•				•	•	•			
	•	•				•	•		•				•	•	•			
	•		•			•	•		•				•	•	•			
•	•	•	•	•		•	•	•	•	•	•	•	•		•			•
	•					•	•		•					•	•			
	•		•		•	•	•	•	•			•	•	•	•			•
	•		•			•	•		•			•	•	•	•			
					•				•				•	•				
	•					•	•		•				•	•	•			
	•					•	•		•				•	•	•			
•	•			•		•	•		•				•	•	•			
	•					•	•		•	•			•	•	•			
•	•		•			•	•	•	•			•	•	•	•			•
	•		•	•		•	•		•			•	•	•	•			•
					•									•				
					•			•										
					•	•	•		•				•	•	•			
						•	•		•					•				
•	•		•			•	•		•				•		•			•
	•				•	•	•		•				•	•	•			
						•	•		•		•		•					
•									•				•	•	•			
•	•	•	•	•		•	•		•				•		•	•	•	•
	•					•		•	•						•			
									•									
	•					•	•		•				•	•	•			•
	•					•	•	•	•				•	•	•			•
	•					•	•		•				•	•	•			
						•	•		•				•	•				
									•				•					
	•				•	•	•		•			•		•	•			
	•					•	•		•					•	•			
	•					•	•		•				•	•	•			
	•					•	•		•				•	•	•			•

	Vacancies	Partners	Total staff	Work placement	Corporate/ commercial	General commercial	Niche	General practice	High street/ legal aid
Goodhand & Forsyth	0	2	31					•	•
Government Legal	40		2000						
Graeme Quar & Co	0	1	9		•				
Gurney-Champion & Co	0	2	8					•	
Hart Reade	0	6	65			•		•	
Heald Solicitors LLP	1(19)	5	30		•	•		•	
Helix Law	2(18)	3	10				•		
Her Majesty's Courts & Tribunals Service	0		1200					•	
Herrington Carmichael LLP	3-4(19)	10	90		•	•		•	
Hill & Abbott	0		40	✔				•	
Hine Solicitors	10	8	180					•	•
HKH Kenwright & Cox	0	2	19	✔	•			•	•
Hodders	0	5	65		•	•		•	•
Holden & Co. LLP	1	4	23					•	•
Horwood & James LLP	0	5	28					•	
Howell Jones LLP	0	14	75					•	
HRJ Foreman Laws	0	5	35			•			
IBB Solicitors	4	28	191		•	•		•	•
Irwin Mitchell	45	269	2700	✔	•	•		•	
John Chapman and Co	0	4	22					•	•
Judge & Priestley LLP	1	11	130					•	
Kaim Todner Solicitors Ltd	0	8	70					•	•
Kennard Wells Solicitors	1	5	35					•	•
Kennedys	16	245	1700	✔	•	•			
Kesar & Co Solicitors	2(19)	1	29	✔					•
Kingsley Smith Solicitors LLP	0	4	20		•	•		•	
Lamport Bassitt	0	11	80		•	•	•		
Larcomes LLP	1	6	40			•		•	•
Lawtons Solicitors	2(18)	2	25						•
Laytons Solicitors LLP	6	29	118	✔	•	•			
Lennons Solicitors Ltd	1(18)	4	32					•	
Leonard Cannings Solicitors LLP	2	3	20						•
Lester Aldridge LLP	8	42	309	✔	•	•	•	•	
Lewis Silkin	Up to 6	59	343	✔	•	•			
Lightfoots LLP	0	9	110		•	•	•	•	
Machins Solicitors LLP	3(19)	12	92		•	•	•	•	•
Mackarness & Lunt	0	2	18					•	
Major & Co	0	1	8	✔				•	
Martin Cray and Co	1	2	22	✔				•	
Martin Murray & Associates	0	9	70					•	•
Martin Searle Solicitors	0	2	15				•		

Banking	Comp/comm	Competition	Construction	Corporate tax	Crime	Dispute resolution	Employment	Environment	Family	Human rights	Insurance	IP	Personal injury	Private client	Property	Shipping	Sport	TMT
					•		•		•				•	•				
•	•	•		•			•	•		•			•	•	•	•	•	•
	•					•	•	•							•			
	•					•	•		•					•	•			
•	•	•	•			•	•	•	•				•		•		•	•
					•													
	•		•	•		•	•		•					•	•			
	•					•	•		•				•	•	•			
			•				•		•					•	•			
						•	•		•			•		•	•			•
	•					•	•		•					•	•			
			•				•		•				•	•	•			
						•	•		•					•	•			
	•						•		•				•	•				
	•		•			•	•	•	•				•	•	•			•
•	•		•			•	•		•		•	•	•	•	•			
•	•	•	•	•	•	•	•	•	•	•	•	•	•	•	•			•
									•				•					
	•					•	•		•		•			•				
			•						•					•				
			•				•		•				•	•	•			
•	•		•			•	•	•	•			•	•		•	•	•	
			•						•	•			•					
	•	•	•			•	•	•		•				•	•		•	•
	•					•	•		•				•	•	•			
	•						•	•	•				•	•	•			
			•															
•	•	•	•	•		•	•	•	•				•	•	•			•
	•					•	•	•	•				•	•	•			
			•				•		•	•								
•	•	•	•	•		•	•	•	•		•	•	•	•	•	•		•
	•		•	•		•	•					•			•		•	•
•	•					•	•		•			•		•	•			
	•		•			•	•	•	•			•	•	•	•			
	•								•					•	•			
	•					•			•				•	•				
			•		•	•	•		•				•	•	•			
					•				•									
							•											

	Vacancies	Partners	Total staff	Work placement	Corporate/ commercial	General commercial	Niche	General practice	High street/ legal aid
Mayo Wynne Baxter LLP	2	31	214					•	
McMillan Williams Solicitors	Varies	60	400	✔	•	•	•	•	•
Moore Blatch LLP	3(19)	42	270					•	
Morrisons Solicitors LLP	2-4(19)	13	140					•	
Mowll & Mowll	0	4	17		•	•			
Mullis & Peake	Poss(18)	7	56					•	
Noble Solicitors	0	3	40	✔					•
Osborne Clarke LLP	20	213	1370	✔	•	•	•		
Owen White	2	6	40		•	•	•		
Owen White and Catlin	3	11	130			•		•	•
Palmers	0	8	90	✔	•	•		•	
Paris Smith LLP	4	37	161	✔	•	•		•	
Parker Bullen LLP	2(19)	7	61	✔	•	•		•	
Paul Robinson Solicitors LLP	1	9	85		•			•	•
Penningtons Manches LLP	12-14	110	600	✔	•	•			
Pictons Solicitors LLP	0	5	50		•			•	
Pitmans LLP	8	40	210		•	•	•		
Pope & Co	0	2	12	✔				•	•
Premier Solicitors LLP	10	6	80	✔				•	
Prettys	3-4	6	75	✔	•	•		•	
Quality Solicitors Large & Gibson	0	2	20		•	•			
QualitySolicitors Howlett Clarke LLP	2(19)	3	45					•	
QualitySolicitors Truemans	0	3	18					•	•
Raj Law Solicitors	0	2	8					•	•
Rawlison Butler LLP	0	14	74		•	•	•		
Reena Ghai Solicitors	0-1	1	6						•
Rix & Kay Solicitors LLP	1(18)	22	125	✔	•				
Robson & Co	0	2	8					•	
Royds Withy King	12	64	470	✔	•	•		•	•
SA Law	2(18)	15	90		•	•			
The Sethi Partnership Solicitors	1	3	25	✔	•	•		•	
Shakespeare Martineau LLP	10	130	850		•				
Sherrards Solicitors LLP	1	15	90		•	•	•		
Shoosmiths	20	175	1550	✔	•	•	•	•	
Silverbeck Rymer	0-3	7	218				•		
SO Legal Limited	5(19)	2	12		•	•		•	
Spelthorne Borough Council	0		7	✔					
Stephen Rimmer LLP	0	6	74			•		•	•
Stephens & Son LLP	0	8	35			•		•	
Stevens & Bolton LLP	5	42	227	✔	•	•		•	
stevensdrake limited	0	7	45		•	•			

Banking	Comp/comm	Competition	Construction	Corporate tax	Crime	Dispute resolution	Employment	Environment	Family	Human rights	Insurance	IP	Personal injury	Private client	Property	Shipping	Sport	TMT
	•					•	•		•			•	•	•	•			•
	•	•	•	•	•	•	•		•	•			•	•	•			•
	•		•			•	•	•	•			•	•	•	•			
•	•			•		•	•		•			•	•	•	•			
	•					•	•		•				•	•	•			
					•													
•	•	•	•	•		•	•	•				•		•	•			•
	•	•				•	•					•		•	•			•
			•				•		•				•	•	•			
	•		•	•	•	•	•		•			•	•	•	•			•
•	•		•	•		•	•	•	•			•	•	•	•		•	•
•	•	•	•		•	•	•		•			•	•	•	•	•	•	•
	•				•	•	•		•			•	•	•	•			•
•	•		•	•		•	•		•			•	•	•	•		•	•
	•					•	•		•				•	•	•			
•	•		•			•	•	•	•		•	•	•	•	•			•
						•	•		•				•	•	•			
	•					•	•		•			•	•	•	•			
	•	•	•	•		•	•	•	•		•	•		•	•	•	•	•
	•				•	•	•		•				•	•	•			
	•					•	•		•			•	•	•	•			
	•					•			•				•	•	•			
					•									•				
	•	•	•			•			•			•	•	•	•		•	•
					•				•					•				
	•		•			•	•		•			•	•	•	•		•	
									•					•				
•	•	•	•	•		•	•		•			•	•	•	•		•	•
•	•					•	•		•				•		•		•	•
	•		•			•	•		•				•	•	•			•
•	•	•	•	•		•	•	•	•		•	•	•	•	•			•
•	•					•	•		•			•		•	•		•	•
•	•	•	•	•		•	•	•	•		•	•	•	•	•	•	•	•
													•	•				
	•		•			•	•								•			
	•					•		•							•			
	•		•		•	•	•		•			•	•	•				
	•				•	•	•		•				•	•	•			
•	•	•	•	•		•	•	•	•		•	•		•	•			•
•	•	•	•	•		•	•		•			•		•	•			•

	Vacancies	Partners	Total staff	Work placement	Corporate/ commercial	General commercial	Niche	General practice	High street/ legal aid
Stone King	4	33	197	✔	•	•	•	•	
Surrey Law Centre	0		9	✔					•
Talbot Walker LLP	1	3	18					•	
Tassells	1	7	21	✔		•		•	
Taylor Walton LLP	2	27	150	✔	•	•		•	
Tees Law	3	20	240	✔				•	
Thackray Williams LLP	3(19)	18	150		•	•		•	•
Thompson Smith and Puxon	Poss	11	75		•	•	•	•	
Thompsons Solicitors	0	50	888				•		
Thomson Snell & Passmore LLP	6	39	230	✔	•	•		•	
Thomson Webb & Corfield	1(18)	9	39		•			•	
Tinklin Springall	2(18)	7	50					•	
Trethowans LLP	3-4	35	214	✔	•	•		•	
TWM Solicitors LLP	0	32	200		•	•		•	
Veale Wasbrough Vizards LLP	8-10	72	411	✔	•	•	•	•	
Vodafone Group Services	0		110	✔	•	•			
W H Matthews & Co	0	12	49					•	
Wannop & Fox	0	6	52					•	•
Warner Goodman LLP	2-4	17	160		•	•		•	•
Warners Solicitors	2(19)	22	111					•	
Weightmans LLP	Up to 18	187	1306	✔	•	•	•		
Wellers Law Group LLP	1(19)	3	85		•	•		•	
White & Co	1(18)	2	12	✔			•		•
Whitehead Monckton	Varies(19)	10	118					•	
Whitworth & Green Solicitors Ltd	4	2	16	✔	•	•		•	•
Wills Chandler	1	3	14					•	•
Wilson & Bird	1	1	6					•	
Wilsons Solicitors	2	1	5	✔				•	•
Winckworth Sherwood LLP	8	58	328	✔			•		
Woodfines LLP	3(19)	20	152	✔	•	•		•	
Wortley Byers LLP	0	11	60		•	•		•	

Banking	Comp/comm	Competition	Construction	Corporate tax	Crime	Dispute resolution	Employment	Environment	Family	Human rights	Insurance	IP	Personal injury	Private client	Property	Shipping	Sport	TMT
	•			•		•	•		•			•		•	•			•
							•		•									
	•					•	•		•			•	•	•	•			
	•		•			•	•		•					•	•			
	•					•	•		•			•		•	•			•
	•					•	•	•	•		•	•	•	•	•			
	•		•			•	•		•				•	•	•			
	•		•			•	•		•				•	•	•			
					•		•		•				•					
	•	•	•	•		•	•	•	•		•	•	•	•	•			•
	•			•		•	•		•					•	•			
	•					•	•		•					•	•			
•	•					•	•		•			•	•	•	•			
	•		•			•	•		•					•	•			
•	•	•	•	•		•	•	•	•			•	•	•	•			•
•	•	•				•						•						•
	•		•		•	•	•		•				•	•	•			
	•				•	•	•		•				•	•	•			
	•	•				•	•		•			•	•	•	•			
	•				•	•	•		•			•	•	•	•		•	•
•	•	•	•	•	•	•	•	•	•		•	•	•	•	•	•	•	•
	•						•	•	•			•	•	•	•			
									•					•				
	•			•		•	•		•			•		•	•			
	•				•	•	•		•				•					
	•					•	•		•				•	•	•			
					•				•					•	•			
	•				•	•	•		•				•	•	•			
•	•		•	•		•	•	•	•			•		•	•			•
	•	•	•		•	•	•	•	•			•	•	•	•			•
	•		•			•	•	•	•			•	•	•	•			•

Southwest

	Vacancies	Partners	Total staff	Work placement	Corporate/ commercial	General commercial	Niche	General practice	High street/ legal aid
Accutrainee	Varies				•	•	•	•	
AMD Solicitors Limited	1	2	30			•		•	•
Ashfords	9	74	540	✔	•	•		•	
Awdry Bailey & Douglas	0	7	95		•	•		•	
Barcan Kirby	0	13	150			•		•	•
Battens Solicitors Limited	0	13	109					•	•
Beale & Company Solicitors LLP	5-6[19]	23	120		•	•	•		
Bennetts Solicitors & Attorneys	0	4	15		•	•	•	•	
Bevan Brittan LLP	8	51	292	✔	•	•			
Beviss & Beckingsale	1[18]	7	50	✔				•	
Blanchards Bailey LLP	0	6	66					•	
BLM	25	210	1700	✔		•			
Bond Dickinson	30	123	1200	✔	•	•			
BPE Solicitors LLP	4	21	130	✔	•	•			
Brain Sinnott & Co	0-1	3	25					•	•
Browne Jacobson LLP	20	115	964	✔	•	•	•		
BS Singh & Co LLP	2	2	4	✔			•	•	
Burges Salmon LLP	30	87	750	✔	•	•		•	
Burroughs Day	1	10	100		•	•		•	
Charles Russell Speechlys	24	148	1001	✔	•	•		•	
Charlesworth Nicholl & Co	0	2	20						•
Clarke & Son Solicitors LLP	0	7	37		•	•		•	
Clarke Willmott LLP	TBC	73	410		•	•		•	
CMS Cameron McKenna Nabarro Olswang LLP	65	1000	7500	✔	•	•			
Coles Miller	3	12	110	✔	•	•		•	•
The Commercial Law Practice	0	1	4	✔	•	•			
Crosse & Crosse	0	8	56		•	•		•	•
Crown Prosecution Service	1[18]		5974				•		
DAC Beachcroft	13[19]	240	2300	✔	•	•		•	
Davies and Partners	1[18]	12	170		•	•		•	
Davies Johnson	0		26				•		
Devon & Cornwall Constabulary	0	1	12				•		
Ellis Jones Solicitors LLP	2	12	130	✔	•	•		•	
Everys	0	10	100		•	•		•	•
Farnfields	0	4	65					•	•
Foot Anstey LLP	12[19]	49	500	✔	•	•		•	
Ford Simey LLP	0	11	64					•	
GA Solicitors	1	15	75		•	•		•	
Gammon Bell & Co	1	2	25					•	
Gilbert Stephens LLP	1	12	126		•	•		•	•

Banking	Comp/comm	Competition	Construction	Corporate tax	Crime	Dispute resolution	Employment	Environment	Family	Human rights	Insurance	IP	Personal injury	Private client	Property	Shipping	Sport	TMT
•	•	•	•	•		•	•	•	•		•	•	•	•	•	•	•	•
								•					•	•				
•	•	•	•	•	•	•	•	•	•		•	•	•	•	•	•	•	•
	•		•			•	•		•				•	•	•			
	•		•			•	•		•				•	•	•			
•	•	•	•	•		•	•	•	•				•	•	•	•		
	•		•			•	•	•			•	•			•			•
•	•		•	•		•	•				•			•		•		•
	•	•	•			•	•	•			•	•			•			•
	•					•		•	•				•	•	•			
	•						•		•				•	•	•			
		•				•	•	•	•		•		•			•		•
•	•	•	•	•		•	•		•		•	•	•	•	•		•	
•	•		•	•		•	•		•				•	•	•			•
					•				•				•	•				
•	•	•	•	•		•	•	•			•	•	•	•	•		•	•
					•	•	•		•				•	•				
•	•	•	•	•		•	•	•	•		•	•	•	•	•		•	•
	•					•	•		•			•	•	•	•			•
•	•	•	•	•		•	•	•	•		•	•	•	•	•		•	•
	•						•		•				•	•	•			
	•					•		•	•				•	•	•			
•	•	•	•	•		•	•	•	•		•	•	•	•	•		•	•
•	•	•	•	•		•	•	•			•	•			•		•	•
	•		•			•	•	•	•			•	•	•	•			•
	•						•							•				
	•		•			•	•	•	•				•	•	•			
					•													
•	•	•	•	•		•	•	•				•	•	•		•		•
	•		•			•	•	•	•				•	•	•	•		•
							•				•			•		•		
					•		•			•			•					
•	•			•	•	•	•		•				•	•	•	•		
	•					•	•		•	•			•	•	•	•		
	•					•	•		•						•	•		
•	•	•	•	•		•	•	•	•		•	•	•	•	•			•
						•			•					•	•	•		
	•					•	•		•				•	•	•	•		
	•					•	•		•				•	•	•			

	Vacancies	Partners	Total staff	Work placement	Corporate/commercial	General commercial	Niche	General practice	High street/legal aid
Gordon Dadds LLP	6(19)	39	236		•	•		•	
Government Legal	40		2000						
Gregg Latchams Limited	2(19)	9	52	✔	•	•		•	
Harrison Clark Rickerbys Solicitors	Approx 10	70	460	✔	•	•		•	
Her Majesty's Courts & Tribunals Service	0		1200					•	
Hine Solicitors	10	8	180					•	•
Hooper & Wollen	0	11	84					•	•
Hotchkiss Warburton	0	2	5					•	
Howard & Over	0	2	32					•	•
Hughes Paddison	2	8	50					•	
Humphreys & Co	1-2	4	35	✔	•	•	•	•	
Humphries Kirk LLP	1(19)	20	180	✔				•	
Irwin Mitchell	45	269	2700	✔	•	•		•	
Jacobs & Reeves	0	6	45		•	•		•	•
John Hodge Solicitors	0	4	65	✔				•	
Kennedys	16	245	1700	✔	•	•			
Kiteleys	0	4	50	✔				•	
Kitsons LLP	Poss(18)	16	100		•	•		•	
Laceys Solicitors LLP	2	13	110					•	
Langley Wellington LLP Solicitors	0	8	70					•	•
Lester Aldridge LLP	8	42	309	✔	•	•	•	•	
Lyons Davidson	4-6	36	1200		•	•		•	
Makka Solicitors Ltd	1	3	8	✔				•	•
McMillan Williams Solicitors	Varies	60	400	✔	•	•	•	•	•
Metcalfes Solicitors	0	6	55		•	•	•	•	
Michelmores LLP	8	64	450	✔	•	•		•	
Middleton & Upsall LLP	0	2	25					•	•
Murrell Associates Limited	0	3	16	✔	•				
Mustoe Shorter	0	7	50					•	•
Nash & Co Solicitors LLP	0	12	72		•	•		•	•
Osborne Clarke LLP	20	213	1370	✔	•	•	•		
Over Taylor Biggs	1	5	20			•			
Pardoes Solicitors LLP	1(19)	8	76					•	•
Paris Smith LLP	4	37	161	✔	•	•		•	
Parker Bullen LLP	2(19)	7	61	✔	•	•		•	
Plexus Law	0	117	1800				•		
Porter Dodson	Poss	22	120		•	•		•	•
Rawlins Davy Plc	0	8	45		•	•		•	
Reynolds Colman Bradley LLP	1	3	22	✔			•		
RJR Solicitors	0	5	45						•
Royds Withy King	12	64	470	✔	•	•		•	•

Banking	Comp/comm	Competition	Construction	Corporate tax	Crime	Dispute resolution	Employment	Environment	Family	Human rights	Insurance	IP	Personal injury	Private client	Property	Shipping	Sport	TMT
•	•	•	•	•		•	•		•		•	•	•	•	•		•	•
•	•	•		•			•	•		•		•	•	•	•	•	•	•
	•				•	•	•	•	•					•	•			
•	•	•	•	•		•	•	•	•		•	•	•	•	•	•	•	•
					•		•		•					•	•			
	•					•	•	•	•				•	•	•	•	•	
															•			
					•				•				•	•				
	•								•				•	•	•			
	•	•	•			•	•	•			•	•	•	•	•		•	•
	•		•			•	•		•			•	•	•	•			
•	•	•	•	•	•	•	•	•	•	•	•	•	•	•	•			•
	•				•	•	•		•			•	•	•	•			
						•	•		•			•	•	•				
•	•		•			•	•	•	•		•	•	•	•	•	•	•	
						•	•	•	•		•	•	•	•				
•	•			•		•	•	•	•			•	•	•	•			
•	•		•			•	•		•			•	•	•	•			•
									•			•	•	•				
•	•	•	•	•		•	•	•	•		•	•	•	•	•	•		•
							•	•	•		•		•	•				
	•					•			•						•			
	•	•	•	•	•	•	•		•	•			•	•	•			•
•	•		•			•	•		•		•	•	•	•	•			•
•	•	•	•	•		•	•	•	•		•	•	•	•				•
	•											•	•		•	•		
					•		•	•		•			•		•			
•	•					•	•		•			•	•	•	•	•	•	•
•	•	•	•	•		•	•	•				•	•	•				•
	•					•	•						•		•			
			•		•	•	•	•	•			•	•	•	•			
•	•		•	•		•	•	•	•			•	•	•	•		•	•
•	•	•	•		•	•	•	•	•			•	•	•	•	•	•	•
			•			•				•			•					
	•		•	•		•	•	•	•			•	•	•	•			
	•					•	•						•		•			
			•			•					•							•
	•				•	•			•				•	•	•			
•	•	•	•	•		•	•		•			•	•	•	•		•	•

	Vacancies	Partners	Total staff	Work placement	Corporate/ commercial	General commercial	Niche	General practice	High street/ legal aid
RPC	12	81	760	✔	•	•			
Samuels	1	3	16	✔				•	
Scott Rowe Solicitors	1(18)	3	26			•		•	
Sewell Mullings Logie LLP	1(19)	7	42				•	•	
Shoosmiths	20	175	1550	✔	•	•	•	•	
Simmons & Simmons LLP	30	250	1600	✔	•	•			
Steele Raymond LLP	2-3(18)	14	75		•	•		•	
Stephens Scown	10	55	300	✔	•			•	
Stone King	4	33	197	✔	•	•	•	•	
Stones Solicitors LLP	2(19)	14	100		•	•	•	•	
Stowe Family Law LLP	Varies	20	60	✔				•	
Thompsons Solicitors	0	50	888					•	
Thorne Segar Ltd	1	2	27	✔				•	
Thrings	10(19)	60	337		•	•	•	•	
TLT LLP	Up to 15	115	1020	✔	•	•		•	
Tozers LLP	Poss	20	120	✔	•	•		•	•
Trethowans LLP	3-4	35	214	✔	•	•		•	
Trowers & Hamlins LLP	23	161	903	✔	•				
Veale Wasbrough Vizards LLP	8-10	72	411	✔	•	•		•	
Waller & Hart Solicitors Limited	0		14			•	•	•	
Wansbroughs	2-3(18)	16	90					•	
Watkins Solicitors	0	3	32	✔			•		•
Willans LLP	0	14	70		•	•		•	
Wilsons Solicitors LLP	4	29	157	✔	•	•	•	•	

Wales

	Vacancies	Partners	Total staff	Work placement	Corporate/ commercial	General commercial	Niche	General practice	High street/ legal aid
Accutrainee	Varies				•	•	•	•	
Acuity Legal Limited	2-3(18)	16	62	✔	•				
Allington Hughes Law	1(19)	14	75					•	•
Anthony Jacobs & Co	2(18)	1	5	✔				•	
Bennetts Solicitors & Attorneys	0	4	15		•	•	•	•	
Blake Morgan LLP	18	101	1000	✔	•	•	•	•	
Bridger & Co Solicitors	1	3	8	✔				•	
Cameron Jones Hussell & Howe	0	5	28					•	
Capital Law	4(18)	18	85	✔	•	•			
Carmarthenshire County Council	0	6	16		•				

Banking	Comp/comm	Competition	Construction	Corporate tax	Crime	Dispute resolution	Employment	Environment	Family	Human rights	Insurance	IP	Personal injury	Private client	Property	Shipping	Sport	TMT
•	•	•	•	•		•	•				•	•	•		•			•
						•							•	•	•			
	•					•	•		•				•	•	•			
	•					•	•		•					•	•			
•	•	•	•	•		•	•	•	•		•	•	•	•	•	•	•	•
•	•	•		•		•	•	•			•	•			•			•
•	•	•	•	•		•	•	•	•			•	•	•	•	•		•
•	•	•	•	•		•	•	•	•	•		•	•	•	•			•
	•			•		•	•		•			•		•	•			•
	•		•	•		•	•		•		•	•	•	•	•		•	•
									•					•				
					•				•				•					
									•					•				
•	•	•	•	•		•	•	•	•		•	•	•	•	•	•	•	•
•	•	•	•	•		•	•	•	•			•		•	•	•	•	•
	•					•	•	•	•			•	•	•	•	•	•	
•	•					•	•		•			•	•	•	•			
•	•			•	•	•	•							•	•			
•	•	•	•	•		•	•	•	•			•	•	•	•			•
	•						•							•	•			
	•		•			•	•	•	•				•	•	•		•	
							•		•						•			
•	•	•	•			•	•		•			•	•	•	•			•
	•	•		•		•	•		•			•		•	•			

Banking	Comp/comm	Competition	Construction	Corporate tax	Crime	Dispute resolution	Employment	Environment	Family	Human rights	Insurance	IP	Personal injury	Private client	Property	Shipping	Sport	TMT
•	•	•	•	•		•	•	•	•		•	•	•	•	•	•	•	•
•	•		•			•	•		•				•		•		•	•
	•				•	•	•		•				•	•	•			
							•		•				•		•			
•	•		•	•		•	•					•		•	•		•	•
•	•	•	•	•		•	•	•	•		•	•	•	•	•	•		•
	•				•	•	•	•	•			•	•	•	•		•	
									•					•				
	•					•	•	•				•			•			•
			•		•	•	•	•	•					•				

	Vacancies	Partners	Total staff	Work placement	Corporate/ commercial	General commercial	Niche	General practice	High street/ legal aid
City and County of Swansea	0		54						
Crown Prosecution Service	1(18)		5974				•		
Cyril Jones & Co	0	5	20					•	•
DAC Beachcroft	13(19)	240	2300	✔	•	•		•	
David & Snape	0	4	26			•		•	•
Dolmans Solicitors	0	9	39		•	•	•		
Douglas-Jones Mercer	1	7	50		•	•		•	
Eversheds Sutherland (International) LLP	50	395	3215	✔	•	•			
Fountain Solicitors Limited	1(18)	1	40	✔				•	•
Gabb & Co	0	6	36					•	
Gamlins Law	2(18)	11	70	✔	•	•		•	•
Geldards LLP	6(19)	57	352		•	•	•		
GHP Legal	0	10	87	✔				•	•
Glamorgan Law	0	4			•	•	•	•	
Gordon Dadds LLP	6(19)	39	236		•	•		•	
Government Legal	40		2000						
Hains & Lewis	0	4	30					•	•
Harding Evans LLP	1	10	120	✔				•	
Her Majesty's Courts & Tribunals Service	0		1200					•	
Hugh James	10	62	690	✔	•	•	•	•	•
Huttons	0	3	25	✔				•	•
JNP Legal	2(18)	4	32					•	•
JW Hughes & Co	0	6	34					•	•
Kirwans	0	5	80			•		•	•
Leo Abse & Cohen	0	13	140		•	•		•	
Lewis Silkin	Up to 6	59	343	✔	•	•			
Lyons Davidson	4-6	36	1200		•	•		•	
Patchell Davies	0	2	7					•	
PJE Solicitors	0	2	10					•	
Quality Solicitors J A Hughes	1	6	30	✔				•	•
RadcliffesLeBrasseur	4	40	170		•	•	•	•	
Slater & Gordon (UK) LLP	53	86	3500			•		•	
Smith Llewelyn Partnership	1	4	40	✔				•	•
The Speakeasy	0		14				•		
Thompsons Solicitors	0	50	888					•	
Wendy Hopkins Family Law Practice	1	4	27				•		

Banking	Comp/comm	Competition	Construction	Corporate tax	Crime	Dispute resolution	Employment	Environment	Family	Human rights	Insurance	IP	Personal injury	Private client	Property	Shipping	Sport	TMT
					•													
							•		•				•	•	•			
•	•	•	•	•		•	•	•			•	•	•		•			•
	•				•	•	•		•				•	•	•			
	•		•			•	•	•			•	•	•	•	•		•	•
•	•		•			•	•		•		•	•	•	•	•			
•	•	•	•	•		•	•	•			•	•	•	•	•	•	•	•
							•		•	•			•					
	•						•							•	•			
	•				•	•	•	•	•			•	•	•	•			
•	•		•	•		•	•		•		•	•	•	•	•		•	•
	•			•		•	•		•				•	•	•			
	•		•			•			•			•		•	•		•	
•	•	•	•	•		•	•		•		•	•	•	•	•		•	•
•	•	•		•			•	•		•		•	•	•	•	•	•	•
					•				•					•	•			
	•				•	•	•		•				•	•	•		•	
•	•		•			•	•	•	•		•	•	•	•	•		•	•
	•				•	•	•		•	•			•	•	•			
						•			•				•	•	•			
						•	•		•				•	•	•			
						•	•		•				•	•	•			
	•					•	•		•		•		•	•	•			
	•		•	•		•	•					•		•	•		•	•
	•						•	•	•		•		•	•	•			
	•						•		•				•	•	•			
	•				•				•				•	•	•			
•	•	•		•	•	•	•	•	•		•	•	•	•	•		•	•
			•		•	•	•		•			•	•	•	•			•
						•	•		•	•			•	•	•		•	
					•		•						•					
									•					•				

	Vacancies	Partners	Total staff	Work placement	Corporate/ commercial	General commercial	Niche	General practice	High street/ legal aid
Accutrainee	Varies				•	•	•	•	
Alsters Kelley	0	4	90		•			•	•
Anthony Collins Solicitors	6	28	260	✔	•	•	•	•	•
Atter Mackenzie & Co	2(18)	5	26			•		•	•
Bell Lax Solicitors	2	3	25					•	
Bevan Brittan LLP	8	51	292	✔	•	•			
BLM	25	210	1700	✔		•			
Browne Jacobson LLP	20	115	964	✔	•	•	•		
Caldicotts	0	4	19	✔					•
Cartwright King	0	26	280					•	•
CBTC Rawstorne	0	1	7		•			•	•
Clarke Willmott LLP	TBC	73	410		•	•		•	
Cocks Lloyd	0	10	50		•			•	•
Cotterhill Hitchman LLP	0	3	13			•			
Coventry City Council	0		70						
Cowlishaw & Mountford	0	1	10					•	
Crown Prosecution Service	1(18)		5974				•		
Cunningtons	Varies	9	60	✔				•	•
DAC Beachcroft	13(19)	240	2300	✔	•	•			
David Phillips & Partners	0	15	75	✔			•	•	
Davies and Partners	1(18)	12	170		•	•		•	
De Marco Solicitors	0	1	12	✔	•	•	•		
Df Legal LLP	2	3	24	✔				•	
DLA Piper UK LLP	Up to 70	1300	8500	✔	•				
DWF LLP	40	329	2600	✔	•	•			
Elliott Bridgman Limited	2	1	21	✔		•	•	•	•
Enoch Evans LLP	Poss(18)	13	75		•	•		•	•
Eversheds Sutherland (International) LLP	50	395	3215	✔	•	•			
FBC Manby Bowdler LLP	0	33	195	✔				•	
Ferdinand Kelly	0	1	5			•	•		
Fieldfisher	18	223	986	✔	•	•			
Fountain Solicitors Limited	1(18)	1	40	✔				•	•
Freeths LLP	20	135	750		•	•		•	
Gateley Plc	14	150	802	✔	•	•			
George Green LLP	2	15	67		•	•			
GHP Legal	0	10	87	✔				•	•
Gough-Thomas & Scott	1	4	18					•	
Government Legal	40		2000						
Gowling WLG (UK) LLP	25	593	3171	✔	•	•	•		
Harrison Clark Rickerbys Solicitors	Approx 10	70	460	✔	•	•		•	
Hatchers Solicitors	0	13	90		•	•	•		•

Banking	Comp/comm	Competition	Construction	Corporate tax	Crime	Dispute resolution	Employment	Environment	Family	Human rights	Insurance	IP	Personal injury	Private client	Property	Shipping	Sport	TMT
•	•	•	•	•		•	•	•	•		•	•	•	•	•	•	•	•
	•				•	•	•		•					•	•	•		
	•		•			•	•		•			•	•	•	•			
				•			•		•	•	•		•	•				
•	•		•			•	•		•		•							
	•	•	•			•	•	•					•	•		•		•
	•		•			•	•	•	•		•		•			•		
•	•	•	•	•		•	•	•	•		•	•	•	•	•		•	•
					•		•		•					•				
					•		•	•	•					•				
	•				•				•					•				
•	•	•	•	•		•	•	•	•		•	•	•	•	•		•	•
	•				•	•	•		•				•	•	•			
	•		•			•	•						•	•	•			
	•				•	•	•	•	•					•				
									•									
					•													
	•					•	•		•				•	•	•			
•	•	•	•	•		•	•	•			•	•	•	•				•
					•				•				•	•				
	•		•			•	•	•	•		•	•	•	•				•
	•						•					•						•
	•					•	•		•				•	•	•		•	
•	•	•	•	•		•	•	•			•	•		•	•	•	•	•
•	•	•	•	•		•	•	•	•		•	•	•	•	•	•	•	•
									•					•	•			
•	•	•	•	•	•	•	•	•	•		•	•	•	•	•		•	•
•	•	•	•	•		•	•	•			•	•	•	•	•	•	•	•
	•					•	•	•	•			•		•	•			•
	•	•				•	•					•	•					
•	•	•	•	•		•	•	•	•		•	•	•	•	•		•	•
								•	•	•				•				
•	•	•	•	•		•	•	•	•	•	•	•	•	•	•		•	•
•	•	•	•	•		•	•	•	•			•		•	•	•	•	•
•	•					•	•	•	•			•		•	•			•
	•			•	•	•	•		•				•	•	•			
						•	•		•				•	•	•			
•	•	•		•		•	•	•		•		•	•	•	•	•	•	•
•	•	•	•	•		•	•	•			•	•		•	•	•	•	•
•	•	•	•	•		•	•	•	•		•	•	•	•	•	•	•	•
	•		•		•	•	•	•	•				•	•	•	•		

	Vacancies	Partners	Total staff	Work placement	Corporate/ commercial	General commercial	Niche	General practice	High street/ legal aid
Her Majesty's Courts & Tribunals Service	0		1200					•	
Herefordshire District Council	0		31						
Hibberts LLP	1(18)	7	96	✔		•		•	•
Higgs & Sons	4-6	35	225		•	•	•	•	
Hine Solicitors	10	8	180					•	•
Irwin Mitchell	45	269	2700	✔	•	•		•	
Kangs Solicitors	1-2(19)	1	10				•		
Kennedys	16	245	1700	✔	•	•			
Kundert Solicitors LLP	0	4	30	✔				•	•
Lanyon Bowdler Solicitors LLP	3(19)	26	220		•				
Lodders Solicitors LLP	3	28	115	✔	•			•	
Lyons Davidson	4-6	36	1200		•	•		•	
Mander Hadley Solicitors	0	9	45		•	•		•	•
Martin-Kaye LLP	Poss	6	60		•	•	•	•	•
mfg Solicitors LLP	2-4(19)	30	140		•	•	•	•	•
Mian & Co	0	2	9						•
Mills & Reeve LLP	18	117	800	✔	•	•			
Newcastle under Lyme Borough Council	0		2						
Painters	0	9	50			•		•	•
Pickerings Solicitors	1	4	33		•	•	•	•	•
Pinsent Masons LLP	72	420	3000	✔	•	•			
Plexus Law	0	117	1800				•		
QualitySolicitors Davisons	0	7	150					•	
Rees Page	0	8	46					•	•
RN Williams & Co	1(18)	3	19					•	•
Scaiff LLP	0	3	21					•	
Shakespeare Martineau LLP	10	130	850		•				
Shoosmiths	20	175	1550	✔	•	•	•	•	
Slater & Gordon (UK) LLP	53	86	3500			•		•	
Squire Patton Boggs (UK) LLP	25	500	2600	✔	•	•			
Terry Jones Solicitors	Poss	4	120					•	
Thaliwal & Co Solicitors	0	1	11	✔			•		
Thompsons Solicitors	0	50	888				•		
Tinsdills	TBC(18)	11	97					•	
TMJ Law Solicitors	2	2	12	✔		•			
Toussaints	0	1	1	✔				•	•
Trowers & Hamlins LLP	23	161	903	✔	•				
Veale Wasbrough Vizards LLP	8-10	72	411	✔	•	•		•	
Wall James Chappell	1	7	35					•	
Wallace Robinson & Morgan	1-2	6	40		•	•		•	
Walters & Plaskitt	Poss	4	60	✔				•	•

Banking	Comp/comm	Competition	Construction	Corporate tax	Crime	Dispute resolution	Employment	Environment	Family	Human rights	Insurance	IP	Personal injury	Private client	Property	Shipping	Sport	TMT
	•	•					•	•	•				•		•			•
	•					•	•		•					•	•			
•	•			•		•	•	•	•				•	•	•			•
				•			•		•					•	•			
•	•	•	•	•	•	•	•	•	•	•	•	•	•	•	•			•
	•						•											
•	•		•			•	•	•	•				•	•	•	•	•	
	•				•		•		•				•	•				
	•		•			•	•	•	•				•	•	•			•
	•						•							•	•			
	•						•	•	•		•		•	•	•			
	•				•	•	•		•				•	•				
	•			•		•	•		•				•	•				
					•													
•	•	•	•	•		•	•	•	•			•	•	•	•		•	•
	•				•	•	•	•					•	•	•			
	•						•	•	•				•	•	•		•	
•	•	•	•	•		•	•	•			•	•		•	•	•	•	•
		•				•					•		•					
						•	•		•				•	•	•			
	•					•	•		•				•	•	•			
					•		•		•				•	•				
	•					•			•				•		•			
•	•	•	•	•		•	•	•	•		•	•	•	•	•			•
•	•	•	•	•		•	•	•	•		•	•	•	•	•	•	•	•
		•			•	•	•		•		•		•					•
•	•	•	•	•	•	•	•	•		•	•	•	•	•	•	•	•	•
	•					•	•		•				•	•				
				•			•						•	•	•			
	•		•			•	•		•				•	•	•			
	•					•	•		•					•	•			
						•	•		•									
•	•		•	•		•	•							•	•			
•	•	•	•	•		•	•	•	•			•		•	•			•
	•					•	•		•					•	•			
	•					•	•		•				•	•	•			
					•				•	•			•	•				

	Vacancies	Partners	Total staff	Work placement	Corporate/ commercial	General commercial	Niche	General practice	High street/ legal aid
Watson Watson Solicitors	2	2	20	✔	•	•	•		
Weightmans LLP	Up to 18	187	1306	✔	•	•	•		
WH Law Ltd	0	3	10				•		
The Wilkes Partnership	4	18	160		•	•			
Wright Hassall LLP	4	35	280	✔	•	•	•	•	
Zyda Law	1	1	5	✔		•	•		

Yorkshire

	Vacancies	Partners	Total staff	Work placement	Corporate/ commercial	General commercial	Niche	General practice	High street/ legal aid
Abode Solicitors	1(19)	4	46	✔			•		
Addleshaw Goddard	37	240	1500	✔	•				
Addlestone Keane Solicitors	1(18)	3	14		•	•	•		
Ashton Bell	1	1	6	✔	•	•	•	•	
Atherton Godfrey	2(19)	5	120				•		
Atteys Solicitors	2	3	48	✔	•				•
Austin Kemp Solicitors Limited	2(18)	1	10	✔			•		
Bassra Solicitors (incorporating John Kelly & Co)	0	2	8						•
Blacks Solicitors LLP	3	16	170	✔	•	•			
Bridge McFarland	2(18)	25	167	✔	•	•		•	•
Bridge Sanderson Munro	0	4	20				•		
Bury & Walkers LLP	0	7	66		•	•		•	•
Cartwright King	0	26	280					•	•
CMS Cameron McKenna Nabarro Olswang LLP	65	1000	7500	✔	•	•			
Conrad King & Solomon Solicitors	2	1	6	✔				•	
Corries Solicitors Ltd	0	2	47					•	
Crockett & Co	0	3	8				•		•
Crown Prosecution Service	1(18)		5974				•		
DAC Beachcroft	13(19)	240	2300	✔	•	•		•	
Devonshires Solicitors	6(19)	34	230		•		•		
DLA Piper UK LLP	Up to 70	1300	8500	✔	•				
DWF LLP	40	329	2600	✔	•	•			
Eaton Smith LLP	0	7	80		•	•		•	•
Emsleys	1(19)	4	120					•	
Eversheds Sutherland (International) LLP	50	395	3215	✔	•	•			
Finn Gledhill	0	6	50					•	

Banking	Comp/comm	Competition	Construction	Corporate tax	Crime	Dispute resolution	Employment	Environment	Family	Human rights	Insurance	IP	Personal injury	Private client	Property	Shipping	Sport	TMT
	•			•											•			
•	•	•	•	•	•	•	•	•	•		•	•	•	•	•	•	•	•
							•	•					•	•				
	•		•		•	•	•						•	•	•			
•	•	•	•	•		•	•		•		•	•	•		•		•	•
							•								•			

Banking	Comp/comm	Competition	Construction	Corporate tax	Crime	Dispute resolution	Employment	Environment	Family	Human rights	Insurance	IP	Personal injury	Private client	Property	Shipping	Sport	TMT
															•			
•	•	•	•	•		•	•	•			•	•		•	•		•	•
	•					•							•		•			
	•					•	•		•			•	•	•	•			•
	•					•	•		•	•		•	•	•	•			
	•					•	•		•				•	•	•			
							•											
				•			•											
	•					•	•		•			•	•	•	•		•	
	•		•	•		•	•		•				•	•	•	•	•	
•	•	•	•	•	•	•	•	•	•	•		•	•	•	•		•	•
						•	•	•	•					•				
•	•	•	•	•		•	•	•			•	•			•		•	•
	•						•		•				•					
											•		•	•				
							•											
				•														
•	•	•	•	•		•	•	•			•	•	•		•			•
•	•		•			•	•		•			•	•	•	•		•	•
•	•	•	•	•		•	•	•			•	•			•	•	•	•
•	•	•	•	•		•	•	•	•		•	•	•	•	•	•	•	•
	•		•	•		•	•		•				•	•	•			•
									•				•	•	•			
•	•	•	•	•		•	•	•			•	•		•	•	•	•	•
	•				•	•	•		•				•	•	•			

	Vacancies	Partners	Total staff	Work placement	Corporate/ commercial	General commercial	Niche	General practice	High street/ legal aid
Forbes Solicitors	4	44	320	✔	•	•	•	•	•
Freeths LLP	20	135	750		•	•		•	
Gateley Plc	14	150	802	✔	•	•			
Gordons LLP	4	26	200		•				
Gosschalks	3	28	124		•	•	•	•	
Government Legal	40		2000						
Graham & Rosen	0	6	45					•	
Grays	0	5	26				•		
Harrowells	0	20	131					•	
Hawkswell Kilvington Ltd	1	3	15				•		
Hempsons	3	46	300				•		
Heptonstalls	1-2	6	100					•	•
Her Majesty's Courts & Tribunals Service	0		1200					•	
Hethertons LLP Solicitors	0	3	31					•	•
hlw Keeble Hawson LLP	4	36	280	✔	•	•	•	•	
HSR Law	0	7	42		•	•		•	•
Irwin Mitchell	45	269	2700	✔	•	•		•	
Jacksons Law Firm	2	11	70		•	•		•	
The Johnson Partnership	1-2	13	110	✔					•
Jordans	2(19)	4	65					•	•
Kennedys	16	245	1700	✔	•	•			
Kingsley Brookes	0	1	5				•		•
LA Steel	0		8	✔			•		
Langleys Solicitors LLP	5	34	340	✔	•	•		•	•
LCF Law	2(18)	21	134		•	•			
Lester Morrill	0	4	38				•		•
Lyons Davidson	4-6	36	1200		•	•		•	
Makin Dixon Solicitors	0	2	70						•
Malcolm C Foy & Co Ltd	1	8	57	✔				•	•
Millan Solicitors	0	1	2	✔				•	
Mills & Reeve LLP	18	117	800	✔	•	•			
Minster Law Solicitors	5		830	✔			•	•	
Morrish Solicitors LLP	0	15	90					•	•
Musa Patels	0	2	16					•	•
North Yorkshire County Council	0		43	✔					
Parker Rhodes Hickmotts	0	3	49					•	•
Pattersons Solicitors	0	1	7						•
Pinsent Masons LLP	72	420	3000	✔	•	•			
Quality Solicitors John Barkers	Poss	2	6	✔	•	•	•	•	
QualitySolicitors Bradbury Roberts & Raby	1(18)	5	47					•	•
RadcliffesLeBrasseur	4	40	170		•	•	•	•	

Banking	Comp/comm	Competition	Construction	Corporate tax	Crime	Dispute resolution	Employment	Environment	Family	Human rights	Insurance	IP	Personal injury	Private client	Property	Shipping	Sport	TMT
	●	●	●	●	●	●	●	●	●	●	●	●	●	●	●		●	●
●	●	●	●	●		●	●	●	●	●	●	●	●	●	●		●	●
●	●	●	●	●		●	●	●	●			●		●	●	●	●	●
	●		●	●		●	●					●	●	●	●			●
●	●		●			●	●	●	●			●		●	●			●
●	●	●		●			●	●		●		●	●	●	●	●	●	●
	●					●	●		●				●	●	●			
						●	●		●				●	●	●			
	●					●	●		●			●	●	●	●			
			●			●												
	●			●		●						●		●	●			
													●					
						●	●		●				●	●	●			
●	●		●			●	●		●			●	●	●	●			●
	●				●	●	●		●				●	●	●			
●	●	●	●	●	●	●	●	●	●	●	●	●	●	●	●			●
	●	●	●		●	●	●	●	●			●	●	●	●			●
					●													
	●				●	●	●		●				●	●	●			
●	●		●			●	●	●				●	●	●		●	●	
					●													
						●	●						●					
●	●		●	●		●	●		●		●	●	●	●	●			
	●					●	●		●			●		●	●		●	●
			●							●			●					
	●					●	●	●	●		●	●	●	●	●			
									●									
						●			●				●	●	●			
									●				●					
●	●	●	●	●		●	●	●	●		●	●			●		●	●
							●						●	●	●			
						●	●		●				●	●	●			
				●											●			
	●	●				●	●	●				●		●	●			
	●						●		●				●	●	●			
					●													
●	●	●	●	●		●	●	●			●	●			●	●	●	●
●	●		●			●	●		●			●	●	●	●			
	●					●	●		●				●	●	●			
●	●	●		●	●	●	●	●	●		●	●	●	●	●		●	●

	Vacancies	Partners	Total staff	Work placement	Corporate/ commercial	General commercial	Niche	General practice	High street/ legal aid
Read Dunn Connell	0	4	20			•		•	
Riaz Solicitors	0			✔				•	•
Rollits	2-3	21	118	✔	•	•			
Schofield Sweeney LLP	3(19)	31	161	✔	•	•			
Sergeant & Collins	0	2	15					•	•
Shulmans LLP	3	25	190		•				
SJP Law	2	5	50	✔	•	•			
Slater & Gordon (UK) LLP	53	86	3500			•		•	
Slater Gordon Solutions Legal Ltd	1	5	1150				•		
Squire Patton Boggs (UK) LLP	25	500	2600	✔	•	•			
Stone King	4	33	197	✔	•	•	•	•	
Stowe Family Law LLP	Varies	20	60	✔			•		
Switalskis Solicitors LLP	0	12	250		•				•
Systech Solicitors Limited	0		25				•		
Thompsons Solicitors	0	50	888				•		
Thorpe & Co	1	8	55					•	•
W Brook & Co	1(18)	2	20						•
Wake Smith Solicitors	1(19)	19	105	✔	•	•		•	
Walker Morris LLP	15	48	450	✔	•	•			
Ward Hadaway	10	85	450	✔	•	•			
Watson Burton LLP	3(19)	14	110	✔	•				
Weightmans LLP	Up to 18	187	1306	✔	•	•	•		
Wilkin Chapman LLP	4	42	360	✔	•	•		•	
Wilkinson Woodward Limited	1-2	8	92					•	•
Wrigley Claydon	1	5	26					•	•
Wrigleys Solicitors LLP	2	21	193				•		
Yorklaw Ltd t/as Burn & Company	0	5	20					•	

Banking	Comp/comm	Competition	Construction	Corporate tax	Crime	Dispute resolution	Employment	Environment	Family	Human rights	Insurance	IP	Personal injury	Private client	Property	Shipping	Sport	TMT
	•					•	•		•				•	•	•			
					•								•					
•	•		•			•	•	•	•				•	•	•			•
•	•		•	•		•	•	•						•	•			•
					•	•			•				•	•	•			
•	•	•	•	•		•	•	•				•	•	•	•		•	•
	•						•	•			•		•	•	•			•
		•				•			•			•	•	•	•			•
													•					
•	•	•	•	•	•	•	•	•		•	•	•	•	•	•		•	•
	•		•			•	•		•		•		•	•				•
								•						•				
		•				•			•	•			•					
		•				•												
			•			•		•					•					
			•			•			•				•	•				
			•			•			•				•					
	•		•	•		•	•		•				•	•	•			•
•	•	•	•	•		•	•	•			•	•	•	•	•		•	•
•	•	•	•	•		•	•	•			•	•	•	•	•		•	•
•	•		•	•		•	•	•			•	•		•				•
•	•	•	•	•	•	•	•	•			•	•	•	•	•	•	•	•
•	•	•	•	•	•	•	•	•					•	•	•	•	•	
	•		•	•		•	•		•				•	•	•			
	•					•	•		•				•	•	•			•
	•						•					•	•	•				
	•						•		•				•	•				

Training contract directory

AARON AND PARTNERS Grosvenor Court, Foregate Street, Chester CH1 1HG **Tel:** 01244 405555 **Email:** careers@aaronandpartners.com **Apply to:** Mrs Samantha Mackie	Working principally for business clients providing general commercial services (property, litigation and company/commercial) plus specialist areas – planning, minerals, environmental, transport, construction and insolvency.	**V** 0 **T** 4 **P** 24 **TS** 124 **WP** no
ABODE SOLICITORS The Studio, Greengate, Harrogate HG3 1GY **Tel:** 01423 535600 **Email:** info@actionconveyancing.co.uk **Apply to:** Mr R Ali	Specialist property firm dealing with residential and commercial property. Welcomes applications from all graduates.	**V** 1[19] **T** 1 **P** 4 **TS** 46 **WP** yes
ABRAHAMS DRESDEN LLP 111 Charterhouse Street, London EC1M 6AW **Tel:** 020 7251 3663 **Email:** alex.protopapas@ad-solicitors.co.uk **Apply to:** Miss Alexandra Protopapas	Small progressive commercial firm committed to providing a superior service and excellent client care. Apply by post only between 1-31 January 2018.	**V** 2[18] **T** 4 **P** 3 **TS** 26 **WP** no
ACA LAW LTD 168-172 Kentish Town Road, London NW5 2AG **Tel:** 020 7485 6677 **Email:** lawyers@acalaw.co.uk **Apply to:** Ms Lisa Cutting	Young, expanding firm involved primarily in publicly funded work, committed to providing high quality advice and representation. The firm is a member of the specialist fraud panel.	**V** Varies **T** 6 **P** 1 **TS** 24 **WP** yes
ACCUTRAINEE 200 Aldersgate Street, London EC1A 4HD **Tel:** 020 7040 0973 **Email:** info@accutrainee.com **Apply to:** Ms Payal Savani	Accutrainee offer bespoke training contracts, sending trainees on secondments to both law firms and in-house. We focus on training, development and mentoring. No application deadline.	**V** Varies **T** 30 **P** - **TS** 0 **WP** no
ACTONS 20 Regent Street, Nottingham NG1 5BQ **Tel:** 0115 910 0200 **Email:** caroline.pearson@actons.co.uk **Apply to:** Mrs Caroline Pearson	Full range of services to businesses and private clients. Particularly strong reputation in insolvency, personal injury commercial and property work.	**V** 2[19] **T** 5 **P** 15 **TS** 70 **WP** no
ACUITY LEGAL LIMITED 3 Assembly Square, Britannia Quay, Cardiff Bay, Cardiff CF10 4PL **Tel:** 029 2048 2288 **Email:** rsellek@acuitylegal.co.uk **Apply to:** Mrs Rachelle Sellek	Commercial firm specialising in corporate finance, commercial property, commercial advice, commercial litigation, construction, employment, commercial projects and public sector.	**V** 2-3[18] **T** 4 **P** 16 **TS** 62 **WP** yes
ADDLESTONE KEANE SOLICITORS G4 Whitehall Waterfront, 2 Riverside Way, Leeds LS1 4EH **Tel:** 0113 244 6700 **Email:** brianaddlestone@aklaw.co.uk **Apply to:** Mr Brian Addlestone	Niche commercial practice advising PLCs, substantial private clients and companies across a broad range including litigation, employment, commercial property and debt recovery.	**V** 1[18] **T** - **P** 3 **TS** 14 **WP** no

V = Vacancies / **T** = Trainees / **P** = Partners / **TS** = Total Staff / **WP** = Work Placement

Addleshaw Goddard

Milton Gate, 60 Chiswell St, London EC1Y 4AG
Tel: 020 7606 8855
Email: grad@addleshawgoddard.com
Web: www.addleshawgoddard.com/graduates

The firm Addleshaw Goddard is a dynamic, international law firm committed to doing all it can to help its clients and its people succeed in their ambitions. Lots of law firms say they are different and talk about the reasons why. Those reasons sound the same. Addleshaw Goddard tries to be different. By listening. By innovating. Through a combination of technical excellence, market insight and commercial decision-making and importantly, by being fun to work with and for. The firm is an FT Innovation Award winner and is pioneering new ways of delivering services which bring outstanding value to its clients and exciting career opportunities for its lawyers. Wherever you are based, you'll also be part of the team from day one, getting first-hand experience of working with blue-chip clients within a supportive yet challenging environment, and benefit from a structured training programme designed with your future success in mind.

Types of work The firm's client portfolio is testament to its strength and range of expertise, and includes financial institutions, public sector bodies, successful businesses and private individuals. It is a leading advisor to FTSE100 companies, and a market leader across its business divisions – commercial services, corporate, finance and projects, litigation and real estate – as well as in specialist fields such as private capital, and across its chosen sectors: financial services, government, energy and infrastructure, retail and consumer and real estate.

Who should apply Students in the UK can apply for a training contract and/or a placement scheme with us from the beginning of your second year onwards. Undergraduate law students studying in Scotland can apply for the summer placement scheme in your third or fourth year (or students in either year of an accelerated course if you are a graduate entrant) or those who have recently completed their LLB and are interested in applying.

Training programme During each six-month seat, there will be regular two-way performance reviews with the supervising partner or solicitor. Trainees may have the opportunity to spend a seat in one of the firm's other offices and there are a number of secondments to clients available. Seated with a qualified solicitor or partner and working as part of a team enables trainees to develop the professional skills necessary to deal with the demanding and challenging work the firm carries out for its clients. Practical training is complemented by high-quality training courses provided by both the in-house team and external training providers. A trainee buddy programme is in place with the trainee predecessor for the first seat. All trainees have a mentor for the duration of their training contract and beyond.

When and how to apply Candidates must complete our online application at www.addleshawgoddard.com/graduates by 31 July 2018 to begin September 2020.

Work placements One-week Easter scheme in London only. Two-week summer scheme in all offices.

Sponsorship Where applicable fees will be paid. Company benefits include corporate gym membership, season ticket loan, subsidised restaurant, pension and private healthcare.

Vacancies	37
Trainees	85
Partners	240
Total staff	1,500

Work placement yes

Training contract deadline
31 July 2018

Apply
Online at graduates.
addleshawgoddard.com

Starting salary
London – £37,000
Leeds and
Manchester – £25,000

Minimum qualifications
2.1 degree, ABB at A level
(excluding General Studies)

Sponsorship
GDL/LPC

Offices
Aberdeen, Edinburgh,
Glasgow, Leeds,
London, Manchester

ADDLESHAW GODDARD

Akin Gump Strauss Hauer & Feld

Eighth Floor, Ten Bishops Square, London E1 6EG
Tel: 020 7012 9600
Email: graduaterecruitment@akingump.com
Web: www.akingump.com/uk-students
🐦 akin_gump

The firm Akin Gump's London office is the main hub of the firm's international offices and its strategy is to grow practices that complement core strengths of the firm. It is an integrated office practising at the top of its markets. We have 20 offices worldwide and our clients range from corporations and financial institutions to foreign governments and individuals.

Types of work Market leading practices including; financial restructuring, corporate transactions (including mergers and acquisitions, joint ventures and private equity), banking and finance, energy, debt and equity capital markets, securities, financial services regulatory, litigation/international arbitration, investment funds (hedge, private equity, real estate and infrastructure), EU competition and tax.

Who should apply We hire the best and brightest. We look for exceptional and consistent academic achievement combined with evidence of a driven outlook through extracurricular achievements.

To thrive in our fast-paced commercial environment our future trainees need to be on track for a 2.1 degree at minimum. You should demonstrate intellectual curiosity, be solution-driven and keen for early responsibility. Diverse professional and personal backgrounds broaden perspectives throughout the firm. Our complementary strengths make for a truly dynamic atmosphere.

Training programme Our London office is an exciting and inspiring environment to train as a lawyer as evidenced by the office winning 'Best Trainer – US Firm in the City' at LawCareers.Net Training and Recruitment Awards 2016. We offer up to four trainee places per year. By focusing on a smaller intake we maintain flexibility and seek to grow through our junior lawyer retention. Trainees have the choice of sitting within the financial restructuring, corporate and M&A, energy, finance, financial regulatory, funds and investment management, litigation and arbitration, competition or tax practice areas. Seats can be tailored to three or six-month durations across the two-year training programme to provide a breadth of experience. Some of our trainees have enjoyed the experience of a seat in an international office.

When and how to apply Online application via firm's website at www.akingump.com/en/careers/uk-students/application-process.html. The deadline for 2020 training contracts is 15 July 2018.

Work placements Our two-week summer vacation scheme is held in July. We introduce participants to our practices and support their exposure to the work the firm does through integration into two practices and tailored development sessions. The application deadline for our 2018 work placement programme is 31 January 2018.

Sponsorship GDL and LPC course fees. Maintenance grants of £8,000 per academic year.

Vacancies	4
Trainees	9
Partners	37
Total staff	170

Work placement | yes

Training contract deadline
15 July 2018

Apply
Online

Sponsorship
GDL/LPC

Offices
Abu Dhabi, Beijing, Dallas, Dubai, Fort Worth, Frankfurt, Geneva, Hong Kong, Houston, Irvine, Longview, London, Los Angeles, Moscow, New York, Philadelphia, San Antonio, San Francisco, Singapore, Washington DC

Akin Gump
STRAUSS HAUER & FELD

ADLAMS LLP
37b Market Square, St Neots, Cambridgeshire
PE19 2AR
Tel: 01480 474061
Email: adlams@adlams.co.uk
Apply to: Ms Connie Johnstone

Long-established small high street practice specialising in conveyancing, family, probate and some commercial work. Good IT skills an advantage for candidates.

V 0
T 1
P 4
TS 23
WP yes

AHMED & CO
67a Camden High Street, London NW1 7JL
Tel: 020 7383 2243
Email: mail@ahmedco.com
Apply to: Ms Nosheen Saleem

Specialist services provided in crime, housing, immigration/nationality and welfare benefits law for individuals who are disadvantaged in some way to enable them to seek justice.

V 0
T 4
P 2
TS 15
WP no

AKIN PALMER LLP
3 Angel Gate, 326 City Road, London EC1V 2PT
Tel: 020 7833 8828
Email: law@akinpalmer.com
Apply to: Mr Dele Ogun

A full service four-partner commercial law firm established since 1997 with a fast-growing reputation.

V 1-2
T 1
P 4
TS 10
WP no

ALAN SIMPSON & CO
Mill Court, 19 London Hill, Rayleigh SS6 7HW
Tel: 01268 745406
Email: ajs@alansimpson.com
Apply to: Mr AJ Simpson

General high street practice serving private and commercial clients.

V 0-1
T 1
P 1
TS 12
WP no

ALFRED NEWTON SOLICITORS
49-51 Wellington Road South, Stockport, Cheshire
SK1 3RX
Tel: 0161 480 6551
Email: mail@alfrednewton.com
Apply to: Mr A Penman

We have three offices based in Stockport providing a wide range of legal services including family, property, wills, probate, mental health, employment, PI and housing.

V 0
T 2
P 4
TS 25
WP no

ALLAN JANES
21-23 Easton Street, High Wycombe HP11 1NT
Tel: 01494 521301
Email: enquiries@allanjanes.com
Apply to: Mr CJG Hitchen

Niche commercial practice focusing on the South Bucks geographical area with a private client department servicing high net worth clients.

V 1
T 1
P 5
TS 20
WP yes

ALLINGTON HUGHES LAW
10 Grosvenor Road, Wrexham LL11 1SD
Tel: 01978 291000
Email: tammy.hughes@allingtonhughes.co.uk
Apply to: Ms Tammy Hughes

V 1[19]
T 2
P 14
TS 75
WP no

ALP LAW LLP
Sherrington House, 66 Chorley Street, Bolton
BL1 4AL
Tel: 01204 454333
Email: mail@alplaw.co.uk
Apply to: Mr TB Walters

A unique and leading firm specialising exclusively in accident cases on a nationwide basis, and dedicated to the pursuit of professionalism and results.

V Poss
T 2
P 4
TS 90
WP no

V = Vacancies / **T** = Trainees / **P** = Partners / **TS** = Total Staff / **WP** = Work Placement

Allen & Overy LLP

One Bishops Square, London E1 6AD
Tel: 020 3088 3399
Email: graduate.recruitment@allenovery.com
Web: www.aograduate.com
f allenoverygrads 🐦 allenoverygrads

The firm Allen & Overy is an international legal practice with approximately 5,300 people in 44 major centres worldwide. Our client list includes many of the world's leading businesses, financial institutions and governments, and naturally, we are committed to providing innovative advice of the highest quality to them. By developing tailored solutions to a wide range of business issues, our partners are recognised as leaders in their areas of expertise and we have earned an enviable reputation and outstanding success in high-profile deals.

Types of work We are renowned for the high quality of our banking, corporate and international capital markets advice, but also have major strengths in areas such as dispute resolution, employment and benefits, real estate and tax.

Who should apply We expect to see a strong, consistent academic performance with at least a 2.1 and 340 UCAS (AAB) (or equivalent) predicted or achieved. At Allen & Overy you will be working in a team where you will manage your own time and workload, so we also look for candidates who can act on initiative, build strong relationships and prioritise effectively.

Training programme The Allen & Overy training contract is characterised by flexibility and choice. The seat structure ensures that you get to see as many parts of the firm as possible and that your learning is hands on, guided by an experienced associate or partner. Your choice of a priority seat is guaranteed unless exceptional business needs or other extenuating circumstances arise. Given the strength of the firm's international finance practice, trainees are required to spend a minimum of 12 months in at least two of the three core departments of banking, corporate and international capital markets. The firm offers its trainees the option of completing a litigation course. This means that trainees do not need to spend time in the firm's litigation and dispute resolution department to gain their contentious experience if they are sure their interests lie elsewhere. There are also opportunities for trainees to undertake an international or client secondment during their final year of training.

Please follow us on facebook www.facebook.com/allenoverygrads and twitter www.twitter.com/allenoverygrads. Plus also add us on snapchat: allenoverygrads.

When and how to apply Both law and non-law students should apply from October 2017. Please visit our website for full details about closing dates.

Work placements We recruit around 50 vacation students across the year from all degree disciplines. We have opportunities for students in their penultimate year and onwards, including graduates, on our vacation schemes. We also offer A&O First as a work experience programme and support network designed exclusively for undergraduate first-year students in the UK. Full details about eligibility requirements and application deadlines are available on our website at www.aograduate.com.

Sponsorship We pay your GDL and LPC course fees and contribute to your maintenance costs. We pay a £8,000 maintenance grant for the Allen & Overy LPC (MA with business) and also for the GDL in London.

Partners	530*
Total staff	5,300*
	*denotes approximate worldwide figures

Work placement yes
(see Insider Report on p69)

Apply
Online at
www.aograduate.com

Starting salary
£44,000

Minimum qualifications
2.1 degree and 340 UCAS (AAB) (or equivalent)

Sponsorship
GDL/LPC

Offices
Abu Dhabi, Amsterdam, Antwerp, Bangkok, Barcelona, Beijing, Belfast, Bratislava, Brussels, Bucharest (associated office), Budapest, Casablanca, Doha, Dubai, Düsseldorf, Frankfurt, Hamburg, Hanoi, Ho Chi Minh City, Hong Kong, Istanbul, Jakarta (associated office), Johannesburg, London, Luxembourg, Madrid, Milan, Moscow, Munich, New York, Paris, Perth, Prague, Riyadh (associated office), Rome, São Paulo, Seoul, Shanghai, Singapore, Sydney, Tokyo, Warsaw, Washington DC, Yangon

ALLEN & OVERY

Affiliated with
🅰🅢 aspiringsolicitors

ALPHA LEXIS LAW FIRM Boundary House, Barnet Lane, Hertfordshire WD6 3JP **Tel:** 0845 194 7340 **Email:** info@alphalexislaw.co.uk **Apply to:** Mr Mahesh Kakkar	We are a forward-thinking, efficient practice specialising in contentious and non-contentious company commercial law, property law and private client work.	V 0 T 0 P 2 TS 8 WP no
ALSTERS KELLEY Hamilton House, 20-22 Hamilton Terrace, Leamington Spa CV32 4LY **Tel:** 01926 356000 **Email:** alison.field@alsterskelley.com **Apply to:** Mrs Julie Richardson	Four-partner, three-office practice in Coventry and Warwickshire undertaking private client and commercial work.	V 0 T 2 P 4 TS 90 WP no
AMD SOLICITORS LIMITED 100 Henleaze Road, Henleaze, Bristol BS9 4JZ **Tel:** 0117 962 1205 **Email:** admin@amdsolicitors.com **Apply to:** Mrs MK Davies	High street firm undertaking residential conveyancing, commercial and company work, probate, trusts, family (both private and legal aid) and education.	V 1 T 0 P 2 TS 30 WP no
AMICUS SOLICITORS LLP 761 Wilmslow Road, Didsbury, Manchester M20 6RN **Tel:** 0161 434 4440 **Email:** enquiries@amicussolicitors.co.uk. **Apply to:** Mr Aneil Naeem	We offer a wide range of services to both international and domestic clients. We have a wealth of experience in a wide range of disciplines.	V 1 T 2 P 2 TS 7 WP yes
AMS SOLICITORS LIMITED Wentworth, 1B Fairways Office Park, Preston PR2 9LF **Tel:** 01772 653 333 **Apply to:** Mr A Suleman	We are an upcoming and rapidly expanding firm specialising in litigation, personal injury and commercial property.	V 2 T 1 P 2 TS 16 WP yes
ANGLO-THAI LEGAL (ATL) 24 Houghton Street, Warrin WA2 7DD **Tel:** 01925 414308 **Email:** john.lewis@anglothailegal.com **Apply to:** Mr John Lewis	Anglo-Thai Legal (ATL) is an international law company regulated to provide legal services in England [SRA no. 559208] and Thailand [Thai Lawyers Council no. 7082/2552].	V Varies T 1 P 1 TS 5 WP yes
ANTHONY COLLINS SOLICITORS 134 Edmund Street, Birmingham B3 2ES **Tel:** 0121 200 3242 **Email:** trainingcontract@anthonycollins.com **Apply to:** Mrs Vicky Paterson	Fast-growing niche commercial and private client practice with a national client base boasting the largest social housing, charities and community regeneration operations outside London.	V 6 T 11 P 28 TS 260 WP yes
ANTHONY GOLD SOLICITORS The Counting House, 53 Tooley Street, London Bridge SE1 2QN **Tel:** 020 7940 4000 **Email:** clare.kelly@anthonygold.co.uk **Apply to:** Ms Clare Kelly	General practice with excellent reputation for family work, plaintiff personal injury/medical negligence and housing. Offices in London Bridge, Streatham and Elephant & Castle.	V 3[19] T 9 P 32 TS 160 WP no

V = Vacancies / **T** = Trainees / **P** = Partners / **TS** = Total Staff / **WP** = Work Placement

ANTHONY JACOBS & CO 91 Albany Road, Cardiff CF24 3LP **Tel:** 029 2048 3509 **Email:** anthonyjacobs@btconnect.com **Apply to:** Mr Anthony Jacobs	General practice with emphasis on property law and family law. No criminal law or legal aid.	V 2^{18} T 2 P 1 TS 5 WP yes
ANTHONY LOUCA SOLICITORS 24 Lisson Grove, Marylebone, London NW1 6TT **Apply to:** Mr F Argyrou	Anthony Louca Solicitors is seeking a trainee solicitor with a good class degree for an early start. No transfers accepted.	V 1 T 0 P 3 TS 7 WP no
ANTONY CLAPP SOLICITORS Holly Bank Chambers, Oasts Business Village, Maidstone ME18 5NN **Tel:** 01622 815 940 **Email:** antony.clapp@antonyclappsolicitors.co.uk **Apply to:** Mr AEJ Clapp	We are a specialist firm dealing exclusively in family law. We have a distinguished reputation built up over many years.	V 0 T 1 P 2 TS 13 WP no
ANTONY HODARI & CO 34 High Street, Manchester M4 1AH **Tel:** 0161 832 4781 **Email:** careers@antonyhodari.co.uk **Apply to:** Mr T Pope	Establsihed in 1984, specialists in RTA personal injury claims.	V 0 T 6 P 6 TS 110 WP no
AP LAW SOLICITORS LTD 257 Balham High Road, London SW17 7BD **Tel:** 020 8672 2488 **Email:** ap@aplaw.co.uk **Apply to:** The Business Manager	High quality of work in specialist areas. Fast expanding, highly motivated young firm. Strong team spirit and excellent opportunities.	V 0 T 5 P 2 TS 50 WP yes
AP SOLICITORS Second Floor, 19 Gerrard Street, London W1D 6JG **Tel:** 020 7287 7880 **Email:** info@apsolicitors.com **Apply to:** Ms Vivienne Poon	A modern and expanding law firm practicing in the heart of London.	V 2 T - P 2 TS 6 WP no
ARBIS SUTHERLAND LLP Marble Quay, St Katharine's Dock, London E1W 1UH **Tel:** 020 7553 8000 **Email:** azm@arbis-sutherland.com **Apply to:** Mr Andrew Murray	Leading shipping and commodity trading boutique with London and Geneva offices, in combination with major US firm Sutherland Asbill & Brennan since March 2014.	V 1-2 T 1 P 5 TS 18 WP no
ARCHON SOLICITORS LIMITED Martin House, 5 Martin Lane, London EC4R ODP **Tel:** 020 7397 9650 **Email:** reception@archonsolicitors.com **Apply to:** Ms Jill Scott	Niche employment law practice offering advice in relation to all aspects of employment law to both employers and senior employees.	V 0 T 1 P 5 TS 19 WP no

V = Vacancies / **T** = Trainees / **P** = Partners / **TS** = Total Staff / **WP** = Work Placement

Arnold & Porter Kaye Scholer LLP

Tower 42, 25 Old Broad Street, London EC2N 1HQ
Tel: 020 7786 6100
Email: graduates@apks.com
Web: www.apks.com

The firm Arnold & Porter Kaye Scholer is a US-based firm with a deserved reputation for its quality of service and expertise in handling the most complex legal and business problems, which require innovative and practical solutions.

Types of work Our London lawyers advise on a full range of regulatory, transactional and litigation matters, and focus especially on intellectual property and technology transactions and litigation, pharmaceuticals and medical device regulation and litigation, telecommunications, internet and media, employment, competition and trade regulation, international arbitration, white collar crime, corporate and securities, bankruptcy, finance, investment management and product liability advice and litigation. Providing our clients with an excellent service is our number one priority, and our lawyers need to be commercially minded, approachable and able to work with our clients as part of a team on complex and often high-profile legal issues.

Who should apply We are looking for talented law and non-law graduates from all backgrounds and cultures who share our commitment to excellence, and who want to be part of the continued growth of our London office and become our next generation of partners and lawyers. Candidates applying to Arnold & Porter Kaye Scholer need to demonstrate a consistently high academic background. We expect candidates to have at least a 2.1 degree, AAB at A level or equivalent, and look for well-rounded individuals who can demonstrate their participation in a range of extra-curricular activities and achievements.

Training programme Trainees will have the opportunity to spend six months working within four of our practice groups: life sciences and healthcare regulatory, intellectual property, corporate, competition, international arbitration and white collar crime. Arnold & Porter Kaye Scholer encourages individuals to work across specialisms, so trainees may find that while working in one practice group, they undertake work in a variety of different areas, and for a variety of partners and fee-earners throughout the firm. Trainees will be expected to work on several matters at once and to assume responsibility at an early stage. We emphasise teamwork and trainees will be exposed to working for a variety of partners and fee earners throughout the office and the firm. Trainees may also have an opportunity to work in our Brussels office and, where the occasion permits, to work on projects in one of our US offices. There are also opportunities for client secondments. Trainees are invited to attend the annual new associates retreat in our Washington DC office. Trainees are encouraged to take part in our pro bono programme, and devote 15% of their time to it, reflecting the firm's strong commitment to pro bono, which helps young lawyers to develop their client management skills from an early stage.

When and how to apply For our 2018 summer vacation scheme, by 4 March 2018. For training contracts commencing in September 2020, by 29 July 2018. Apply online at the London trainees page of our website.

Work placements We take around 10 summer vacation students each year. Students will spend two weeks working on a variety of projects and workshops with partners and associates throughout the London office. In addition to this, social events are organised for our summer vacation students to encourage them to meet the partners and associates in our London office.

Sponsorship Arnold & Porter Kaye Scholer will pay your fees for the LPC and GDL. In addition we will pay a maintenance grant for each course.

Vacancies	2
Trainees	4
Partners	28
Total staff	126

Work placement yes

Training contract deadline
29 July 2018

Apply to
Graduate Recruitment

Starting salary
£45,000

Minimum qualifications
2.1 degree

Sponsorship
GDL/LPC

Offices
London, Washington DC, Brussels, Chicago, Frankfurt, New York, Los Angeles, Denver, Houston, San Francisco, Shanghai, Silicon Valley, West Palm Beach

ARNOLD & PORTER
KAYE SCHOLER

ARLINGTONS SHARMAS SOLICITORS 6 Arlington Street, St James's, London SW1A 1RE **Tel:** 020 7299 8999 **Email:** law@arlingtons.co.uk **Apply to:** Mrs Awal	A well-established firm with a strong client base covering commercial work, litigation, property (commercial and residential), employment, trusts, probate and private client work.	V Poss T 1 P 2 TS 14 WP yes
ARNOLD GREENWOOD SOLICITORS LTD Exchange Chambers, 8 & 10 Highgate, Kendal, Cumbria LA9 4SX **Tel:** 01539 720049 **Email:** brichardson@arnoldgreenwood.co.uk **Apply to:** Miss B Richardson		V 0 T 1 P 4 TS 16 WP no
ASB LAW LLP Origin Two, 106 High Street, Crawley, West Sussex RH10 1BF **Tel:** 01293 603600 **Email:** hr.team@asb-law.com **Apply to:** Ms Kelly-Anne Goodall	Award-winning practice servicing businesses, public sector bodies and private clients with recognised expertise in a number of sectors including aviation and travel.	V 2^{18} T 4 P 17 TS 134 WP yes
ASCHFORDS LAW 79 College Road, Harrow, Middlesex HA1 1BD **Tel:** 020 3586 4050 **Email:** info@aschfordslaw.com **Apply to:** Ms Shalini V Bhargava	Aschfords Law Solicitors is a UK based immigration specialist firm. We are authorised to train trainee solicitors. We also provide the opportunity to enthusiasts looking for work experience (unpaid) and paralegals.	V 1 T 1 P 3 TS 5 WP yes
ASHFORDS Ashford House, Grenadier Road, Exeter EX1 3LH **Tel:** 01392 333 634 **Email:** traineerecruitment@ashfords.co.uk **Apply to:** Ms Jordan Harris	Ashfords is a leading UK law firm delivering high quality legal and professional services to businesses and individuals throughout the UK and abroad.	V 9 T 28 P 74 TS 540 WP yes
ASHTON BELL 19 Hanover Square, Leeds LS3 1AP **Tel:** 0113 2438688 **Apply to:** Ms Maxine Brown	Predominantly private client practice. Most high street work undertaken except crime. Significant personal injury and divorce work. Apply in writing with CV and handwritten letter.	V 1 T 0 P 1 TS 6 WP yes
ASHTONS LEGAL Beacon House, Kempson Way, Suffolk Business Park, Bury St Edmunds IP32 7AR **Tel:** 01284 732120 **Email:** graduaterecruitment@ashtonslegal.co.uk **Apply to:** Miss Claire Hughes	A leading East Anglia medium-sized law firm. This award winning practice stands out through its reputation for excellence and its friendly, approachable ethos.	V 4^{19} T 6 P 30 TS 300 WP yes
ASTON BOND 135-137 High Street, Slough SL1 1DN **Tel:** 01753 486 777 **Email:** info@astonbond.co.uk **Apply to:** Mr Stephen Puri	We are a young energetic and entrepreneurial law firm specialising in general commercial and corporate matters involving property and have a strong reputation for excellence.	V 1 T 1 P 3 TS 20 WP yes

V = Vacancies / **T** = Trainees / **P** = Partners / **TS** = Total Staff / **WP** = Work Placement

Ashurst LLP

Broadwalk House, 5 Appold Street, London EC2A 2AG
Tel: 020 7638 1111
Email: gradrec@ashurst.com
Web: www.ashurst.com/en/careers
f ashursttrainees

The firm With 25 offices in 15 countries and a number of referral relationships we offer the reach and insight of a global network, combined with the knowledge and understanding of local markets. Our 400 partners and further 1,000 lawyers work across 10 different time zones, responding to our clients wherever and whenever they need us.

Types of work Ashurst advance; banking and finance; capital markets; competition and antitrust; corporate and M&A; digital economy; dispute resolution; employment; financial regulation; insurance and reinsurance; intellectual property; investigations; investment funds; projects; real estate; restructuring, insolvency and special situations; tax.

Who should apply We expect a lot of ourselves – and so, as you would expect, you will need to be comfortable with challenges and pressure. You should also be able to express yourself confidently on paper and out loud, whether that's among your team or in a client's boardroom.

You'll need to become a shrewd negotiator, have an ability to read both balance sheets and behaviours, and become a commercial strategist with a deep understanding of specific industries.

Training programme We will plan closely with you four seats of six months each, that will broaden your world view and hone your talents. At least one seat will be in a finance practice and another within a transactional department. You will also have the opportunity to apply for an overseas or client secondment.

When and how to apply Online application form addressed to Nick Wong, graduate recruitment partner. We will be accepting training contract applications to start in September 2020/March 2021 from 1 October 2017. There will be two windows to apply for training contracts with the firm. These will be from 1 October 2017 to 7 January 2018 and then again from 1 May 2018 to 31 July 2018.

Work placements We run a one-week winter vacation scheme and two three-week vacation schemes during the summer. Our winter and summer vacation schemes are for all penultimate-year law students and beyond, as well as final-year students and graduates studying a non-law degree. Our first-year scheme runs in the spring. Law students are eligible to apply.

Applications open on 1 September 2017 and close on 5 November 2017 for the winter scheme and 7 January 2018 for the summer schemes. We also host a first-year programme in the spring for law students. Apply online between 1 September 2017 and 7 January 2018.

Sponsorship For the Graduate Diploma in Law (GDL) and Legal Practice Course (LPC), we offer scholarships that cover your course fees and provide £8,000 per year towards the cost of maintenance (£7,000 if you choose to study the GDL outside of London).

Vacancies	40-45
Trainees	90
Partners	400
Total staff	3,100

Work placement yes
(see Insider Report on p71)

Training contract deadline
31 July 2018

Apply
Online

Starting salary
£42,000

Minimum qualifications
2.1 degree

Sponsorship
GDL /LPC

Offices
Abu Dhabi, Beijing, Brisbane, Brussels, Canberra, Dubai, Frankfurt, Glasgow (support office), Hong Kong, Jakarta (associated office), Jeddah (associated office), London, Madrid, Melbourne, Milan, Munich, New York, Paris, Perth, Port Moresby, Shanghai, Singapore, Sydney, Tokyo, Washington DC

ASTON CLARK SOLICITORS 225-227 High Street, Acton, London W3 9BY **Tel:** 020 8752 1122 **Email:** solicitors@astonclark.co.uk **Apply to:** Personnel Department	Busy high street practice offers a professional, efficient, friendly, cost-effective service from pleasant West London offices.	V 0 T 1 P 3 TS 12 WP no
ATHERTON GODFREY 8 Hall Gate, Doncaster, South Yorkshire DN1 3LU **Tel:** 01302 320 621 **Email:** d.parker@athertongodfrey.co.uk **Apply to:** Ms Diane Parker	A high street firm doing claimant personal injury work, clinical negligence, family, company and commercial, domestic conveyancing, wills and probate and general litigation.	V 2[19] T 2 P 5 TS 120 WP no
ATKINS HOPE 74-78 North End, Croydon, Surrey CR9 1SD **Tel:** 020 8680 5018 **Email:** cc@atkinshope.co.uk **Apply to:** Ms Greta Carpenter	*Chambers* listed and Jordans Awards shortlisted firm with four partners and three offices, undertaking all aspects of family law, mediation, PI and non-contentious work.	V 0 T 1 P 4 TS 35 WP yes
ATTER MACKENZIE & CO Bridge Court, 64 Bridge Street, Evesham WR11 4RY **Tel:** 01386 425300 **Email:** ah@attermackenzie.co.uk **Apply to:** Mr Amer Hussain	Legal aid franchised high street general practice. Litigation orientated.	V 2[18] T 3 P 5 TS 26 WP no
ATTEYS SOLICITORS 82 Cleveland Street, Doncaster DN1 3DR **Tel:** 01302 762900 **Apply to:** Ms Christine Burton	Three-partner firm with two offices. Doncaster: company commercial, employment, commercial litigation, commercial property. Retford: private client, personal injury, wills, trusts, probate, conveyancing.	V 2 T 5 P 3 TS 48 WP yes
AUSTIN KEMP SOLICITORS LIMITED 7 Northumberland Street, Huddersfield HD1 1RL **Tel:** 0845 862 5001 **Email:** mail@austinkemp.co.uk **Apply to:** Vivienne Rudd	Niche firm of specialist divorce lawyers with a particular focus on high-net worth complex finance divorce cases.	V 2[18] T 1 P 1 TS 10 WP yes
AVADIS & CO SOLICITORS 7-9 Ferdinand Street, London NW1 8ES **Tel:** 020 7267 8864 **Email:** lavadis@aol.com **Apply to:** Mr L Avadis	We are offering an opportunity for some hands-on unpaid work experience for law students. Please forward your CV and covering letter.	V 1 T - P 1 TS 5 WP yes
AVERY EMERSON Gloucester House, 335 Green lane, Ilford, Essex IG3 9TH **Tel:** 020 8215 0884 **Email:** reception@ae-law.co.uk **Apply to:** The Recruitment Officer	Proactive and innovative law firm which undertakes a wide variety of work: employment; immigration; conveyancing; family; wills and probate; landlord and tenant; litigation; and business.	V 2 T 1 P 1 TS 6 WP yes

V = Vacancies / **T** = Trainees / **P** = Partners / **TS** = Total Staff / **WP** = Work Placement

Baker McKenzie LLP

100 New Bridge Street, London EC4V 6JA
Tel: 020 7919 1000
Email: londongraduates@bakermckenzie.com
Web: www.bakermckenzie.com/londongraduates
f bakermckenziegraduates 🐦 bakermckenzie

The firm Baker McKenzie is a leading global law firm based in over 75 locations in nearly all of the world's leading financial and commercial centres, our strategy is to provide the best combination of local legal and commercial knowledge, international expertise and resources.

Our trainee solicitors are a vital part of that strategy, exposed to the international scope of the firm from the moment they start. There is also the possibility of an overseas secondment, with recent secondees spending time in San Francisco, Brussels, Moscow, Johannesburg and Hong Kong.

Types of work London is home to the firm's largest office where Baker McKenzie has been well established since its opening in 1961. With more than 400 legal professionals, we have a substantial presence in the legal and business community.

As a full-service office, we deliver high-quality local solutions across a broad range of practices and offer global advice in conjunction with our international offices. Our client base consists primarily of venture capital funds, investment banks, technology powerhouses and household name brands. And as a firm with a very strong international client base, we have considerable expertise in acting on, and coordinating, complex cross-border transactions and disputes.

Who should apply The firm strives to enable trainees to be the best they can be. We are looking for trainees who are stimulated by intellectual challenge and respect and enjoy the diversity of cultural, social and academic backgrounds found in the firm. Effective communication skills, together with the ability to be creative and practical problem solvers, team players and to have a sense of humour, are qualities which will help them stand out from the crowd.

Training programme The two-year training contract comprises of four six-month seats which include a corporate and a contentious seat, usually within our highly regarded dispute resolution department, together with the possibility of a secondment abroad or with a client. During each seat you will have formal and informal reviews to discuss your progress and regular meetings to explore subsequent seat preferences. Your training contract commences with a highly interactive and practical induction programme which focuses on key skills including practical problem solving, presenting and the application of information technology. The firm's training programmes include important components on management and other business skills, as well as seminars and workshops on key legal topics for each practice area. There is a trainee solicitor liaison committee which acts as a forum for any new ideas which may occur during the training contract.

When and how to apply The firm is aiming to recruit 30 individuals looking to commence their training contracts in either March 2020 or September 2020. Application is by way of an online application form which can be found on our website along with our deadlines.

Work placements Spring and summer vacation schemes, open days and first year programme. Please see website for details.

Sponsorship Payment of full fees and maintenance grant of £8,000 for the LPC and £6,000 for the CPE/GDL.

Vacancies	30
Trainees	62
Partners	90
Total staff	891*

*denotes London figure

Work placement yes

Apply to
Graduate Recruitment Team

Starting salary
£45,000

Minimum qualifications
340 UCAS points,
2.1 degree or equivilent

Sponsorship
CPE/GDL/LPC

Offices
Over 75 offices in nearly 50 countries

Baker McKenzie.

Affiliated with

Remember to cite *The Training Contract & Pupillage Handbook* on your application form if you apply to this firm.

AWDRY BAILEY & DOUGLAS 33 St Johns Street, Devizes SN10 1BW **Tel:** 01380 722311 **Email:** david.turley@awdrys.co.uk **Apply to:** Mr Andrew Douglas	General high street practice.	V T P TS WP	0 5 7 95 no
BANNER JONES 24 Glumangate, Chesterfield S40 1UA **Tel:** 01246 560 560 **Email:** info@bannerjones.co.uk **Apply to:** Mr Robert Banner	General firm with six offices throughout North Derbyshire and Sheffield. The firm incorporated in 2008 and has 10 directors and a staff of approaching 90.	V T P TS WP	0 0 10 90 no
BARCAN KIRBY 36 High Street, Thornbury, Bristol BS35 2AJ **Tel:** 0117 3252929 **Email:** b.humanresources@barcankirby.co.uk **Apply to:** Mrs Claire Pennell	Six office practice with offices in Bristol, Kingswoood and Thornbury.	V T P TS WP	0 2 13 150 no
BARGATE MURRAY 44 Worship Street, London EC2A 2EA **Tel:** 020 7375 1393 **Email:** info@bargatemurray.com **Apply to:** Mr Quentin Bargate	We are an expanding City of London law firm with niche expertise in superyachts, shipping, litigation, ADR, commercial and corporate.	V T P TS WP	0 0 3 11 no
BARKER GOTELEE 41 Barrack Square, Martlesham Heath, Ipswich IP5 7RF **Tel:** 01473 611211 **Email:** bg@barkergotelee.co.uk **Apply to:** Mr Toby Pound	A regional commercial and private client firm with a national reputation in agricultural, property and private client work. We offer broad and practical training.	V T P TS WP	0 2 8 54 no
BARLOW ROBBINS LLP The Oriel, Sydenham Road, Guildford, Surrey GU1 3SR **Tel:** 01483 562 901 **Email:** trainees@barlowrobbins.com **Apply to:** Mrs Jo Vernon	Established Surrey practice specialising in corporate commercial, IT/IP, employment, commercial property, dispute resolution, family, personal injury and clinical negligence, private client and residential property.	V T P TS WP	4 8 18 150 no
BARNETTS Southport Buiness Park, Wight Moss Way, Kew, Southport PR8 4HQ **Tel:** 0844 800 5600 **Email:** andrea.parry@barnetts.co.uk **Apply to:** Mrs Andrea Parry	Niche property and personal injury practice. Applicants must have completed both LLB (or equivalent) and LPC and work as an assistant for 12 months.	V T P TS WP	2 12 6 135 no
BARON GREY Langtry House, 441 Richmond Road, Middlesex TW1 2EF **Tel:** 020 8891 4311 **Email:** info@barongrey.co.uk **Apply to:** Mr Vincent Hambleton-Grey	Multi-discipline practice with general commercial and family clientele, specialising in litigation, conveyancing and probate.	V T P TS WP	0 1 1 9 yes

V = Vacancies / **T** = Trainees / **P** = Partners / **TS** = Total Staff / **WP** = Work Placement

BASINGSTOKE & DEANE BOROUGH COUNCIL		
Civic Offices, London Road, Basingstoke, Hampshire RG21 4AH **Tel:** 01256 845402 **Email:** chris.guy@basingstoke.gov.uk **Apply to:** Mrs Nicki Beck	Leading e-enabled local government practice. High value development, regeneration and commercial property projects. Trainees have own caseloads with opportunities for advocacy. Applications continually sought.	V 1-2 T 4 P 1 TS 20 WP no

BASSRA SOLICITORS (INCORPORATING JOHN KELLY & CO)		
89/93 Manningham Lane, Bradford, West Yorkshire BD1 3DN **Tel:** 01274 307060 **Apply to:** Mr John Kelly	Small North West Yorkshire firm specialising in crime. Legal aid franchise.	V 0 T 2 P 2 TS 8 WP no

BASTIAN LLOYD MORRIS LLP		
Sovereign Court, Witan Gate East, Milton Keynes MK9 2HP **Tel:** 01908 546 580 **Email:** jab@blmsolicitors.co.uk **Apply to:** Mr Syvil Lloyd Morris	Bastian Lloyd Morris Solicitor Advocates specialise in all aspects of criminal law, including police stations, family law, including care proceeding and injunctive relief.	V 0 T 1 P 3 TS 14 WP yes

BATCHELORS		
Charles House, 35 Widmore Road, Bromley, Kent BR1 1RW **Tel:** 020 8768 7000 **Email:** batchelors@batchelors.co.uk **Apply to:** Ms Sarah Brannigan	Medium-sized practice providing services for commercial and private clients including housing management, real estate, wills, trust and probate. No vacancies at present.	V 0 T 0 P 14 TS 55 WP no

BATES WELLS BRAITHWAITE		
10 Queen Street Place, London EC4R 1BE **Tel:** 020 7551 7777 **Email:** training@bwbllp.com **Apply to:** Mrs Hayley Ferraro	BWB – "City firm with a conscience". Practice areas: charity; commercial; general litigation; administrative; media; sports; employment; immigration/asylum; and property.	V 6 T 10 P 38 TS 248 WP yes

BATTENS SOLICITORS LIMITED		
Mansion House, Princes Street, Yeovil BA20 1EP **Tel:** 01935 846000 **Email:** b.sinclair@battens.co.uk **Apply to:** Mrs Bex Sinclair	Battens is a long established but progressive firm with four offices in Somerset and Dorset. Extremely strong presence in all practice areas, except criminal law.	V 0 T 3 P 13 TS 109 WP no

BEALE & COMPANY SOLICITORS LLP		
Capital House, 85 King William Street, London EC4N 7BL **Tel:** 020 7469 0400 **Email:** traineeapplications@beale-law.com **Apply to:** Mrs Donna Clarke	A commercial law firm with specialist experience in construction, engineering and infrastructure, insurance, and technology sectors.	V 5-6[19] T 10 P 23 TS 120 WP no

BEETENSON & GIBBON SOLICITORS		
12-18 Frances Street, Scunthorpe, North Lincolnshire DN15 6NS **Tel:** 01724 847888 **Email:** ruth.gilliatt@bgsolicitors.com **Apply to:** Miss J Moorhouse	Friendly high street practice specialising in personal injury, family and property.	V 0 T 1 P 5 TS 30 WP no

V = Vacancies / **T** = Trainees / **P** = Partners / **TS** = Total Staff / **WP** = Work Placement

BELL LAX SOLICITORS New Bank House, 21 Maney Corner, Sutton Coldfield B72 1QL **Tel:** 0121 355 0011 **Email:** liam.owen@belllax.com **Apply to:** Mr Liam Owen	Specialist litigation practice – 65% commercial litigation, 35% personal injury and relationship disputes. Trainees given considerable responsibility, but benefit from close supervision on all matters.	V 2 T 2 P 3 TS 25 WP no
BEN HOARE BELL LLP 47 John Street, Sunderland SR1 1QU **Tel:** 0191 565 3112 **Email:** rachelfloyd@benhoarebell.co.uk **Apply to:** Miss Rachel Floyd	Clinical negligence, crime, housing, family, mental health, personal injury. Strong links to universities and other key agencies.	V 0 T 6 P 8 TS 75 WP no
BENNETTS SOLICITORS & ATTORNEYS Barley Wood Stables, Long Lane, Wrington, Bristol BS40 5QB **Tel:** 01934 862786 **Email:** info@bennettlaw.co.uk **Apply to:** Mr Craig Smith	Training at Bennetts is practical, gives broad but specialist commercial and private client experience, develops problem solving, client care and high professional standards.	V 0 T - P 4 TS 15 WP no
BERG 35 Peter Street, Manchester M2 5BG **Tel:** 0161 833 9211 **Email:** trainee@berg.co.uk **Apply to:** Ms Alison Loveday	Undertakes all aspects of commercial work. The firm's mission is to be recognised as the clever choice, giving imaginative advice and value for money.	V 2[19] T 4 P 7 TS 50 WP yes
BERMANS Exchange Station, Tithebarn Street, Liverpool L2 2QP **Tel:** 0151 224 0500 **Email:** alex.chapman@bermans.co.uk **Apply to:** Mr Alex Chapman	Manchester office in 2017. No nonsense business lawyers. Niches in factoring/leasing and leisure/creative.	V 1[18] T 3 P 12 TS 70 WP no
BERRY & BERRY 1-5 Longley Road, Worsley, Manchester M28 3JB **Tel:** 0161 790 1411 **Apply to:** Ms Margaret McCormack	A well-established general practice with four offices in Greater Manchester covering matrimonial, crime, personal injury, commercial conveyancing and litigation. Legal aid franchise.	V 1 T 3 P 8 TS 52 WP no
BERRY & LAMBERTS SOLICITORS 11 Church Road, Tunbridge Wells TN1 1JA **Tel:** 01892 526344 **Email:** schapman@the-solicitors.co.uk **Apply to:** Miss Sue Chapman	A general practice carrying out contentious and non-contentious work for individuals and businesses. A member of LawNet. Applications only accepted in January and February.	V 1[18] T 3 P 12 TS 80 WP no
BERWIN LEIGHTON PAISNER Adelaide House, London Bridge, London EC4R 9HA **Tel:** 020 3400 1000 **Email:** traineerecruit@blplaw.com **Apply to:** Graduate Recruitment	Top City law firm with offices in London, Abu Dhabi, Beijing, Berlin, Brussels, Dubai, Frankfurt, Hong Kong, Manchester, Moscow, Paris, Singapore, Tel Aviv and Yangon.	V 40 T 114 P 200 TS 1417 WP yes

V = Vacancies / **T** = Trainees / **P** = Partners / **TS** = Total Staff / **WP** = Work Placement

BEVAN BRITTAN LLP Kings Orchard, 1 Queen Street, Bristol BS2 0HQ **Tel:** 0370 194 1000 **Email:** hr.training@bevanbrittan.com **Apply to:** HR Department	Bevan Brittan provides practical, high quality and commercially relevant legal advice to public, private and third sector organisations.	V 9 T 19 P 58 TS 403 WP yes
BEVISS & BECKINGSALE Law Chambers, Silver Street, Axminster, Devon EX13 5AH **Tel:** 01297 630700 **Email:** enquiries@bevissandbeckingsale.co.uk **Apply to:** Ms Anna Leavy	Award-winning law firm across East Devon and Somerset specialising in private client, agricultural matters, residential and commercial property work, litigation and family law.	V 1[18] T 1 P 7 TS 50 WP yes
BG GROUP PLC 100 Thames Valley Park Drive, Reading RG6 1PT **Tel:** 0118 935 3222 **Email:** info@bg-group.com **Apply to:** Mr Howard Landes	BG is a global business and a leader in exploration, production and delivery of natural gas. Our lawyers are integral to our success.	V 1 T 2 P - TS 100 WP no
BHATIA BEST 12 Carrington Street, Nottingham NG1 7FF **Tel:** 0115 950 3231 **Email:** info@bhatiabest.co.uk **Apply to:** Ms Jayne Sheehan	A city centre legal aid franchise practice with a dynamic, progressive approach. Specialising in crime, matrimonial, public law, community care, civil litigation, PI, commercial debt.	V 0 T 4 P 11 TS 128 WP no
BHATT MURPHY 10 Tyssen Street, London E8 2FE **Tel:** 020 7729 1115 **Email:** mail@bhattmurphy.co.uk **Apply to:** Ms Diane Fisher	Bhatt Murphy is a human rights practice specialising in the protection of civil liberties, dealing particularly with actions against the police, public and prison law.	V 0 T 5 P 2 TS 33 WP yes
BHOGAL PARTNERS SOLICITORS 174 High Street, Hounslow, London TW3 1BQ **Tel:** 020 8572 9867 **Email:** info@bhogalpartners.co.uk **Apply to:** Mr Kritpal Bhogal	Established for over 19 years, we are a dynamic and forward thinking legal firm providing services in various areas of law and notarial services.	V 1 T 3 P 3 TS 19 WP yes
BHP LAW Westgate House, Faverdale, Darlington DL3 0PZ **Tel:** 01325 466 794 **Email:** lisac@bhplaw.co.uk **Apply to:** Mrs Lisa Cairns		V 0 T 4 P 10 TS 125 WP no
BHW SOLICITORS 1 Smith Way, Grove Park, Enderby, Leicester LE19 1SX **Tel:** 0116 289 7000 **Email:** jack.khurana@bhwsolicitors.com **Apply to:** Mr Jack Khurana	A progressive eight partner firm providing a high quality legal service to business clients ranging from national PLCs to local entrepreneurs.	V 2-4[19] T 4 P 8 TS 50 WP yes

V = Vacancies / **T** = Trainees / **P** = Partners / **TS** = Total Staff / **WP** = Work Placement

Firm	Description	V	T	P	TS	WP
BILTON HAMMOND The Corner House, Union Street, Mansfield, Nottinghamshire NG18 1RP **Tel:** 01623 675 800 **Email:** markbilton@biltonhammond.co.uk **Apply to:** Mr Mark Bilton	Progressive firm specialising in family, crime and property. Only applicants living within 10 miles of Chesterfield or Mansfield will be considered for the vacation scheme.	0	2	6	35	yes
BINDMANS LLP 275 Gray's Inn Road, London WC1X 8QB **Tel:** 020 7833 4433 **Email:** info@bindmans.com **Apply to:** Ms Lynn Knowles	A highly successful law firm offering a wide range of services with a reputation for excellence, we are often at the cutting edge of legal developments.	0	9	14	114	no
BIRCHALL BLACKBURN LAW 36-48 Avenham Street, Preston PR1 3BN **Tel:** 01772 561663 **Email:** cjharris@birchallblackburn.co.uk **Apply to:** Mrs Christine Harris	Well-established and progressive firm with seven offices, offering services to business and private clients. Also cover insolvency and are specialists in family law, particularly childcare.	0	2	21	240	no
BIRCHAM DYSON BELL LLP 50 Broadway, London SW1H 0BL **Tel:** 020 7227 7000 **Email:** graduate@bdb-law.co.uk **Apply to:** Graduate Recruitment Team	Broad based, friendly firm with strong private client, charities and parliamentary public law and planning practices. Trainees given good training with responsibility under supervision of partners.	5	10	47	280	yes
BIRD & BIRD 12 New Fetter Lane, London EC4A 1JP **Tel:** 020 7415 6000 **Email:** london.graduates@twobirds.com **Apply to:** Graduate Recruitment & Trainee Development Team	Bird & Bird is an international law firm serving clients in 118 countries from 28 offices across Europe, the Middle East and the Asia-Pacific region.	18	36	298	3000	yes
BIRD & CO SOLICITORS LLP 15 Castlegate, Grantham, Lincolnshire NG31 6SE **Tel:** 01476 591711 **Email:** enquiries@birdandco.co.uk **Apply to:** Mrs E Conron	Four-partner firm with offices in Grantham, Newark and Lincoln. Young and progressive high street practice. Core areas are criminal, family, civil litigation, PI, conveyancing, wills and probate.	0	2	4	50	no
BIRKETT LONG LLP 1 Amphora Place, Sheepen Road, Colchester CO3 3QG **Tel:** 01206 217300 **Email:** liz.omahony@birkettlong.co.uk **Apply to:** Miss Liz O'Mahony	Pre-eminent Essex firm – general services; specialisms in commercial, environmental, agricultural, education, employment, computer law, family and private client. Other offices in Chelmsford and Basildon.	0	6	24	175	yes
BIRKETTS LLP 24-26 Museum Street, Ipswich IP1 1HZ **Tel:** 01473 232300 **Email:** graduate-recruitment@birketts.co.uk **Apply to:** Ms Suzannah Rogers	Award-winning, top 100 law firm based in the East of England, providing a full range of legal services: corporate and commercial, property and private client.	7	20	59	504	yes

V = Vacancies / **T** = Trainees / **P** = Partners / **TS** = Total Staff / **WP** = Work Placement

Blake Morgan LLP

New Kings Court, Tollgate Chandler's Ford, Eastleigh Hampshire SO53 3LG
Tel: 0238 090 8090
Email: graduateinfo@blakemorgan.co.uk
Web: www.blakemorgan.co.uk
f blakemorganllp 🐦 bm_careers

The firm At Blake Morgan we have always excelled in finding the best possible solutions for our clients. With exceptional talent and leading lawyers working across southern England and Wales, Blake Morgan has a highly skilled workforce, giving our clients access to a wide range and depth of skills and experience. We act for large corporates, entrepreneurs and owner-managed businesses, public sector, charity organisations and private individuals.

Types of work Banking and finance, commercial contracts, commercial recoveries, construction and engineering, corporate transactions, dispute resolution, driver defence, employment, family, financial services, franchising, insurance, intellectual property, licensing, pensions and benefits, planning, professional regulatory, property litigation, public procurement, real estate, regulatory risk and compliance, residential property, restructuring and insolvency, rural and agriculture, interventions, technology and outsourcing, trademarks and registrations, wills, probate, tax and trusts.

Who should apply When recruiting our trainee solicitors we are looking for ability, enthusiasm, commitment and contribution. We recruit high-calibre people with proven analytical ability, strong interpersonal skills, good commercial awareness and an excellent academic record. We look for individuals with a record of significant personal achievement, who are willing and flexible, and who care about their communities as much as we do. To be successful at the application screening stage, we need to see evidence of the skills and attributes needed to be a successful lawyer within your application, including those such as attention to detail, research and individuality.

Training programme Training is carefully structured and designed to provide variety, responsibility and intellectual challenge. Working closely alongside partners and associates, the aim is to give you experience of a wide range of clients and practice areas through a series of six-month placements. We also offer client secondment opportunities. Your seat supervisor will involve you directly in work so you learn from personal experience as well as observation and instruction. The more competence you demonstrate, the more responsibility we will give you. We offer a comprehensive development programme alongside the compulsory Professional Skills Course. You will have a review meeting every three months with your supervisor and the trainee regional partner to monitor your progress.

When and how to apply All applications must be made via our online application form at www.blakemorgan.co.uk. We regret that we cannot accept applications made by any other means.

Work placements We offer a one-week vacation scheme to those applying for a training contract. We structure the week to allow you to spend quality time within a legal team learning about the work they do and their clients. It is also important to us that you have a chance to really understand our culture and what being a trainee at Blake Morgan is like so you also complete client research and charity-related projects. The final day is an assessment day where candidates will have a first-round interview with an associate and take part in group and individual exercises. Insights days are a great way to learn more about us and to confirm that we're the right firm for you. After a warm welcome from the trainee regional partner, you'll hear more about Blake Morgan, attend a recruitment workshop and enjoy a networking lunch before shadowing a current trainee for the afternoon.

Vacancies	18
Trainees	33
Partners	118
Total staff	1,000
Work placement	yes

Training contract deadline
31 May 2018

Apply
Online

Sponsorship
LPC

Offices
Cardiff, London, Southampton, Portsmouth, Oxford, Reading

BLAKE 🌟
MORGAN

Remember to cite *The Training Contract & Pupillage Handbook* on your application form if you apply to this firm.

Blaser Mills LLP

40 Oxford Road, High Wycombe HP11 2EE
Tel: 020 3814 2020
Email: enquiries@blasermills.co.uk
Web: www.blasermills.co.uk
🐦 blasermills

The firm Blaser Mills is a leading law firm based in the South East with over 60 lawyers. We are a full-service firm, offering a comprehensive range of legal services to businesses and private individuals. We act for blue-chip companies that are household names as well as SMEs, entrepreneurs and not-for-profit organisations. The firm has a rich history and we have retained our reputation for high-quality legal advice from lawyers who are experts in their fields. At the same time, our modern and innovative approach means that we deliver practical and cost-effective solutions.

Types of work Commercial, commercial property, employment and dispute resolution, residential property and development, wills, trusts and probate, personal and serious injury, family and divorce (including child care), criminal defence.

Who should apply We are proud of the diversity of our teams of lawyers, in terms of experience, background and approach. We look for diversity in our trainees too. As well as a strong academic background, excellent communication skills and analytical ability, we look for talented individuals who have a strong team ethic, ambition and who embrace responsibility. Trainees are right at the heart of the firm and nothing demonstrates this more clearly than the fact that the majority of our partners trained with us. Progression to partnership is strictly on merit and excellence is continuously rewarded.

Training programme Training starts in September with a full induction day that introduces trainees to the firm. Trainees will have varied (four six-month) seats in both non-contentious and contentious practice areas, giving them the opportunity to gain experience across a broad range of legal disciplines in a variety of locations. From day one, trainees are given plenty of responsibility and hands-on experience, with the ongoing support from experienced training supervisors. In addition, we operate a mentor scheme that gives trainees confidential access to recently qualified lawyers who can offer first-hand experience and advice. Part of the mentor scheme includes getting the trainees together three times a year for social events. Trainees are also actively encourage to attend networking events to help develop their personal and professional skills.

When and how to apply For training contracts to commence September 2020, applications open on 2 March 2018 and close on 29 June 2018. Please complete the online application form accessible on our website. We no longer accept applications by CV and covering letter.

Vacancies	4
Trainees	8
Partners	22
Total staff	125

Work placement yes

Training contract deadline
29 June 2018

Apply
Online

Offices
High Wycombe, Amersham, Rickmansworth, London

 **BlaserMills**

BLM

Kings House, 42 Kings Street West, Manchester M3 2NU
Tel: 0161 236 2002
Email: graduaterecruitment@blmlaw.com
Web: www.blmlaw.com/graduatecareers
🐦 blm_grads

The firm With strong ambitions for growth and expansion, BLM's goal is to be recognised as one of the leading global insurance and risk law specialists by 2020. The firm has now broken through the £100m barrier and has the strength and breadth to work with more customers across more lines of business and in more locations. In 2014, we restructured our business to reflect our customers' needs. Today, we are more than an insurance and risk law firm – we understand and are firmly embedded into our sector.

Types of work Insurance and risk law, including (but not limited to): catastrophic injury, casualty, clinical negligence, fraud, housing litigation,motor, occupational disease and product liability.

Who should apply Trainees represent a significant investment for the business and so we need to ensure that you are up for the challenge.

We look for a blend of high academic ability and people who fit with our dynamic, ideas led and ambitious culture. Please note that we do not screen any candidates out of the process based purely on academic results, we consider your entire application.

Training programme Our two-year trainee solicitor programme has been designed to maximise your potential. You'll complete four six-month seats, giving you exposure to a variety of teams across the business. You'll also gain the experience and develop the skills required of a qualified solicitor within insurance law. You may also have the opportunity to spend time on secondment with one of our customers or with the Association of British Insurers. Throughout your programme you will work with our partners and associates on a variety of cases from low to complex, high-value claims, from initial investigation through to trial. You will have all of the support that you need from your assigned supervisor and our in-house talent development team. Partners encourage early responsibility and expect trainees to manage workloads autonomously and as part of a team. We will provide a supportive and friendly working environment and you can expect clear opportunities for career progression and a broad scope of challenging and interesting work.

When and how to apply Please apply directly through our website www.blmlaw.com/join-us/graduates.

Work placements BLM's vacation scheme gives you the opportunity to spend two weeks in one of our offices. You'll be paired up with one of our current trainees and will have the opportunity to really get to grips with what we do day-to-day. You'll work with our partners and associates too, contributing to live cases and be given real responsibility.

During your vacation scheme you will also have the opportunity to network with colleagues outside of your team so you can start building relationships and start to get to know our people. We will provide you with a blend of practice group presentations, training and other development opportunities too. It's not all work though – we will also arrange a number of social events. The vacation scheme isn't just about you impressing us... it's also about you deciding if we're the right firm for you.

Sponsorship BLM will fund the LPC for future trainees who have not already completed this.

Vacancies	25
Trainees	50
Partners	210
Total staff	1,700
Work placement	yes

Apply
Online

Starting salary
London – £31,000
Regional offices – £22,000

Minimum qualifications
2.1 degree

Sponsorship
LPC

Offices
Edinburgh, Glasgow, Liverpool, Manchester, Birmingham, London, Southampton

BISHOP & SEWELL LLP
59-60 Russell Square, London WC1B 4HP
Tel: 020 7631 4141
Email: mail@bishopandsewell.co.uk
Apply to: Mr Michael Gillman

Bishop & Sewell is a firm offering comprehensive range of legal services to both private and commercial clients. We are not currently inviting applications for training contracts.

V	0
T	2
P	9
TS	54
WP	no

BLACKHURST SWAINSON GOODIER LLP T/A BSG SOLICITORS
10 Chapel Street, Preston PR1 8AY
Tel: 01772 253841
Email: info@bsglaw.co.uk
Apply to: Mr Keith G Parr

General practice. Holder of legal aid franchise. Applications for training contracts and vacation placements accepted at any time.

V	1
T	1
P	6
TS	22
WP	no

BLACKS SOLICITORS LLP
Citypoint, 29 King Street, Leeds LS1 2HL
Tel: 0113 207 0000
Email: tmoyes@lawblacks.com
Apply to: Mr Tom Moyes

General commercial practice with increasing emphasis on company commercial and commercial property areas of work but also servicing private clients.

V	3
T	6
P	16
TS	170
WP	yes

BLANCHARDS BAILEY LLP
Bunbury House, Stour Park, Blandford St Mary, Dorset DT11 9LQ
Tel: 01258 459361
Email: pat.mapstone@blanchardsbailey.co.uk
Apply to: Ms Pat Mapstone

Blanchards Bailey is a six-partner firm with approximately 66 staff across three offices dealing with a wide range of legal work.

V	0
T	1
P	6
TS	66
WP	no

BLANDY & BLANDY LLP
One Friar Street, Reading RG1 1DA
Tel: 0118 951 6800
Email: hr@blandy.co.uk
Apply to: Mrs Anne Laflin

The firm offers a full range of commercial and private client services (except criminal work). Clients include public and private companies, landed estates and individuals.

V	2-3
T	5
P	20
TS	104
WP	yes

BOLT BURDON
Providence House, Providence Place, London N1 0NT
Tel: 020 7288 4700
Email: people@igloolaw.co.uk
Apply to: Ms Lucy Croucher

A modern professional firm providing swift practical advice and the highest levels of service to business and personal clients, and in negligence cases.

V	0
T	1
P	5
TS	70
WP	no

BOND DICKINSON
4 More London Riverside, London SE1 2AU
Tel: 0845 415 0000
Email: joanne.smallwood@bonddickinson.com
Apply to: Joanne Smallwood

A dynamic UK law firm, providing a comprehensive legal service to our clients in a wide range of legal sectors across eight UK cities.

V	30
T	54
P	123
TS	1200
WP	yes

BONNETT SON & TURNER LLP
33 Bath Road, Hounslow TW3 3BW
Tel: 020 8570 5286
Apply to: Mrs N Bowman

Established practice with two offices specialising in company, commercial property, litigation, employment, residential conveyancing, and wills and probate.

V	0
T	1
P	3
TS	30
WP	no

V = Vacancies / **T** = Trainees / **P** = Partners / **TS** = Total Staff / **WP** = Work Placement

Boyes Turner

Abbots House, Abbey Street, Reading RG1 3BD
Tel: 0118 952 7191
Email: graduates@boyesturner.com
Web: www.boyesturner.com
🐦 boyesturner

The firm Boyes Turner is continuing to flourish in the Thames Valley legal market. The strategy for 2018 and onwards is to continue the growth and development of the firm, its employees and its work.

The firm demands a high standard of quality work from its partners, associates, assistants and trainee solicitors, together with those employees providing support services. However, the firm also recognises its employees' desire to enjoy their time outside of work which results in highly motivated employees.

The firm's values fall into the following categories: accessibility, quality client contact, commercial awareness, approachability, openness, honesty, enthusiasm and respect. Boyes Turner prides itself on being a modern, forward thinking, friendly team.

Types of work We are one of the UK's leading full-service law firms. Our lawyers regularly work with many of the world's largest multinationals as well as successful UK and European businesses. Our highly ranked commercial and specialist claims groups are regularly rated amongst the best in the UK.

Who should apply If you are an enthusiastic, practical and pragmatic individual who takes pride in your work and are prepared to go the extra mile to provide high quality services to clients, colleagues and the firm as a whole, then apply to Boyes Turner for a 2020 training contract.

Training programme The training principal, Andrew Chalkley, and the human resources manager, Helen Barnett, oversee the training of all trainee solicitors. Each trainee has a tutor who is one of the firm's partners. The tutors meet the trainees on a regular basis throughout the training contract to review the trainees' progress on two levels: (a) how the trainees are developing as lawyers and (b) how the trainees are developing as individuals.

Training seats are currently organised into six-month seats in four practice areas, offering our trainees experience in both commercial and private client areas of law. For each area, a supervisor from the relevant practice group will oversee day-to-day training and work. Boyes Turner seeks to give as much client contact to trainees as possible.

When and how to apply If you are interested in applying for a training contract with Boyes Turner commencing in 2020, please do so via our online application at www.boyesturner.com. The deadline for receipt of 2020 applications is June 2018. The application form will be published on our website from January 2018.

Work placements Boyes Turner's vacation placement scheme provides a unique opportunity to gain an insight into what it is like to work for our law firm. We offer eight students one week placements (four placements in the spring and four placements in the summer). We use the vacation placement scheme to identify potential recruits for our training contracts. The placement also allows you to find out if you would like to train with us.

Sponsorship Candidates who accept a training contract with Boyes Turner prior to beginning their LPC will receive part sponsorship of LPC tuition fees.

Vacancies	3
Trainees	6
Partners	23
Total staff	160

Work placement yes

Training contract deadline
June 2018

Apply
Online at
www.boyesturner.com

Minimum qualifications
2.1 degree

Sponsorship
LPC

Offices
Heading

B P Collins LLP

Collins House, 32-38 Station Road, Gerrards Cross SL9 8EL
Tel: 01753 889995
Email: jacqui.symons@bpcollins.co.uk
Web: www.bpcollins.co.uk
🐦 bpcollinslaw

The firm Established in 1966 and with over 60 lawyers, B P Collins LLP is an award-winning law firm based in Gerrards Cross, Buckinghamshire. Heralded a 'regional heavyweight' and top ranked by independent legal directories, its teams of legal experts provide advice and support to both businesses and private individuals across a range of corporate, employment, real estate, dispute resolution, family law and wills, trusts and probate matters.

Celebrating 50 years in 2016, the firm has built its reputation helping successful people with significant assets achieve peace of mind. Its lawyers are dedicated to delivering the best legal advice, through solving problems, managing risk and adding value. Lexcel accredited, B P Collins' commitment to and enduring relationships with clients, whether a private individual or thriving business, ensure delivery of an outstanding service.

Most lawyers have worked in London, but have opted to work in more congenial surroundings where they can enjoy a higher quality lifestyle. Gerrards Cross is a very pleasant town surrounded by beautiful countryside, but within 20 minutes commuting distance of London Marylebone. It is an affluent area and we are conveniently located to serve the extremely active business communities of West London, Heathrow, Uxbridge, Slough and High Wycombe.

Types of work Corporate and commercial, commercial and residential property, employment law, family law, litigation and dispute resolution and private client.

Who should apply Bright, hard-working, lateral thinkers who are good communicators with plenty of initiative will thrive in the B P Collins environment. You should be adaptable and self starting in approach and possess a degree of robustness to cope with the changing demands which you will face during the contract.

Training programme The firm aims to have six to eight trainee solicitors at different stages of their training contracts at all times. Trainees complete five months in four different practice groups of their choice. The final four months is spent in the practice group in which the trainee intends to specialise. The firm has a training partner with overall responsibility for all trainees and each practice group has its own trainee supervisor who is responsible for day-to-day supervision. Trainees are given early responsibility which includes plenty of client contact and professional work. There are regular meetings between the supervisor and the trainee to monitor progress and a review meeting with the training partner midway through and at the end of each practice group seat. Trainees are encouraged to participate in social and marketing events. The firm has a very high trainee retention rate.

When and how to apply CV with a handwritten letter from 1 March through to 31 May 2018 (email applications will not be considered).

Work placements See website for details.

Sponsorship The firm makes a contribution towards LPC fees.

Vacancies	3-4
Trainees	7-8
Partners	16
Total staff	105

Work placement   yes

Training contract deadline
31 May 2018

Apply to
Jacqui Symons,
HR Manager

Starting salary
£26,400

Minimum qualifications
2.1 degree, As and Bs at
A level

Sponsorship
LPC

Offices
Gerrards Cross, Bucks

Remember to cite *The Training Contract & Pupillage Handbook* on your application form if you apply to this firm.

BPE Solicitors LLP

St James House, St James Square, Cheltenham GL50 3PR
Tel: 0124 222 4433
Email: amanda.coleman@bpe.co.uk
Web: www.bpe.co.uk
f bpecommunity **𝕏** bpe_solicitors

The firm BPE Solicitors is an entrepreneurial firm working with like-minded businesses and individuals, supporting them at home and at work. Many clients have been retained for decades and the firm has supported young businesses in their growth to become multi-million pound, multi-national operations.

With more than 130 staff including 60 lawyers, BPE continues to grow through its collaborative approach, providing clients with a team of specialists. Its lawyers have extensive sector experience and great networks of contacts. As comfortable working directly with owner-managers and directors of growing firms, as with in-house counsel, government agencies, or private clients seeking help with family issues, BPE provides versatility, expertise and a personal approach.

Headquartered in Cheltenham, Gloucestershire and with an office in London and a presence in Bristol and Oxford, BPE clients are located throughout the UK.

Operating for close to 35 years, for the past eight the firm has been led by senior partner John Workman, who was joined in 2017 by chief executive Paul Browne in steering its continued growth.

Types of work Property, corporate, construction and engineering, commercial, employment, litigation, science and technology, family, private client, contentious probate and residential.

Who should apply BPE is different. We want you to share our ambition. We are looking for bright, passionate and driven individuals who are able to think on their feet, learn from each other, and enjoy being part of a dynamic, entrepreneurial team. You will need a minimum 2.1 degree with strong A levels and relevant work experience.

Training programme Each trainee will spend six months in four seats across the firm. We offer corporate and commercial seats along with a private client seat option, covering both contentious and non-contentious disciplines, giving you the chance to find out which area of law suits you best.

Our teams provide an exciting and stimulating training environment with a very hands on approach. You will find yourself getting involved in client matters, networking events, conference calls, ADR, target client research, and much more. We guarantee your training will be wide ranging, intensive and well balanced.

But it's not all work and no play – we make the most of any opportunity to get together and have fun! From our mix of sports teams and Friday nights out to firm-wide summer and Christmas parties and team away days, there's always plenty of opportunities to get to know your colleagues outside of work.

When and how to apply Contact HR Manager Amanda Coleman at amanda.coleman@bpe.co.uk for more information.

Work placements Placements are available all year round depending on the availability of both the student and BPE.

Sponsorship We do not offer any form of sponsorship.

Vacancies	4
Trainees	10
Partners	21
Total staff	130

Training contract deadline
31 May 2018

Apply
Online

Starting salary
£22,000

Minimum qualifications
2.1 degree

Offices
Cheltenham, Stonehouse

Remember to cite *The Training Contract & Pupillage Handbook* on your application form if you apply to this firm.

BOODLE HATFIELD LLP 240 Blackfriars Road, London SE1 8NW **Tel:** 020 7629 7411 **Email:** traineesolicitors@boodlehatfield.com **Apply to:** Miss Jenny Andrews	Boodle Hatfield is a highly successful law firm which advises wealthy individuals, families, property owners and businesses in the United Kingdom and internationally.	V 4 T 9 P 34 TS 150 WP yes	
BOSLEY & CO 5 Marlborough Place, Brighton BN1 1UB **Tel:** 01273 608 181 **Email:** sb@bosley.co.uk **Apply to:** Mr Stanley Bernard		V 1 T 0 P 3 TS 13 WP yes	
BOTT & COMPANY SOLICITORS LTD St Ann's House, Parsonage Green, Wilmslow, Cheshire SK9 1HG **Tel:** 01625 415 800 **Email:** info@bottonline.co.uk **Apply to:** Ms Claire Walsh		V 0 T 0 P 3 TS 102 WP no	
BOWCOCK CUERDEN LLP South Cheshire House, Manor Road, Nantwich, Cheshire CW5 5LX **Tel:** 01270 611106 **Email:** jpc@bowcockcuerden.co.uk **Apply to:** Mr JP Cuerden	Three-partner LLP niche commercial firm with specialist private client department; longstanding Lexcel accreditation; progressive; quality oriented. NFU legal panel firm covering Cheshire and Derbyshire.	V 1 T 0 P 3 TS 28 WP no	
BRACHERS LLP Somerfield House, 59 London Road, Maidstone ME16 8JH **Tel:** 01622 690691 **Email:** humanresources@brachers.co.uk **Apply to:** Mrs Jacqueline Shepherd	Providing extensive legal services to corporate and private clients throughout London and the South East.	V 2[19] T 4 P 23 TS 180 WP yes	
BRAIN SINNOTT & CO 1 Moravian Road, Kingswood, Bristol BS15 8LY **Tel:** 0117 960 6880 **Apply to:** Mrs Claire Haycroft	A general local practice dealing principally in criminal and matrimonial legal aid matters with a small civil litigation client base together with a non-contentious department.	V 0-1 T 1 P 3 TS 25 WP no	
BRAMSDON & CHILDS 141 Elm Grove, Southsea, Portsmouth PO5 1HR **Tel:** 023 92821251 **Apply to:** Mr Andrew White	Well-established firm with offices in Southsea, Portsmouth and Fareham with a general practice.	V 1 T 1 P 5 TS 34 WP no	
BRAY & BRAY Spa Place, 36-42 Humberstone Road, Leicester LE5 0AE **Tel:** 0116 254 8871 **Email:** info@braybray.co.uk **Apply to:** Mr ID Lewis	Well-established firm with strong private client and SME commercial client base. Wide variety of work including legal aid.	V 1 T 1 P 12 TS 95 WP no	

V = Vacancies / **T** = Trainees / **P** = Partners / **TS** = Total Staff / **WP** = Work Placement

Brabners LLP

1 Horton House, Exchange Flags, Liverpool L2 3YL
Tel: 0151 600 3000
Email: trainees@brabners.com
Web: www.brabners.com
🐦 brabnersllp

The firm One of the top Northwest commercial firms, Brabners LLP, in Liverpool, Manchester and Preston, has the experience, talent and prestige of a firm with a 200-plus year history. Brabners LLP is a dynamic, client-led specialist in the provision of excellent legal services to clients ranging from large plcs to private individuals.

Types of work The firm carries out a wide range of specialist legal services and its client base includes plcs, public sector bodies, banks and other commercial, corporate and professional businesses. Brabners LLP is organised into client-focused departments: banking, corporate, commercial, employment, litigation, property (including construction), social housing and private client.

Who should apply Graduates and those undertaking the GDL or LPC, who can demonstrate intelligence, intuition, humour, approachability and commitment.

Training programme The LLP is one of the few law firms that holds Investor in People status and has a comprehensive training and development programme. Trainees are given a high degree of responsibility and are an integral part of the culture of the firm. Each trainee will have partner-level supervision. Personal development appraisals are conducted at three six-monthly intervals to ensure that trainee progress is valuable and informed. The training programme is overseen by the firm's director of training, Dr Tony Harvey, and each centre has designated trainee partners.

It is not all hard work and the firm has an excellent social programme.

When and how to apply Apply online by 30 June 2018 for training contracts commencing September 2020.

Vacancies	6
Trainees	12
Partners	64
Total staff	356

Training contract deadline
30 June 2018

Apply
Online

Starting salary
Not less than £24,000

Minimum qualifications
2.1 degree or postgraduate degree

Offices
Liverpool, Manchester, Preston

Brabners

BREEZE & WYLES SOLICITORS LTD Second Floor, Stag House, Old London Road, Hertford SG13 7LA **Tel:** 01992 558411 **Email:** recruitment@breezeandwyles.co.uk **Apply to:** Miss Amy Collins	Established for 100 years, progressive and forward thinking. Covers domestic conveyancing/ commercial conveyancing and litigation, company commercial, matrimonial, probate and private client.

V	4^{18}
T	8
P	9
TS	180
WP	no

BRIAN KOFFMAN & CO New Maxdov House, 130 Bury New Road, Prestwich, Manchester M25 0AA **Tel:** 0161 832 3852 **Email:** briankoffman@motoringoffencesolicitors.co.uk **Apply to:** Mr B Koffman	Privately funded road traffic and crime.

V	0
T	-
P	1
TS	2
WP	no

BRIDGE MCFARLAND Sibthorp House, 351-355 High Street, Lincoln LN5 7BN **Tel:** 01522 518888 **Email:** recruitment@bmcf.co.uk **Apply to:** Mrs Tracey Inkpin	Offices in Grimsby, Lincoln, Hull, Louth and Market Rasen. Particular expertise in medical negligence, personal injury, commercial, civil and construction litigation, family, and property.

V	2^{18}
T	3
P	25
TS	167
WP	yes

BRIDGE SANDERSON MUNRO 55 Hallgate, Doncaster DN1 3PD **Tel:** 01302 321621 **Email:** info@bsmlaw.co.uk **Apply to:** Mr PD Davies	Long-established franchised general practice with four partners in three offices.

V	0
T	0
P	4
TS	20
WP	no

BRIDGER & CO SOLICITORS Old Bank Chambers, 35 High Street, Builth Wells, Powys LD2 3DL **Tel:** 01982 559292 **Email:** philip@bridgerandco.co.uk **Apply to:** Mr Philip Bridger	Bridger & Co is a fast growing practice, based at Llandovery, Llandrindod Wells and Builth Wells with plans to open further branches. We specialise predominantly in high street work as well as agriculture and planning.

V	1
T	2
P	3
TS	8
WP	yes

BRIGHOUSE WOLFF Whelmar House, Southway, Skelmersdale WN8 6NX **Tel:** 01695 722577 **Email:** mgh@brighouse-wolff.co.uk **Apply to:** Mr MG Hagerty	Large general practice specialising in conveyancing probate litigation, crime, mental health and family law. Legal aid franchise and estate agency.

V	1
T	1
P	10
TS	80
WP	no

BRIGNALLS BALDERSTON WARREN Forum Chambers, The Forum, Stevenage, Hertfordshire SG1 1EL **Tel:** 01438 359311 **Apply to:** Mr B C Lendrum	General high street practice dealing with conveyancing, probate, wills and trusts, family, crime, corporate and commercial matters, employment and general civil litigation.

V	0
T	2
P	13
TS	57
WP	no

BROOKS & PARTNERS Lyons House, 2 Station Road, Camberley, Surrey GU16 7JA **Tel:** 01276 681217 **Email:** law@brooks-partners.co.uk **Apply to:** Mrs V Lennard	A progressive law firm based in Surrey handling a wide range of private client and business work. Our strength is the quality of our people.

V	0
T	1
P	1
TS	24
WP	no

V = Vacancies / **T** = Trainees / **P** = Partners / **TS** = Total Staff / **WP** = Work Placement

Bristows LLP

100 Victoria Embankment, London EC4Y 0DH
Tel: 020 7400 8000
Email: trainee.recruitment@bristows.com
Web: training.bristows.com
🐦 bristowsgrad

The firm Bristows is a medium-sized firm that handles the types of work you might normally associate with only the very largest firms. Established 180 years ago, we have built up a client list that includes leading businesses from a variety of cutting-edge industries. Working with so many ambitious organisations, we are often advising on issues that shape entire industries and on which a company's future might depend.

Our strength in the intellectual property field means we have a great many clients from the life sciences, technology and consumer products sectors, as these are areas where organisations often need to protect their ideas, inventions and brands. Our clients range from fast-growing start-ups and medium-sized enterprises, to global corporations, financial institutions and high-profile charities. It's a real mix of organisations and, whatever your specialism, as a lawyer at Bristows you could find yourself working with any of them.

Types of work Bristows has one of the foremost intellectual property practices in the world. Our lawyers are recognised as leading authorities in a wide variety of legal disciplines and as a firm we offer a true breadth of expertise. Our core practice areas are: IP, IT and data protection, corporate, commercial technology and copyright disputes, real estate, regulatory, EU and competition, employment, tax and charities.

Who should apply Each year we ask around 10 graduates to join our team and are extremely selective because we are looking for trainees with true partner potential. We place great importance on having a diverse and inclusive environment and recruit trainees from all degree disciplines (including those with a science and engineering background) from a wide range of universities.

Training programme As part of a small, select and high-calibre intake, our trainees work alongside our partners dealing directly with clients right from the start. There's plenty of responsibility, but this is matched by an extremely supportive and friendly culture so trainees are never far from encouragement and advice when they need it. During the two years' training we offer a mixture of three-month and six-month seats which may include a three-month secondment to the UK in-house legal department of one of our leading multi-national clients. We also guarantee a seat in IP – this is rare even among firms with a strong IP practice!

When and how to apply To apply for a training contract position commencing in September 2020, please complete our online application form which can be found on the firm's trainee recruitment webpage. The deadline for training contract applications is 31 July 2018.

Work placements We run a number of two-day workshops and open days which offer the chance to find out more about Bristows and are a great opportunity to assess whether law as a career, and Bristows as a firm, are for you. While in the office you will take part in a range of activities to enable you to get a real sense of the firm and find out first-hand what life is like as a lawyer at Bristows. Please visit our website for the dates of our winter, spring and summer workshops, our open days and application deadlines.

Sponsorship Payment of full fees and a maintenance grant of £8,000 for both the LPC and GDL (where applicable).

Vacancies	10
Trainees	20
Partners	41
Total staff	275

Work placement yes
(see Insider Report on p73)

Training contract deadline
31 July 2018

Apply
Online

Starting salary
£38,000

Minimum qualifications
2.1 degree preferred

Sponsorship
GDL/LPC

Offices
London

BRISTOWS

Remember to cite *The Training Contract & Pupillage Handbook* on your application form if you apply to this firm.

BROSS BENNETT Stable House, 64A Highgate High Street, London N6 5HX **Tel:** 020 8340 0444 **Email:** gen@brossbennett.co.uk **Apply to:** Mrs Sharon Bennett	The firm specialises in family law and is one of the largest niche practices outside of central London.	V T P TS WP	0 1 5 20 yes
BROWN RUDNICK LLP 8 Clifford Street, London W1S 2LQ **Tel:** 020 7851 6000 **Email:** employmentopportunities@brownrudnick.com **Apply to:** Ms Valerie Jones	An AmLaw 200 firm with offices in the United States and Europe. The firm represents clients from around the world in high stakes litigation and business transactions.	V T P TS WP	3[18] 5 29 100 no
BROWNE JACOBSON LLP Mowbray House, Castle Meadow Road, Nottingham NG2 1BJ **Tel:** 0808 1789064 **Email:** traineeapplications@brownejacobson.com **Apply to:** Trainee Recruitment	A full service national law firm with expertise across both private and public sector specialisms. Offering excellent opportunities for quality people.	V T P TS WP	20 32 115 964 yes
BRYAN AND ARMSTRONG The New Meeting House, Station Street, Mansfield NG18 1EF **Tel:** 01623 624505 **Email:** enquiries@bryanandarmstrong.co.uk **Apply to:** Mr N Croston	Legal aid, matrimonial, personal injury and litigation, commercial and residential property, small business advice. One office in Mansfield. Lexcel and CQC accredited	V T P TS WP	0 1 4 21 no
BRYAN CAVE 88 Wood Street, London EC2V 7AJ **Tel:** 020 3207 1100 **Email:** clinton.baker@bryancave.com **Apply to:** Mr Clinton Baker	Extensive banking, corporate/commercial practice with offices worldwide. Bryan Cave is one of the leading firms in the US and offers clients a comprehensive service.	V T P TS WP	0 4 15 80 yes
BS SINGH & CO LLP 182 Stapleton Road, Easton, Bristol BS5 0NZ **Tel:** 0117 935 4500 **Email:** info@bssinghsolicitors.co.uk **Apply to:** Mr Bhupinder Singh	Bristol-based high street niche practice. Specialising in immigration, family, children matters, conveyancing (residential, commercial), wills and probate, litigation, employment, crime and general.	V T P TS WP	2 - 2 4 yes
BTMK SOLICITORS LLP 19 Clifftown Road, Southend-On-Sea, Essex SS1 1AB **Tel:** 01702 339222 **Email:** info@btmk.co.uk **Apply to:** Ms Judith Kundi	One of the largest commerical and personal law firms in Essex with expertise covering all aspects of company and business law and personal legal services.	V T P TS WP	2[18] 5 10 70 yes
BUCKLES SOLICITORS LLP Grant House, 101 Bourges Boulevard, Peterborough PE1 1NG **Tel:** 01733 888722 **Email:** hr@buckles-law.co.uk **Apply to:** Mrs Christine Walker	Buckles Solicitors LLP are a regional firm dedicated to the provision of quality legal services to individual and commercial clients. We are a progressive and developing firm.	V T P TS WP	2 2 14 100 no

V = Vacancies / **T** = Trainees / **P** = Partners / **TS** = Total Staff / **WP** = Work Placement

Burges Salmon

1 Glass Wharf, Bristol BS2 0ZX
Tel: 0117 939 2229
Email: frances.bennett@burges-salmon.com
Web: www.burges-salmon.com
f burgessalmontrainee 🐦 burgessalmonts

The firm Burges Salmon is the independent UK law firm which delivers the best mix of advice, service and value. We pride ourselves on delivering an excellent standard of legal and business advice to our clients, which has led to many of our practice areas and sectors winning awards and recognition as best in class. Our national and international client base ranges from private individuals to government departments and FTSE 100 companies including The Crown Estate, Nationwide, Lloyds Banking Group, John Lewis, The Nuclear Decommissioning Authority, FirstGroup and the Crown Commercial Service. We believe it is our people that make the firm great. Our values of ambition, collaboration, commitment, fairness, quality and respect shape our distinctive culture and are evident across the firm. All our people are based in our HQ in Bristol. This means we all know and work with each other. In fact, team playing is core to our approach to delivering a great client experience. We are accredited by Investors in People Gold and offer our people a generous benefits package, career development and progression, and a strong corporate responsibility programme.

Types of work The quality of the firm's expertise is widely recognised across its main departments including banking and finance, commercial, corporate, dispute resolution, employment, private client, projects and real estate.

Who should apply There is no 'standard' Burges Salmon trainee. The one thing all our people have in common is their ambition and drive to deliver top quality work for colleagues and clients. We therefore welcome applications from the widest pool of candidates. As an undergraduate you can apply from your penultimate year. We also welcome applications from graduates and those considering a change in career. Successful candidates will have achieved or expect to achieve a 2.1 at degree level in any discipline and have achievements which demonstrate the exceptional personal skills necessary to become a lawyer at Burges Salmon.

Training programme Our six-seat training contract is designed to provide you with the greatest breadth of experience possible as a trainee. While traditional training contracts normally include four six-month seats, ours includes six four-month placements. This ensures you gain the maximum exposure to our varied practice areas and experience a wide range of contentious and non-contentious work from across our main departments.

When and how to apply Our online application form can be found within the careers section of our website.

Work placements We run winter (one-week), spring and summer (two-week) schemes across the year. During the vacation scheme you will have the opportunity to visit two departments of your choice. The emphasis is on 'real work' and, under the guidance of your supervisor, you will have the chance to attend court visits or client meetings as well as skills sessions run by trainees and solicitors. In addition to this, there are many social and sports events throughout the placement that offer a real insight into life as a trainee solicitor. Allowance: £250 per week.

Sponsorship The firm pays GDL and LPC fees. Maintenance grants of £7,000 are paid to LPC students and £14,000 to students studying for both the GDL and LPC (£7,000 pa).

Vacancies	30
Trainees	56
Partners	87
Total staff	750

Work placement   yes

Training contract deadline
31 July 2018

Apply
Online

Starting salary
£35,000

Minimum qualifications
2.1 degree, any discipline

Sponsorship
GDL/LPC

Offices
Bristol, London

BURNETTS
6 Victoria Place, Carlisle CA1 1ES
Tel: 01228 552222
Email: kas@burnetts.co.uk
Apply to: Mrs Kate Sowerby

We are one of the largest law firms in Northern England providing grounded and expert legal advice nationally to individuals, businesses and the public sector.

V	2
T	2
P	10
TS	126
WP	no

BURROUGHS DAY
14 Charlotte Street, Bristol BS1 5PT
Tel: 0117 929 0333
Email: recruitment@bd4law.com
Apply to: Ms Michelle Groom

Burroughs Day Solicitors is a leading South West law firm offering advice to start-ups, owner-managed businesses and individuals.

V	1
T	1
P	10
TS	100
WP	no

BURTON & BURTON SOLICITORS LTD
Fox House, 17 Dale Street, Nottingham, Nottinghamshire NG2 4LE
Tel: 01159 859 059
Email: enquiries@burtonandburton.co.uk
Apply to: Mr Mohammed Mahruf

High street firm which also deals with wide range of work specialising in immigration, family, personal injury and property.

V	0-1
T	2
P	4
TS	20
WP	no

BURTON & CO LLP
Stonebow, Lincoln LN2 1DA
Tel: 01522 523215
Email: inmail@burtonlaw.co.uk
Apply to: Mrs Judith Brennan

A very well established, well known firm located in the centre of Lincoln, undertaking all types of work for a small city and country clientele.

V	0
T	1
P	5
TS	40
WP	yes

BURY & WALKERS LLP
Britannic House, Regent Street, Barnsley S70 2EQ
Tel: 01226 733533
Email: info@burywalkers.con
Apply to: Mr John Clark

V	0
T	1
P	7
TS	66
WP	no

BUSS MURTON LAW LLP
Wellington Gate, 7-9 Church Road, Tunbridge Wells, Kent TN1 1HT
Tel: 01892 510222
Email: psimpson@bussmurton.co.uk
Apply to: Ms Patricia Simpson

Medium-sized regional law firm covering most aspects of the law in both commercial and private client areas. Four operating divisions broken down into specialist areas.

V	1[19]
T	2
P	9
TS	80
WP	no

BUTCHER & BARLOW LLP
2 Bank Street, Bury BL9 0DL
Tel: 0161 764 4062
Email: cb@butcher-barlow.co.uk
Apply to: Mr Charles Barlow

We prefer candidates who can develop their careers in any of our offices in Greater Manchester and Cheshire.

V	2[19]
T	4
P	24
TS	139
WP	no

BWF SOLICITORS
529 Kingsland Road, Dalston, London E8 4AR
Tel: 020 7241 7180
Email: admin@bwfsolicitors.com
Apply to: Mr B Owusu

Small highly professional solicitors, specialising in family, immigration, civil litigation, conveyancing, personal injury and wills and probate.

V	2
T	0
P	2
TS	5
WP	no

V = Vacancies / **T** = Trainees / **P** = Partners / **TS** = Total Staff / **WP** = Work Placement

CAINS ADVOCATES LIMITED Fort Anne, Douglas, Isle of Man IM1 5PD **Tel:** 01624 638300 **Email:** richard.vanderplank@cains.com **Apply to:** Mr Richard Vanderplank	Cains advises many of the world's largest financial and commercial institutions in areas including project finance, corporate law, financial services, commercial litigation and commercial property.	V 2 T 2 P 9 TS 50 WP yes
CALDICOTTS 21 Burgess Street, Leominster, Herefordshire HR6 8DE **Tel:** 01568 614168 **Email:** lawyers@caldicotts.com **Apply to:** Mr Bruce Gray		V 0 T 3 P 4 TS 19 WP yes
CAMERON JONES HUSSELL & HOWE 1/3 Grove Place, Port Talbot, West Glamorgan SA13 1HX **Tel:** 01639 885261 **Email:** jghussell@cjhh.com **Apply to:** Mr JG Hussell	Sound base in conveyancing and probate. Experienced in civil litigation. Franchise for matrimonial and family work including child care.	V 0 T - P 5 TS 28 WP no
CAMPBELL CHAMBERS 25 Hatton Garden, London EC1N 8BQ **Tel:** 020 7691 8777 **Apply to:** Ms A Campbell	The firm is progressive and forward-thinking, valuing the diversity of its client base. We aim to recruit a workforce that reflects this. No vacancies at present.	V 0 T 4 P 2 TS 10 WP no
CAMPBELL-TAYLOR SOLICITORS 3 Bradbury Street, London N16 8JN **Tel:** 020 7923 9583 **Email:** admin@rhctlegal.co.uk **Apply to:** Mr Rod Campbell-Taylor		V 0 T 1 P 1 TS 10 WP yes
CAMPS 1 Europa House, Conway Street, Birkenhead CH41 4FT **Tel:** 0151 201 8080 **Email:** cdb@camplaw.co.uk **Apply to:** Mr Colin Billing	Specialist plaintiff litigation using dedicated software.	V 0 T 0 P 5 TS 170 WP yes
CANNINGS CONNOLLY SOLICITORS 16 St Martin's-le-Grand, London EC1A 4EE **Tel:** 020 7003 8124 **Email:** sjones@cclaw.co.uk **Apply to:** Mr Simon Jones	Two six-month seats in real estate and a further six months in each of dispute resolution and corporate.	V 1[19] T 2 P 7 TS 25 WP no
CANTER LEVIN & BERG The Temple, 1 Temple Square, 24 Dale Street, Liverpool L2 5RL **Tel:** 0151 239 1000 **Email:** martinmalone@canter-law.co.uk **Apply to:** Ms Hayley Roberts	Offices in Liverpool and Kirkby.	V 1-2 T 1 P 10 TS 91 WP yes

V = Vacancies / **T** = Trainees / **P** = Partners / **TS** = Total Staff / **WP** = Work Placement

CAPITAL LAW Capital Building, Tyndall Street, Cardiff CF10 4AZ **Tel:** 0333 2400 489 **Email:** recruitment@capitallaw.co.uk **Apply to:** Miss Lauren Peach	Specialising in commercial litigation, employment, non-contentious corporate/commercial matters, insolvency and commercial property.	V 4^{18} T 6 P 18 TS 85 WP yes
CARMARTHENSHIRE COUNTY COUNCIL County Hall, Carmarthen, Carmarthenshire SA31 1JP **Tel:** 01267 224012 **Email:** direct@carmarthenshire.gov.uk **Apply to:** Mr Lyn Thomas	Local government legal service.	V 0 T 2 P 6 TS 16 WP no
CARPENTER & CO 46 Woodcote Road, Wallington, Surrey SM6 0NW **Tel:** 020 8669 5145 **Apply to:** Mr David Greenfield	A general well-established high street practice including family, conveyancing, probate and civil litigation.	V 0-1 T 0 P 3 TS 25 WP no
CARTER BELLS LLP Kings' Stone House, 12 High Street, Kingston-upon-Thames KT1 1HD **Tel:** 020 8939 4000 **Email:** mail@carterbells.co.uk **Apply to:** Mr Frank Horder	This well-established high street practice covers all areas of law apart from crime and can provide a good grounding for enthusiastic trainees.	V 0 T 0 P 7 TS 25 WP no
CARTMELL SHEPHERD Viaduct House, Carlisle CA3 8EZ **Tel:** 01228 516666 **Email:** scott.garson@cartmells.co.uk **Apply to:** Mr Scott Garson	Cartmell Shepherd is a large, broadly-based general practice with five offices throughout Cumbria and Northumbria.	V 2 T 5 P 7 TS 90 WP yes
CARTWRIGHT KING Lock House, Wilford Road, Nottingham NG2 1AG **Tel:** 0115 9587 444 **Email:** personnel@cartwrightking.co.uk **Apply to:** Mrs Ellen Nightingale	We are a national firm specialising in areas such as family and care, mental health, court of protection, motoring, fraud immigration and crime.	V 0 T 2 P 26 TS 280 WP no
CBTC RAWSTORNE 27a Windsor Street, Stratford-Upon-Avon CV37 6NL **Tel:** 01789 267 646 **Email:** enquiries@cbtcrawstorne.co.uk **Apply to:** Mrs Melanie Mellichap	Main areas of practice are criminal, mental health, family, childcare, civil litigation, residential conveyancing, company and commercial, wills, trust and probate law.	V 0 T 0 P 1 TS 7 WP no
CFG LAW (PART OF THE CLIENT FIRST GROUP) Oakwater House, 4 Oakwater Avenue, Cheadle Royal Business Park, Cheshire SK8 3SR **Tel:** 0161 437 9999 **Email:** recruitment@cfglaw.co.uk **Apply to:** Ms Allyson McCahill	Specialist personal injury practice with a commitment to providing an interesting and challenging case load, excellent training and full support.	V 4 T 6 P 1 TS 75 WP yes

V = Vacancies / **T** = Trainees / **P** = Partners / **TS** = Total Staff / **WP** = Work Placement

Charles Russell Speechlys LLP

5 Fleet Place, London EC4M 7RD
Tel: 020 7203 5353
Web: www.charlesrussellspeechlys.com
🐦 crs_trainees

The firm Charles Russell Speechlys is one of a small number of law firms which provides personalised, considered advice to dynamic and entrepreneurial organisations, as well as astutely commercial advice to individuals and their families. We are uniquely positioned to provide comprehensive advice where these two sets of needs overlap and as a result we work with some of the world's most successful entrepreneurs, wealthy families and growth businesses. Our approach is to take both a long-term and broad view, helping our clients to make the right decisions now and for the future. We adapt to the needs of each of our clients and work with them in a highly responsive and personal way, sensitively guiding them to the right outcome. Many much larger commercial clients find our approach a refreshing alternative to that of larger, but less personal law firms.

Types of work Banking and finance, commercial, commercial dispute resolution, construction, engineering and projects, contentious trusts and estates, corporate, corporate tax, corporate restructuring and insolvency, employment, pensions and immigration, family, financial services, IP litigation, private property, property litigation, real estate and tax, trusts and succession. These practice areas are focused on the following sector areas: charities/not for profit, energy and natural resources, family, financial services, healthcare, private wealth, real estate and construction, retail and leisure, sport and TMT.

Who should apply We require candidates to achieve a minimum of a 2.1 in their degree and be able to demonstrate other key attributes outside of academia, such as teamwork, leadership, communication skills and initiative. People come to us from all backgrounds and degree disciplines, with a range of views that combine to give us our distinctive perspective on the law.

Training programme The two-year training contract at Charles Russell Speechlys is divided into four seats, giving trainees the opportunity to experience a range of different practice areas before qualification. This gives our trainees the chance to engage in high level work with both private clients and commercial clients. Throughout the training contract, there are regular meetings and reviews between the trainees and their supervisors to ensure they are continuing to receive a broad range of quality work and that they are developing the required skills and knowledge as they progress through their seats. Benefits include private medical care; PHI and life assurance; pension; season ticket loan; cycle to work; 25 days' holiday and a subsidised restaurant in the London office.

When and how to apply Online applications to be submitted via our website www.charlesrussellspeechlys.com. Applications open in December each year. The deadline for our summer placement scheme is 31 January, and applications for our training contract will close on 30 June 2018.

Work placements Our summer placement scheme takes place in both our London and Guildford offices and offers a detailed introduction into the legal world. Each week is spent in a different practice area where you will carry out real fee earning work that could include attending client meetings and going to court. You will have support from trainees and solicitors in each of the teams and have the opportunity to meet a number of different people, either at organised social events or as part of your day to day interactions.

Sponsorship We undertake to pay GDL and/or LPC course fees together with a maintenance grant.

Vacancies	24
Trainees	48
Partners	148
Total staff	1,001

Work placement yes

Training contract deadline
30 June 2018

Apply
Online via www.charlesrussellspeechlys.com

Starting salary
London – £38,000
Guildford – £32,000
Cheltenham – £28,500

Sponsorship
GDL/LPC

Offices
London, Guildford, Cheltenham, Paris, Geneva, Luxembourg, Zurich, Manama, Doha

CHADBOURNE & PARKE (LONDON) LLP Regis House, 45 King William Street, London EC4R 9AN **Tel:** 020 7337 8000 **Email:** recruitmentldn@chadbourne.com **Apply to:** Mr Andy Garside	Leading US law firm with a focus on high quality, international work for sophisticated clients. Professional, yet relaxed and welcoming culture with access to partners.	V 1 T 2 P 15 TS 73 WP no
CHAMBERLINS 4, 5 & 6 Crown Road, Great Yarmouth, Norfolk NR30 2JP **Tel:** 01493 857621 **Email:** info@chamberlins.demon.co.uk **Apply to:** Mr JB Thackray	General practice with four branches. The firm has been established for over 100 years. The first firm in Great Yarmouth to be recommended for a legal aid franchise.	V 0 T 0 P 5 TS 32 WP no
CHARLESWORTH NICHOLL & CO 31 High Street, Crediton, Devon EX17 3AJ **Tel:** 01363 774706 **Email:** sp@charlesworthnicholl.co.uk **Apply to:** Miss CS Nicholl	A high street practice specialising in residential, agricultural and commercial property work, wills and probate, and family work. We have Lexcel and Investors in People.	V 0 T 1 P 2 TS 20 WP no
CHATHAM CHAMBERS SOLICITORS 136 Chatham Street, Reading, Berkshire RG1 7HT **Tel:** 0118 958 5855 **Email:** contact@chathamchambers.co.uk **Apply to:** Mr I Nawaz-Chechi	We are a dynamic high street practice specialising in immigration, property and private client work Based in Reading.	V 1 T 1 P 2 TS 6 WP yes
CHELMSFORD BOROUGH COUNCIL Legal Services, Civic Centre, Duke Street, Chelmsford CM1 1JE **Tel:** 01245 606606 **Email:** susan.deval@chelmsfordbc.gov.uk **Apply to:** Mrs Susan De Val	An in-house service providing a comprehensive range of legal services to the council and other public bodies including advice, litigation, advocacy and mediation services.	V 0 T 0 P 0 TS 16 WP no
CHENERY MAHER 21 Church Street, Clithero, Lancs BB7 2DF **Tel:** 01200 422264 **Email:** mail@chenerymaher.co.uk **Apply to:** Mrs N Bradbury	Small semi-niche firm committed to provision of quality professional services in conveyancing, wills and probate, and family specialisation.	V 0 T 0 P 2 TS 11 WP no
CHHOKAR & CO 29a The Broadway, Southall, Middlesex UB1 1JY **Tel:** 020 8574 2488 **Email:** law@chhokar.com **Apply to:** Mr SS Chhokar	Established quality driven West London practice committed to delivering a superior service in property (residential and commercial), family, wills and probate, immigration and litigation.	V 1 T 1 P 3 TS 11 WP no
CHURCHERS BOLITHO WAY 13-18 Kings Terrace, Portsmouth PO5 3AL **Tel:** 023 92820747 **Apply to:** Mr DJ Grinstead	General practice with specialism in commercial work (particularly software licensing). Applications by post.	V 0 T 2 P 7 TS 22 WP yes

V = Vacancies / **T** = Trainees / **P** = Partners / **TS** = Total Staff / **WP** = Work Placement

CITY AND COUNTY OF SWANSEA Civic Centre, Oystermouth Road, Swansea SA1 3SN **Tel:** 01792 636000 **Email:** vivienne.rees@swansea.gov.uk **Apply to:** Legal Services Department	Large, busy local government legal department dealing with litigation, commercial property, planning, contracts, employment, housing, social services, childcare and education matters. LEXCEL accredited.	V 0 T 1 P - TS 54 WP no
CLARKE & SON SOLICITORS LLP Manor House, 8 Winchester Road, Basingstoke RG21 8UG **Tel:** 01256 320555 **Email:** nwharry@clarkeandson.co.uk **Apply to:** Mrs Nia Wharry	Established 1862, our goal is to be the best law firm in Basingstoke. An experienced and dynamic team, our primary focus is our clients.	V 0 T 1 P 7 TS 37 WP no
CLARKE KIERNAN 2-4 Bradford Street, Tonbridge TN1 1DU **Tel:** 01732 360 999 **Email:** cmc@clarkekiernan.com **Apply to:** Ms Catherine McCarthy	Two offices. High street practice offering specialist departments in family and criminal work, growing litigation, housing and prison law departments, principally legal aid work.	V 1[18] T 1 P 2 TS 27 WP no
CLARKE WILLMOTT LLP 138 Edmund Street, Birmingham B3 2ES **Tel:** 0845 209 1729 **Email:** heather.cooper@clarkewillmott.com **Apply to:** Ms Grace Larbey	A UK law firm with a national reputation in key commercial and private client services.	V TBC T 10 P 73 TS 410 WP no
CLARKSLEGAL LLP One Forbury Square, The Forbury, Reading RG1 3EB **Tel:** 0118 958 5321 **Email:** contact@clarkslegal.com **Apply to:** Ms Denise Taylor	Based in Reading and London, a leading commercial practice offering a comprehensive service to a wide range of business clients.	V 2 T 4 P 13 TS 70 WP no
CLARKSON WRIGHT & JAKES LTD Valiant House, 12 Knoll Rise, Orpington BR6 0PG **Tel:** 01689 887887 **Email:** hr@cwj.co.uk **Apply to:** Ms Jill Lawton	CWJ sees itself as providing capital quality to its clients (corporate, commercial and private client) without the rat race for its staff.	V 0 T 1 P 15 TS 77 WP no
CLIFFORD HARRIS & CO 58 Queen Anne Street, London W1G 8HW **Tel:** 020 7486 0031 **Email:** sv@cliffordharris.co.uk **Apply to:** Mr Sunil Varma	Small West End commercial practice dealing with general litigation, insolvency, conveyancing, and company/commercial work for established corporate and private clients.	V 0 T 1 P 2 TS 8 WP no
CLIFTON INGRAM LLP 22/24 Broad Street, Wokingham, Berkshire RG40 1BA **Tel:** 0118 9780099 **Email:** stephanierose@cliftoningram.co.uk **Apply to:** Mrs Stephanie Rose	Our trainees are valued members of the Clifton Ingram team – we provide a structured, supportive training environment, 'real' experience, client exposure and skill development.	V 1 T 2 P 12 TS 70 WP no

V = Vacancies / **T** = Trainees / **P** = Partners / **TS** = Total Staff / **WP** = Work Placement

Cleary Gottlieb Steen & Hamilton LLP

City Place House, 55 Basinghall Street, London EC2V 5EH
Tel: 020 7847 6860
Email: longraduaterecruit@cgsh.com
Web: www.cgsh.com/careers/london

The firm Pioneers in the globalisation of the legal profession, we are a leading international law firm with 16 integrated offices located in major financial and political centres around the world. We operate as a single global partnership. Consistent with the vision of our founders, we remain committed to openness, diversity, individuality and collaboration.

Types of work Our core areas of practice in London are mergers and acquisitions, financing and restructuring, capital markets, international litigation and arbitration, and competition. In addition, we have established successful self-standing practices in tax, financial regulation, intellectual property and information technology.

Who should apply We look for candidates who are excited by the challenge of working on groundbreaking matters in a dynamic international setting. While academic excellence is a pre-requisite, we place particular emphasis on recruiting candidates with whom we and our clients will enjoy working. A sense of humour is just as important as an ability to think critically and creatively about cutting-edge legal issues.

Training programme We do not believe in a 'one size fits all' training solution. By recruiting 15-20 trainees each year, we are able to offer training that is tailored to each trainee's interests, experience and aptitudes. Nor do we believe that the transition from trainee solicitor to associate occurs overnight on qualification. So we encourage our trainees to take responsibility as soon as they are ready to do so. Given appropriate levels of supervision and support, trainees operate as lawyers from the day they join us.

When and how to apply Candidates for trainee solicitor positions should apply before 31 July, two years in advance of the year in which the training contract is due to commence. All candidates should submit a cover letter and full curriculum vitae via the firm's website, including details of all public examination results.

Work placements Our London office offers 48 vacation places each year (12 in winter, 12 in spring and 12 in each of two summer schemes). To provide a practical insight into life as a Cleary lawyer, we involve applicants directly in client work. To ensure exposure to the full range of work that we undertake in London, we provide a series of practice overview sessions. We also organise a number of external social events that offer applicants the opportunity to get to know our partners, associates and trainees in an informal setting.

We actively encourage all candidates who are considering applying for a trainee solicitor position to undertake a vacation placement with us. Applications for winter vacation placements should be received by 3 November. The deadline for spring and summer vacation scheme applications is 19 January.

Sponsorship We fund the LPC for all our future trainee solicitors. For non-law graduates, we also fund the GDL. A maintenance grant of £8,000 is paid for each year of professional study.

Vacancies	15-20
Trainees	27
Partners	193
	(21 in London)
Total staff	2,500
	(200 in London)

Work placement yes

Training contract deadline
31 July 2018

Apply to
Claire Astbury

Starting salary
1st year – £48,000
2nd year – £52,000

Minimum qualifications
High 2.1 degree

Sponsorship
GDL/LPC

Offices
London, New York, Washington DC, Paris, Brussels, Frankfurt, Cologne, Rome, Milan, Moscow, Hong Kong, Beijing, Buenos Aires, São Paulo, Abu Dhabi, Seoul

CLEARY GOTTLIEB

Remember to cite *The Training Contract & Pupillage Handbook* on your application form if you apply to this firm.

(312) THE TRAINING CONTRACT & PUPILLAGE HANDBOOK

Clifford Chance

10 Upper Bank Street, Canary Wharf, London E14 5JJ
Tel: 020 7006 4005
Email: graduate.recruitment@cliffordchance.com
Web: www.cliffordchancegraduates.com
f cliffordchancegrads 🐦 ccgradsuk

The firm We are one of the world's pre-eminent law firms, with significant depth and range of resources across five continents. As a single, fully integrated, global partnership, we pride ourselves on our approachable, collegial and team-based way of working. We always strive to exceed the expectations of our clients, which include corporates from all the commercial and industrial sectors, governments, regulators, trade bodies and not-for-profit organisations. We provide them with the highest-quality advice and legal insight, which combines the firm's global standards with in-depth local expertise.

Types of work Our clients look for expert advice and solutions for a host of different commercial issues, which we divide into six key practice areas: corporate; finance; capital markets; real estate; litigation and dispute resolution, and risk management; and tax, pensions and employment.

Who should apply We are looking for individuals with a strong and consistent academic record along with a keen interest in commercial affairs and the law. This is a client-orientated vocation so excellent commnication skills are key. Teamwork, resilience, planning and organisation, problem solving and attention to detail are all vital attributes we are looking for in our applicants.

Training programme Over the course of the 24-month training contract you'll rotate through four of our core areas: finance, corporate, capital markets and one other of your choice. In each seat, you'll have in-depth, sector-specific training, which will bring you up-to-date with the latest trends, ideas and innovations in that area. You'll also have the support of our graduate development team, as well as a dedicated supervisor.

The support doesn't end there either. You'll also have access to not just a legal support manager and a career development partner, but also the award-winning Clifford Chance academy. This acclaimed centre works to develop innovative learning tools and offers exceptional training courses, led by internal and external experts. The academy also holds regular talks with clients, to give you an idea of the wider industry.

We offer client secondments and international seats as part of the training contract subject to business need.

When and how to apply Apply via our website www.cliffordchancegraduates.com for training contracts in 2020. All of our applications open in October 2017 – January 2018.

Work placements We are running two first-year springboard schemes and one summer vacation scheme. We will also be hosting open days throughout the year so please visit our website to find out more and how to apply.

Sponsorship Please refer to website for details.

Vacancies	Up to 80
Trainees	200
Partners	567
Total staff	6,025

Work placement yes
(see Insider Report on p74)

Training contract deadline
3 January 2018

Apply
Online

Starting salary
1st year – £44,800
2nd year – £50,500
(September 2017)

Minimum qualifications
340 UCAS points

Sponsorship
Please refer to website

Offices
Abu Dhabi, Amsterdam, Bangkok, Barcelona, Beijing, Brussels, Bucharest, Casablanca, Dubai, Düsseldorf, Frankfurt, Hong Kong, Istanbul, Jakarta, London, Luxembourg, Madrid, Milan, Moscow, Munich, New York, Paris, Perth, Prague, Rome, São Paulo, Seoul, Shanghai, Singapore, Sydney, Tokyo, Warsaw, Washington DC

C L I F F O R D

C H A N C E

CMS Cameron McKenna Nabarro Olswang

Cannon Place, 78 Cannon Street, London EC4N 6AF
Tel: 020 7367 3000
Email: grad.rec@cms-cmno.com
Web: www.cms.law
f cmsuk_graduates 𝕏 cmsuk_graduates

The firm In 2017, CMS UK, Nabarro LLP and Olswang LLP combined in what was the largest ever merger in the UK legal industry. The new combined firm, CMS, is now the sixth largest in the UK by revenue and the sixth largest globally by headcount. CMS is a new kind of future-facing law firm. Combining top quality sector expertise with international scale across its six core sectors of energy, financial services, infrastructure and project finance, life sciences and healthcare, real estate and technology, media and communications, the firm is modern and ambitious.

Types of work Our main practice areas include banking and finance, commercial, competition and EU, consumer products, corporate/M&A, dispute resolution, employment and pensions, energy, funds, hotels and leisure, infrastructure and projects, insurance, intellectual property, life sciences, private equity, public procurement, real estate and construction, tax, technology, media and communications.

Who should apply We have a range of graduate opportunities which are open to law and non-law students and students who are currently at university or who have already graduated. Eligibility for our graduate opportunities will vary depending on your year of study; therefore, please visit our website for further details. Our minimum criteria requires candidates to have an ABB at A level (or equivalent) and be on track to achieve/have achieved a 2.1 at degree level (or equivalent).

Training programme CMS trainee solicitors embark on a two-year training contract in London, Bristol, Sheffield, Aberdeen, Edinburgh or Glasgow. Prior to starting a training contract, all trainees attend a comprehensive induction programme that includes a week residential course at IMD, Switzerland – a top-ranked business school for executive development. During the training contract, our trainees undertake four six-month seats across the various practice areas and given responsibility within high-profile transactions and cases. There is also a guaranteed secondment, which includes secondments to one of the firm's clients or to one of its UK or international offices.

When and how to apply Online application via graduates.cms-cmck.com. The process will include an online application, online tests and assessment day. Application dates are available on our website at: graduates.cms-cmck.com.

Work placements The CMS academy is CMS's next generation vacation scheme starting with business of law training in London for one week. This comprises panel discussions with clients, case studies, work simulation exercises and client visits amongst other things!

The second part of the programme includes a two-week internship within one of our UK offices. Participants gain real experience in a commercial environment and develop skills needed to succeed as a trainee solicitor at a modern future-facing law firm. A supervisor and buddy will be your main point of contact and will provide high quality work which will give you an accurate insight into the work of a trainee solicitor.

Our first steps programme offers an introduction to commercial law and working in a global elite law firm. The programme comprises an introduction to CMS, skills sessions and an opportunity to shadow our fee earners. A case study and social events will both enhance your technical skills, interpersonal skills and networking skills.

Vacancies	65
Trainees	130
Partners	1,000*
Total staff	7,500

* denotes worldwide figure

Work placement yes

Training contract deadline
Please visit our website for all deadlines

Apply
Online via website

Starting salary
£40,000 (London)
£37,000 (Bristol),
£24,000 (Aberdeen,
Edinburgh and Glasgow),
£26,000 (Sheffield)

Minimum qualifications
ABB at A level and 2.1 degree or equivalent

Sponsorship
GDL/LPC

Offices
71 offices in over 40 countries

C/M/S/
Law . Tax

Remember to cite *The Training Contract & Pupillage Handbook* on your application form if you apply to this firm.

CLINTONS 55 Drury Lane, London WC2B 5RZ **Tel:** 020 7379 6080 **Email:** pnewton@clintons.co.uk **Apply to:** Mr Paul Newton	One of the foremost law practices in entertainment, sport and media, with an extensive general practice covering contentious and non-contentious commercial work, family and property.

V	2
T	4
P	21
TS	75
WP	no

CLYDE & CO LLP The St Botolph Building, 138 Houndsditch, London EC3A 7AR **Tel:** 020 7876 5555 **Email:** graduaterecruitment@clydeco.com **Apply to:** Ms Rebecca Babb	Clyde & Co is a sector-focused global law firm. We advise on a full range of contentious, non-contentious and transactional matters.

V	45-50
T	100
P	375
TS	3600
WP	yes

COCKS LLOYD Riversley House, Coton Road, Nuneaton, Warwickshire CV11 5TX **Tel:** 024 7664 1642 **Email:** sol@cockslloyd.co.uk **Apply to:** Mrs Sharon Wilkinson	Largest firm in Nuneaton/North Warwickshire; all general practice areas covered including some significant commercial work more normally associated with larger 'city' practices.

V	0
T	0
P	10
TS	50
WP	no

COFFIN MEW LLP 1000 Lakeside, North Harbour, Portsmouth PO6 3EN **Tel:** 023 9238 8021 **Email:** perfectfit@coffinmew.co.uk **Apply to:** Mrs Claire Cordy	A full service firm providing services for individuals and business across the Solent region and beyond, with a strong focus on delivering client service excellence.

V	4
T	9
P	16
TS	137
WP	no

COHEN DAVIS SOLICITORS Warlies Park House, Horseshoe Hill, Upshire EN9 3SL **Tel:** 020 7183 4123 **Email:** support@cohendavis.co.uk **Apply to:** Mrs Marcia Cohen	Award winning firm focused on cutting edge social media and internet law. We offer high achievers an exciting opportunity to develop personally and professionally.

V	3[18]
T	1
P	1
TS	4
WP	yes

COLEMANS-CTTS T/A SIMPSON MILLAR 25-29 High Street, Kingston Upon Thames KT1 1LL **Tel:** 020 8296 9966 **Email:** hr@colemans-ctts.co.uk **Apply to:** The HR Manager	Colemans-ctts is a progressive and dynamic national law firm. Client relationships and the delivery of high levels of service are the hallmarks of its reputation.

V	0
T	4
P	12
TS	200
WP	no

COLES MILLER 44-46 Parkstone Road, Poole BH15 2PG **Tel:** 01202 673011 **Email:** acormack@coles-miller.co.uk **Apply to:** Mr Adrian Cormack	The firm has four offices covering the Bournemouth/Poole conurbation and seeks to provide a wide range of services to both private and commercial clients.

V	3
T	4
P	12
TS	110
WP	yes

COLLAS CRILL Glategny Court, PO Box 140, Glategny Esplanade, St Peter Port, Guernsey GY1 4EW **Tel:** 01481 734278 **Email:** recruitment@collascrill.com **Apply to:** Ms Katherine Mercer	Collas Crill is a leading global offshore firm providing a comprehensive range of services to the international and local finance and business communities, and HNWI.

V	3[18]
T	8
P	33
TS	183
WP	no

V = Vacancies / **T** = Trainees / **P** = Partners / **TS** = Total Staff / **WP** = Work Placement

Cooley (UK) LLP

Dashwood, 69 Old Broad Street, London EC2M 1QS
Tel: 020 7583 4055
Email: uktrainee@cooley.com
Web: www.cooley.com/uktrainee

The firm Cooley lawyers solve legal issues for entrepreneurs, investors, financial institutions and established companies. Clients partner with Cooley on transformative deals, complex IP and regulatory matters and high-stakes, complex litigation, often where innovation meets the law. Cooley is one of the pre-eminent law firms for technology and life sciences. The firm has 900 lawyers across 12 offices in the US, China and Europe. The firm has received a number of recent accolades; it was named one of *Fortune*'s '100 best places to Work For' in 2015, 2016 and 2017, as well as being recognised as an elite 'Top-5 Innovative Law Firm' by the *Financial Times*. Cooley opened in London in January 2015 and since opening has been named London Office of the Year at the 2015 British Legal Awards and was recognised at the *Legal Week* Innovation Awards for International Law Firm Innovation in 2016.

Types of work The UK practice has strengths across many of Cooley's core practice areas, among them corporate/M&A, private equity and venture capital, banking and finance, tax, technology and life sciences transactions, IP, complex high-stakes litigation, insurance and reinsurance, competition, employment, privacy and data protection.

Who should apply To join Cooley you need to be stimulated by solving business and legal challenges. Academic excellence (minimum 2.1 and at least 320 UCAS points or equivalent), great analytical skills and a rigorous approach are essential. You should demonstrate plenty of energy, drive and determination. Your understanding of business and commercial considerations should be of a good standard. You will also be adaptable, capable of thinking on your feet and have developed great communication and interpersonal skills from a variety of situations. Understanding teamwork, evidence of leadership and seeking responsibilities are vital. Interesting achievements and making the most of non-academic and work experience (not necessarily all legal) opportunities will help applicants stand-out.

Training programme The Cooley training experience will revolve around small groups of trainees and really hands-on involvement. We truly believe in learning by doing. Trainees spend four six-month periods in some of the firm's contentious and non-contentious corporate/transactional and litigation areas. Trainees give preferences for seats and there may also be opportunities for client secondments from time to time. The focus is on your development as a truly commercial lawyer. Supplementing your hands-on learning will be a programme designed to increase your knowledge and skill for the work Cooley does. You'll also develop your finance, marketing and commercial understanding. Practice group programmes and firm-wide opportunities will enhance this. Working alongside and learning from some of the best lawyers in their fields will give you a fantastic start to your professional life. A multilevel support network of partners, mentors and a buddy system ensures you have a targeted level of guidance.

When and how to apply The summer placement scheme is the route into being considered for a training place. Apply online by 31 January 2018.

Work placements Two structured two-week placements for eight (two groups of four) students. The dates for 2018 are 25 June to 6 July and 16 to 27 July.

Sponsorship Course fees and a living allowance while studying: £8,000 pa if studying in London, £7,500 outside London.

Vacancies	4
Trainees	7
Partners	27
Total staff	145 (London)

Work placement yes

Apply
Online

Starting salary
£44,000

Minimum qualifications
2.1 degree, at least ABB at A level (not including general studies) or equivalent

Sponsorship
GDL/LPC

Offices
Boston, Colorado, London, Los Angeles, New York, Palo Alto, Reston, San Diego, San Francisco, Seattle, Shanghai, Washington DC

Cooley

COLLINS SOLICITORS 20 Station Road, Watford WD17 1AR **Tel:** 01923 223324 **Email:** collins@collinslaw.co.uk **Apply to:** Mrs Lesley Collins	Niche practice specialising in personal injury plus full range of legal services. Situated opposite county court building, adjacent to Watford Junction station, 20 minutes from Euston.	V 0 T 3 P 5 TS 24 WP no
COLLYER BRISTOW LLP 4 Bedford Row, London WC1R 4TF **Tel:** 020 7242 7363 **Email:** recruitment@collyerbristow.com **Apply to:** Mrs Corinne Johnson	Collyer Bristow is based in central London and has 30 partners. The firm has a strong client base in both the commercial and private client sectors.	V 4-5[19] T 8 P 30 TS 138 WP yes
THE COMMERCIAL LAW PRACTICE 47 Peverell Avenue West, Poundbury, Dorchester DT1 3SU **Tel:** 01305 544 015 **Email:** lw@thecommerciallawpractice.com **Apply to:** Ms Lee Wilkins	The Commercial Law Practice is located in Dorchester specialising in residential and commercial property, business acquisitions, debt recovery, commercial mediation and other related commercial and corporate work.	V 0 T 1 P 1 TS 4 WP yes
COMMUNITY LAW CLINIC SOLICITORS 101 Chamberlayne Road, London NW10 3NP **Tel:** 020 8960 3200 **Email:** law@clcsolicitors.co.uk **Apply to:** Ms Amrik Bains	Specialists in immigration and social welfare law. Committed to legal aid work dealing with immigration, housing, debt, benefits, welfare benefits employment, family and community care.	V 0 T 2 P 1 TS 24 WP no
CONRAD KING & SOLOMON SOLICITORS 836-840 Leeds Road, Bradford BD3 9TX **Tel:** 01274 656 465 **Email:** info@nursolicitors.com **Apply to:** Mr Adam Green	A young and energetic practice with an established reputation for providing excellent client care and specialist advice in civil litigation, education, immigration, business and commercial, property, and wills and probate.	V 2 T 0 P 1 TS 6 WP yes
CORRIES SOLICITORS LTD 1st Floor, Rowntree Wharf, Navigation Road, York YO1 9WE **Tel:** 0845 241 5566 **Email:** sarah.haskins@corries.co.uk **Apply to:** Mrs Kerry Stojanovic	Corries is a modern and progressive law firm, specialising in personal injury claims, asbestos claims, criminal injuries and medical negligence.	V 0 T 2 P 2 TS 47 WP no
COTTERHILL HITCHMAN LLP Atlas House, 4-6 Belwell Lane, Sutton Coldfield B74 4AB **Tel:** 0121 323 1860 **Email:** mail@cotterhillhitchman.co.uk **Apply to:** Ms Saima Zulfiqar	Small niche firm. Mainly commercial, private client, litigation, and employment work.	V 0 T 1 P 3 TS 13 WP no
COVENTRY CITY COUNCIL Legal & Democratic Services, Council House, Coventry CV1 5RR **Tel:** 024 76833000 **Email:** jobs@coventry.gov.uk **Apply to:** Legal Services Manager	Legal and democratic services is part of the resources directorate of the council providing advice and support across the full range of council services.	V 0 T 1 P - TS 70 WP no

V = Vacancies / **T** = Trainees / **P** = Partners / **TS** = Total Staff / **WP** = Work Placement

Covington & Burling LLP

265 Strand, London WC2R 1BH
Tel: 020 7067 2000
Email: graduate@cov.com
Web: www.cov.com/en/careers/lawyers/london-graduate-recruitment-programme
🐦 covingtonllp

The firm Covington & Burling LLP was founded in Washington DC nearly a century ago. Today, the firm has over 1,000 lawyers globally across offices in Beijing, Brussels, Dubai, Johannesburg, London, Los Angeles, New York, San Francisco, Seoul, Shanghai, Silicon Valley and Washington DC. Covington's London office, overlooking the Royal Courts of Justice, was established over 25 years ago. We offer services across a wide range of practice areas, advising clients on their most challenging and complex matters. Most of the work has an international element, and all our practice groups operate across borders. Covington has been rated a Top Ranked Leading Law Firm in *Chambers UK 2017* and appears in *The Lawyer* Top 30 International Law Firm, as well as Legal Business Global 100 surveys. At Covington, you will have an opportunity to work on cutting-edge deals for international and UK corporates such as Microsoft, Astra Zeneca and Facebook, *Fortune 100* businesses and leading technology, life sciences and media companies.

Types of work Corporate advisory (including capital markets, M&A, finance, private equity, venture capital and funds), commercial litigation, data privacy, employment, financial services, insurance coverage disputes, intellectual property, internal investigations and compliance, international arbitration, life sciences, project and finance, tax, technology and media. As a trainee you will receive work assignments designed to develop your skills and will get the support and training to excel in your work. In addition, all our lawyers, including trainees, are encouraged to undertake pro bono work.

Who should apply We are looking for candidates with consistently high academic results (on target for a 2.1 degree or above and with strong A-level results), commercial awareness, strong interpersonal skills and the ability to work well in a team.

Training programme You will do four six-month seats, rotating between departments. All trainees will undertake a seat in corporate and a seat in dispute resolution. We offer optional seats in employment, life sciences, project and finance, technology and media and client secondments may also be available. We aim to distinguish our trainee programme by offering a genuine support network which includes assigning associate buddies and undertaking regular performance reviews. We have an excellent record of retaining trainees on qualification and we aim to recruit trainees who are interested in making a long term commitment to the firm.

When and how to apply Please submit an application form via the online application system, the details of which can be found on our website. Please apply by 17 July 2018.

Work placements Each year we offer up to 10 summer placements on each of our two-week programmes. Participants sit with a senior lawyer and will be given as much hands-on experience as possible. Students will spend each of their two weeks in a different practice area and will be given as much hands-on experience as possible. They will also get involved in a research project, participate in group activities and attend a series of presentations. We also organise a number of social events so that students can have some fun and get to know us.

Sponsorship Successful training contract applicants will receive payment of tuition fees for both the GDL and the LPC, as well as a maintenance grant of up to £8,000. We do not pay fees retrospectively for completed courses.

Vacancies	8
Trainees	15
Partners	283
Work placement	yes

Training contract deadline
17 July 2018

Apply
Online

Starting salary
1st year – £43,000
2nd year – £47,000
NQ – £95,000

Minimum qualifications
2.1 degree

Sponsorship
GDL/LPC

Offices
Beijing, Brussels, Dubai, Johannesburg, Los Angeles, New York, San Francisco, Seoul, Shanghai, Silicon Valley, Washington DC

COVINGTON

Remember to cite *The Training Contract & Pupillage Handbook* on your application form if you apply to this firm.

318 THE TRAINING CONTRACT & PUPILLAGE HANDBOOK

COWANS SOLICITORS LLP 114 South Street, Dorking RH4 2EW **Tel:** 01306 886622 **Email:** enquiries@cowansdorking.co.uk **Apply to:** Miss Sarah Delahunty	General practice including litigation, family and matrimonial, crime, conveyancing, and wills and probate. Committed to legally aided work. No set recruitment schedule for trainees or paralegals.	V 0 T 0 P 2 TS 25 WP no
COWLISHAW & MOUNTFORD 90 High Street, Uttoxeter ST14 7JD **Tel:** 01889 565211 **Apply to:** Mr Paul Hopkins	General practice in a country town with a mix of private and franchised legal aid work.	V 0 T 0 P 1 TS 10 WP no
COZENS-HARDY LLP Castle Chambers, Opie Street, Norwich NR1 3DP **Tel:** 01603 625231 **Email:** djtaylor@cozens-hardy.com **Apply to:** Mr David Taylor		V 1[18] T 2 P 13 TS 70 WP no
CRIPPS LLP Number 22, Mount Ephraim, Tunbridge Wells TN4 8AS **Tel:** 01892 515121 **Email:** graduates@cripps.co.uk **Apply to:** Mrs Katie Slade	A key regional law firm serving clients nationally and internationally from offices in Kent and London. Recognised countrywide for commercial, private client and property work.	V 10 T 14 P 51 TS 350 WP yes
CROCKETT & CO 260 Harehills Lane, Leeds LS9 7BD **Tel:** 0113 226 0111 **Email:** info@crockettsolicitors.co.uk **Apply to:** Miss H Crockett	Lexcel accredited specialist family law firm dealing in contact, care, divorce, ancilliary, domestic violence and other niche legal work.	V 0 T 0 P 3 TS 8 WP no
CROSSE & CROSSE 14 Southernhay West, Exeter EX1 1PL **Tel:** 01392 258451 **Apply to:** Mr TP Selley	Well established (1915) firm dealing with all main areas of work. Legal aid franchise. Specialises in personal injury, civil and family.	V 0 T 2 P 8 TS 56 WP no
CROWN PROSECUTION SERVICE CPS HQ - Rose Court, 2 Southwark Bridge, London SE1 9HS **Tel:** 0151 239 6553 **Email:** strategic.resourcing@cps.gsi.gov.uk **Apply to:** Mr Jamie Booth	The CPS recruits pupil barristers and trainee solicitors across England and Wales with permanent Crown Prosecutor posts available upon successful qualification.	V 1[18] T 30 P - TS 5974 WP no
CUMBRIA LAW CENTRE 8 Spencer Street, Carlisle, Cumbria CA1 1BG **Tel:** 01228 515 129 **Email:** reception@comlaw.co.uk **Apply to:** Ms Claire Burton	Cumbria's law centre, free specialist practice in housing, employment, welfare benefits and debt; also human rights and anti-discrimination.	V 0 T 1 P 0 TS 13 WP no

V = Vacancies / **T** = Trainees / **P** = Partners / **TS** = Total Staff / **WP** = Work Placement

CUNNINGTONS
Great Square, Braintree CM7 1UD
Tel: 013 7632 6868
Email: info@cunningtons.co.uk
Apply to: Mr Aaron Coombs

Cunningtons have over 260 years legal experience with branches nationwide. We offer a complete range of legal services including: residential and commercial conveyancing, family law, wills, trusts, probate, civil litigation and employment.

V	Varies
T	0
P	9
TS	60
WP	yes

CURTIS LAW SOLICITORS LLP
Witton Chambers, Witton Business Park, Cartmel Road, Blackburn BB2 2TA
Tel: 01254 297 130
Email: info@curtislaw.co.uk
Apply to: Miss T Riaz

We are a dynamic rapidly growing legal practice with a strong client base and a large spectrum of specialist areas.

V	8
T	2
P	4
TS	115
WP	yes

CURTIS MALLET-PREVOST COLT & MOSLE LLP
99 Gresham Street, London EC2V 7NG
Tel: 020 7710 9800
Email: recruitmentlondon@curtis.com
Apply to: Tuula Davis

US-headquartered firm with 17 offices worldwide. London specialises in international arbitration and corporate/commercial, and provides the ideal balance between friendly local office and varied international work.

V	0
T	3
P	4
TS	14
WP	no

CURWENS LLP
Crossfield House, Gladbeck Way, Enfield EN2 7HT
Tel: 020 8363 4444
Email: enfield@curwens.co.uk
Apply to: Ms Lisa Dearman

'Mini-regional' firm covering Hertfordshire and North London. A general practice also having particular strengths in litigation, employment, and company/commercial work.

V	2[18]
T	5
P	15
TS	90
WP	no

CURZON GREEN SOLICITORS
114-116 Oxford Road, High Wycombe, Buckinghamshire HP11 2DN
Tel: 01494 451355
Email: training@curzongreen.co.uk
Apply to: Miss Jennifer Sole

Curzon Green is a distinguished law firm servicing the needs of businesses and individuals. We offer our trainees a supporting environment to develop their careers.

V	2[18]
T	6
P	3
TS	22
WP	yes

CYRIL JONES & CO
17 Egerton Street, Wrexham LL11 1NB
Tel: 01978 367 830
Apply to: Mr Gareth Jones

Small general practice in North Wales, varied workload covering most areas of law, mainly conveyancing, family and probate and PI. Legal aid franchise.

V	0
T	2
P	5
TS	20
WP	no

DAC BEACHCROFT
100 Fetter Lane, London EC4A 1BN
Tel: 020 7242 1011
Email: trainee@dacbeachcroft.com
Apply to: Graduate Recruitment Team

A leading international legal business currently employing over 2,300 people across a number of locations with global coverage and ambitious plans for future growth.

V	13[19]
T	26
P	240
TS	2300
WP	yes

DAKERS MARRIOTT SOLICITORS
Quayside Chambers, 353-357 High Street, Rochester ME1 1DA
Tel: 01634 813 300
Email: mail@dakersmarriott.co.uk
Apply to: Mr Mark Marriott

A city practice in the provinces. We are a very busy practice where quality advice is available.

V	0
T	0
P	3
TS	12
WP	no

V = Vacancies / **T** = Trainees / **P** = Partners / **TS** = Total Staff / **WP** = Work Placement

DARBYS SOLICITORS LLP Midland House, West Way, Botley, Oxford OX2 0PH **Tel:** 01865 811700 **Email:** crose@darbys.co.uk **Apply to:** Mrs Cherie Rose	A regional practice with specialist team providing a wide range of legal services to both business and private clients.	V T P TS WP	4 8 38 219 yes
DARLINGTON BOROUGH COUNCIL Feethams, Darlington, County Durham DL1 5QT **Tel:** 01325 405490 **Email:** luke.swinhoe@darlington.gov.uk **Apply to:** Mr Luke Swinhoe	Local authority. Have previously had trainees but do not have trainee currently as post deleted.	V T P TS WP	0 0 - 19 no
DARLINGTONS Darlingtons House, 7 Spring Villa Park, Edgware HA8 7EB **Tel:** 020 8951 6666 **Email:** sakers@darlingtons.com **Apply to:** Mr Stephen Akers		V T P TS WP	1 2 6 42 yes
DAVID & SNAPE Old Castle Offices, South Street, Bridgend CF31 3ED **Tel:** 01656 661115 **Email:** sue.smith@davidandsnape.com **Apply to:** Ms Susan Smith	A busy, friendly and progressive high street firm with membership of several law society panels and a legal services commission franchise.	V T P TS WP	0 0 4 26 no
DAVID GRAY SOLICITORS LLP Old County Court, 56 Westgate Road, Newcastle Upon Tyne NE1 5XU **Tel:** 0191 232 9547 **Email:** lawyers@davidgray.co.uk **Apply to:** Ms Debora Sanderson	Private work and LAA contracted firm. Working within crime, family, immigration, commercial and residential conveyancing, wills/ probate, elderly client care and mental health.	V T P TS WP	1[18] 4 9 67 yes
DAVID PHILLIPS & PARTNERS 202 Stanley Road, Bootle L20 3EP **Tel:** 0151 922 5525 **Apply to:** Mrs Susan Christopher	London office deals with high profile criminal cases. Bootle office is a general practice with an emphasis on legal aid work, both criminal and civil.	V T P TS WP	0 3 15 75 yes
DAVIES AND PARTNERS Rowan House, Barnett Way, Barnwood, Gloucester GL4 3RT **Tel:** 01452 612345 **Email:** recruitment@daviesandpartners.com **Apply to:** Ms Suzanne Williams	Regional commercial practice with an emphasis on heavyweight property law, clinical negligence and commercial litigation. Integrated offices in Bristol, Gloucester, Birmingham and London.	V T P TS WP	1[18] 9 12 170 no
DAVIES JOHNSON Old Harbour Office, Guy's Quay, Sutton Harbour, Plymouth PL4 0ES **Tel:** 01752 226020 **Email:** info@daviesjohnson.com **Apply to:** Mr Charles Patterson	Specialist shipping and commercial practice.	V T P TS WP	0 0 0 26 no

V = Vacancies / **T** = Trainees / **P** = Partners / **TS** = Total Staff / **WP** = Work Placement

Davis Polk & Wardwell London LLP

5 Aldermanbury Square, London EC2V 7HR
Tel: 020 7418 1300
Email: londonrecruiting@davispolk.com
Web: careers.davispolk.com

The firm Davis Polk is a global law firm. For more than 160 years, its lawyers have advised industry-leading companies and major financial institutions on their most challenging legal and business matters. Davis Polk ranks among the world's preeminent law firms across the entire range of its practice. With over 900 lawyers across the globe, the firm operates from the key business centres around the world to provide clients with seamlessly integrated legal services of the highest calibre.

Types of work Our London based team now consists of over 60 UK and US lawyers covering a range of high profile complex and cross-border securities offerings, mergers and acquisitions and financing transactions. The corporate and finance teams are supported by first rate corporate tax, financial regulatory and anti-trust practices.

Who should apply We seek to hire applicants from a variety of backgrounds with outstanding academic and non-academic achievements, personal skills and creativity, and with a demonstrated willingness to take initiative. We strive to find exceptional lawyers who share our commitment to excellence and who will be collaborative and supportive colleagues.

Training programme Trainees will undertake a number of rotations through our corporate, credit and specialist practice areas, providing each trainee with the variety of experiences necessary to lay the foundation for a successful legal career.

Davis Polk trainees will also have the opportunity to experience a six-month secondment to our New York office.

Each trainee will be assigned a senior lawyer who will serve as a mentor and provide advice and guidance throughout the program.

When and how to apply Please visit our website at careers.davispolk.com for information on how to apply. Please note that we will be recruiting our 2020 intake of trainees directly from our Summer 2018 vacation schemes.

Work placements Please visit our website at careers.davispolk.com for information on how to apply for a place on Davis Polk's 2018 summer vacation scheme. We will accept applications from 1 December 2017 through to 14 January 2018.

Sponsorship GDL and LPC fees and maintenance grants are paid.

Vacancies	Approx 4
Trainees	8
Partners	10
Total staff	90

Work placement yes

Apply
Online at
careers.davispolk.com

Starting salary
1st year – £50,000
2nd year – £55,000

Minimum qualifications
2.1 degree or higher

Sponsorship
GDL/LPC

Offices
New York, Menlo Park, Washington DC, São Paulo, London, Paris, Madrid, Tokyo, Beijing, Hong Kong

Davis Polk

Remember to cite *The Training Contract & Pupillage Handbook* on your application form if you apply to this firm.

322   THE TRAINING CONTRACT & PUPILLAGE HANDBOOK

DAVIS & CO St Michaels Rectory, St Michaels Alley, Cornhill, London EC3V 9DS **Tel:** 020 7621 1091 **Email:** trevor.davis@davis-solicitors.com **Apply to:** Mr Trevor Davis	Niche City firm specialising in utilities litigation with blue-chip client base. Candidates should have a good academic background and have an interest in advocacy.	V T P TS WP	1 0 1 2 no
DAVIS BLANK FURNISS 90 Deansgate, Manchester M3 2QJ **Tel:** 0161 832 3304 **Email:** carole.burleigh@dbf-law.co.uk **Apply to:** Mrs Carole Burleigh	While having a successful corporate and business department, the firm is firmly committed to retaining private client work. Training in a wide range of work.	V T P TS WP	2 4 10 60 no
DAWSON CORNWELL 15 Red Lion Square, London WC1R 4QT **Tel:** 020 7242 2556 **Email:** mail@dawsoncornwell.com **Apply to:** Ms Rhiannon Lewis	A specialist family law firm, described in *Chambers 2015* as "a leader in the field, not just nationally but internationally".	V T P TS WP	1[19] 3 11 34 yes
DAWSON HART The Old Grammar School, Church Street, Uckfield TN22 1BH **Tel:** 01825 762281 **Email:** info@dawson-hart.co.uk **Apply to:** Mr Trevor Mersh	We invest valuable time with our trainees and aim to offer them a career with us, assisting them through all stages up to partnership level.	V T P TS WP	0 - 7 42 no
DAYBELLS LLP 43-45 Broadway, Stratford, London E15 4BL **Tel:** 020 8555 4321 **Email:** info@daybells.com **Apply to:** Mr Qaiser Malik	We are an established local practice with specific emphasis on client care. The firm has developed a niche in residential and commercial conveyancing.	V T P TS WP	1[19] 1 3 10 yes
DE MARCO SOLICITORS 1 Generator Hall, Electric Wharf, Sandy Lane, Coventry CV1 4JL **Tel:** 024 7699 8055 **Email:** enquiries@demarcosolicitors.com **Apply to:** Miss Sandra Garlick	De Marco Solicitors is niche *Legal 500* firm specialising in employment and company/commercial law. No current vacancies.	V T P TS WP	0 0 1 12 yes
DEAN MANSON LLP – SOLICITORS 243 Mitcham Road, Tooting, London SW17 9JQ **Tel:** 020 8767 5000 **Email:** info@deanmanson.com **Apply to:** Mr Ejaz Baig	Applications are invited for four prospective trainees under apprentice scheme each with language skills in Polish, Tamil, Arabic and Hindi.	V T P TS WP	4 2 2 10 yes
DEAN SOLICITORS 123 Drake Street, Rochdale, Lancashire OL16 1PZ **Tel:** 01706 661400 **Email:** info@deansolicitors.co.uk **Apply to:** Mr M Din	General practice with LEXCEL accreditation specialising in personal injury, conveyancing and immigration.	V T P TS WP	0 2 2 9 no

V = Vacancies / **T** = Trainees / **P** = Partners / **TS** = Total Staff / **WP** = Work Placement

Debevoise & Plimpton LLP

65 Gresham Street, London EC2V 7NQ
Tel: 020 7786 9000
Email: london-recruit@debevoise.com
Web: www.debevoise.com

The firm Debevoise & Plimpton LLP is a leading international law firm with offices in New York, Washington DC, London, Paris, Frankfurt, Moscow, Hong Kong, Shanghai and Tokyo. The London office works on many of the highest profile and most complex transactions in Europe and worldwide. We do this by virtue of our English and New York law expertise and our close integration with our other offices.

Types of work In developing our practice in London, we have sought to replicate the core strengths of our practice worldwide. Our focus is on private equity, insurance, international disputes and investigations, financial institutions, M&A, finance, capital markets and tax.

Clients include: AIA Group Limited, Alta One Capital, American International Group, Baring Vostok, The Carlyle Group, Clayton, DH Equity Partners, Clayton Dubilier & Rice, Deutsche Bank, Global Infrastructure Partners, HarbourVest Partners, Helios Investment Partners, Interros, Metric Capital, Morgan Stanley, Norilsk Nickel, Oaktree Capital Management, Park Square Capital Partners, Polyus Gold, Rexel, Stone Point Capital, Tishman Speyer, Triton and Uralkali.

Who should apply We look for students whose personal qualities, academic records and other achievements demonstrate exceptional ability, motivation and potential for growth. The training contract is open to both law and non-law graduates. We are looking for individuals who have consistently high levels of achievements both at A level (or equivalent) and at university. Applicants should be expecting to achieve at least a 2.1 in any degree discipline and have a minimum of 360 UCAS points at A level (or equivalent).

Training programme One of Debevoise's basic principles is that each of our associates should become a 'well rounded' lawyer – an effective counsellor, advisor, and advocate – who can combine specific legal knowledge with the ability to deal with a broad range of situations. We believe that lawyers best develop their skills through a combination of formal training and on-the-job experience, in a respectful and collegial environment. The two years are split into four six-month seats and trainees have the opportunity to gain experience in at least three distinct areas of law.

When and how to apply Applications for a training contract commencing September 2020 can be made between 1 May 2018 and 31 July 2018. An online application form will be available on our website at this time. Anyone interested in a training contract at Debevoise is strongly encouraged to apply for a vacation scheme place. If you wish to speak with someone about training contracts at Debevoise, please contact Rian Champion.

Work placements Debevoise offers a two-week summer vacation scheme, which runs between June and August each year. Applications for 2018 can be made between 1 December 2017 and 15 January 2018 by completing the online application form that will be available on our website during this time.

Sponsorship Full tuition fees are paid for GDL and LPC, together with a maintenance grant of £9,000 per year.

Vacancies	8-10
Trainees	15
Partners	19
Total staff	215

Work placement yes

Training contract deadline
31 July 2018

Apply to
london-recruit@
debevoise.com

Starting salary
1st year – £50,000
2nd year – £55,000

Minimum qualifications
2.1 degree

Sponsorship
GDL/LPC

Offices
New York, Washington DC, London, Paris, Frankfurt, Moscow, Hong Kong, Shanghai, Tokyo

Debevoise
&Plimpton

Remember to cite *The Training Contract & Pupillage Handbook* on your application form if you apply to this firm.

324 THE TRAINING CONTRACT & PUPILLAGE HANDBOOK

DEAN WILSON LLP Ridgeland House, 165 Dyke Road, Brighton BN3 1TL **Tel:** 01273 249200 **Email:** jbh@deanwilson.co.uk **Apply to:** Mr Julian Hunt	An award-winning firm with a national reputation for property, landlord and tenant and employment law; solicitors to various national associations; family, probate.	V 2[19] T 2 P 13 TS 69 WP no
DEBENHAMS OTTAWAY LLP Ivy House, 107 St Peters Street, St Albans AL1 3EW **Tel:** 01727 837 161 **Email:** recruitment@debenhamsottaway.co.uk **Apply to:** Mrs Alexandra Langley	Regional practice with specialist teams dealing with private client, family, employment, dispute resolution, commercial and residential property, company commercial and corporate.	V 0 T 3 P 12 TS 120 WP no
DEBIDINS 6 Broadway, London W13 0SR **Tel:** 020 8567 6343 **Email:** info@debidins.co.uk **Apply to:** Mr D Debidins	General high street pratice of long-standing with full range of legal service. No legal aid franchise.	V 0 T 0 P 2 TS 4 WP no
DECHERT LLP 160 Queen Victoria Street, London EC4V 4QQ **Tel:** 020 7184 7000 **Email:** graduate.recruitment@dechert.com **Apply to:** Graduate Recruitment	Dechert is an international law firm with offices throughout the USA, Europe and Asia. Our largest offices are in Philadelphia, New York and London.	V 10 T 20 P 312 TS 2295 WP yes
DENBY & CO 119 Duke Street, Barrow-In-Furness LA14 1XE **Tel:** 01229 822366 **Email:** info@denbyco.co.uk **Apply to:** Mr John H Denby	Franchised high street general practice. Offices in Barrow and Ulverston. Personal injury, family, crime, conveyancing and probate.	V 1 T 1 P 5 TS 26 WP no
DEREK B FORREST SOLICITORS 71 Hough Lane, Leyland PR25 2SA **Tel:** 01772 424999 **Email:** derek@solicitordirect.com **Apply to:** Mr Derek Forrest	A high street solicitor and estate agent working nationwide over phone and internet. Heavily computerised without secretaries.	V 1 T 1 P 2 TS 8 WP no
DEVON & CORNWALL CONSTABULARY Middlemoor, Exeter EX2 7HQ **Tel:** 0139 2452863 **Apply to:** Mr Brent Davision	The force's legal services provide legal support for the chief constable of Devon and Cornwall constabulary across a number of disciplines. Mainly litigious work.	V 0 T 1 P 1 TS 12 WP no
DEVONSHIRES SOLICITORS 30 Finsbury Circus, London EC2M 7DT **Tel:** 020 7628 7576 **Email:** trainee.recruit@devonshires.co.uk **Apply to:** Ms Katy Perry	Leading City firm with an established reputation for delivering a personal and bespoke service to both public and private sector organisations.	V 6[19] T 15 P 34 TS 230 WP no

V = Vacancies / **T** = Trainees / **P** = Partners / **TS** = Total Staff / **WP** = Work Placement

DEXTER MONTAGUE LLP
105 Oxford Road, Reading RG1 7UD
Tel: 0118 939 3999
Email: info@dextermontague.co.uk
Apply to: Mr William Montague

DMP is a medium-sized Thames Valley practice specialising in property, business/commercial, private client, family, and civil litigation, including PI, employment and housing. LSC contracts in family and housing.

V	119
T	1
P	4
TS	24
WP	yes

DF LEGAL LLP
62/63 High Street, Tewksbury, Gloucestershire GL20 5BJ
Tel: 01684 850 750
Apply to: Mr JG Daniels

Expanding forward-looking private practice with specialisms in interesting areas of work.

V	2
T	4
P	3
TS	24
WP	yes

DH LAW SOLICITORS LTD
130-132 Uxbridge Road, Hanwell, London W7 3SL
Tel: 020 8840 8008
Email: rheian@dhlaw.org.uk
Apply to: Ms Rheian Davies

An award-winning firm. We hold legal aid franchises in mental health, housing, family and community care.

V	0
T	2
P	1
TS	10
WP	yes

DLA PIPER UK LLP
3 Noble Street, London EC2V 7EE
Tel: 08700 111 111
Email: recruitment_graduate@dlapiper.com
Apply to: Ms Katie Sands

DLA Piper is one of the world's largest law firms, supporting businesses with commercial legal needs. We offer up to 70 training contracts a year.

V	Up to 70
T	450
P	1300
TS	8500
WP	yes

DMA LAW
56 Duke Street, Darlington DL3 7AN
Tel: 01325 482299
Email: enquiries@dma-law.co.uk
Apply to: Mr John Relton

The firm offers a friendly yet challenging environment. Career development is taken seriously. Donnelly Adamson sets high standards wihin the profession and expects nothing less.

V	0
T	0
P	5
TS	34
WP	no

DMH STALLARD LLP
Gainsborough House, Pegler Way, Crawley RH11 7FZ
Tel: 01293 605067
Email: recruitment@dmhstallard.com
Apply to: Graduate Recruitment

DMH Stallard LLP is an innovative and progressive firm that seeks opportunities to stand out from the crowd.

V	0
T	4
P	59
TS	259
WP	yes

DOLMANS SOLICITORS
One Kingsway, Cardiff CF10 3DS
Tel: 029 2034 5531
Email: philipb@dolmans.co.uk
Apply to: Ms Clare Hoskins

Specialist public sector and insurance litigation practice. Dynamic business services including corporate finance, commercial, property, sports law, employment and dispute resolution. Established private client department.

V	0
T	-
P	9
TS	39
WP	no

DONALD RACE & NEWTON
5/7 Hargreaves Street, Burnley BB11 1EA
Tel: 01282 864500
Apply to: Mr David Rogers

Burnley-based, three-office general practice specialising in crime, family and personal injury with commercial and domestic conveyancing. LSC contract. Please note that we do not currently have any vacancies.

V	0
T	2
P	6
TS	47
WP	yes

V = Vacancies / **T** = Trainees / **P** = Partners / **TS** = Total Staff / **WP** = Work Placement

DORSEY 199 Bishopsgate, London EC2M 3UT **Tel:** 020 7031 3700 **Email:** london@dorsey.com **Apply to:** Ms Roselynne Atkins	The London office has over 30 lawyers and trainees and continues to build on its strengths in corporate law, litigation, corporate tax, property and IP.	V 2 T 3 P 14 TS 45 WP no
DOUGLAS-JONES MERCER 16 Axis Court, Mallard Way, Swansea Vale, Swansea SA7 0AJ **Tel:** 01792 650000 **Email:** bjd@djm.law.co.uk **Apply to:** Mr Barry Davies	South Wales practice dealing with private client, and ever growing commercial departments. Offices in Swansea. Clients vary from large companies to private individuals.	V 1 T 2 P 7 TS 50 WP no
DOWSE & CO 23-25 Dalston Lane, London E8 3DF **Tel:** 020 7254 6205 **Email:** mh@dowse.co.uk **Apply to:** Mr Myles Hickey	Small high street legal aid practice specialising in employment, family, housing and PI.	V 0 T 4 P 3 TS 14 WP no
DRUCES LLP Salisbury House, London Wall, London EC2M 5PS **Tel:** 020 7638 9271 **Email:** info@druces.com **Apply to:** Mrs Moira Lapper	Druces LLP is an ambitious City firm, embarking on exciting times and change. It is renowned for the openness and approachability of its staff and the close relationships it develops and maintains with clients.	V 2 T 4 P 20 TS 78 WP yes
DRYSDALES SOLICITORS LLP Cumberland House, 24-28 Baxter Avenue, Southend-on-Sea SS2 6HZ **Tel:** 01702 423 400 **Email:** a.murrell@drysdales.net **Apply to:** Mr AD Murrell		V 1 T 1 P 3 TS 20 WP no
DUNCAN GIBBINS SOLICITORS Forum House, Kings Park, Knowsley L34 1BH **Tel:** 0151 949 5757 **Email:** info@duncangibbins.com **Apply to:** Mr M Dean	We are a specialist claimant personal injury firm operating in the North West but with a nationwide client base. We also have a small wills and probate department.	V 2 T 5 P 2 TS 34 WP no
DUNCAN LEWIS SOLICITORS LTD Spencer House, 29 Grove Hill Road, Harrow HA1 3BN **Tel:** 020 7923 4020 **Email:** darsheetav@duncanlewis.com **Apply to:** Ms Darsheeta Vaghela	Fastest growing legal aid firm; over 20,000 clients each year. Quality committed (12 quality marks) and largest number of training contracts at high-street level.	V 100 T 68 P 33 TS 421 WP yes
DW LAW Suite 2, Marquis House, 68 Great North Road, Hatfield, Hertfordshire AL9 5ER **Tel:** 01707 261177 **Email:** office@dwlaw.co.uk **Apply to:** Mr Francis Domingo	A firm that specialises in criminal defence work that can provide the challenge and satisfaction of achievement in an increasingly demanding environment in criminal litigation.	V 1 T 1 P 2 TS 8 WP yes

V = Vacancies / **T** = Trainees / **P** = Partners / **TS** = Total Staff / **WP** = Work Placement

DWF LLP

1 Scott Place, 2 Hardman Street, Manchester M3 3AA
Tel: 0333 320 2220
Email: trainees@dwf.law
Web: www.dwf.law/join-us/graduate
f dwf-llp-graduate-recruitment **𝕏** dwf_graduates

The firm Described by market commentators as 'blazing a trail', DWF is an award-winning legal business with a strong reputation for excellent client service and effective operational management. Recognised by the *Financial Times* as one of Europe's top 50 most innovative law firms, for innovation in culture, strategy, technology and human resources, DWF's strategic aim is to make legal services a more powerful enabler of its clients' success.

Types of work The business has core strengths in corporate and banking, insurance and litigation, and in-depth industry expertise in eight core sectors, namely energy and industrials; financial services; insurance; public sector; real estate; retail, food and hospitality; technology; and transport and logistics, which underpin its go-to-market strategy. DWF is focused on delivering service excellence to all of its clients in the UK and internationally, which include major household names and FTSE-listed companies such as Adidas, Aviva, DHL, Expedia, Royal Bank of Scotland, RSA, Serco, Telefonica, Virgin Trains, Whitbread and Zurich.

Who should apply We welcome applications from penultimate-year law students, final-year students (law and non-law) and graduates. We're looking for people who are committed to a career in law, who enjoy working as part of a busy team and respond positively to a challenge.

Our trainees need a 2.1 or higher in any degree discipline and AAB at A level (or equivalent)/AAABB at Scottish Higher Level.

Commercial acumen, good organisational skills and a fresh way of thinking about client needs are all hallmarks of a DWF team member.

Training programme DWF's training contract gives you a real taste of the variety of work on offer, giving responsibility and client contact from the get go. Many DWF trainees also have the opportunity to complete a client secondment.

When and how to apply Applications must be made online via our website www.dwf.law/join-us/graduate. Training contract applications will be accepted from October 2017 until 6 July 2018. Apply by 5 January 2018 for the vacation scheme.

Work placements DWF summer vacation scheme takes place in June, dates of which depend on location. If you are in your penultimate year of a law degree, or final year of a non-law degree then you are eligible to apply. Applications are usually open from the start of October until January, and you must make an online application.

The business recruits the majority of its trainees through the vacation scheme, so it's a good opportunity to get ahead and see why DWF is the right business for you. The two-week vacation scheme gives you the chance to work with partners, associates and trainees across two different practice groups. You'll work on live legal matters and will be given responsibility right from the start.

This is combined with a variety of internal workshops and presentations, helping you understand DWF as a business. You'll also complete a group project that's designed to aid your professional development and provide you with some of the essential skills of a successful commercial lawyer.

Sponsorship DWF sponsors the LPC/Scottish Diploma fees.

Vacancies	Up to 40
Trainees	87
Partners	329
Total staff	2,600

Work placement   yes

Training contract deadline
6 July 2018

Apply
Online

Starting salary
£22,000-£36,000

Minimum qualifications
2.1 in any subject and AAB in A levels or equivalent

Sponsorship
LPC/Scottish Diploma fees

Offices
Manchester, Birmingham, Leeds, Newcastle, Bristol, Edinburgh, Liverpool, Milton Keynes, London, Chicago, Toronto, Glasgow, Brussels, Dublin, Cologne, Dubai, Munich, Paris, Berlin, Sydney, Belfast, Singapore, Preston

Remember to cite *The Training Contract & Pupillage Handbook* on your application form if you apply to this firm.

EAST HAMPSHIRE DISTRICT COUNCIL Council Offices, Penns Place, Petersfield, Hampshire GU31 4EX **Tel:** 01730 234 069 **Email:** tracy.beavis@easthants.gov.uk **Apply to:** Mr Nick Leach	Legal services department within a local authority providing a wide range of services to the council, councillors and officers.	V 0 T 0 P 0 TS 7 WP no
EATON SMITH LLP 14 High Street, Huddersfield HD1 2HA **Tel:** 01484 821300 **Email:** mail@eatonsmith.co.uk **Apply to:** Mrs Janet Hogg	We provide a complete legal service to both the commercial and private client.	V 0 T - P 7 TS 80 WP no
EB LEGAL Astute House, Wilmslow Road, Cheshire SK9 3HP **Tel:** 01625 544 797 **Email:** info@eblegal.co.uk **Apply to:** Mrs Elizabeth Tselepis-Beesley	We are a relatively new but dynamic firm specialising primarily in personal injury and consumer credit law. We are looking for trainees wishing to specialise in these areas.	V 1 T 1 P 1 TS 5 WP yes
EDMONDSON HALL 25 Exeter Road, Newmarket CB8 8AR **Tel:** 01638 560556 **Email:** solicitors@edmondsonhall.com **Apply to:** Mr Mark Edmondson	Leading niche bloodstock and sports law practice. Equine litigation. Vet negligence, sale and purchase disputes etc. Award-winning sports lawyers. Friendly but forward thinking. Smart offices. Partners recognised specialists.	V 0 T 1 P 3 TS 20 WP yes
EDWARDS DUTHIE 269-275 Cranbrook Road, Ilford IG1 4TG **Tel:** 020 8514 9000 **Email:** allinfo@edwardsduthie.com **Apply to:** Mrs Coral Joyce	A substantial, diverse practice with particular expertise in personal injury, crime and property. Four offices across East London and Essex. Legal aid franchises in all areas.	V 0 T 7 P 12 TS 85 WP no
EDWIN COE LLP 2 Stone Buildings, Lincoln's Inn, London WC2A 3TH **Tel:** 020 7691 4000 **Email:** recruitment@edwincoe.com **Apply to:** Mrs Liz Austin	Ranked as 'UK-200' law firm, Edwin Coe LLP provides high-quality partner led legal advice to a broad spectrum of UK and international clients.	V 4 T 8 P 38 TS 160 WP yes
ELBORNE MITCHELL LLP 88 Leadenhall Street, London EC3A 3BP **Tel:** 020 7320 9000 **Email:** lawyers@elbornes.com **Apply to:** Ms Margaret Martin	The firm is a friendly high flyer, the clients professional or substantial business people, and work is specialised and intellectually challenging.	V 2 T 4 P 9 TS 33 WP no
ELLIOTT BRIDGMAN LIMITED 66-70 Court Street, Madeley, Telford TF7 5EP **Tel:** 01952 684544 **Email:** info@elliottbridgman.com **Apply to:** Mrs Joanne Foulkes	Lexcel accredited private law firm dealing with private client, notary public, probate and conveyancing, children and family matters and mental health law.	V 2 T 0 P 1 TS 21 WP yes

V = Vacancies / **T** = Trainees / **P** = Partners / **TS** = Total Staff / **WP** = Work Placement

ELLIS JONES SOLICITORS LLP Sandbourne House, 302 Charminster Road, Bournemouth BH8 9RU **Tel:** 01202 525333 **Email:** email@ellisjones.co.uk **Apply to:** Miss Sabre King	Progressive and expanding partnership in the south of England. Banking litigation, commercial property, residential property, company commercial, personal injury, private client, family and civil litigation.	**V** **T** **P** **TS** **WP**	2 4 12 130 yes
ELLISONS Headgate Court, Head Street, Colchester CO1 1NP **Tel:** 01206 764477 **Email:** recruitment@ellisonslegal.com **Apply to:** Mr Alan Dearsley		**V** **T** **P** **TS** **WP**	1[19] 4 17 160 no
EMD LAW LLP 13 Warrior Square, St Leonards-On-Sea, East Sussex TN37 6BA **Tel:** 01580890600 **Email:** lcb@emdlaw.co.uk **Apply to:** Mrs Elizabeth Dumbleton		**V** **T** **P** **TS** **WP**	0 0 3 13 no
EMERY JOHNSON ASTILLS 3 & 5 Welford Road, Leicester LE2 7AD **Tel:** 0116 2554855 **Email:** legal@emeryjohnson.com **Apply to:** Ms Isabel Wilson	Leicester firm specialising in criminal, family, childcare, conveyancing and private client law. Young, dynamic team committed to providing a quality service to clients.	**V** **T** **P** **TS** **WP**	0 3 5 45 yes
EMSLEYS 35b Main Street, Garforth, Leeds LS25 1DS **Tel:** 011 3287 8717 **Email:** corinne.pujara@emsleys.co.uk **Apply to:** Mrs Corinne Pujara	A four director general practice firm with specialised claimant personal injury and property departments.	**V** **T** **P** **TS** **WP**	1[19] 1 4 120 no
THE ENDEAVOUR PARTNERSHIP LLP St Mark's Court, Teesdale Business Park, Stockton on Tees TS17 6QW **Tel:** 01642 610300 **Email:** careers@endeavour.law **Apply to:** Ms Sharon Hutchinson	We are exclusively a business law firm, that's what we do. Providing commercial legal advice for over 15 years to companies and organisations around the Tees Valley area and beyond.	**V** **T** **P** **TS** **WP**	3 6 8 50 yes
ENGLAND & CO 7-8 South Quay, Great Yarmouth NR30 2QN **Tel:** 01493 844308 **Email:** pmason@englandandco.co.uk **Apply to:** Mr Peter Mason	A well-established firm providing a wide range of legal services. We are committed to public funding and have Investors in People and Lexcel status.	**V** **T** **P** **TS** **WP**	0 0 6 25 no
ENOCH EVANS LLP St Pauls Chambers, 6-9 Hatherton Road, Walsall WS1 1XS **Tel:** 01922 720333 **Email:** ss@enoch-evans.co.uk **Apply to:** Miss Sukie Shemar	Full service commercial firm serving a cross section of both commercial and private clients with specialist departments covering a wide range of legal services.	**V** **T** **P** **TS** **WP**	Poss[18] 4 13 75 no

V = Vacancies / **T** = Trainees / **P** = Partners / **TS** = Total Staff / **WP** = Work Placement

EMW Law LLP

Seebeck House, One Seebeck Place, Knowlhill, Milton Keynes MK5 8FR
Tel: 0345 070 6000
Email: hr@emwllp.com
Web: www.emwllp.com
🐦 emwlaw

The firm EMW is a progressive and well-established corporate and commercial law firm. We have rapidly gained recognition as a leading law firm offering niche legal services. We work with our clients to provide solutions, which often involves drawing on expertise from a number of our specialist areas and putting together a tailor-made team to ensure we achieve the best possible results. We are also very conscious about the future and are constantly responding to the changing needs of the commercial world by renewing and developing our services. This not only benefits our clients but creates opportunities for existing staff and new recruits. We are not a firm that stands still.

Types of work Recognised as having leading teams in corporate and commercial including banking and finance; and real estate including planning and construction. We also have a strong reputation for employment, dispute resolution, arbitration and property litigation, insolvency, restructuring and asset based lending, intellectual property, technology and wills, trust and probate. We are currently ranked top tier in the *Legal 500* South East region, in our key service areas.

Who should apply Our success is built on our people and we take our trainee solicitor recruitment very seriously. We are looking for candidates who have a 2.1 degree or above, who are approachable, have great communication skills and an appetite for success. However, if you have not achieved a 2.1 degree but still think you have something to offer us please email us telling us why we should still consider you.

Training programme We actively promote a friendly, supportive, practical and business-like approach to your training by offering a comprehensive induction training programme, quarterly trainee seminars, practical workshops with particular emphasis on developing your business development skills and a detailed appraisal at the end of each seat.

We aim to give all trainees the best commercial grounding by giving you the opportunity to complete your training contract by way of six-month seats within corporate finance, real estate and dispute resolution, with the fourth seat allocation to be decided between either employment or commercial contracts. Trainees are given the opportunity to take on responsibility and be involved in a wide range of legal work.

We pride ourselves on our 'open door' policy and encourage coaching and mentoring throughout the training contract. The quality of our training programme was recognised by LawCareers.Net Training and Recruitment Awards by winning the 'Best Trainer' Award in 2013 and winning the 'Best Recruiter' Award in 2014 and 2015. In 2017, Stephen Kay (our training principal) was nominated for Best Training Principal (small trainee intake). We achieved Investors in People Gold Status in June 2015.

Benefits include: BUPA, income protection, death in service benefit together with the following in-house schemes: childcare vouchers, car share, cycle to work and public transport schemes. We aim to recruit our trainees on qualification and encourage their continued development through to associate and partner level; four of our current partners started their career with the firm as trainees.

When and how to apply Please visit careers.emwllp.com and apply by 31 August 2018 for a 2020 training contract.

Vacancies	5
Trainees	10
Partners	34
Total staff	172

Training contract deadline
31 August 2018

Apply
Online

Starting salary
£24,750 minimum

Minimum qualifications
2.1 degree

Offices
London, Milton Keynes

Remember to cite *The Training Contract & Pupillage Handbook* on your application form if you apply to this firm.

ERIC ROBINSON SOLICITORS 5a St John, Hedge End, Southampton SO30 4AA **Tel:** 01489 788922 **Email:** recruitment@ericrobinson.co.uk **Apply to:** Ms Catherine Maxfield	Six offices in Southampton region. General practice including legal aid, probate, large matrimonial, crime, personal injury and property. Developing commercial department.	V T P TS WP	2 2 9 140 no
ESSEX LEGAL SERVICES SEAX House, Victoria Road South, Chelmsford CM1 1QH **Tel:** 033301 39993 **Email:** paul.turner@essex.gov.uk **Apply to:** Mr Paul Turner	Local authority wide-ranging practice including child care, employment, prosecutions, land, commercial, insurance and civil litigation.	V T P TS WP	0 0 - 120 no
EVERATT'S SOLICITORS First Floor Offices, 17 St. Ann's Road, Harrow, Middlesex HA1 1JU **Tel:** 020 8424 0088 **Email:** shilan@everatts.co.uk **Apply to:** Mr Shilan Shah	Small well-established general practice with commercial and litigation bias, no legal aid work.	V T P TS WP	1 1 1 6 no
EVERSHEDS SUTHERLAND (INTERNATIONAL) LLP 1 Wood Street, London EC2V 7WS **Tel:** 0845 497 9797 **Email:** gradrec@eversheds-sutherland.com **Apply to:** Graduate Recruitment	Eversheds Sutherland is one of the world's largest full-service law firms operating as one team across Europe, the US, Africa, Asia and the Middle East.	V T P TS WP	50 165 395 3215 yes
EVERYS The Laurels, 46 New Street, Honiton EX14 1BY **Tel:** 01404 43431 **Email:** law@everys.co.uk **Apply to:** Mrs Jo Garrod	Progressive, well-established practice with offices in London, Exeter, Honiton, Exmouth, Ottery St Mary, Sidmouth, Seaton, Budleigh, Salterton and Taunton.	V T P TS WP	0 2 10 100 no
EWINGS & CO 148 High Street, London SE20 7EU **Tel:** 020 8778 1126 **Email:** enquiry@ewings.uk.com **Apply to:** Mrs DM Ewings	General high street practice centrally located. Committed to expansion of its private and publicly funded work. Quality mark holders in family and crime.	V T P TS WP	0 2 3 30 no
EXPRESS SOLICITORS Resolution House, 319 Palatine Road, Northenden, Manchester M22 4HH **Tel:** 0161 9044 660 **Email:** recruitment@expresssolicitors.co.uk **Apply to:** Mr James Maxey	Top 200 personal injury and clinical negligence firm. Legal 500. Typical entry Litigation Assistant in New Client Team. Fast Track scheme for top 1% available.	V T P TS WP	5 15 15 185 yes
FARADAYS SOLICITORS 142 Seven Sisters Road, London N7 7NS **Tel:** 020 72811001 **Email:** enquiries@faradayssolicitors.co.uk **Apply to:** Mrs Caroline Lewis	Energetic four-partner firm that specialises in criminal law, family law and personal injury. We are established with an excellent reputation.	V T P TS WP	Varies 1 4 20 yes

V = Vacancies / **T** = Trainees / **P** = Partners / **TS** = Total Staff / **WP** = Work Placement

Faegre Baker Daniels LLP

7 Pilgrim Street, London EC4V 6LB
Tel: 020 7450 4500
Email: stephen.llewellyn@faegrebd.com
Web: www.faegrebd.com
f faegrebd 🐦 faegrebd

The firm Faegre Baker Daniels LLP offers a full complement of legal services to clients ranging from emerging enterprises to multinational companies. The firm's 750 plus legal and consulting professionals handle complex transactions and litigation matters throughout Europe, the United States and Asia. Faegre Baker Daniels is one of the 75 largest firms in the US.

Types of work In London we focus on advising clients which range from *Fortune 500* companies to high quality emerging companies meeting their legal needs, both domestically and internationally.

Corporate: includes mergers and acquisitions, takeovers, management buy-outs, joint ventures, private equity, financing, flotations (IPOs), fundraisings and corporate reorganisations. We have particular expertise in advising on AIM listings.

Business litigation: general commercial litigation with a growing emphasis on mediation and arbitration, much of which is international.

Commercial: a wide range of contentious and non-contentious commercial and IP matters for a diverse client base. Our expertise also covers franchising, outsourcing, international data privacy, e-commerce and digital media.

Employment: advice on a broad range of employment issues from recruitment to dismissal and also on employers' duties on business sales and reorganisations, share option and incentive plans, global mobility and immigration and termination issues such as redundancy, unfair and wrongful dismissal and restrictive covenants.

Real estate: advice on all aspects of property investments and management, development and finance, as well as corporate real estate issues.

Who should apply We are looking for motivated people not only with strong academics, but who are also team players with good all-round ability, common sense and ambition. In addition, strong communication skills and an appreciation of our clients' commercial interests are essential.

Training programme The London office is split into four main practice groups. We offer training in each of these groups and trainees will assist a number of partners or solicitors within any group. This provides a good breadth of experience and you will quickly become integrated within the firm. Our aim is for trainees to be one of the team and to have responsibility (subject to appropriate supervision) at an early stage. We provide some in-house training, and trainees are encouraged to attend outside lectures and courses where appropriate. Appraisals are undertaken every three months.

When and how to apply Online application form available at www.faegrebd.com/25458. Your application should be received by 15 July two years before the commencement of the training contract. Interviews take place during September each year.

Work placements There are a limited number of places available each year. You should apply using our online application form by 31 March 2018.

Sponsorship LPC fees.

Vacancies	2
Trainees	4
Partners	7
Total staff	40

Work placement yes

Training contract deadline
15 July 2018

Apply to
Online

Starting salary
£38,000 (September 2017)

Minimum qualifications
2.1 degree

Sponsorship
LPC

Offices
Beijing, Boulder, Chicago, Denver, Des Moines, Fort Wayne, Indianapolis, London, Los Angeles, Minneapolis, Shanghai, Silicon Valley, Washington DC

FAEGRE BAKER
DANIELS

Farrer & Co LLP

66 Lincoln's Inn Fields, London WC2A 3LH
Tel: 020 3375 7000
Email: graduaterecruitment@farrer.co.uk
Web: www.farrer.co.uk

The firm Farrer & Co is a successful law firm with a distinguished history and an excellent reputation built up over many years.

The firm provides a full service to clients as well as having outstanding expertise in a number of niche sectors. This is coupled with careful attention to personal service and quality, and a strong emphasis on the human touch based on the goodwill of numerous close client relationships.

We have over 400 staff, including 256 lawyers, many of whom are leaders in their fields and some 73 of whom are partners.

Types of work Farrer & Co has expertise in a number of diverse fields including intellectual property, sports, media, matrimonial, heritage, employment, estates work, charity law and financial services. Clients range from national institutions, museums, galleries, schools and universities to high profile individuals and companies such as banks and media organisations.

Who should apply Those applicants who appear eager to break the mould – as shown by their initiative for organisation, leadership, exploration or enterprise. We look for trainees who are highly motivated individuals with keen intellects and engaging and interesting personalities.

Training programme The training programme involves each trainee in probably the widest range of cases, clients and issues possible in a single law firm. This provides a broad foundation of knowledge and experience, with the opportunity to make an informed choice about the area of law in which to specialise. A high degree of involvement in client work is encouraged under the direct supervision of associates and partners. Trainees attend regular internal and external seminars. The training principal reviews trainees' progress at the end of each seat and extensive feedback is given. The firm has a friendly atmosphere and holds regular sporting and social events.

When and how to apply You can apply at any time. The closing date for training contract applications is 31 July 2018. Applications are dealt with online via the firm's website. A covering letter forms part of the online application.

Work placements Farrer & Co runs Easter and summer vacation schemes for those considering a career in law. An allowance of £300 per week will be paid. The dates for the 2018 vacation schemes will be available from the autumn of this year. The deadline is 31 January 2018 for all schemes. Approximately 100 applicants for summer vacation schemes will be invited to one of three open days held at the firm's offices in March 2018, which present a good opportunity to get to know the firm. These will help us make the final selection of successful candidates.

Sponsorship Fees for GDL and LPC and £7,000 grant per year.

Vacancies	10
Trainees	20
Partners	73
Total staff	415

Work placement yes

Training contract deadline
31 July 2018

Apply to
Trainee Recruitment
Consultant

Starting salary
£37,000 (September 2017)

Minimum qualifications
2.1 degree

Sponsorship
GDL/LPC

Offices
London

FARRER&Co

Remember to cite *The Training Contract & Pupillage Handbook* on your application form if you apply to this firm.

334 THE TRAINING CONTRACT & PUPILLAGE HANDBOOK

FARLEYS SOLICITORS LLP 22-27 Richmond Terrace, Blackburn BB1 7AF **Tel:** 01254 606000 **Email:** n.molyneux@farleys.com **Apply to:** Mr Nicholas Molyneux	We are a large practice offering a full range of work areas based across East Lancashire and Manchester.	**V** 2^{18} **T** 6 **P** 12 **TS** 170 **WP** no
FARNFIELDS The Square, Gillingham SP8 4AX **Tel:** 01747 825432 **Email:** info@farnfields.com **Apply to:** Ms Susan Lacey	As a 'high street' practice operating in four locations our core services are property (residential and commercial), private client, family and mediation.	**V** 0 **T** 0 **P** 4 **TS** 65 **WP** no
FBC MANBY BOWDLER LLP George House, St John's Square, Wolverhampton WV2 4BZ **Tel:** 01902 578000 **Email:** hr@fbcmb.co.uk **Apply to:** Miss Charlotte Clode	We aim to develop exceptional people who intelligently deliver a stellar service from trainee through to partner.	**V** 0 **T** 6 **P** 33 **TS** 195 **WP** yes
FEARON & CO Westminster House, 7 Faraday Road, Guildford, Surrey GU1 1EA **Tel:** 01483 540 840 **Email:** enquiries@fearonlaw.com **Apply to:** Mr AJ Phillips	Niche firm of solicitors established in 1825 and based just outside Guildford town centre specialising in property, probate and litigation.	**V** 0 **T** 1 **P** 1 **TS** 6 **WP** no
FELLOWES SOLICITORS LLP 21 Church Hill, Walthamstow, London E17 3AD **Tel:** 020 8520 7392 **Email:** info@fellowes.org **Apply to:** Mrs Judith Stalley	Long-established general high street practice based in East London, covering conveyancing and probate with a franchise in criminal. Recruitment is open – no deadlines.	**V** 1 **T** 1 **P** 4 **TS** 14 **WP** yes
FENTONS 55 Princess Street, Manchester M2 4EW **Tel:** 0161 2386400 **Email:** melanie.ridgewell@fentons.co.uk **Apply to:** Miss Melanie Ridgewell	Personal injury, employment, probate and wills, clinical negligence and serious injury.	**V** 0 **T** 0 **P** 24 **TS** 210 **WP** no
FERDINAND KELLY 96 Broad Street, Birmingham B15 1AU **Tel:** 0121 643 7733 **Email:** info@ferdinandkelly.co.uk **Apply to:** The Recruitment Partner	Niche commercial firm. Specialisms: commercial litigation, commercial property, employment, European law; commercial work generally, sometimes with an international element.	**V** 0 **T** 0 **P** 1 **TS** 5 **WP** no
FIELD SEYMOUR PARKES 1 London Street, Reading RG1 4QW **Tel:** 0118 951 6200 **Email:** lisa.cross@fsp-law.com **Apply to:** Ms Lisa Cross	Dynamic Thames Valley full-service practice with an impressive and growing client base, active in both commercial and private client work areas.	**V** 3 **T** 8 **P** 20 **TS** 110 **WP** yes

V = Vacancies / **T** = Trainees / **P** = Partners / **TS** = Total Staff / **WP** = Work Placement

FIELDFISHER
2 Swan Lane, London EC4R 3TT
Tel: 020 7861 4000
Email: graduaterecruitment@fieldfisher.com
Apply to: Mrs Amelia Spinks

Fieldfisher is a European law firm providing commercial solutions across a range of industry sectors.

V	18
T	28
P	223
TS	986
WP	yes

FIELDINGS PORTER
Silverwell House, Silverwell Street, Bolton BL1 1PT
Tel: 01204 387742
Email: info@fieldingsporter.co.uk
Apply to: Mr Fraser Young

Long established general practice dealing with a wide variety of work from high value commercial to PI and legal aid franchises.

V	3-4
T	5
P	11
TS	76
WP	no

FINN GLEDHILL
1-4 Harrison Road, Halifax HX1 2AG
Tel: 01422 330000
Email: barbara.lee@finngledhill.co.uk
Apply to: The Training Principal

A Yorkshire general practice with two offices, undertaking both commercial and private client work. Has a legal aid franchise.

V	0
T	0
P	6
TS	50
WP	no

FISHER JONES GREENWOOD SOLICITORS
Charter Court, Newcomen Way, Colchester Business Park, Colchester CO4 9YA
Tel: 01206 835300
Email: info@fjg.co.uk
Apply to: Mrs Rebecca Greene

Dynamic, modern, friendly firm undertaking commercial, property, family, litigation, crime, employment, wills and probate, landlord and tenant etc with specialist immigration and human rights department.

V	0
T	2
P	21
TS	143
WP	no

FISHER MEREDITH
7th Floor, 322 High Holborn, London WC1V 7PB
Tel: 020 7091 2700
Email: hr@fishermeredith.co.uk
Apply to: Ms Jo Secker

Fisher Meredith is an award winning London firm with an outstanding reputation for acting on behalf of individuals, businesses and organisations with highly successful results.

V	2[19]
T	6
P	11
TS	41
WP	no

FISHERS
4-8 Kilwardby Street, Ashby De La Zouch, Leicestershire LE65 2FU
Tel: 01530 412167
Email: fishers@fisherslaw.co.uk
Apply to: Mr MCA Killin

A long-established practice with strong client base and niche areas in company and commercial, commercial property, taxations and trusts.

V	0
T	1
P	5
TS	38
WP	no

FITZ SOLICITORS
Chappell House, The Green, Datchet SL3 9EH
Tel: 01753 592 000
Email: info@fitz-legal.com
Apply to: Mr JF Fitzgerald

A boutique practice offering outstanding service to discerning clients in corporate/commercial, environmental, conveyancing, wills & probate, civil litigation and family.

V	0
T	1
P	1
TS	5
WP	no

FLADGATE LLP
16 Great Queen Street, London WC2B 5DG
Tel: 020 3036 7000
Email: trainees@fladgate.com
Apply to: Mrs Nicola Thomas

A leading commercial practice – our property, corporate and litigation departments provide wide-ranging legal services to a diverse portfolio of UK and international clients.

V	6
T	12
P	75
TS	265
WP	no

V = Vacancies / **T** = Trainees / **P** = Partners / **TS** = Total Staff / **WP** = Work Placement

Foot Anstey

Salt Quay House, 4 North East Quay, Sutton Harbour, Plymouth PL4 0BN
Tel: 01752 675000
Email: contact@footanstey.com
Web: www.footanstey.com/careers
🐦 joinfootanstey

The firm Foot Anstey is a leading regional law firm. Through a network of five offices across the South West plus our newly opened Southampton office, we work as one national team offering specialist legal advice and services to regional, national and international clients, both businesses and individuals. We pride ourselves on offering premium services, delivered by recognised experts in their field. Our approach is flexible and client-focused. The advice which we give is personal, practical and cost effective. We are among the UK's top 100 law firms, with just under 50 partners and around 500 staff. We have achieved consistent growth and strong financial performance despite a challenging economic environment. We like to think that our approach to business and developing client relationships makes us distinctly different to traditional law firms and also attractive. As does our desire to ensure our lawyers and trainees operate in an environment where everything is tailored towards delivering specialist and forward thinking advice to our clients. Whatever the reason you want to join us, we promise you a progressive working environment. We can offer you an open and supportive culture that is committed to ensuring you realise your maximum potential. We will invest in you, train you and value you. We have received high profile recognition for our culture and strategy. We have been named as the Law Firm of the Year at the Bristol Law Society Awards for the second time in three years.

Types of work Foot Anstey advises a wide variety of clients on a wider range of services. Advising regional, national and international clients, the pace is fast and interesting. The firm is arranged into four main practice groups; real estate, business (which includes commercial, corporate and employment), dispute resolution, private wealth and clinical negligence (which has recently been rebranded as Enable Law). We also have a niche Islamic finance practice.

Who should apply We welcome applications from all law and non-law graduates who have a strong academic background, exceptional communication skills and the vision to be part of our future. We are an ambitious firm; we want people that will help take us forward.

Training programme Our training programme is designed to help you reach your full potential. Our trainees undertake six seats of four months' duration with regular, open communication between the trainees and supervisors as standard. You'll get exposure to situations to develop your legal and commercial expertise, in an environment that is friendly and supportive. All trainees are entitled to the flexible, forward thinking 'choices' benefits package which includes: 25 days' holiday, options to buy/sell holiday, contributory pension scheme, life assurance, cycle scheme and paid sabbaticals every five years (after 10 years' service). In addition, we offer a popular lifestyle hour, the chance to take one hour off work each week to promote a healthy work/life balance.

When and how to apply All applications for either a training contract or our summer placement scheme should be made online, at www.footanstey.com/careers. Deadlines; training contacts 1 June 2018 and summer vacation scheme by 1 April 2018

Work placements Our summer placement scheme offers a week of work experience, providing a valuable insight into our business and the different areas of legal expertise.

Sponsorship Grants available towards GDL/LPC and living expenses.

Vacancies	12
Trainees	24
Partners	49
Total staff	500

Work placement yes

Training contract deadline
1 June 2018

Apply
Online at
www.footanstey.com/
careers

Starting salary
Competitive

Minimum qualifications
Usually 2.1 degree

Sponsorship
GDL/LPC

Offices
Bristol, Exeter,
Plymouth, Taunton,
Truro, Southampton

Forbes Solicitors

73 Northgate, Blackburn BB2 1AA
Tel: 01254 580000
Email: graduate.recruitment@forbessolicitors.co.uk
Web: www.forbessolicitors.co.uk

The firm Forbes has eight offices across the North of England, over 320 employees, 44 partners and is the largest legal practice in the North West outside the major cities. We offer a full range of legal services to both individuals and commercial clients. We believe that the trainee solicitors we appoint are the future partners of our firm. We aim to provide our trainees with hands on experience in a City practice environment from the outset. This is done in a supportive and nurturing way which focuses on developing each trainee solicitors' potential. It is an exciting time to join the firm as we continue to expand our work areas and client base.

Types of work Commercial departments including – corporate, commercial, housing and regeneration, commercial property, residential property, dispute resolution, employment, wills, trusts and probate, insurance litigation, claimant litigation, crime, family/matrimonial.

Who should apply We look for high calibre recruits who can demonstrate a strong academic track record together with legal work experience. We want individuals who have strong local connections, who are keen team players, friendly and approachable and client and quality focused. In addition, applicants will be confident and resilient, and will look forward to assuming real responsibility right from the start. You should be able to demonstrate high academic ability, with at least a 2.1, or expected 2.1 in any degree, plus BBB at A level (or equivalent).

Training programme During our award-winning training contract, based within the Preston, Blackburn, Manchester and Leeds offices, you will have the opportunity to experience four six-month seats in a variety of practice areas that are available. Supervision is paramount and you will experience two formal reviews in each seat with the principal and the graduate training partner, as well as daily supervision from your departmental supervisor. A dedicated trainee mentor will also available for you to speak to during the course of your training contract. You will be guaranteed first-rate work and a high level of involvement with our clients – we believe in offering challenges, responsibility and opportunities from the outset. Some trainees will have the opportunity to undertake a secondment to one of our clients, which is a great opportunity to build your own networks and experience a client's business first-hand.

When and how to apply Apply online by 31 July 2018 for a 2020 training contract.

Work placements The best way to understand Forbes' unique culture, and the way that we work, is to gain first-hand experience by working with us! Our vacation scheme will give you the opportunity to spend a week in one of our offices. You will be paired up with one of our current trainee supervisors and will have the opportunity to really get to grips with what we do day to day. You'll also work with our partners and associates, contributing to live cases and be given real responsibility. During your vacation scheme you will also have the opportunity to network with colleagues outside of your team so you can start building relationships and get to know our people.

Vacancies	4
Trainees	10
Partners	44
Total staff	320

Work placement yes

Training contract deadline
31 July 2018

Apply
Online

Starting salary
Competitive

Minimum qualifications
2.1 degree

Offices
Manchester, Leeds, Preston, Blackburn, Chorley, Accrington

forbessolicitors.

Remember to cite *The Training Contract & Pupillage Handbook* on your application form if you apply to this firm.

Forsters LLP

31 Hill Street, London W1J 5LS
Tel: 020 7863 8333
Web: www.forsters.co.uk

The firm We are a dynamic, successful firm committed to being the best at what we do. Based in Mayfair, Forsters was founded in 1998 and has since more than trebled in size. While we are best known for our top-flight real estate and private client practices, we also have thriving corporate and dispute resolution teams. Forsters offers interesting, intellectually challenging work, high quality clients and fantastic people to work with and learn from. We are dedicated to giving outstanding client service in a highly professional, collaborative and supportive environment.

Types of work The firm has a strong reputation for all aspects of commercial and residential real estate work. The real estate groups deal with investment funding, development, planning, construction, landlord and tenant, property taxation and residential investment and development. Forsters is also recognised as having one of the leading private client practices in London with a client base comprising a broad range of individuals and trustees in the UK and offshore. Our corporate practice specialises in company acquisitions and disposals, financings and joint ventures and shareholder arrangements. The dispute resolution group handles and resolves a wide variety of commercial disputes through litigation, arbitration and mediation as well as working alongside the firm's private client group in relation to trust and probate disputes.

Who should apply We recruit graduates from a broad range of backgrounds and welcome both graduate and undergraduate applicants with degrees in any discipline. Our standard criteria are a minimum of 320 UCAS points from three A level results excluding general studies and a 2.1 or higher degree classification (achieved or predicted). Beyond this, we are looking for ambitious, personable and motivated candidates who thrive on responsibility within a team environment.

Training programme A training contract with Forsters consists of six four-month seats. In the first year, this usually involves seats in three of the following departments: real estate, private client, corporate or dispute resolution. In the second year, the four-month pattern still applies, but if an area is of particular interest, it may be possible to spend additional time in the relevant department. As the training contract progresses, increasing responsibility is given; trainees start working on their own files and talking to and meeting with clients. Supervision and guidance is always available but we are keen that our trainees quickly start playing a real role in our teams. In addition to on the job training, there are regular in-house seminars on legal and commercial topics as well as training on our IT and other in-house systems. Our trainees also attend a bespoke Professionals Skills Course, provided by a leading training supplier and designed for Forsters.

When and how to apply All applications should be made online at www.graduates.forsters.co.uk. The closing date for training contracts commencing in September 2020 is 31 July 2018.

Work placements Forsters offers up to 14 vacation scheme places during the summer, each for a two-week period. Please see our website for more details.

Sponsorship We have an exclusive arrangement with The University of Law for the provision of GDL and LPC courses to our future trainees, but we do not mind if you have already completed either course elsewhere. Payment of course fees, plus a maintenance grant of £5,500 per year of study, is offered to future trainees who have yet to complete these courses.

Vacancies	7-9
Trainees	18
Partners	52
Total staff	390 approx

Work placement yes

Training contract deadline
31 July 2018

Apply
Online

Starting salary
1st year – £38,000
2nd year – £40,000

Minimum qualifications
2.1 degree, 320 UCAS points (excluding General Studies)

Sponsorship
GDL/LPC

Offices
London

FORSTERS

FLETCHER DERVISH
582 Green Lanes, London N8 0RP
Tel: 020 8800 4615
Email: law@fletcherdervish.co.uk
Apply to: Mr D Dervish

Long-established practice committed to high standard of work. Franchised in family, crime, housing, immigration with departments in PI, consumer/general contract, property and wills/probate.

V	0
T	3
P	1
TS	20
WP	no

FORD SIMEY LLP
The Forum, Barnfield Road, Exeter EX1 1QR
Tel: 01392 274126
Email: info@fordsimey.co.uk
Apply to: Mr David Williams

General practice with specialist teams dealing with private client, family, personal injury and commercial. Welcomes non-law graduates.

V	0
T	0
P	11
TS	64
WP	no

FORRESTERS SOLICITORS LIMITED
117 Duke Street, Barrow In Furness LA14 1XA
Tel: 01229 820 297
Email: mail@forresterssolicitors.co.uk
Apply to: Mrs Emma Scott

V	0
T	-
P	2
TS	15
WP	no

FOSTERS
William House, 19 Bank Plain, Norwich NR2 4FS
Tel: 01603 620508
Email: hbrown@fosters-solicitors.co.uk
Apply to: Mr Iain McClay

Winner of UK Law Firm of the Year (Regional) 2013, and Law Society Excellence Award. Applications ongoing.

V	0
T	3
P	13
TS	130
WP	no

FOUNTAIN SOLICITORS LIMITED
ManderHouse, 36 Bardford Street, Walsall WS1 3QA
Tel: 01922 645 429
Email: info@fountainsolicitors.com
Apply to: Mr Ramzan Sharif

We specialise in immigration, asylum, family, personal injury, public law, leases, social welfare law, criminal law and employment law.

V	1[18]
T	1
P	1
TS	40
WP	yes

FOX WILLIAMS LLP
10 Finsbury Square, London EC2A 1AF
Tel: 020 7628 2000
Email: application@foxwilliams.com
Apply to: Graduate Recruitment Team

We are City lawyers with an uncompromising focus on quality, value and our clients' commercial success.

V	3[19]
T	6
P	32
TS	112
WP	no

FRANCES LINDSAY & CO
48 Broadway, Maidenhead, Berkshire SL6 1LU
Tel: 01628 634667
Email: info@franceslindsay.co.uk
Apply to: Ms Frances Lindsay

Specialist family law practice. Non-legal aid.

V	0-1
T	1
P	1
TS	5
WP	no

FRANK BRAZELL & PARTNERS
97 White Lion Street, Islington, London N1 9PF
Tel: 020 7689 8989
Apply to: Mr FW Brazell

We have an experienced team of solicitors. We specialise in all areas of criminal and family work and have an expanding private client department.

V	0
T	3
P	3
TS	28
WP	no

V = Vacancies / **T** = Trainees / **P** = Partners / **TS** = Total Staff / **WP** = Work Placement

Freeths LLP

Cumberland Court, 80 Mount Street, Nottingham NG1 6HH
Tel: 0845 274 6815
Email: carole.wigley@freeths.co.uk
Web: www.freeths.co.uk
🐦 freeths

The firm Freeths is a top 100 national law practice, turning over in excess of £70 million annually, with some 135 partners and 750 staff working in a network of 11 offices throughout England. This means that we have considerable strength, extensive legal knowledge and are able to offer a quick and responsive service across all business areas. In recognition of high levels of employee engagement, we have been awarded Two Star status by Best Companies for 2017, Silver Investors in People and we are a *Sunday Times* Best Company to Work For 2017. The *Legal 500*'s UK rankings recommended 93 of Freeths' lawyers and named 17 of them as Elite Leading Lawyers. 63 of our partners are named by *Chambers UK* as leaders in their field.

Types of work Freeths offers a complete commercial service covering the bigger picture of commercial operations and dispute resolution within a variety of sector specialisms. However, while we specialise in commercial advice, we also advise our business clients on their personal affairs including wills, care of the elderly and disabled, clinical negligence, Court of Protection, debt recovery and trust formation, personal injury, and administration and taxation.

Who should apply There is no such thing as a typical Freeths candidate. So if you are a bright and talented individual who will make a real difference to our firm over the coming years then we are interested in your application. We are flexible in our approach to finding the best talent hence we have no minimum criteria and we welcome applications from both law and non-law students and from those who have already graduated or completed either their LPC or GDL.

Training programme At Freeths we "think differently" and this also applies to the flexible graduate programmes we offer. We believe that it is your career therefore you should be the one to choose how it starts. So if you prefer to focus on gaining valuable work experience prior to commencing either your LPC or training contract, then our legal assistant foundation programme could be for you. However, if you prefer to study part time while working then our flexible route could suit you better. Equally, if you prefer a more traditional route to qualification then our direct entry route allows you the opportunity to complete your academic qualifications prior to starting your training contract with us.

When and how to apply To apply for one of our training schemes, you will need to complete our online application form which can be found either on our website www.freeths.co.uk/training-contracts or at www.apply4law.com/freeths. If you have any specific access requirements or are unable to complete the online application form please contact carole.wigley@freeths.co.uk.

Sponsorship If you are offered a place on one of our flexible graduate programmes then we provide funding to cover relevant LPC and GDL fees. Loans may be available for the direct entry route.

Vacancies	20
Trainees	40
Members	135
Total staff	750

Work placement no

Apply to
Online

Starting salary
£25,000

Sponsorship
GDL/LPC

Offices
Birmingham, Derby, Leeds, Leicester, London, Manchester, Milton Keynes, Nottingham, Oxford, Sheffield, Stoke-on-Trent

FREETHS

Remember to cite *The Training Contract & Pupillage Handbook* on your application form if you apply to this firm.

TRAINING CONTRACT DIRECTORY 341

Fried, Frank, Harris, Shriver & Jacobson LLP

41 Lothbury, London EC2R 7HF
Tel: 020 7972 9600
Email: londonhumanresources@friedfrank.com
Web: www.friedfrank.com
🐦 friedfrank

The firm Fried, Frank, Harris, Shriver & Jacobson LLP advises the world's leading corporations and financial institutions on their most critical legal needs and business opportunities. The firm's approximately 450 lawyers are based in North America and Europe.

Types of work Corporate, M&A/private equity, asset management, finance, real estate, restructuring and insolvency, tax, antitrust and litigation.

Who should apply If you are applying to Fried Frank during your studies, we would recommend that you apply in either the penultimate year of your law degree or the final year of a non-law degree. Fried Frank also welcomes graduates and those changing careers.

Training programme Fried Frank offers a fresh and individualistic training programme, working as part of a close-knit team with a practical and hands-on approach to learning. Trainees will have direct access to a combination of US and UK expertise, working for clients on European and international transactions. Trainees will spend six months working with partners and associates across four departments, gaining a broad knowledge of the law to become a commercial partner to clients.

When and how to apply If you are interested in joining an international firm which will provide you with quality work and training, please apply by completing our application form, located on our firm's careers website. Once complete, please return your form to londonhumanresources@friedfrank.com.

Work placements Fried Frank offers one and three-month internship placements in our litigation department. Interns will gain experience within the legal industry, while gaining exposure to top quality work and clients. Our internship programme details and application form can be found on our careers website. Please note that applications for our internship programme are separate to those for our training contract.

Sponsorship For future trainees of the firm, we will sponsor both the GDL and LPC, and will provide an annual maintenance grant of £7,000.

Vacancies	2
Trainees	4
Partners	14
Total staff	99

Work placement yes

Training contract deadline
31 July 2018

Apply
Online

Starting salary
£45,000

Minimum qualifications
2.1 degree

Sponsorship
GDL/LPC

Offices
London, New York, Washington DC, Frankfurt, Paris

FRIED FRANK

FRANKLINS SOLICITORS LLP 8 Castilian Street, Northampton NN1 1JX **Tel:** 01604 828282 **Email:** emma.mcnally@franklins-sols.co.uk **Apply to:** Ms Emma McNally	A well-established firm specialising in corporate commercial services, employment, conveyancing, family, wills, trusts and probate, delivering a high quality service to all our clients.	V 0 T 3 P 14 TS 100 WP yes
FRASER BROWN 84 Friar Lane, Nottingham NG1 6ED **Tel:** 0115 9888 777 **Email:** info@fraserbrown.com **Apply to:** Ms Sarah Poole		V 0 T 2 P 16 TS 93 WP no
FREEMAN JOHNSON 11 Victoria Road, Darlington DL1 5SP **Tel:** 01325 466221 **Apply to:** Mr Kevin Campbell	Offices at Darlington, Durham and Spennymoor. All general private client work. Legal aid franchise in personal injury, matrimony and criminal. Some company commercial.	V 1 T 2 P 8 TS 45 WP yes
FRESHFIELDS BRUCKHAUS DERINGER LLP 65 Fleet Street, London EC4Y 1HT **Tel:** 020 7785 5554 **Email:** ukgraduates@freshfields.com **Apply to:** Graduate Recruitment	We are a leading international law firm providing first-rate legal services to corporations, financial institutions and governments worldwide.	V 80 T 160 P 391 TS 4960 WP yes
FURLEY PAGE LLP 39 St Margaret's Street, Canterbury CT1 2TX **Tel:** 01227 863118 **Email:** hr@furleypage.co.uk **Apply to:** Mrs Karen Cook	One of the leading law firms in Kent and South East, acknowledged for its expertise and client service by *Legal 500* and *Chambers & Partners*.	V 2 T 2 P 18 TS 150 WP yes
GA SOLICITORS Gill Akaster House, 25 Lockyer Street, Plymouth PL1 2QW **Tel:** 01752 203500 **Email:** stuart.elford@gasolicitors.com **Apply to:** Mr Stuart Elford	We look for those who share our values and deliver a high quality service.	V 1 T 1 P 15 TS 75 WP no
GABB & CO 32 Monk Street, Abergavenny NP7 5NW **Tel:** 01873 852432 **Email:** abergavenny@gabb.co.uk **Apply to:** Mrs Betty Harriot-Pole		V 0 T 0 P 6 TS 36 WP no
GABY HARDWICKE 33 The Avenue, Eastbourne, East Sussex BN21 3YD **Tel:** 01323 435900 **Email:** ann.townsend@gabyhardwicke.co.uk **Apply to:** Ann Townsend	A major Sussex firm with 20 partners and 150 staff servicing private and commercial clients with specialist corporate, property, probate and litigation departments.	V 2[19] T 2 P 20 TS 150 WP no

V = Vacancies / **T** = Trainees / **P** = Partners / **TS** = Total Staff / **WP** = Work Placement

GALBRAITH BRANLEY
18 Friern Park, North Finchley, London N12 9DA
Tel: 020 8446 8474
Email: solicitors@galbraithbranley.com
Apply to: Mr Anthony Branley

Legal aid/private firm undertaking criminal defence and family law work. All prospective trainees start as paralegals.

V	1
T	3
P	1
TS	15
WP	no

GAMLINS LAW
31-37 Russell Road, Rhyl LL18 3DB
Tel: 01745 343500
Email: gamlins@gamlins.co.uk
Apply to: Mrs Kate Sutherland

The largest firm in North Wales specialising in: commercial, property, personal injury/clinical negligence, litigation, matrimonial/family law, private client, crime and regulatory matters.

V	2[18]
T	5
P	11
TS	70
WP	yes

GAMMON BELL & CO
91 Leigh Road, Eastleigh SO50 9DQ
Tel: 023 8062 9009
Apply to: The Recruitment Partner

Small general practice with two partners, three assistant solicitors, two managing clerks and one trainee. High street location. Established local clients. Emphasis on conveyancing and court work.

V	1
T	1
P	2
TS	25
WP	no

GARDEN HOUSE SOLICITORS
23 London Road, Hertford SG13 7LG
Tel: 01992 422128
Email: ruth@ghslaw.co.uk
Apply to: Mrs Ruth Allen

Efficient Lexcel accredited general practice in Hertford Town. Personal injury, private client, dispute resolution, employment, family.

V	1[18]
T	-
P	1
TS	12
WP	no

GATELEY PLC
One Eleven, Edmund Street, Birmingham B3 2HJ
Tel: 0121 234 0000
Email: graduaterecruitmentengland@gateleyuk.com
Apply to: Graduate Recruitment

Commercial practice advising all businesses including major financial institutions and plcs. Specialisms include corporate, banking, employment, construction, property, insolvency, CDR, commercial, tax and shipping.

V	14
T	29
P	150
TS	802
WP	yes

GC SOLICITORS
27 Leys Avenue, Letchworth Garden City SG6 3ED
Tel: 01462 483800
Email: admin@gcsols.co.uk
Apply to: Mr Ben Singh

We are a friendly high street practice specialising in the areas of personal injury, crime (including motoring offences and transport/regulatory law), family and childcare.

V	0
T	0
P	2
TS	17
WP	no

GELDARDS LLP
Dumfries House, Dumfries Place, Cardiff CF10 3ZF
Tel: 029 2039 1777
Email: recruitment@geldards.com
Apply to: HR department

Geldards LLP is an established commercial practice with three main offices (Cardiff, Derby and Nottingham) offering interesting and challenging work in a friendly atmosphere.

V	6[19]
T	12
P	57
TS	352
WP	no

GEORGE GREEN LLP
195 High Street, Cradley Heath, West Midlands B64 5HW
Tel: 013 8441 0410
Email: vpalmer@georgegreen.co.uk
Apply to: Ms Vanessa Palmer

George Green LLP is a leading full service law firm. Our lawyers make a difference by helping our clients succeed.

V	2
T	5
P	15
TS	67
WP	no

V = Vacancies / T = Trainees / P = Partners / TS = Total Staff / WP = Work Placement

GEPP & SONS SOLICITORS LLP 58 New London Road, Chelmsford CM2 0PA **Tel:** 01245 493939 **Email:** training@gepp.co.uk **Apply to:** Mrs Karen Mollison	A large and long established Legal 500 and Lexcel accredited practice in Essex, offering a full range of legal services to businesses and private clients.	V 2^{18} T 4 P 17 TS 85 WP no
GHP LEGAL 26-30 Grosvenor Road, Wrexham LL11 1BU **Tel:** 01978 291456 **Email:** wrexham@ghplegal.com **Apply to:** The Practice Manager	Leading regional firm, offering a complete and comprehensive service, with experts specialising in all aspects of private, commercial and legal aid work.	V 0 T 4 P 10 TS 87 WP yes
GIBSON DUNN & CRUTCHER LLP Telephone House, 2-4 Temple Avenue, London EC4Y 0HB **Tel:** 020 7071 4000 **Email:** graduaterecruitment@gibsondunn.com **Apply to:** Mr Stephen Trowbridge	Gibson Dunn is a top global law firm, offering full-service capabilities on a wide range of business issues to organisations with international operations and ambitions.	V 8 T 13 P 26 TS 130 WP yes
GIDE LOYRETTE NOUEL LLP 125 Old Broad Street, London EC2N 1AR **Tel:** 020 7382 5500 **Email:** tcapplications@gide.com **Apply to:** Ms Stephanie Leduc	Gide Loyrette Nouel, an international firm founded in France, has a highly-renowned, specialist banking and finance and dispute resolution practice in the City of London.	V 4 T 4 P 6 TS 42 WP no
GILBERT STEPHENS LLP 15-17 Southernhay East, Exeter EX1 1QE **Tel:** 01392 424242 **Email:** hr@gilbertstephens.co.uk **Apply to:** Ms Sarah Judd	A long-established highly respected firm offering a comprehensive range of legal services. The firm also has its own financial services department.	V 1 T 0 P 12 TS 126 WP no
GILL & CO Trevian House, 422-426 Ley Street, Ilford, Essex IG2 7BS **Tel:** 020 8554 1011 **Email:** info@gillsolicitors.com **Apply to:** Mrs GK Bhogal		V 1 T 1 P 2 TS 14 WP no
GILL TURNER TUCKER Colman House, King Street, Maidstone ME14 1JE **Tel:** 01622 759051 **Email:** michael.trigg@gillturnertucker.com **Apply to:** Mr Michael Trigg	Established in 1949 we are a general practice with an emphasis on commercial and matrimonial work.	V 0 T 0 P 4 TS 27 WP no
GIRLINGS 16 Rose Lane, Canterbury CT1 2UR **Tel:** 01227 768374 **Email:** judithneenan@girlings.com **Apply to:** Mrs Judith Neenan	The firm recruits two paralegals in October/November each year to commence work in January. Subject to satisfactory performance, they begin their training contracts in September. A 2.1 degree and LPC pass is essential.	V 2^{19} T 2 P 12 TS 81 WP no

V = Vacancies / **T** = Trainees / **P** = Partners / **TS** = Total Staff / **WP** = Work Placement

Firm	Description	V	T	P	TS	WP
GLAISYERS SOLICITORS LLP One St James's Square, Manchester M2 6DN **Tel:** 0161 832 4666 **Email:** kxc@glaisyers.com **Apply to:** Mrs Karen Culliney	Medium-sized practice which provides the wealth of work types that satisfy our clients' needs from minor private client matters up to large commercial transactions.	0	3	11	85	yes
GLAMORGAN LAW 51 The Parade, Cardiff CF24 3AY **Tel:** 029 2049 1271 **Email:** jarter@ccj-law.co.uk **Apply to:** Mr Jonathan Arter		0	0	4	-	no
GLANVILLES West Wing Cams Hall, Cams Hill, Fareham, Hampshire PO16 8AB **Tel:** 01329 282841 **Email:** fareham@glanvilles.co.uk **Apply to:** Ms Alison Blanch	Three offices situated in South Hampshire and the Isle of Wight. Mix of commercial and private client work. Long established.	1	2	12	100	no
GLOVERS SOLICITORS LLP 6 York Steet, London W1U 6QD **Tel:** 020 7935 8882 **Email:** central@glovers.co.uk **Apply to:** Mrs Mandy Marson	Property law specialists. Early responsibility encouraged and full involvement in all areas – commercial property, property finance, property litigation, general commercial litigation, construction and employment.	2[19]	3	11	38	no
GLP SOLICITORS 672 Bolton Road, Pendlebury, Swinton, Manchester M27 8FH **Tel:** 0161 793 0901 **Email:** pendlebury@glplaw.com **Apply to:** Mr Sheldon Fagelman	A modern progressive law firm specialising in personal injury, family law and conveyancing.	0-1	0	4	9	no
GOODHAND & FORSYTH 76 Station Road, Redhill, Surrey RH1 1PL **Tel:** 01737 773 533 **Email:** elainebrown@goodhandandforsyth.co.uk **Apply to:** Mr Keith Goodhand		0	0	2	31	no
GOODMAN RAY 5 Cranwood Street, London EC1V 9AE **Tel:** 020 7608 1227 **Email:** mail@goodmanray.com **Apply to:** Mr Miles Honour	Family practice. Central London area. No training contracts until further notice.	0	2	5	20	no
GOODY BURRETT LLP St Martin House, 63 West Stockwell Street, Colchester CO1 1WD **Tel:** 01206 577676 **Email:** law@goodyburrett.co.uk **Apply to:** Mr BC Johnston	One of the oldest firms in Colchester (over 250 years), offers friendly, relaxed but professional legal services to private clients and companies.	1[19]	1	4	30	yes

V = Vacancies / **T** = Trainees / **P** = Partners / **TS** = Total Staff / **WP** = Work Placement

Goodman Derrick LLP

10 St Bride Street, London EC4A 4AD
Tel: 020 7404 0606
Email: law@gdlaw.co.uk
Web: www.gdlaw.co.uk
🐦 goodmanderrick

The firm Goodman Derrick LLP is an established London law firm with a broad commercial practice and a particularly strong reputation for high-profile media work. We represent both UK and international clients. Our emphasis is on providing high quality yet practical legal advice tailored to our clients' business needs.

Types of work Our practice is focused on corporate, property and dispute resolution work. We provide a range of services throughout five departments: corporate; property; dispute resolution (including family); private client and employment. Within these departments we have specialists in media, IP/IT, hotels, charities, film finance and collector cars. The firm has an impressive client list acting for many public figures, public and large private companies, large retail chains, property companies, publishers, television companies, broadcasters and independent producers, charities and trade associations. We aim to offer a supportive and stimulating working environment where trainees are given maximum client contact and responsibility from the start.

Who should apply Applicants should ideally have a minimum 2.1 degree (not necessarily law) and a strong academic background. In addition we look for trainees who are confident, motivated and practically-minded to suit our working environment.

Training programme We invest a lot of time and resource in our trainees and our training is aimed at producing solicitors with well-rounded knowledge, skills and abilities. Hands-on experience is supplemented by internal and external training courses.

Trainees undertake four seats of six months each selected from our five departments. Where possible these will include corporate, property and a dispute resolution based seat, as we believe the skills learned in these practice areas are essential for a trainee's development. Trainees gain experience of media work within our dispute resolution and corporate departments.

Trainees are not assigned exclusively to any particular partner, but are treated as part of the department's team from day one, enabling them to experience the breadth of the department's work. Trainees are, however, supervised by and will share a room with a fee earner (usually a partner) to maximise their experience.

Trainees will play an active and essential role working with partners and fee earners on larger cases and transactions, but where possible trainees also run their own files. We like to encourage initiative and responsibility at an early stage. Trainees are also given maximum client contact.

When and how to apply The closing date for training contracts commencing in September 2020 is 30 June 2018. Apply by online application form available on our website www.gdlaw.co.uk.

Sponsorship Funding for the LPC fees at the institution of your choice and a maintenance grant of £4,000 during the LPC.

Vacancies	3
Trainees	6
Partners	32
Total staff	102

Work placement no

Training contract deadline
30 June 2018

Apply
Online

Starting salary
1st year – £33,000
2nd year – £34,500

Minimum qualifications
2.1 degree, A-C at A level

Offices
London

GOODMAN DERRICK LLP

Remember to cite *The Training Contract & Pupillage Handbook* on your application form if you apply to this firm.

TRAINING CONTRACT DIRECTORY **347**

Gordon Dadds

6 Agar Street, London WC2N 4HN
Tel: 020 7493 6151
Email: recruitment@gordondadds.com
Web: www.gordondadds.com
🐦 gordondadds

The firm Gordon Dadds is a top 100 law firm and the legal and professional services firm of choice for ambitious individuals and organisations. We are one of London's most innovative law firms with a growing global footprint. Over recent years we have expanded from a highly regarded but modestly sized practice to become one of the UK's most ambitious full-service firms, with over 100 fee-earners specialising in every major area of the law. Our legal services are complemented by our consulting arm, a growing and important part of our service for our clients. Our head office is in London and we also have offices in Cardiff and Bristol. We are the exclusive English member of Globalaw, a top 10 international network of independent law firms, through which we are able to service our clients' international needs.

Types of work We are a full service law firm offering both personal and business legal services, and offer other professional services through our consulting arm. Our business services include arbitration, banking, business recovery, restructuring and insolvency, commercial contracts, commercial real estate, corporate, corporate finance, employer's issues including immigration, insurance, intellectual property and brand management, licensing, betting, gaming and regulatory, litigation and dispute resolution, mediation, tax compliance and planning. Our personal services include administration of estates, director, partnership and shareholder disputes, issues at work, litigation and dispute resolution, mediation, powers of attorney, private wealth, relationship formation and breakdown, reputational issues and defamation, residential real estate, tax compliance and planning, wills and succession planning. Our consultancy services include automatic enrolment, company in a box, compliance and risk advice and training, crisis management, employee benefits, human resources, legal process and consultancy, pensions and actuarial consultancy, competition investigations and financial markets consulting and services.

Who should apply We welcome applications from enthusiastic, high-calibre individuals who are determined to succeed in the law. You will need to have excellent communications skills and to thrive in a fast-paced, quality-orientated environment. We are a forward thinking firm and welcome candidates who will develop an innovative and modern approach to the practice of the law.

Training programme A period of recognised training at Gordon Dadds offers an opportunity to gain experience, skills and knowledge in a wide range of practice areas (corporate and commercial (including IP), dispute resolution and litigation, regulatory solutions, property, family, private client and employment) typically on a six-month rotation basis. Our period of recognised training aims to go beyond the traditional rotation structure and also seeks to develop other essential skills such as networking, business development and business management , all of which we look for in our future partners. On average, we recruit five or six trainees a year. Applications from both law and non-law graduates are welcome. To be considered for a period of recognised training with the firm you should be able to demonstrate a consistently high level of academic and personal achievement.

When and how to apply Please visit www.gordondadds.com for further details.

Work placements As well as period of recognised training, we offer a number of work experience opportunities at both our London and Cardiff offices. If you are interested in a career in the law, and would like some first-hand experience at a leading firm, please contact us through our website.

Vacancies	6
Trainees	14
Partners	47
Total staff	239

Training contract deadline
31 July 2018

Apply
Online

Starting salary
1st year – £33,000
2nd year – £35,000

Minimum qualifications
2.1 degree

Offices
London, Cardiff

GORDON DADDS

Gordons LLP

Riverside West, Whitehall Road, Leeds LS1 4AW
Tel: 0113 227 0100
Email: recruitment@gordonsllp.com
Web: www.gordonsllp.com
🐦 gordonsllp

The firm Gordons is a leading independent Yorkshire firm with offices in Leeds and Bradford. We are a modern, straight-talking, ambitious law firm dedicated to delivering a comprehensive and integrated range of legal services to corporate and individual clients including some of the UK's most successful companies and well-loved brands. We aim to be the law firm of choice in our region, providing a genuine alternative to the national firms.

Types of work As a result of our strong reputation and recognised expertise in both corporate and private work, our client base extends far beyond the Yorkshire region.

A full-service firm, areas of work include commercial property, planning and environmental, retail, construction, corporate/commercial, insolvency, commercial litigation, intellectual property, employment, personal injury, private client and residential property.

Who should apply Academically our entry standard is a 2.1 degree although we will take a broader view for those that just miss out.

In recruiting trainees we are looking to select our solicitors and indeed partners of the future. We therefore require committed and loyal trainees who are keen to build a successful career in the region and specifically with us. We offer a broad-based training which gives early and increasing responsibility to trainees in a supportive environment. Applicants must therefore be willing to be challenged from day one.

The firm takes pride in its ability to build enduring relationships with clients. It is therefore essential that our trainees have the potential to be at ease with clients, be able to relate well to them in both a business and a social context, and most importantly inspire trust and confidence in the legal advice that they give. So interpersonal skills, a professional yet friendly manner and sound commercial awareness are criteria we use to measure the suitability of applicants.

Training programme The training contract consists of four six-month seats. During the second year of the training contract trainees are able to express their preference of department and we try to accommodate these requests where possible. Trainees spend time at both Leeds and Bradford offices, and are actively encouraged to get involved in marketing, networking, training and other events hosted by the firm and/or clients. The environment is supportive and friendly, with trainees having regular meetings with their supervisors to ensure their progress.

Outside of working hours the firm has frequent activities that trainees can get involved in, both social and in support of our charity of the year.

When and how to apply The deadline for our 2020 intake is 31 July 2018. Application is via our online form which can be found on the trainee section of our website at www.gordonsllp.com/careers/trainee-recruitment.

Sponsorship The firm contributes £5,000 towards LPC fees.

Vacancies	4
Trainees	8
Partners	26
Total staff	200

Training contract deadline
31 July 2018

Apply
Online

Starting salary
1st year – £24,000
2nd year – £26,000

Minimum qualifications
2.1 degree

Offices
Leeds, Bradford

GORDONS

Government Legal

Tel: 0845 300 0793
Email: glstrainees@tmpw.co.uk
Web: www.gov.uk/gls

The firm Government lawyers provide legal advice to the government of the day and represent it in court proceedings.

Whether the government is creating new laws, buying goods and services, employing people or defending its decisions in court, it needs significant levels of legal advice on a whole range of complex issues. To carry out this work, the government needs its own lawyers, who understand its business, to provide legal services to a wide client base – including a range of central government departments and other government bodies.

Types of work Education and adoption, exiting the European Union, trade, immigration, consumer rights, national security and welfare reform. These are just some examples of the work our lawyers have been involved in recently. The diversity of our work reflects the wide range of activities within government. These range across issues of national and international significance and across public and private law, embracing advisory and legislative work, litigation, commercial and a wealth of specialist areas.

Who should apply We are looking for people with excellent analytical ability and communication skills. Since our lawyers have the opportunity to work in different legal areas throughout their careers, rather than specialise in a single area of law, we need evidence of innovative thinking. And because our work has a significant and positive impact upon the lives of millions across the country, you must be passionate about public service.

Training programme Two-year training opportunities are primarily available within the Government Legal Department (GLD), HM Revenue and Customs (HMRC) and potentially other government departments and agencies. If your application is successful, you will join one of these departments and the structure of your training period will vary accordingly. A valued member of your legal team, you will be fully involved in a broad range of work. You will have an active role to play in casework. You will liaise with government ministers, senior policy makers and counsel. And you will have the opportunity to participate in the legislative process itself.

When and how to apply Trainees and pupils are usually recruited two years in advance. Applicants will, typically, complete an application form (including a situational judgement test), a verbal reasoning test and critical reasoning test. The final stage is a half-day assessment centre in London.

Work placements Around 30 placements are usually available each year through the GLS diversity summer scheme. Please check www.gov.uk/gls for further information.

Sponsorship Departments will pay your Legal Practice Course (LPC) or Bar Professional Training Course (BPTC) fees in full provided you have not yet started either course. Where the course has begun, departments will pay your fees for the remainder of the course. If you intend to study the LPC or BPTC on a full-time basis, you may be eligible for a grant of about £5,400-£7,600. Retrospective payments to candidates who have completed their courses cannot be made. Funding for the GDL may be available. If your application is successful, you will need to discuss GDL funding with your department.

Vacancies	40
Trainees	50-60
Total lawyers	2,000
Work placement	no

Apply
Online

Starting salary
1st year – £28,000

Minimum qualifications
2.2 degree

Sponsorship
LPC/BPTC

Offices
Mostly London although there are GLS legal teams located in Bootle, Bristol, Leeds and Manchester

GLS Government Legal Service

Remember to cite *The Training Contract & Pupillage Handbook* on your application form if you apply to this firm.

Gowling WLG (UK) LLP

Two Snowhill, Snow Hill Queensway, Birmingham B4 6WR
Tel: 0800 096 9610
Email: gradmail@gowlingwlg.com
Web: gowlingwlgcareers.co.uk
f gowlingwlgtrainees 𝕐 gowlingtrainees

The firm We're a leading sector-focused international law firm. But we're different. What sets us apart is a growing reputation for client experience, outstanding people and creative energy. You'll find us in Canada, Europe, Middle East, Asia and the UK, focused on key global sectors including real estate, energy, financial services, life sciences, natural resources, infrastructure and technology. We're a firm with momentum, making bold moves in the international legal market, where we've significantly increased our footprint and capability. And we have an appetite for further international growth.

Types of work Our areas of expertise include: real estate, corporate, dispute resolution, banking and finance, employment, pensions, tax, antitrust, public law and regulatory, corporate recovery and insolvency, intellectual property, IT, projects, outsourcing and general commercial.

Who should apply Penultimate-year law students, final-year non-law students and graduates. We welcome applications from exceptional candidates with well-rounded personalities from diverse cultures and different backgrounds. We're not prescriptive when it comes to qualifications, so we don't ask for particular grades at A level or degree. If you are intelligent, talented, willing to learn and work hard, we think you deserve the chance to prove yourself.

Training programme Treated as a lawyer from day one, you'll enjoy rewarding early responsibility, international opportunities and exposure to big-ticket work as you learn from legal experts across the globe. Our training contracts consist of four six-month seats and we'll get you started with a full and comprehensive induction, designed to help you settle into life here. Choosing from our broad-ranging practice areas, your programme will typically include a contentious seat, a non-contentious seat, real estate and an optional seat (which could be an international secondment or working for a client). You'll get deeply involved in interesting casework for an exceptional scope of clients, enjoying top tier training in a high performing, hugely encouraging culture. It'll be a continuous learning journey with one-to-one guidance from a partner mentor, a dedicated supervisor, the graduate recruitment team and, of course, the strong support network of legal experts all around you.

When and how to apply The first stage of the selection procedure is an online application form. After we receive your application form, we'll invite you to complete a situational judgement test. If successful, you will then be asked to complete an online test and a video interview. Assessment days are the final part of our selection procedure for places on our vacation schemes and for training contract applications.

Work placements We run vacation schemes at our London and Birmingham offices, during spring, summer and winter. You'll experience life at an international law firm first-hand, meet our people and clients, and gain an insight into our work and culture. One of our current trainees will help you settle in and is on hand to answer any queries you may have. You'll have a dedicated supervisor who will ensure you receive quality work, support and constructive feedback. There will also be plenty of social events to help you network and build up professional relationships (while enjoying yourself too, of course).

Sponsorship We cover your Legal Practice Course (LPC) and Graduate Diploma in Law (GDL) fees, as well as providing a maintenance grant for each course.

Vacancies	25
Trainees	60
Partners	593
Total staff	3171

Work placement yes

Apply
Online at
gowlingwlgcareers.co.uk

Starting salary
Birmingham – £27,500
London – £40,000

Sponsorship
GDL/LPC

Offices
Beijing, Birmingham, Brussels, Calgary, Dubai, Guangzhou, Hamilton, London, Monaco, Montréal, Moscow, Munich, Ottawa, Paris, Singapore, Stuttgart, Toronto, Vancouver, Waterloo

 GOWLING WLG

Remember to cite *The Training Contract & Pupillage Handbook* on your application form if you apply to this firm.

GOSSCHALKS Queens Gardens, Hull HU1 3DZ **Tel:** 01482 324252 **Email:** rjt@gosschalks.co.uk **Apply to:** Mr Richard Taylor	Purpose built city centre offices. Major national clients with emphasis on commercial and licensing work. Many partners recognised as specialists in their own field.	V T P TS WP	3 6 28 124 no
GOTELEE 31-41 Elm Street, Ipswich IP1 2AY **Tel:** 01473 211121 **Email:** sally.benjafield@gotelee.co.uk **Apply to:** Mrs Sally Benjafield	A well-established firm with a strong client base covering most areas of commercial private client and litigation work.	V T P TS WP	0 2 20 127 no
GOUGH-THOMAS & SCOTT 8 Willow Street, Ellesmere, Shropshire SY12 0AQ **Tel:** 01691 622413 **Apply to:** Mr MJ Kendall	Offices in Ellesmere and Oswestry, a young go ahead firm in a rural area dealing with general practice.	V T P TS WP	1 1 4 18 no
GRAEME QUAR & CO Orchard House, Furzehall Farm, Fareham PO16 7JH **Tel:** 01329 827 004 **Email:** gquar@quar.co.uk **Apply to:** Mr Graeme Quar	A law firm advising business.	V T P TS WP	0 0 1 9 no
GRAHAM & ROSEN 8 Parliament Street, Hull HU1 2BB **Tel:** 01482 323123 **Email:** ajg@graham-rosen.co.uk **Apply to:** Helen Drewery	General practice including private client, personal injury and matrimonial. Member of network of European lawyers. No vacancies at present.	V T P TS WP	0 1 6 45 no
GRAYS Duncombe Place, Duncombe Place, York YO1 7DY **Tel:** 01904 634771 **Email:** brianmitchell@grayssolicitors.co.uk **Apply to:** Mr Brian Mitchell	Matters handled include private client work, landed and settled estates, tax, trusts and probate, charities, property litigation, professional negligence, agricultural, commercial and domestic conveyancing, and landlord and tenant work.	V T P TS WP	0 0 5 26 no
GREATER MANCHESTER POLICE Professional Standards Branch - Legal Services, Force Headquarters, Central Park, Northampton Road, Manchester M40 5BP **Apply to:** Ms Tricia Harris		V T P TS WP	0 0 - 0 no
GREENBERG TRAURIG LLP The Shard, Level 8, 32 London Bridge Street, London SE1 9SG **Tel:** 020 3349 8700 **Email:** gradrecruit@gtlaw.com **Apply to:** Training Principal	GT is the multidisciplinary London office of international firm Greenberg Traurig and prides itself on its reputation for client focused service and building long-term relationships.	V T P TS WP	4+[18] 7 25 105 yes

V = Vacancies / **T** = Trainees / **P** = Partners / **TS** = Total Staff / **WP** = Work Placement

GREENHOUSE STIRTON & CO 1-2 Faulkner's Alley, Cowcross Street, London EC1M 6DD **Tel:** 020 7490 3456 **Email:** greehousestirton@mediationlawyers.co.uk **Apply to:** Mr M Stirton	Private client firm specialising in court of protection, probate charity and mediation.	V T P TS WP	0 0 2 3 yes
GREENWOODS SOLICITORS LLP Monkstone House, City Road, Peterborough PEI 1JE **Tel:** 01733 887700 **Email:** rmpreston@greenwoods.co.uk **Apply to:** Mrs Rosa Preston	Greenwoods is a leading regional firm with offices in Peterborough, Cambridge and London offering a comprehensive range of commercial legal services.	V T P TS WP	3 4 8 100 yes
GREGG LATCHAMS LIMITED 7 Queen Square, Bristol BS1 4JE **Tel:** 0117 906 9400 **Email:** enquiries@gregglatchams.com **Apply to:** Mr Richard Gore	Bristol-based commercial and general practice with expertise in all areas of the law.	V T P TS WP	2[19] 3 9 52 yes
GREGORY ABRAMS DAVIDSON LLP 20-24 Matthew Street, Liverpool L2 6RE **Tel:** 0151 236 5000 **Email:** info@gadllp.co.uk **Apply to:** The Personnel Manager	Dynamic, forward-thinking practice that has achieved particular recognition for property, commercial, personal injury, family, crime and education law. A friendly yet challenging environment for trainees.	V T P TS WP	0 2 9 78 yes
GREGORY ROWCLIFFE MILNERS 1 Bedford Row, London WC1R 4BZ **Tel:** 020 7242 0631 **Email:** law@grm.co.uk **Apply to:** Mr Tim Moloney	Long-established private client, company/commercial and litigation practice with strongly developed Anglo-German, and other connections including Anglo-German trade organisations.	V T P TS WP	1 2 13 55 no
GROSS & CO 83/84 Guildhall Street, Bury St Edmunds IP33 1LN **Tel:** 01284 763333 **Email:** gdk@gross.co.uk **Apply to:** Mr Graeme Kirk	An independent firm providing a quality service throughout the world.	V T P TS WP	0 0 5 28 no
GUILDFORD BOROUGH COUNCIL Millmead House, Millmead, Guildford, Surrey GU2 4BB **Tel:** 01483 505050 **Email:** businesssupportlegal@guildford.gov.uk **Apply to:** Mrs Sandra Herbert	Local government in-house legal practice dealing primarily with planning, housing, public entertainment and taxi licensing, conveyancing, procurement, contracts and general local government law.	V T P TS WP	0 2 - 23 no
GUILE NICHOLAS SOLICITORS 43 Lodge Lane, North Finchley, London N12 8JG **Tel:** 020 8492 2290 **Email:** hr@gnlaw.co.uk **Apply to:** HR Department	Specialist firm: family, housing, court of protection, employment, wills/probate, mental health, AVP and general civil litigation. Private and legal aid work.	V T P TS WP	0 5 5 30 yes

V = Vacancies / **T** = Trainees / **P** = Partners / **TS** = Total Staff / **WP** = Work Placement

GURNEY-CHAMPION & CO 104 Victoria Road North, Southsea, Portsmouth PO5 1QE **Tel:** 023 9282 1100 **Email:** ngc@championlawyers.co.uk **Apply to:** Mr N C A Gurney-Champion	Traditional high street practice, dealing with residential and commercial conveyancing, wills and probate, family, civil litigation, landlord and tenant, and general business matters.	V T P TS WP	0 1 2 8 no
HAINS & LEWIS Penffynnon, Hawthorn Rise, Haverfordwest SA61 2BQ **Tel:** 0834 4080 125 **Email:** law@hainsandlewis.co.uk **Apply to:** Miss V H Hains	General high street/legal aid practice – two branch offices. Five solicitors specialising in family, property, probate, public law, general civil litigation and some crime.	V T P TS WP	0 2 4 30 no
HALL SMITH WHITTINGHAM 1 Dysart Buildings, Nantwich, Cheshire CW5 5DP **Tel:** 01270 610 300 **Email:** law@hswsolicitors.co.uk **Apply to:** Mrs Kay Master	General practice but known for strength in family, agriculture, private client work. Only candidates with a 2.1 degree are interviewed and preference is given to local candidates.	V T P TS WP	0 2 5 40 no
HANNE & CO St. Johns Chambers, 1C St Johns Hill, Clapham Junction, London SW11 1TN **Tel:** 020 7228 0017 **Email:** info@hanne.co.uk **Apply to:** Ms Grainne Fahy	Hanne & Co is a full service law firm with an outstanding reputation. We are always looking for ambitious people to join our team.	V T P TS WP	3[18] 9 10 57 no
HARBOTTLE & LEWIS LLP Hanover House, 14 Hanover Square, London W1S 1HP **Tel:** 020 7667 5000 **Email:** graduaterecruitment@harbottle.com **Apply to:** Lisa Lacuna	The firm specialises in the media, entertainment, leisure and aviation industries. Regarded by *Legal 500* as a leading firm across all its industry areas.	V T P TS WP	6 11 42 186 no
HARDING EVANS LLP 2 North Street, Newport, Gwent NP20 1TE **Tel:** 01633 244233 **Email:** thomasn@hevans.com **Apply to:** Miss Nikki Thomas	For our 2018 intake the firm are identifying and recruiting our future trainee solicitors through our internal paralegal pool.	V T P TS WP	1 3 10 120 yes
HARPER & ODELL 61-63 St John Street, London EC1M 4AN **Tel:** 020 7490 0500 **Email:** law@harperandodell.co.uk **Apply to:** Mr RA Hussein	Long-established, busy central London commercial practice specialising in personal injury, landlord and tenant and contractual claims, property disputes and residential and commercial conveyancing.	V T P TS WP	TBC 2 2 5 no
HARRIS WATERS & CO 406-408 High Road, Ilford, Essex IG1 1TW **Tel:** 020 8478 0888 **Email:** roger@harriswaters.com **Apply to:** Mr R Waters	We are an expanding dynamic firm with a growing reputation for our professional yet warm and friendly services in family law, litigation, residential and commercial conveyancing.	V T P TS WP	1 1 2 11 yes

V = Vacancies / **T** = Trainees / **P** = Partners / **TS** = Total Staff / **WP** = Work Placement

HARRISON CLARK RICKERBYS SOLICITORS 5 Deansway, Worcester WR1 2JG **Tel:** 01905 746 453 **Email:** cengland@hcrlaw.com **Apply to:** Miss Charlotte England	Harrison Clark Rickerbys is listed as first tier in the prestigious legal directories *Legal 500* and *Chambers & Partners* and is Lexcel accredited.	V Approx 10 T 20 P 70 TS 460 WP yes
HARROWELLS 1 St Saviourgate, York YO1 8ZQ **Tel:** 01904 558600 **Email:** careers@harrowells.co.uk **Apply to:** Mrs Louise Osborne		V 0 T 7 P 20 TS 131 WP no
HART READE 104 South Street, Eastbourne BN21 4LW **Tel:** 01323 727321 **Email:** info@hartreade.co.uk **Apply to:** Mrs Fiona Gausden	Established and respected high street firm which advises private and business clients on all main areas of law. Lexcel, CQS, ALEP accredited.	V 0 T 0 P 6 TS 65 WP no
HATCHERS SOLICITORS Welsh Bridge, 1 Frankwell, Shrewsbury SY3 8LG **Tel:** 01743 248545 **Email:** mail@hatchers.co.uk **Apply to:** Mr Patrick Gittins	General practice with some specialisms. Broad client base. Three offices in Central and North Shropshire. Specialisms: environment, agriculture, debt, PI, crime, family, private client, corporate and employment.	V 0 T 1 P 13 TS 90 WP no
HATTON 1 Sheaf Street, Daventry, Northants NN11 4AA **Tel:** 01327 301201 **Email:** jhatton@msn.com **Apply to:** Mr Jonathan Hatton	Fraud, commercial and chancery.	V 1-2 T 1 P 1 TS 6 WP yes
HAWKSWELL KILVINGTON LTD 17 Navigation Court, Calder Park, Wakefield, West Yorkshire WF2 7BJ **Tel:** 01924258719 **Email:** ltankard@hklegal.co.uk	We are based south of Leeds in a modern business park. We have established a national reputation as a niche construction law practice.	V 1 T 2 P 3 TS 15 WP no
HAY & KILNER LAW FIRM Merchant House, 30 Cloth Market, Newcastle upon Tyne NE1 1EE **Tel:** 0191 232 8345 **Email:** ros.sparrow@hay-kilner.co.uk	We are looking for confident and commercially aware individuals with excellent communication skills. We will provide you with a broad training programme.	V 3 T 3 P 24 TS 82 WP yes
HAYES + STORR 18-19 Market Place, Fakenham, Norfolk NR21 9BH **Tel:** 01328 863231 **Email:** law@hayes-storr.com **Apply to:** Mr Alex Findlay	Busy, dynamic and expanding practice with six offices across North and West Norfolk. We offer a broad range of services to individuals and commercial clients.	V 2 T 2 P 13 TS 105 WP no

V = Vacancies / **T** = Trainees / **P** = Partners / **TS** = Total Staff / **WP** = Work Placement

HEALD SOLICITORS LLP Artemis House, 4 Bramley Road, Milton Keynes MK1 1PT **Tel:** 01908 662277 **Email:** liz.linton@healdlaw.com **Apply to:** Mr Martin Banham-Hall	We mainly serve businesses (mostly owner-managed), their owners and key personnel. Commercial property, corporate and commercial, dispute resolution, family and private client departments.	V T P TS WP	1[19] 1 5 30 no
HELIX LAW 1 Frederick Terrace, Frederick Place, Brighton BN1 1AX **Tel:** 01273 761990 **Email:** careers@helix-law.com **Apply to:** Mr Alex Cook	We are a firm specialising in dispute resolution, litigation and adjudication. We look for hard working ambitious people who deliver.	V T P TS WP	2[18] 4 3 10 no
HEMPSONS 40 Villiers Street, London WC2N 6NJ **Tel:** 020 7839 0278 **Email:** erecruitment@hempsons.co.uk **Apply to:** The Trainee Solicitor Coordinator	Offices: London, Harrogate, Newcastle and Manchester, offering a full range of legal services to NHS and healthcare clients (both individuals and institutional) and charities.	V T P TS WP	3 3 46 300 no
HENRY'S SOLICITORS LIMITED 72-74 Wellington Road South, Stockport, Cheshire SK1 3SU **Tel:** 0161 477 8558 **Apply to:** Mr Kieran Henry	A criminal and prison law specialist company with a fraud contract. We are one of the North West's leading criminal law providers.	V T P TS WP	1 3 - 25 yes
HEPTONSTALLS 7-13 Gladstone Terrace, Goole DN14 5AH **Tel:** 01405 765661 **Email:** recruitment@heptonstalls.co.uk **Apply to:** Ms Sharon Speirs	A friendly general practice firm with a strong emphasis on personal injury and medical negligence work. Applications should be made using the application form.	V T P TS WP	1-2 0 6 100 no
HER MAJESTY'S COURTS & TRIBUNALS SERVICE Legal Operations Team, 102 Petty France, London SW1H 9AJ **Tel:** 020 3334 2582 **Email:** benjamin.wood@hmcts.gsi.gov.uk **Apply to:** Mr Benjamin Wood	HMCTS employs 1,200 lawyers who are mostly responsible for providing advice to magistrates on matters of law, practice and procedure. Legal roles also exist in other jurisdictions, albeit in smaller numbers.	V T P TS WP	0 0 0 1200 no
HEREFORDSHIRE DISTRICT COUNCIL Brockington, 35 Hafod Road, Hereford HR1 1SH **Tel:** 01432 260266 **Apply to:** Ms Erica Hermon	A busy legal practice serving both Herefordshire Council and a range of local public sector organisations.	V T P TS WP	0 0 0 31 no
HERRINGTON CARMICHAEL LLP Building 9, Riverside Way, Watchmoor Business Park, Camberley, Surrey GU15 3YL **Tel:** 012 7668 6222 **Email:** kate.hardesty@herrington-carmichael.com **Apply to:** Mrs Kate Hardesty	General practice with offices in Camberley and Wokingham. Specialist commercial and private client departments dealing with most areas of work except crime or legal aid.	V T P TS WP	3-4[19] 8 10 90 no

V = Vacancies / **T** = Trainees / **P** = Partners / **TS** = Total Staff / **WP** = Work Placement

Herbert Smith Freehills LLP

Exchange House, Primrose Street, London EC2A 2EG
Tel: 020 7374 8000
Email: graduates.uk@hsf.com
Web: www.herbertsmithfreehills.com
f hsfgraduatesuk **𝕐** hsfgraduatesuk

The firm World-class disputes practice. Market-leading corporate practice. Top-tier specialist teams. We've got it all. We are a truly global elite law firm and we work with some of the largest international organisations on some of their most ambitious projects. Our international presence is demonstrated by over 3,000 lawyers in 26 offices across Asia, Australia, Europe, the Middle East and the USA. Working across borders is a key part of our philosophy. Thanks to the quality of our international network, we're able to offer our clients services across the globe, giving you the chance to work in a truly international way.

Types of work Our work is incredibly varied. We provide top quality tailored legal advice to major corporations, governments and financial institutions as well as various commercial organisations. We advise more FTSE 100 clients than any other UK or US-headquartered firm. Our dispute resolution practice is number one in the UK, Asia and Australia and this includes both our leading international arbitration practice and award-winning in-house advocacy unit. We can therefore offer a complete litigation service and a realistic alternative to the Bar. And that's not all. Our other practice areas include finance, competition, regulation and trade, real estate and employment, pensions and incentives as well as specialist areas like intellectual property and tax. Herbert Smith Freehills prides itself on being a global elite law firm that brings together ambitious people to achieve the best results for clients.

Who should apply Herbert Smith Freehills is a place where you have both global exposure and a supportive network. You'll focus on technical excellence and a client led approach. If you've got the drive to make the most of the opportunities on offer and the ambition and potential to become a brilliant lawyer, don't compromise. Be a part of everything at Herbert Smith Freehills. The minimum academic qualification required is a 2.1 degree (or equivalent); applications are accepted from students with law and non-law backgrounds and those looking to change careers.

Training programme Herbert Smith Freehills' trainees can be a part of it all. The training contract balances contentious and non-contentious work with pro bono opportunities and real responsibility. Trainees rotate around four six-month seats with the opportunity to go on secondment either to a client or to one of the firm's international offices.

When and how to apply Applications for training contracts open on 18 September 2017. The deadline for 2020 training contracts is 29 December 2017. The application form can be completed online at careers.herbertsmithfreehills.com/uk/grads.

Work placements Spring, summer and winter vacation schemes offered.

Sponsorship Herbert Smith Freehills provides funding and a maintenance allowance for GDL and LPC courses.

Vacancies	60
Trainees	147
Partners	476
Total staff	4,965

Work placement yes

Training contract deadline
29 December 2017

Apply
Online at careers.
herbertsmithfreehills.com/
uk/grads

Starting salary
£44,000

Minimum qualifications
2.1 degree

Sponsorship
GDL/LPC

Offices
Throughout Asia, Australia, Europe, the Middle East and the USA

HERBERT
SMITH
FREEHILLS

Hewitsons LLP

Elgin House, Billing Road, Northampton NN1 5AU
Tel: 0160 423 3233
Email: carolinelewis@hewitsons.com
Web: www.hewitsons.com
🐦 hewitsons

The firm Hewitsons is ranked among the UK's foremost regional law firms with 46 partners and around 100 lawyers based at its main centres in Northampton and Cambridge.

Types of work The firm has a strong reputation in a range of specialisms and a national and international client base, particularly in Europe and across North America. Its areas of noted expertise include corporate and commercial work, technology, employment, competition law, property, construction, planning, environment, insolvency, bioscience, agriculture, tax, trusts and charities.

Who should apply The firm welcomes applications from candidates who have achieved a high standard of academic success, with a minimum of a 2.1 degree, and who are bright, personable, have initiative and enjoy working as part of a team.

Training programme Training contracts are offered at Northampton and Cambridge, with placements in London and Milton Keynes. Trainees complete four placements of six months each in a range of different legal specialisms. During each seat, the trainee is supervised closely by a partner or senior solicitor, and progress is monitored on a day-by-day basis as well as in a formal three-monthly review, carried out mid-seat and at end of seat. The firm provides a comprehensive induction programme specifically tailored for the needs of trainee solicitors. The Professional Skills Course is coupled with an extensive programme of trainee solicitors' seminars provided by specialist in-house lawyers.

When and how to apply Telephone the director of human resources, Caroline Lewis, on 0160 423 3233 or email carolinelewis@hewitsons.com. Applications for training contracts to start in September 2020 should be made between July and August 2018.

Work placements The firm operates a vacation scheme and placements are available throughout the year.

Vacancies	15
Trainees	15
Partners	46
Total staff	243

Work placement yes

Training contract deadline
August 2018

Apply to
Caroline Lewis

Starting salary
£23,500

Minimum qualifications
2.1 degree

Offices
Northampton, Cambridge, Milton Keynes, London

HFW

Friary Court, 65 Crutched Friars, London EC3N 2AE
Tel: 020 7264 8000
Email: grad.recruitment@hfw.com
Web: www.hfw.com
🐦 hfwgrads

The firm We are a sector-focused, entrepreneurial law firm. But there's more to us than that. We have a passion for the sectors we work in – whether we are solving complex issues across construction, aviation and shipping, or providing advice across insurance, commodities and energy. We're people who like to get things done. It's this pragmatism, combined with our creative approach, that makes us our clients' go-to commercial advisers.

And we are, unapologetically, absolute experts in what we advise our clients on. So yes, we're different. Our clients say "less traditional" – "progressive", even. We say we're specialist lawyers here to add value to our clients.

Types of work Aviation, commodities, construction, energy, financial institutions, insurance and reinsurance, logistics, mining, ports and terminals, shipping, space, yachts, travel, cruise and leisure.

Who should apply Our trainees share our entrepreneurial spirit and are bright and commercial. We look for individuals who are eager to solve problems in new and practical ways, and who want to build collaborative relationships. Strong communication skills are a must. In addition, as our training contract is truly international we look for individuals who have a global perspective and an interest in completing international work.

Our trainees come from a variety of backgrounds and disciplines and we welcome applications from both law and non-law students and undergraduates and experienced individuals alike.

Training programme Every year we recruit only a small number of trainees – 15 per year split across a September and March intake. This enables us to give every trainee our full attention, and means that your individual contribution makes a real difference. A training contract at HFW consists of four six-month seats – typically three contentious seats and one transactional seat, with at least one seat spent outside of London in an international office. Overall, we aim to provide you with a dynamic, supportive and varied environment in which you are challenged to become the best lawyer you can be and encouraged to contribute to the success of our global business.

When and how to apply Apply online via our website: www.hfw.com/graduate-recruitment. The deadline for vacation scheme applications is 31 January 2018. The deadline for training contract applications is 31 July 2018.

Work placements Our vacation schemes are a key part of our recruitment process for trainees and we consider all of our vacation scheme participants for a training contract. Completing a vacation scheme enables you to experience our work first hand, and also provides you with valuable insight into our industry sectors, our global reach and our culture. Alongside spending time in at least one department of your choice, you can expect to attend presentations, social events and a final round partner interview for a training contract.

Each year we run a one-week spring vacation scheme and various summer vacation schemes (ranging between one and two weeks in duration).

Sponsorship GDL/LPC fees paid and a maintenance grant of £7,000 (£5,500 outside London) is available for each year of study.

Vacancies	15
Trainees	33
Partners	170
Total staff	972

Work placement yes

Training contract deadline
31 July 2018

Apply
Online

Starting salary
1st year – £37,000
2nd year – £39,000

Sponsorship
CPE/GDL/LPC

Offices
Beirut; Brussels; Dubai; Geneva; Hong Kong; Houston; Kuwait; London; Melbourne; Paris; Perth; Piraeus; Riyadh; São Paulo; Shanghai; Singapore; Sydney

HFW

Affiliated with
ⱭS aspiringsolicitors

Remember to cite *The Training Contract & Pupillage Handbook* on your application form if you apply to this firm.

TRAINING CONTRACT DIRECTORY 359

HERTFORDSHIRE COUNTY COUNCIL County Hall, Pegs Lane, Hertford SG13 8DE **Tel:** 01992 555510 **Email:** hertsdirect@hertscc.gov.uk **Apply to:** Mr D Simon		V T P TS WP	0 3 - - no
HETHERTONS LLP SOLICITORS Northern House, 7-9 Rougier Street, York Y01 6HZ **Tel:** 01904 625 327 **Email:** law@hethertons.co.uk **Apply to:** The Staff Partner	General legal practice with offices in York and Boroughbridge. Private and publicly funded work and a comprehensive range of legal services.	V T P TS WP	0 1 3 31 no
HEWITTS 207 Newgate Street, Bishop Auckland DL14 7EL **Tel:** 01388 604691 **Email:** enquiries@hewitts.co.uk **Apply to:** Ms Laura Saunders-Jerrom	General legal practice with five offices situated in rural South West Durham and Teeside.	V T P TS WP	0 2 13 103 no
HEXTALLS LTD 28 Leman Street, London E1 8ER **Tel:** 020 7488 1424 **Email:** janeclark@hextalls.com **Apply to:** Ms Emma Bond	Specialises in national and international insurance/reinsurance and other commercial litigation/dispute resolution, shipping, transport/travel and sports and leisure.	V T P TS WP	0 0 8 30 no
HIBBERTS LLP 144 Nantwich Road, Crewe, Cheshire CW2 6BG **Tel:** 01270215117 **Email:** cjb@hibberts.com **Apply to:** Ms Carolyn Brooksbank	Long established and highly regarded practice located in Cheshire and Shropshire. We pride ourselves in providing personal, practical and professional advice to all our clients.	V T P TS WP	1[18] 2 7 96 yes
HILL & ABBOTT Burgundy Court, 64-66 Springfield Road, Chelmsford CM2 6JY **Tel:** 01245 258892 **Email:** cst@hill-abbott.co.uk **Apply to:** Mrs Kerry Huggins	General practice with specialisms in personal injury, family, child care, trusts, commercial and conveyancing.	V T P TS WP	0 2 - 40 yes
HILLIERS HRW Mindenhall Court, High Street, Stevenage SG1 3UN **Tel:** 01438 346 000 **Email:** admin@hilliershrw.co.uk **Apply to:** Mrs Fiona Nash	Offices at present in Bedfordshire & Hertfordshire. An extremely forward thinking firm in IT and all business matters.	V T P TS WP	0 1 2 32 no
HILLYER MCKEOWN LLP Gorse Stacks House, George Street, Chester, Cheshire CH1 3EQ **Tel:** 01244 318 131 **Email:** enquiries@law.uk.com **Apply to:** Mr Richard Burnett	Hillyer McKeown LLP is a full service commercial and private client firm. The firm's three offices cover Chester, North Wales and the Wirral Pensinsula. No vacancies at present.	V T P TS WP	1 2 12 80 no

V = Vacancies / **T** = Trainees / **P** = Partners / **TS** = Total Staff / **WP** = Work Placement

Higgs & Sons

3 Waterfront Business Park, Brierley Hill DY5 1LX
Tel: 0345 111 5050
Email: growyourfuture@higgsandsons.co.uk
Web: www.higgsandsons.co.uk
f higgsandsonsgrads ➤ higgsandsons

The firm Higgs & Sons is one of the largest and most respected law firms in the West Midlands, operating out of offices in Brierley Hill and employing over 200 staff. The firm's headquarters are situated in a modern, purpose designed facility at the prestigious Waterfront Business Park. We are well recognised in the *Legal 500* and *Chambers & Partners* guide to the legal profession. In 2011 the firm was awarded Law Firm of the Year (16+ partners) by the Birmingham Law Society.

Higgs & Sons is different from the typical law firm. We successfully combine traditional values with an innovative approach to legal problems which has helped to attract an impressive client base while also staying true to our local community. Clients and staff alike are attracted to Higgs' offer an all round service in a number of areas. We are proud to provide a supportive and friendly working environment within which colleagues can thrive. The opportunity for career progression is clear as almost half of our partners trained with the firm.

Types of work For the business client: corporate and commercial; insolvency; employment; commercial litigation; and commercial property.

For the private client: wills; probate and trusts and tax; employment; personal injury; clinical negligence; conveyancing; dispute resolution; and matrimonial/family.

Who should apply Applications are welcome from law and non-law students who can demonstrate consistently high academic records, a broad range of interpersonal skills and extra-curricular activities and interests. We would like to hear about what you have done to develop your wider skills and awareness. We are looking for people who want to get involved and participate fully in the business.

Training programme A training contract at Higgs is different from those offered by other firms. There is the unique opportunity to undertake six four-month seats in a variety of departments, including a double seat in the department into which you wish to qualify as you approach the end of your training contract. Throughout the training contract you will receive a mix of contentious and non-contentious work and an open door policy means that there is always someone on hand to answer questions and supervise your work. Regular appraisals take place at the end of each seat and a designated partner oversees you throughout the duration of your training contract, acting as a mentor. Participation in BTSS events and an active Higgs social environment ensures an effective work life balance.

Benefits include private medical insurance, contributory pension, life assurance, 25 days' holiday and BTSS membership.

When and how to apply The deadline for the September 2020 intake is 31 July 2018. Apply online at www.higgsandsons.co.uk.

Sponsorship Professional Skills Course.

Vacancies	4-6
Trainees	11
Partners	35
Total staff	225

Training contract deadline
31 July 2018

Apply
Online

Starting salary
1st year – £23,500
2nd year – £25,000

Minimum qualifications
2.1 preferred

Offices
Brierley Hill

HIGGS
&SONS
S O L I C I T O R S

Hill Dickinson LLP

No 1 St Paul's Square, Liverpool L3 9SJ
Tel: 0151 600 8000
Email: recruitment@hilldickinson.com
Web: www.hilldickinson.com
🐦 hd_trainees

The firm We're an award-winning, international law firm with big clients, great people and fantastic opportunities. With around 1,000 people, including 190 partners and legal directors, we have offices in Liverpool, London and Manchester in the UK, alongside international bases in Singapore, Piraeus, Monaco and Hong Kong.

Types of work We're a full-service commercial law firm, so we cover all areas of law and work across a number of sectors, including: insurance, retail, aviation, sports, media, health and marine.

Who should apply Academically, you'll need at least a 2.1 and ABB or equivalent. We want our trainees to show a commitment to learning throughout their careers. We want trainees with the insight and awareness to understand our clients' demands and what is expected of us as an international law firm, so we want to hear about your business background. You'll need to have experiences that demonstrate your passion for a career in law and the motivation you've got to get there.

Training programme Modest numbers: we recruit to retain, so for 2020, we're taking on 14 trainees which means that we'll have the resources and time to give you as much support as you need.

Immediate responsibilities: because of our small intake, there's lots of interesting work to go around and you'll be given challenges from the start.

Choices: you'll work four seats and be able to select preferences from a variety of different areas of law.

A mentor: your mentor (a Hill Dickinson solicitor) will be on hand from day one and throughout your training contract to offer advice, guidance and support.

Office sharing: you'll share an office with a partner, who will help you develop your legal knowledge and be there to support you.

A social scene: our trainees work really hard and as you'd expect, it's not all fun and games. But when they do let their hair down, they get together and do it properly! You're welcome to get involved in the firm's sports and CSR teams, too.

When and how to apply Apply via our online form at www.hilldickinsontrainees.com which opens 1 November 2017, 31 January 2018 for vacation schemes and 31 July 2018 for training contracts.

Work placements We have up to 44 vacation scheme places available in our northern offices and 10 in London. Apply online by 31 January 2018.

Vacancies	14
Trainees	25
Partners	132
Total staff	1,000

Work placement	yes

Training contract deadline
31 July 2018

Apply
Online

Starting salary
1st year – £24,000
2nd year – £26,000
London:
1st year – £32,000
2nd year – £34,000

Minimum qualifications
2.1 degree

Sponsorship
LPC plus maintenance grant

Offices
Liverpool, Manchester, London, Piraeus, Singapore, Monaco, Hong Kong

HILL DICKINSON

Hodge Jones & Allen LLP

180 North Gower Street, London NW1 2NB
Tel: 020 7874 8300
Email: eantoniades@hja.net
Web: www.hja.net
🐦 hodgejonesallen

The firm Hodge Jones & Allen was founded in 1977 and to this day remains committed to providing first-class legal help to both individuals and organisations.

Our philosophy has always been to enable individuals to have access to justice where otherwise they might be denied it and this ethos remains as strong today as it did back then. We strive to right wrongs, achieve justice for all and get the very best result for our clients. People have always been at the heart of our firm and this is recognised by our Investors in People Gold accreditation.

"We have been on the forefront of the legal sector – changing lives, making headlines and advancing the law, since our inception and hope to continue this for many years to come." – Patrick Allen, senior partner.

Types of work Civil liberties, criminal defence, employment, family, wills and probate, medical negligence, personal injury, dispute resolution, social housing, serious fraud, military claims, industrial disease, property disputes and court of protection.

Who should apply Applications from both law and non-law graduates are welcome. You should be able to demonstrate a consistently high level of academic and personal achievement. We generally expect an upper second class degree.

The firm is looking for people who:
Communicate clearly and effectively;
Have an excellent academic record;
Can demonstrate they are interested and committed to the work the firm does;
Are hard-working and dedicated;
Understand and share the ethos of the firm; and
Have a record of achievement in extracurricular activities

Training programme Trainees have a full induction on joining Hodge Jones & Allen covering the work of the firm's main departments, procedural matters and professional conduct. Training consists of four six-month seats. Formal reviews of progress are held at least once during the seat. The training is well structured and the trainees have the benefit of a mentoring scheme. The firm provides good clerical support so trainees can concentrate on legal work rather than administration. The firm has an excellent IT infrastructure and continues to invest heavily in IT to keep pace with innovation.

When and how to apply Applications are invited by 27 July 2018 for training contracts to begin in September 2019. All recruitment information is available on our website at www.hja.net.

Applications are by application form only, downloaded from our website. Guidance notes, a job description and FAQs can be accessed on our website.

Sponsorship Sponsorship contributions may be considered, but not generally available.

Vacancies	7
Trainees	14
Partners	41
Total staff	210

Work placement · no

Training contract deadline
27 July 2018

Apply to
Trainee Solicitor Scheme

Starting salary
1st year – £24,000
2nd year – £26,000

Minimum qualifications
2.1 degree

Offices
London

hodge jones & allen
solicitors

Remember to cite *The Training Contract & Pupillage Handbook* on your application form if you apply to this firm.

TRAINING CONTRACT DIRECTORY **363**

Hogan Lovells

Atlantic House, Holborn Viaduct, London EC1A 2FG
Tel: 020 7296 2000
Email: graduate.recruitment@hoganlovells.com
Web: www.hoganlovells.com/graduates
f hoganlovellsgradsuk ♥ @hlgraduatesuk

The firm A practical, straight-talking approach to law. Open, honest and deep relationships with clients. Training that keeps on evolving. A global community where everyone is on the same wavelength – but always encouraged to be themselves. All of this gives Hogan Lovells a different dynamic to other global law firms.

Types of work It's why many prestigious, forward-thinking clients choose to work with us. The firm has a reputation not just for the consistently high quality of its 2,500 lawyers, but also for its sense of community. The network of 45 global offices collaborates closely and constructively. Together, our teams of corporate, finance, dispute resolution, government regulatory and intellectual property lawyers tackle some of the most intricate legal and commercial issues that businesses face.

Training programme Each year, the firm takes on up to 60 trainee solicitors – both law and non-law graduates. The two-year training contract is split into four six-month seats. During this time, trainee solicitors move around four different practice areas, including corporate, finance and dispute resolution. You will gain exposure to and develop a rounded understanding of international law, and you will have an opportunity to apply for an international or client secondment.

When and how to apply Law students should apply by 31 July 2018 at the latest. Non-law students and non-law graduates should apply by 31 January 2018. Applicants should visit our website at www.hoganlovells.com/graduates and complete an online application form.

Work placements Hogan Lovells runs highly-regarded spring, summer and winter vacation schemes. Up to 65 places are available in total. Each lasts up to three weeks and gives participants the chance to work alongside partners, associates and trainees in major practice areas. Students are exposed to two or three practice areas and learn to draft documents, carry out legal research, attend meetings and, in some cases, attend court. This hands-on learning is complemented by tailored workshops, case studies and social events.

The closing date for the winter vacation scheme is 31 October 2017. The closing date for the spring and summer vacation scheme is the 7 January 2018.

Sponsorship Maintenance grants are available for GDL and accelerated LPC. GDL is £7,000 outside of London and £8,000 within London.

Vacancies	Up to 60
Trainees	120
Partners	800
Total staff	5,000

Work placement yes
(see Insider Report on p77)

Training contract deadline
31 July 2018

Apply
Online at
hoganlovells.com/graduates

Starting salary
Year 1 – £44,000
Year 2 – £49,000

Minimum qualifications
2.1 degree (or equivalent)

Sponsorship
GDL/LPC

Offices
Alicante, Amsterdam, Baltimore, Beijing, Brussels, Budapest, Caracas, Colorado Springs, Denver, Dubai, Düsseldorf, Frankfurt, Hamburg, Hanoi, Ho Chi Minh City, Hong Kong, Houston, Jakarta, Johannesburg, London, Los Angeles, Louisville, Luxembourg, Madrid, Mexico City, Miami, Milan, Minneapolis, Monterrey, Moscow, Munich, New York, Northern Virginia, Paris, Perth, Philadelphia, Riyadh, Rio de Janeiro, Rome, San Francisco, São Paulo, Shanghai, Silicon Valley, Singapore, Sydney, Tokyo, Ulaanbaatar, Warsaw, Washington DC, Zagreb

Affiliated with
ᴢ aspiringsolicitors

Remember to cite *The Training Contract & Pupillage Handbook* on your application form if you apply to this firm.

HINE SOLICITORS 285 Banbury Road, Summertown, Oxford OX2 7JF **Tel:** 01865 514348 **Email:** recruitment@hinesolicitors.com **Apply to:** Abi Wilson	The training contract will have a heavy emphasis on criminal law. Presently training seats are also offered in prison law and conveyancing.	V 10 T 21 P 8 TS 180 WP no
HKH KENWRIGHT & COX Mountsview House, 202-212 High Road, Ilford, Essex IG1 1QB **Tel:** 020 8553 9600 **Email:** admin@hkhsol.com **Apply to:** Mr KS Mian	Specialist criminal and family firm. Handles residential and commercial conveyancing. Serious Fraud Panel members. Private immigration and work permits. Legal aid and private client base.	V 0 T 1 P 2 TS 19 WP yes
HLW KEEBLE HAWSON LLP Commercial House, Commercial Street, Sheffield S1 2AT **Tel:** 0114 2765555 **Email:** lisalimb@hlwkeeblehawson.co.uk **Apply to:** Mr Giles Searby	One of the North's leading law firms, hlw Keeble Hawson LLP offers dynamic and commercial legal advice through its offices in Sheffield, Leeds and Doncaster.	V 4 T 12 P 36 TS 280 WP yes
HODDERS Po Box 344, 11 Station Road, Harlesden, London NW10 4UD **Tel:** 020 8965 9862 **Apply to:** Ms Nycki Gray-Cooper	A medium-sized five partner law firm with offices in Northwest London, Wembley, Battersea and High Wycombe.	V 0 T 2 P 5 TS 65 WP no
HOLDEN & CO. LLP 32-33 Robertson Street, Hastings TN34 1HT **Tel:** 01424 722422 **Email:** law@holdenandco.co.uk **Apply to:** Mr David Nessling	General high street practice of a legal aid plus private work Lexcel accredited firm.	V 1 T 1 P 4 TS 23 WP no
HOLMES & HILLS Bocking End, Braintree, Essex CM7 9AJ **Tel:** 01376 320 456 **Email:** legaladvice@holmes-hills.co.uk **Apply to:** Mrs Sue Bushell	Holmes & Hills offers a full range of legal assistance from personal, family and property services to comprehensive support for your business.	V 0 T - P 6 TS 95 WP no
HOOD VORES & ALLWOOD The Priory, Church Street, Dereham NR19 1DW **Tel:** 0845 3724240 **Email:** roger.margand@hoodvoreslaw.co.uk **Apply to:** Mr Roger Margand	Mid-Norfolk medium-sized rural firm able to offer excellent experience, particularly in private client and property work.	V 0 T 1 P 5 TS 25 WP no
HOOPER & WOLLEN Carlton House, 30 The Terrace, Torquay TQ1 1BS **Tel:** 01803 213251 **Email:** lawyers@hooperwollen.co.uk **Apply to:** Mr Clive Meredith	Leading South Devon firm. Departments include trust and probate, conveyancing – domestic and commercial, civil litigation, personal injury, family/child care, LSC franchise and company/commercial.	V 0 T 4 P 11 TS 84 WP no

V = Vacancies / **T** = Trainees / **P** = Partners / **TS** = Total Staff / **WP** = Work Placement

HORWICH FARRELLY	Easter and summer vacation	V	15
Alexander House, 94-96 Talbot Road, Old Trafford,	schemes available. Horwich Farrelly	T	30
Manchester M16 OSP	hire students into paralegal roles.	P	35
Tel: 0161 413 1937	Once probation is completed	TS	730
Email: sarah.halliwell@h-f.co.uk	paralegals are eligible to apply for	WP	yes
Apply to: Miss Sarah Halliwell	training contracts.		

HORWOOD & JAMES LLP	Business and private client	V	0
7 Temple Square, Aylesbury, Buckinghamshire	lawyers, established in Aylesbury,	T	1
HP20 2QB	Buckinghamshire, for over 200 years.	P	5
Tel: 01296 487361		TS	28
Email: enquiries@horwoodjames.co.uk		WP	no
Apply to: Miss Jill Swift			

HOTCHKISS WARBURTON	Small high street firm specialising in	V	0
34 High Street, Crediton, Devon EX17 3JP	conveyancing, wills and probate.	T	0
Tel: 01363 774752		P	2
Email: enquiries@hotchkiss-warburton.co.uk		TS	5
Apply to: Mrs L Stone		WP	no

HOWARD & OVER	Offices at Devonport, Plymstock and	V	0
114 Albert Road, Devonport, Plymouth PL2 1AF	Ivybridge. General practice with two	T	0
Tel: 01752 556606	partners and 10 other fee-earners.	P	2
Email: admin@howard-over.co.uk	The firm has a legal aid franchise in	TS	32
Apply to: Ms Katherine Millman	two categories.	WP	no

HOWARD KENNEDY	We are a full-service firm, with core	V	10[19]
No1 London Bridge, London SE1 9BG	real estate, corporate and dispute	T	16
Tel: 020 3755 6000	resolution departments, and further	P	53
Email: trainee.recruitment@howardkennedy.com	teams in employment, private client	TS	350
Apply to: Trainee Recruitment	and family.	WP	no

HOWARTH GOODMAN	Commercial property, employment,	V	Poss
First Floor, The Lexicon, 10 Mount Street,	landlord and tenant, company,	T	1
Manchester M2 5NT	building contract disputes.	P	2
Tel: 0161 832 5068		TS	11
Email: sb@howarthgoodman.com		WP	yes
Apply to: Mr Steven Baddiel			

HOWELL JONES LLP	We offer a broad range of services	V	0
75 Surbiton Road, Kingston upon Thames, Surrey	including company commercial,	T	0
KT1 2AF	litigation, personal injury, property,	P	14
Tel: 020 8549 5186	matrimonial and private client.	TS	75
Email: keith.howell-jones@howell-jones.com		WP	no
Apply to: Mr Simon Carter			

HRJ FOREMAN LAWS	Company/commercial and property	V	0
25 Bancroft, Hitchin, Hertfordshire SG5 1JW	are our forte – with a practice geared	T	3
Tel: 01462 458711	to the business community.	P	5
Email: simon.cousins@foremanlaws.co.uk		TS	35
Apply to: Mr Simon Cousins		WP	no

V = Vacancies / **T** = Trainees / **P** = Partners / **TS** = Total Staff / **WP** = Work Placement

Howes Percival LLP

Nene House, 4 Rushmills, Northampton NN4 7YB
Tel: 0160 423 0400
Email: katy.tebbutt@howespercival.com
Web: www.howespercival.com
🐦 howespercival

The firm Howes Percival LLP is a leading commercial law firm with offices in Cambridge, Leicester, Manchester, Milton Keynes, Northampton and Norwich. Our working environment is progressive and highly professional, and our corporate structure means that fee earners are rewarded on merit and can progress to associate or partner status quickly.

Types of work The firm is a recognised market leader in corporate and commercial, commercial property, planning, employment, commercial and property litigation, construction, IP/IT, insolvency, regulatory, family and private client, among other things.

The top quality work we do means that we are instructed by major companies. We were shortlisted for Regional Law Firm of the Year 2016 in *The Lawyer* awards which recognises our ambitious strategy for growth over the past two years, which has seen us modernise and improve every aspect of our business.

Who should apply Well-educated, focused, enthusiastic, commercially aware graduates with a minimum 2.1 degree in any discipline. We welcome confident communicators with strong interpersonal skills who share our desire to be the best.

Training programme Trainees usually complete four six-month seats. They report direct to a partner or director and after three months and again towards the end of each seat will be formally assessed by the fee earner training them. Trainees will be given every assistance by the fee-earners in their department to develop quickly, and will be given responsibility as soon as they are ready.

Staff benefit from a flexible benefits package, including contributory pension and private medical insurance.

When and how to apply The closing date for training applications in 2020 is 13 July 2018. Our application form is online and can be found on the graduate page of our website.

Work placements These are available in June and July. Please apply via the online application form found on the graduate page of our website.

Sponsorship GDL and LPC up to a cap. Details available upon request.

Vacancies	8
Trainees	13
Partners	43
Total staff	229

Work placement   yes

Training contract deadline
13 July 2018

Apply
Online

Minimum qualifications
2.1 degree

Sponsorship
GDL/LPC

Offices
Cambridge, Leicester, Manchester, Milton Keynes, Northampton, Norwich

Remember to cite *The Training Contract & Pupillage Handbook* on your application form if you apply to this firm.

TRAINING CONTRACT DIRECTORY   367

HSR LAW The Law Chambers, 7/8 South Parade, Doncaster, South Yorkshire DN1 2ED **Tel:** 01302 347800 **Email:** richard.allwood@hsrlaw.co.uk **Apply to:** Mr Richard Allwood	Three offices organised in five teams: civil litigation/PI; family (franchised); private client; crime(franchised); business/agriculture; and property and corporate.	V 0 T 1 P 7 TS 42 WP no
HUGH JAMES Hodge House, 114-116 St Mary Street, Cardiff CF10 1DY **Tel:** 029 20224871 **Email:** diane.brooks@hughjames.com **Apply to:** Mrs Diane Brooks	Hugh James is a top 100 and Wales' largest regional law firm. For any additional information please contact Diane Brooks, HR director.	V 10 T 20 P 62 TS 690 WP yes
HUGHES PADDISON 10 Royal Crescent, Cheltenham GL50 3DA **Tel:** 01242 574244 **Email:** info@hughes-paddison.co.uk **Apply to:** Mrs Jane Brothwood	Medium-sized high street practice providing services across the board including family, private client, residential conveyancing, commercial property, civil litigation, business law and commercial disputes.	V 2 T 4 P 8 TS 50 WP no
HUMPHREYS & CO 14 King Street, Bristol BS1 4EF **Tel:** 0117 929 2662 **Email:** lawyers@humphreys.co.uk **Apply to:** Ms Amanda Weaver	Central Bristol niche practice. Commercial: intellectual property; employment; litigation; company/ commercial; property. Private client: planning, residential property; defamation; professional negligence; asbestos litigation.	V 1-2 T 3 P 4 TS 35 WP yes
HUMPHRIES KIRK LLP Glebe House, North Street, Wareham, Dorset BH20 4AN **Tel:** 01929 552141 **Email:** m.knight@hklaw.eu **Apply to:** Mrs Melanie Knight	Specialised practice offering family, conveyancing, private client, PI, IP, construction, commercial litigation, company/commercial and commercial property work from offices in Dorset, London and Europe.	V 1[19] T 3 P 20 TS 180 WP yes
HUNT AND COOMBS SOLICITORS 35 Thorpe Road, Peterborough PE3 6AG **Tel:** 01733 882800 **Email:** andrew.cave@hcsolicitors.co.uk **Apply to:** Mr Andrew Cave	General practice firm with specialities in family, property, probate, crime and dispute resolution. Has legal aid franchises, Lexcel and IIP. Committed to IT solutions and training.	V 2 T 0 P 8 TS 85 WP no
HUNTERS 9 New Square, Lincoln's Inn, London WC2A 3QN **Tel:** 020 7412 0050 **Email:** trainingcontracts@hunters-solicitors.co.uk **Apply to:** The Training Principal	Traditionally known for private client, charity and matrimonial work. Now a broadly based Lincoln's Inn practice with a significant presence in other fields.	V 1-2 T 4 P 28 TS 71 WP yes
HUTTONS 16 St Andrew's Crescent, Cardiff CF10 3DD **Tel:** 029 20378621 **Email:** stuart.hutton@huttons-solicitors.co.uk **Apply to:** Ms C Strowbridge	We are niche litigation practice covering clinical negligence, commercial litigation, contentious probate, criminal and family law and some non contentious property, trusts and corporate work.	V 0 T 1 P 3 TS 25 WP yes

V = Vacancies / **T** = Trainees / **P** = Partners / **TS** = Total Staff / **WP** = Work Placement

IBB Solicitors

Capital Court, 30 Windsor Street, Uxbridge UB8 1AB
Tel: 0345 638 1381
Email: lydia.bayly@ibblaw.co.uk
Web: www.ibblaw.co.uk
🐦 ibb_solicitors

The firm IBB Solicitors is a distinctly different, award-winning regional law firm that prioritises the needs of its clients beyond everything else. We have a stellar reputation for delivering exceptional legal services across all our legal specialisms and pride ourselves not only on the high-quality, complex legal work we provide, but on the positive contributions we make to our community. We can trace the firm's history back to 1774 and we continue to innovate and adapt to the changing legal environment, constantly finding ways to be better. Our strength lies in the diversity of our committed and caring people.

Types of work IBB's practice areas are divided into four groups – real estate, community legal services, commercial services and private client. Each group comprises teams focused on different niche specialisms championed by leaders in their fields. Clients include UK subsidiaries of large multinationals, SME's, residential developers, high-net worth individuals, charitable organisations, and community bodies, many of which are household names.

Who should apply IBB looks for talented individuals who are confident, resilient, dynamic, self-motivated, and aspirational, with strong academic credentials and commercial awareness. At IBB, you will have access to interesting, high-quality work, a supportive environment and be given early responsibility and client exposure. Both offices are open plan, creating a collaborative, engaging and non-hierarchical environment in which learning and development are actively encouraged and supported. We are an ambitious firm with a clear vision to be the best and we are looking for candidates who feel the same. If you are bold, personable and can demonstrate a commitment to succeeding in the legal profession by consistent academic and vocational achievements, we welcome your application.

Training programme Training at IBB begins with a comprehensive induction that lays the foundations for success. Our training programme typically comprises of six-monthly placements, at either of our Uxbridge and Chesham offices, on a rotation basis driven by business needs, and range from commercial property, commercial services and private client. In each seat you will be supported by a senior solicitor who will act as guide and mentor, ensuring that you have the necessary exposure and support to develop you for your future career. IBB encourages trainees to take ownership of their period of recognised training (PORT) contracts by chairing quarterly trainee meetings with the trainee principal and human resources and making insightful recommendations on process improvements and training. In-house training seminars covering a range of topics are offered throughout the PORT enabling continuing development. Open communication is encouraged to ensure all trainees feel valued and listened to. From the start of their PORT, trainees will experience hands-on responsibility and involvement in complex legal work, marketing and client contact, differentiating a training contract at IBB from our City comparatives. Trainee engagement in business development activity and wider community initiatives is encouraged.

When and how to apply Applications for training contracts to commence in September 2020 should be made online at www.apply4law.com/ibb. Applications are accepted between 1 October 2017 and 31 July 2018. The selection process involves an assessment centre in Autumn 2018. Details on the structure of the assessment centre can be found on the trainee recruitment page of our website. Please note that direct applications and CVs are not accepted.

Vacancies	4
Trainees	8
Partners	28
Total staff	191

Training contract deadline
31 July 2018

Apply
Online

Offices
Chesham, Uxbridge

IBBsolicitors

Ince & Co LLP

Aldgate Tower, 2 Leman Street, London E1 8QN
Tel: 020 7481 0010
Email: graduate.recruitment@incelaw.com
Web: incegraduates.com
f incelaw 🐦 incelaw

The firm With over 140 years of experience, we're one of the oldest law firms in the City. We are a growing firm, boasting 13 offices worldwide, with our most recent office opening in Marseille in February 2017. The firm is continuing to develop, with a 16% year-on-year increase in turnover in 2016-2017 and 100% of our trainees being offered an NQ position on qualification.

Our success is built upon always taking a collaborative and innovative approach by looking for new ways to apply legal strategies and create new law. While our international presence and world leading reputation was initially built on shipping and insurance, we have successfully explored new territory and established our expertise across a number of specific industries.

We've invested heavily in new IT and infrastructure, supporting agile working and relocating to modern offices in Hong Kong and London, with employees now working from Surface Pro 4s. Ince regularly hosts client events throughout the year in our dedicated client suites, including annual shipping and insurance parties. Ince also hosts events internally, including the annual black tie May ball and monthly 'Ince drinks', which is a great opportunity to get to know people from across the firm.

Types of work Ince has five core business groups: aviation, energy, insurance and reinsurance, international trade and shipping. Within these five sectors we have a broad range of expertise including; EU law, competition and regulation, commercial disputes, insolvency and cooperate recovery, emergency response, ports and maritime infrastructure. Our corporate and finance practice has grown significantly in recent years, and the firm has developed a strong transactional business to complement our dispute resolution work.Clients range from insurers, brokers and banks to oil and shipping companies, airlines, aircraft manufacturers, entrepreneurs and major international trading groups.

Who should apply Academically you'll need a 2.1 and AAB at A level. We recruit a mix of law and non-law graduates from a wide range of backgrounds. You will be self-motivated and able to juggle competing priorities and take a proactive approach to your training. Naturally the ability to understand the law and apply or challenge it in real-time fast moving situations is essential.

Training programme Ince sees things differently with around 70% of our partners having trained with us. We not only regard our trainees as future solicitors and potential partners, but our training programme is different too. With us you'll get involved with real legal work from day one, with flexibility to work across different departments and retain a portion of your cases as you progress through your training.

When and how to apply Online via incegraduates.com. We will be accepting applications between 1 December 2017 and 31 January 2018 for our 2018 trainee recruitment placement scheme, and between 1 February 2018 and 31 July 2018 for our 2020 trainee intake.

Work placements Running during the Easter period, our two-week trainee recruitment placement scheme (TRPS) gives you a practical insight into life as an Ince trainee. We welcome a maximum of five people on the TRPS at any one time so that we can give you all the support you need. You'll also work on real cases – which may involve attending court and hearings, meeting clients, drafting correspondence or doing legal research.

Vacancies	10
Trainees	20
Partners	100
Total staff	550

Work placement yes
(see Insider Report on p75)

Training contract deadline
31 July 2018

Apply
Online

Starting salary
1st year – £37,750
2nd year – £41,800

Sponsorship
GDL/LPC

Offices
Beijing, Cologne, Dubai, Hamburg, Hong Kong, Le Havre, London, Marseille,Monaco, Paris, Piraeus, Shanghai, Singapore

INCE & CO

IKIE SOLICITORS LLP 20 Marischal Road, Lewisham, London SE13 5LG **Tel:** 020 8463 0808 **Email:** ikiesolicitors@aol.com **Apply to:** Mr A N Ikie	Small firm with services offered in high street general practices. Applicants must have a minimum 2.1 degree.	V 0 T 2 P 2 TS 5 WP no
INGHAMS 32-38 North Albert Street, Fleetwood FY7 6AW **Tel:** 01253 873481 **Email:** enquiries@inghams-law.co.uk **Apply to:** HR Department	A general high street practice, with four offices across the Fylde Coast in Lancashire, undertaking a broad range of legal work, including publicly funded.	V Poss T 1 P 7 TS 43 WP yes
IRENA SPENCE & CO 68-70 Castle Street, Cambridge CB3 0AJ **Tel:** 01223 713300 **Email:** mail@irenaspence.co.uk **Apply to:** Mrs Irena Spence	Small-medium general practice with two offices in the city of Cambridge and surrounding villages. Caseload is litigation and property mix particularly family, employment and personal injury.	V 1 T 2 P 4 TS 24 WP yes
IRWIN MITCHELL Riverside East, 2 Millsands, Sheffield S3 8DT **Tel:** 0370 1500 100 **Email:** graduaterecruitment@irwinmitchell.com **Apply to:** Mrs Nicola Stanley	A national, full service law firm that prides itself on 'exceeding the expectations of every client' from private individuals, right through to multinational corporations.	V 45 T 108 P 269 TS 2700 WP yes
JACKSON LEES GROUP 44/45 Hamilton Square, Birkenhead CH41 5AR **Tel:** 0151 647 9381 **Email:** recruitment@lees.co.uk **Apply to:** Mrs Joanna Kingston-Davies	Business and property, dispute resolution, personal injury, clinical negligence, court of protection, family, wills/estates. Lexcel, Investors in People. Offices: Birkenhead, Heswall, West Kirby.	V 0 T 0 P 5 TS 100 WP no
JACKSONS LAW FIRM 17 Falcon Court, Preston Farm Industrial Estate, Stockton-on-Tees TS18 3TU **Tel:** 01642 356500 **Email:** recruitment@jacksons-law.com **Apply to:** Ms Adrienne Patterson	Jacksons' philosophy is based upon a modern approach to business, incorporating the most up to date information technology and a commercial style management structure.	V 2 T 4 P 11 TS 70 WP no
JACOBS & REEVES 153 High Street, Poole, Dorset BH15 1AU **Tel:** 01202 674425 **Email:** jsingleton@jacobsreeves.co.uk **Apply to:** Ms Janice Singleton	Well-established firm with three offices in Poole and Wimborne. Strong client base covering most areas of general practice, commercial, private client and litigation.	V 0 T 1 P 6 TS 45 WP no
JAMES MURRAY SOLICITORS 41 Merton Road, Bootle, Liverpool L20 7AP **Tel:** 0151 933 3333 **Email:** info@jamesmurray.law.co.uk **Apply to:** Ms J Thomas	We offer training contracts on merit to in-house paralegals usually within one year. Vacancies arise through expansion and CVs received are kept on file.	V 0 T 6 P 4 TS 68 WP no

V = Vacancies / **T** = Trainees / **P** = Partners / **TS** = Total Staff / **WP** = Work Placement

JAY VADHER & CO 185 Romford Road, London E15 4JF **Tel:** 020 8519 3000 **Apply to:** Mr BND Vadher	High street firm with litigation and conveyancing departments. CLS franchises.	V 1 T 1 P 3 TS 8 WP no
JEFFREY GREEN RUSSELL LIMITED Waverly House, 7-10 Noel Street, London W1F 8GQ **Tel:** 020 7339 7000 **Email:** humanresources@jgrlaw.co.uk **Apply to:** Human Resources Manager	Jeffrey Green Russell is a medium-sized commercial West End practice with a diverse client base specialising in company/commercial, litigation, property, gaming, licensing and leisure, and private client.	V 2 T 4 P 21 TS 76 WP no
JEREMY ROBERTS & CO 51 Park Road, Peterborough PE1 2TH **Tel:** 01733 343943 **Email:** jeremyroberts.co@btconnect.com **Apply to:** Mr J Roberts	A small, friendly, high street solicitors in Peterborough specialising in family, criminal, employment, accident and general litigation with some conveyancing and general work.	V 1 T 0 P 1 TS 8 WP yes
JH POWELL & CO Cathedral Chambers, 2 Amen Alley, Derby DE1 3GT **Tel:** 01332 372211 **Email:** djt@jhpowell.co.uk **Apply to:** Mr David Tomlinson	City centre commercial and private client practice.	V 0 T 2 P 6 TS 20 WP no
JMW SOLICITORS No 1 Byrom Place, Manchester M3 3HG **Tel:** 0161 832 8087 **Email:** trainee@jmw.co.uk **Apply to:** Mr Richard Powell	Main work areas are personal injury, clinical negligence, commercial property, corporate, insolvency, commercial litigation, intellectual property, employment, family, sports and media, crime and private client.	V Approx 10 T 10 P 35 TS 380 WP no
JNP LEGAL 15 Glebeland Street, Merthyr Tydfil CF47 8AU **Tel:** 01685 350421 **Email:** law@jnplegal.org **Apply to:** Mr Antony Williams	Busy high street practice providing a first class service, combining excellent client care and modern practices.	V 2[18] T 1 P 4 TS 32 WP no
JOELSON JD LLP 30 Portland Place, London W1B 1LZ **Tel:** 020 7580 5721 **Email:** training@joelsonlaw.com **Apply to:** Mr Niall McCann	Founded in 1957, we undertake company/commercial, gambling/liquor licensing, litigation, property, private client, employment, immigration, IP and international work for commercial clients.	V 4[18] T 5 P 14 TS 80 WP no
JOHAR & CO Beckville House, 66 London Road, Leicester LE2 OQD **Tel:** 0116 2543345 **Email:** deepakjohar@johars.com **Apply to:** Mr DK Johar	Franchised firm with IIP. General high street practice dealing with conveyancing, litigation, matrimonial, PI and immigration; clients both corporate and individual.	V 1 T 3 P 2 TS 25 WP no

V = Vacancies / **T** = Trainees / **P** = Partners / **TS** = Total Staff / **WP** = Work Placement

Jones Day

21 Tudor Street, London EC4Y 0DJ
Tel: 020 7039 5959
Email: recruit.london@jonesday.com
Web: www.jonesdaylondon.com
f jonesdaygraduatesuk **𝕏** jonesday

The firm Jones Day is a truly global law firm – probably the most integrated in the world. Our 2,500 lawyers across 43 locations in major business and finance centres worldwide have vast transactional and contentious experience and are at the forefront of globalisation and the advancement of the rule of law. Our strengths in London reflect those of the firm: our 200 London lawyers (including around 60 partners and 40 trainees) have a sophisticated understanding of risk and draw on specialist insights and skills from across the globe to guide clients through their toughest challenges.

Types of work In London's critical financial centre, our lawyers are perfectly placed to address the most demanding and complex global matters: including cross-border M&A; real estate and finance transactions (including banking, capital markets, investment funds, private equity and structured finance); global disputes; and regulatory matters involving the UK, US and other authorities. Additional specialist areas include business restructuring; competition/antitrust; corporate criminal investigations; corporate tax planning; employment and pensions; intellectual property; and projects and infrastructure.

Who should apply We recruit people who are committed to a legal career and want to become partners of the future. Around half our London partners trained with the firm. Successful candidates have either a law or non-law degree; strong intellectual ability; good communication skills; and demonstrate resourcefulness, drive and dedication. 70% of our current trainees are non-law graduates and 35% were graduates or postgraduates when they applied to us.

Training programme The firm operates a distinctive, non-rotational training system, designed to provide flexibility and responsibility from the start. Our trainees work across different practice areas at the same time and are encouraged to assume their own workload. This allows for a high level of client contact, faster development of potential and the opportunity to compare and contrast different disciplines alongside one another. As our trainees do not move to a different department every six months they don't miss the end of deals or trials that they have worked on. Work will vary from small cases which trainees may handle alone (under the supervision of a senior lawyer) to matters where they will assist a partner or an associate solicitor. The firm runs a structured seminar programme to support the practical teaching trainees receive from lawyers with whom they work.

When and how to apply Apply for a placement if you want to train at Jones Day. We expect to recruit our trainees from our placement candidates. All our placement schemes are open to final-year law and non-law students, graduates and postgraduates; our placement schemes are also open to penultimate-year students undertaking a qualifying law degree. Applications open on 1 September 2017. We recruit on a rolling basis, so cannot guarantee availability. Early applications are always advised. Final deadlines are 27 October 2017 (winter scheme); 15 December 2017 (spring scheme) and 10 January 2018 (summer scheme).

Work placements 72 places for two-week placements in winter, spring and summer holidays. Attendees experience work in a truly global law firm and see how our non-rotational training system works in practice by taking on real work from a variety of practice areas. They are also able to meet a range of lawyers at various social events. We pay an allowance of £400 per week.

Sponsorship GDL and LPC fees paid and £9,000 maintenance per year. Fast track LPC for sponsored students from August to end February each year with six-month gap before commencing training.

Vacancies	20
Trainees	40 approx
Partners	60 approx
Total staff	350 approx

Work placement yes
(see Insider Report on p79)

Training contract deadline
10 January 2018

Apply to
Graduate Recruitment Manager

Starting salary
£47,000 (2017)

Minimum qualifications
2.1 degree and ideally AAA at A level/36 points for international baccalaureate (or equivalent)

Sponsorship
GDL and LPC

Offices
London, Continental Europe, Asia, United States, Latin America, Middle East, Asia Pacific

Firm	Description	V	T	P	TS	WP
JOHN CHAPMAN AND CO 152-154 Epsom Road, Sutton SM3 9EU **Tel:** 020 8337 3801 **Apply to:** Mr Andrew Larner	Conveyancing, wills and probate, litigation – personal injury, matrimonial, children. There are no vacancies at present.	0	0	4	22	no
JOHN HODGE SOLICITORS 10/11 Morston Court, Aisecome Way, Weston-Super-Mare BS22 8NG **Tel:** 01934 410910 **Email:** jane.banks@johnhodge.co.uk **Apply to:** Mrs Jane Banks	Well-established general practice. Training offered in family law, personal injury, conveyancing, dispute resolution and probate.	0	0	4	65	yes
JOHNS & SAGGAR LLP 34-36 Grays Inn Road, London WC1X 8HR **Tel:** 020 3490 1475 **Email:** info@johnsandsaggar.co.uk **Apply to:** Mr Khalid Sofi	Our specialist team are able to deal with a wide range of legal services to individuals, businesses and organisations.	0	0	2	13	yes
THE JOHNSON PARTNERSHIP Cannon Courtyard, Long Row, Nottingham NG1 6JE **Tel:** 0115 941 9141 **Email:** mail@thejohnsonpartnership.co.uk **Apply to:** Mr Bill Soughton	Criminal work. Vacancies start as work experience and possibly lead onto training contracts.	1-2	4	13	110	yes
JORDANS Neil Jordan House, Wellington Road, Dewsbury, West Yorkshire WF13 1HL **Tel:** 01924 457 171 **Email:** recruitment@jordanssolicitors.co.uk **Apply to:** Mrs S Taylor	An independent, medium-sized practice serving both the business community and private individuals across a broad range of specialisms.	2[19]	8	4	65	no
JOSEPH HILL & CO 220-224, High Road, Tottenham N14 4AJ **Tel:** 020 8880 3535 **Email:** josephhillsols@yahoo.co.uk **Apply to:** Mr Phaedon Georgiou	Large criminal law practice requires dedicated and ambitious candidates. Successful applicants will gain experience in serious and complex cases and undertake police station accreditation.	4[18]	4	2	13	yes
JOVES SOLICITORS 312 Lewisham Road, London SE13 7PA **Tel:** 020 8852 4544 **Apply to:** Mr AA Ekwekwu	Friendly firm specialising in immigration, employment and civil litigation and contracts.	0	1	-	3	yes
JUDGE & PRIESTLEY LLP Justin House, 6 West Street, Bromley BR1 1JN **Tel:** 020 8290 7406 **Email:** gcollier@judge-priestley.co.uk **Apply to:** Ms Lucy El-Aawar	J&P are a leading firm in North Kent providing expert, professional and friendly advice to individuals and businesses in every major industry sector.	1	2	11	130	no

V = Vacancies / **T** = Trainees / **P** = Partners / **TS** = Total Staff / **WP** = Work Placement

K&L Gates LLP

One New Change, London EC4M 9AF
Tel: 020 7648 9000
Email: traineerecruitment@klgates.com
Web: www.klgates.com
🐦 klgates

The firm K&L Gates LLP comprises approximately 2,000 lawyers who practise in fully integrated offices located on five continents. K&L Gates represents leading global corporations, growth and middle-market companies, capital markets participants and entrepreneurs in every major industry group as well as public sector entities, educational institutions, philanthropic organisations and individuals. Our practice is a robust full market practice – cutting edge, complex and dynamic, at once regional, national and international in scope. Over each of the last six years our revenues exceeded $1 billion.

Types of work K&L Gates is active in the areas of corporate/M&A, debt capital markets, private equity, restructuring and insolvency, banking and asset finance, structured finance, derivatives, aviation, funds, antitrust, competition and trade regulation, public policy, real estate, planning and environment, intellectual property, media and sport, construction, energy, infrastructure and resources, insurance coverage, regulatory, tax, employment, litigation, international arbitration, investigations, enforcement and white collar crime plus other forms of dispute resolution.

Who should apply The firm welcomes applications from both law and non-law students. The firm also welcomes applications from relevant postgraduates. You should be highly motivated, intellectually curious, with an interest in commercial law and be looking for comprehensive training.

Training programme The firm ensures each trainee is given exceptional opportunities to learn, experience and develop so that they can achieve their maximum potential. Trainees spend six-month seats in four of the areas mentioned above. Each trainee sits with a supervisor and is allocated an individual mentor to ensure all round supervision and training. The firm has a thorough induction scheme and career development programme. High importance is placed on the acquisition of business and professional skills, with considerable emphasis on client contact and early responsibility. The training programme consists of weekly legal education seminars, workshops and a full programme of skills electives. Pro bono and corporate social responsibility activities are also encouraged.

When and how to apply Apply between 1 November 2017 and 31 July 2018 to begin in September 2020.

Work placements The firm's formal summer legal work placement scheme is open to law and non-law students and other relevant postgraduates. Your two weeks with us in July will provide you with broad exposure to opportunities in diverse areas. We aim to give you a seat in at least two departments, and wherever possible we will allocate you to a seat of your choice.

Sponsorship GDL funding: fees paid plus £5,000 maintenance grant.
LPC funding: fees paid plus £7,000 maintenance grant.

Vacancies	TBD
Trainees	17
Partners	55
Total staff	244

Work placement yes

Training contract deadline
31 July 2018

Apply to
Hayley Atherton

Minimum qualifications
2.1 degree

Sponsorship
GDL/LPC

Offices
Austin, Beijing, Berlin, Boston, Brisbane, Brussels, Charleston, Charlotte, Chicago, Dallas, Doha, Dubai, Fort Worth, Frankfurt, Harrisburg, Hong Kong, Houston, London, Los Angeles, Melbourne, Miami, Milan, Munich, Newark, New York, Orange County, Palo Alto, Paris, Perth, Pittsburgh, Portland, Raleigh, Research Triangle Park, San Francisco, São Paulo, Seattle, Seoul, Shanghai, Singapore, Sydney, Taipei, Tokyo, Warsaw, Washington DC, Wilmington

Firm	Description		

JW HUGHES & CO
Bank House, Lancaster Square, Conwy, Gwynedd LL32 8AD
Tel: 01492 593442
Apply to: Mr DC Roberts

Established and busy general practice with well appointed offices in Conwy and Llandudno. Departmental structure dealing with areas of law in which the firm specialises.

V	0
T	1
P	6
TS	34
WP	no

JWK SOLICITORS
19 Northumberland Street, Morecambe LA4 4AZ
Tel: 01524 416960
Apply to: Mr D Harrison

A multi-discipline practice comprising three offices: Morecambe; Lancaster; and Great Eccleston. Supported by IT for the future. Broad commercial private/legal aid client base.

V	0
T	0
P	5
TS	34
WP	no

K J COMMONS & CO
2-6 Upper Jane Street, Workington, Cumbria CA14 4AY
Tel: 01900 604 698
Email: helen.mcneil@kjcommons.co.uk
Apply to: Ms Helen McNeil

Franchised firm in crime, family, PI and clinical negligence. Large criminal practice. Other areas covered – conveyancing and wills. Offices also in Carlisle and Whitehaven.

V	Poss
T	3
P	2
TS	55
WP	no

KAIM TODNER SOLICITORS LTD
11 Bolt Court, London EC4A 3DQ
Tel: 020 7353 6660
Email: recruitment@kaimtodner.com
Apply to: Ms Edina Balogh

V	0
T	4
P	8
TS	70
WP	no

KANGS SOLICITORS
2a Wake Green Road, Birmingham B13 9EZ
Tel: 0121 449 9888
Email: enquiries@kangssolicitors.co.uk
Apply to: Mr H Kang

Niche criminal firm specialising in white collar crime/serious fraud work. Member of LSC specialist fraud panel.

V	1-2[19]
T	1
P	1
TS	10
WP	no

KC LAW CHAMBERS SOLICITORS
Unit B2, 62 Beechwood Road, London E8 3DY
Tel: 020 7254 3353
Email: info@kclawchambers.com
Apply to: Ms Roma Aheer

We are a firm of solicitors based in London, providing a wide range of legal service, with emphasis on personal injury, immigration employment and intellectual property law.

V	2[18]
T	0
P	2
TS	5
WP	yes

THE KEITH JONES PARTNERSHIP
First Floor Birkenhead House, 17-21 Price Street, Birkenhead, Merseyside CH41 6JN
Tel: 0151 650 6830
Email: info@kjplaw.co.uk
Apply to: Mrs Karen Doleman

We are a niche firm who specialise in commercial litigation and general commercial matters.

V	0
T	1
P	3
TS	15
WP	yes

KENNARD WELLS SOLICITORS
84a High Street, Epping, Essex CM16 4AE
Tel: 01992 570505
Apply to: Mr Richard Cohen

General family based practice with wide ranged private client work and legal aid franchises.

V	1
T	1
P	5
TS	35
WP	no

V = Vacancies / **T** = Trainees / **P** = Partners / **TS** = Total Staff / **WP** = Work Placement

Kennedys

25 Fenchurch Avenue, London EC3M 5AD
Tel: 020 7667 9667
Email: hradmin@kennedyslaw.com
Web: www.kennedyslaw.com
f kennedystrainees

The firm Kennedys is a top 30 international legal firm with unrivalled expertise in litigation and dispute resolution, particularly in the insurance/ reinsurance and liability industries. The firm has over 1,700 people in 11 countries across the world. We also have an active network of 32 offices across the world.

From an initial base in the City of London, we have grown a network of 10 offices in Belfast, Birmingham, Cambridge, Chelmsford, Edinburgh, Glasgow, Manchester, Sheffield and Taunton. Our UK staff are proud to be part of Kennedys' growing international network that is well resourced to help clients handle and resolve cases all around the world.

Kennedys is here to provide answers, recommendations, strategy and tactics. We deliver these in plain English and it's what we call: Legal advice in black and white.

We deeply value the relationships we build with our clients and we know that they value our warm, friendly, human approach.

Types of work Our specialist lawyers are passionate about resolving disputes and claims in the most complex industry sectors including insurance/reinsurance, healthcare, construction, transport, shipping, public sector and international trade.

Who should apply We offer a vibrant and supportive working environment built upon our core values; we are approachable and responsive, we show respect for people, we are trustworthy and straightforward and we ensure that we deliver economic solutions for our clients. Our trainees experience early responsibility and client contact as we find that this produces excellent solicitors capable of running their own caseload once they qualify. We therefore recruit graduates who are confident, articulate and sociable, who are team players, self-aware and resourceful.

Training programme The purpose of the training contract is to give trainees a mix of experience and skills that will set you up in a legal career as a solicitor with Kennedys. Our ability to consistently offer the majority of trainees positions on qualification is attributable to producing newly qualified lawyers who are competent, confident and commercially driven. A balance of work experience, responsibility, supervision and formal training achieves this. We ensure that our trainee solicitors are given a sound training in the core disciplines. We have an open-door policy, and partners and supervisors are readily accessible.

When and how to apply Applications for our 2020 training contracts open on the 1 May 2018 and will close on the 31 December 2018. Applications for our 2019 winter vacation scheme will also open on the 1 May 2018 and close on the 30 September 2018.

Vacancies	16
Trainees	41
Partners	245
Total staff	1,700

Work placement yes

Training contract deadline
31 December 2018

Apply
Online via our website
www.kennedyslaw.com

Starting salary
£36,000 (London)
£26,000 (regional)

Minimum qualifications
2.1 degree, any discipline, 300 UCAS points or equivalent at A level

Offices
Belfast, Birmingham, Cambridge, Chelmsford, Edinburgh, Glasgow, London, Manchester, Sheffield, Taunton, Auckland, Bogota, Brussels, Copenhagen, Dubai, Dublin, Hong Kong, Lima, Lisbon, Madrid, Mexico City, Miami, Moscow, Santiago, São Paulo, Singapore, Sydney, Basking Ridge, New York, Austin, Philadelphia, Chicago

Kennedys

Kingsley Napley LLP

Knights Quarter, 14 St Johns Lane, London EC1M 4AJ
Tel: 020 7814 1200
Email: recruitment@kingsleynapley.co.uk
Web: www.kingsleynapley.co.uk
🐦 kingsleynapley

The firm We are a central London law firm advising nationally and internationally based clients covering a wide range of specialist areas from family and criminal to corporate and property work. Our wide range of expertise means that we can provide support for our clients in all areas of their business and private lives. Our reputation is strong, many of our lawyers are leaders in their field and our practice areas are highly ranked by the legal directories. We are known for combining creative solutions with pragmatism and a friendly sensitive approach, where the relationship between lawyer and client is key. We look for exceptional people with a wide range of skills to provide the breadth of service our clients require. In return, we offer a culture of individual responsibility, autonomy and development.

Types of work Criminal litigation, dispute resolution, clinical negligence and PI, employment, family and divorce, immigration, private client, company and commercial, real estate, public law and regulatory and professional discipline.

Who should apply Applications are welcomed from both legal and non-legal graduates who have a strong academic background (achieved a 2.1 degree). A trainee will need to demonstrate commercial awareness, motivation and enthusiasm. To be successful you will need excellent communication skills with the ability to be a creative, practical problem solver. We look for team players who bring something to the table and have a long-term interest in Kingsley Napley and the areas of legal practice it focuses on. Successful short-listed candidates will be asked to attend an assessment centre and partner interview as part of the selection process.

Training programme You will not be a bag carrier as a trainee at Kingsley Napley. By choosing to start your career with us you will be given meaningful and good quality experience working alongside and being supervised by highly experienced lawyers, who are specialists in their legal field. Trainees complete four six-month seats, providing a wide range of practical experience and skills in contentious and non-contentious work. The training programme is broader than most other firms due to the wide ranging areas of law practised here. Individual preference for seats is sought and will be balanced with the firm's needs. Trainees work closely with partners and solicitors in a supportive team structure, and have regular reviews to assist development. The firm maintains a friendly and open environment and it is the firm's policy that each trainee sits with a partner or senior solicitor while working for a department as a whole. The firm gives trainees the chance to meet clients, be responsible for their own work and join in marketing and client development activities.

When and how to apply Individuals are invited to apply from October 2017 with a closing date of 31 May 2018. A link to the online application form can be found on our website. For queries relating to training contracts at Kingsley Napley please email Vicki Tavener at vtavener@kingsleynapley.co.uk.

Work placements Kingsley Napley offer a limited number of one-week legal work placements during March to September each year. Work experience students have an opportunity to experience a number of aspects of life in a law firm, for example: general administration, library research and shadowing our qualified solicitors. To apply, a CV and covering letter should be submitted in the work experience section of our website www.kingsleynapley.co.uk/careers/work-experience.

Vacancies	6
Trainees	13
Partners	52
Total staff	352

Work placement yes

Training contract deadline
31 May 2018

Apply
Online

Minimum qualifications
2.1 degree

Offices
London

Kirkland & Ellis International LLP

30 St Mary Axe, London EC3A 8AF
Tel: 020 7469 2000
Web: ukgraduate.kirkland.com

The firm Kirkland & Ellis International LLP is a leading international law firm with approximately 1,900 lawyers representing global clients.

Types of work Corporate: Kirkland has one of the most active and highly regarded private equity practices encompassing all aspects of this rapidly changing field.

Finance: Kirkland's leading finance practice includes the representation of both borrowers and lenders in a wide variety of transactions.

Investment funds: Kirkland is uniquely positioned to serve its clients in connection with the organisation and operation of private equity, real estate and hedge funds.

Financial services regulatory: Kirkland advises clients of the firm that are regulated by the UK Regulator, the US Regulator or both.

Tax: Kirkland has a strong international reputation for providing sophisticated tax counselling and effectively representing clients in tax disputes worldwide.

Restructuring: Kirkland has earned a distinguished international reputation acting for a varied range of clients in complex corporate restructuring, work-out and bankruptcy planning, negotiation and litigation.

International arbitration and litigation: Kirkland represents multinational corporations, governments and government-owned entities in international arbitration and litigation cases around the world.

Technology and IP transactions: Kirkland represents clients in all areas of IP, patent litigation, trademark matters, outsourcing, computer software, licensing, distribution, joint venture agreements, biotechnology, data protection and e-commerce issues.

Antitrust/competition: Kirkland's antitrust and competition practice has decades of experience in litigation and transaction clearance.

Capital markets: Kirkland represents issuers, sponsors and underwriters in a wide variety of international securities transactions, with a particular focus on offerings of high-yield and other complex debt securities.

Who should apply Successful candidates will have a strong academic record and be motivated to work hard in a professional, friendly and entrepreneurial team.

Training programme You will be given early responsibility to work on complex multi-jurisdictional matters. On the job training is actively supported by an extensive education programme, carefully tailored to meet your needs. Trainees will have the opportunity to apply for an overseas secondment.

When and how to apply Apply online by 7 January 2018 for spring and summer vacation schemes, and by 15 July 2018 for training contracts beginning in September 2020.

Work placements Two-week vacation schemes across the spring and summer.

Sponsorship Full sponsorship of GDL and LPC fees, plus a maintenance grant of £8,000.

Vacancies	10
Trainees	20
Partners	850*
Total staff	3,811*
	* denotes worldwide figure

Work placement yes
(see Insider Report on p81)

Training contract deadline
15 July 2018

Apply to
Emma Ridley

Starting salary
1st year – £50,000
2nd year – £55,000

Minimum qualifications
2.1 degree

Sponsorship
GDL/LPC

Offices
Beijing, Boston, Chicago, Hong Kong, Houston, London, Los Angeles, Munich, New York, Palo Alto, San Francisco, Shanghai, Washington DC

KIRKLAND & ELLIS

Affiliated with
aspiringsolicitors

Remember to cite *The Training Contract & Pupillage Handbook* on your application form if you apply to this firm.

KESAR & CO SOLICITORS 20-25 Market Square, Bromley, Kent BR1 1NA **Tel:** 020 8181 3100 **Email:** recruitment@kesarandcosolicitors.co.uk **Apply to:** Mr Mladen Kesar	Preference may be given to the IAAS accredited candidates.	V T P TS WP	219 - 1 29 yes
KINGSLEY BROOKES Estate Buildings, Railway Street, Huddersfield HD1 1JY **Tel:** 01484 302800 **Email:** practice.manager@kingsleybrookes.co.uk **Apply to:** Mrs Sam Goodall	A specialist criminal litigation firm, set up in 1998 with offices based in Huddersfield.	V T P TS WP	0 0 1 5 no
KINGSLEY SMITH SOLICITORS LLP 81/87/89 High Street, Chatham, Kent ME4 4EE **Tel:** 01634 811118 **Email:** mail@kslaw.co.uk **Apply to:** Mrs Elizabeth Kingsley-Smith	We provide quality legal advice in a full range of legal services to individuals and businesses in the Medway towns and across Kent.	V T P TS WP	0 0 4 20 no
KIRWANS 363 Woodchurch Road, Birkenhead, Merseyside CH42 8PE **Tel:** 0151 608 9078 **Email:** sbirchall@kirwans.co.uk **Apply to:** Mrs Sarah Birchall	Practice covering wills and estates, crime, conveyancing, family, personal injury, general civil, private client, general commercial, housing. LEXEL and Investor in People accreditation.	V T P TS WP	0 4 5 80 no
KITELEYS 7 Stephens Court, 15-17 St Stephens Road, Bournemouth BH2 6LA **Tel:** 01202 299992 **Email:** office@kiteleys.co.uk **Apply to:** Mrs Paula Rose	One of the fastest growing law firms in the South with seven offices across Dorset and Hampshire, each committed to providing the best possible service to a wide range of clients.	V T P TS WP	0 2 4 50 yes
KITSONS LLP Minerva House, Orchard Way, Torquay TQ2 7FA **Tel:** 01803 202020 **Email:** recruitment@kitsons-solicitors.co.uk **Apply to:** Miss Louise Mason	Established 1826. Serves private and commercial clients. Lexcel, investor in people, CQS, resolution, ELA, SFE, STEP, law society's family panel and alternative dispute resolution accredited.	V T P TS WP	Poss[18] 4 16 100 no
KOTECHA & CO 40b Station Road, North Harrow, Harrow, Middlesex HA2 7SE **Tel:** 020 8426 0014 **Email:** info@kotechasolicitors.co.uk **Apply to:** Ms Nayna Kotecha	Small friendly high street practice carrying out property work, wills & probate, matrimonial, landlord and tenant and personal injury.	V T P TS WP	0 1 2 5 yes
KUIT STEINART LEVY 3 St Mary's Parsonage, Manchester M3 2RD **Tel:** 0161 832 3434 **Email:** alisonpearse@kuits.com **Apply to:** Ms Alison Pearse	This UK200-listed Manchester commercial law firm advises and services businesses, their owners and high-net-worth individuals, including SMEs, financial institutions, property investment companies and PLCs.	V T P TS WP	6 13 35 185 yes

V = Vacancies / **T** = Trainees / **P** = Partners / **TS** = Total Staff / **WP** = Work Placement

KUNDERT SOLICITORS LLP 4 The Quadrant, Coventry CV1 2EL **Tel:** 024 7622 7741 **Email:** chris@kundert.co.uk **Apply to:** Mr CJD Jones	General practice, two office locations in the centre of Coventry and at the north of the city. Mixed practice of contentious and non-contentious work.	V 0 T 1 P 4 TS 30 WP yes
LA STEEL Oxford Villa, 123 Dodworth Road, Barnsley, South Yorkshire S70 2EJ **Tel:** 01226 770 909 **Email:** enquiries@lasteelsolicitors.com **Apply to:** Mr LA Steel	Specialists in civil litigation, including personal injury, consumer law and professional and clinical negligence. Referrals solely through satisfied clients. No charge win or lose.	V 0 T 0 P 0 TS 8 WP yes
LACEYS SOLICITORS LLP 5 Poole Road, Bournemouth BH2 5QL **Tel:** 01202 557256 **Email:** info@laceyssolicitors.co.uk **Apply to:** Mr Sam Freeman	A progressive *Legal 500*, Investors in People and Lexcel firm. Strong with both commercial and private clients.	V 2 T 2 P 13 TS 110 WP no
LADERMAN AND CO 4 The Shrubberies, George Lane, London E18 1BD **Tel:** 020 8530 7319 **Apply to:** Mr Daniel C Laderman		V Poss T 2 P 2 TS 13 WP no
LAMPORT BASSITT 46 The Avenue, Southampton SO17 1AX **Tel:** 023 80634931 **Email:** e-mail@lamportbassitt.co.uk **Apply to:** Mr John Newton	The firm does not offer training contracts to external candidates. It recruits candidates as paralegals, and may internally promote these to trainees after one year's employment.	V 0 T 3 P 11 TS 80 WP no
LAND LAW LLP 10-14 Market Street, Altrincham WA14 1QB **Tel:** 0161 928 8383 **Email:** aawprivate@land-law.co.uk **Apply to:** Mr AAF Whyte	Niche commercial property firm.	V 0 T 3 P 6 TS 46 WP no
LANGLEY WELLINGTON LLP SOLICITORS Royal House, 60 Bruton Way, Gloucester GL1 1EP **Tel:** 01452 521286 **Email:** lawyers@langleywellington.co.uk **Apply to:** Miss Helen Stephens	A long-established Gloucester firm, offering a wide range of legal services. Investors in People accredited.	V 0 T - P 8 TS 70 WP no
LANGLEYS SOLICITORS LLP Queens House, Micklegate, York YO1 6WG **Tel:** 01904 610886 **Email:** recruitment@langleys.com **Apply to:** Mrs Jude Lean	Based in Lincoln and York, Langleys is a full-service firm providing legal services in insurance law, commercial law, private law and residential conveyancing.	V 5 T 11 P 34 TS 340 WP yes

V = Vacancies / **T** = Trainees / **P** = Partners / **TS** = Total Staff / **WP** = Work Placement

LANYON BOWDLER SOLICITORS LLP
Chapter House North, Abbey Lawn, Abbey
Foregate, Shrewsbury SY2 5DE
Tel: 01743 280280
Email: colin.spanner@lblaw.co.uk
Apply to: Mr Colin Spanner

General practice. Six Shropshire and
Herefordshire offices. Significant
corporate and commercial, planning,
commercial property and litigation
work. Also specialists in personal
injury and clinical negligence.

V	3[19]
T	8
P	26
TS	220
WP	no

LARCOMES LLP
168 London Road, North End, Portsmouth
PO2 9DN
Tel: 023 9244 8100
Email: enquiries@larcomes.co.uk
Apply to: Mr Julian Quartermain

V	1
T	0
P	6
TS	40
WP	no

LATHAM & WATKINS
99 Bishopsgate, London EC2M 3XF
Tel: 020 7710 1000
Email: londongraduates@lw.com
Apply to: Rosie Buckley

Latham & Watkins is a major
international law firm with an
established London office.

V	24
T	48
P	75
TS	530
WP	yes

LATIMER HINKS
5-8 Priestgate, Darlington DL1 1NL
Tel: 01325 341500
Apply to: Mr Paul Saunders

General long-established practice
providing legal services for
commercial, agricultural and private
clients in Durham, Teesside and
North Yorkshire.

V	Poss
T	2
P	9
TS	51
WP	no

LATIMER LEE
35 Bury New Road, Prestwich, Manchester
M25 9JY
Tel: 0161 798 9000
Email: customerservices@latimerlee.com
Apply to: Mr SR Latimer

Large local firm dedicated in
providing exceptional work.

V	0
T	0
P	-
TS	-
WP	yes

LAWTONS SOLICITORS
19-25 Salisbury Square, Hatfield, Hertfordshire
AL9 5BT
Tel: 01707 270905
Email: stephenhalloran@lawtonslaw.co.uk
Apply to: Mr Stephen Halloran

Leading criminal defence solicitors
covering Bedfordshire, Hertfordshire
and London. We seek individuals
with good academic records and
commitment to criminal work.

V	2[18]
T	2
P	2
TS	25
WP	no

LAYTONS SOLICITORS LLP
2 More London Riverside, London SE1 2AP
Tel: 020 7842 8000
Email: careers@laytons.com
Apply to: Mr John Skelly

Laytons is a commercial law firm
whose primary focus is developing
dynamic business. Practice areas
include: corporate/commercial,
IP and data protection, property/
construction, dispute resolution and
employment.

V	6
T	5
P	29
TS	118
WP	yes

LCF LAW
2 The Embankment, Sovereign Street, Leeds
LS1 4BP
Tel: 0113 244 0876
Email: rspencerrobb@lcf.co.uk
Apply to: Mrs Rachel Spencer Robb

LCF Law has offices in Leeds
Bradford, Harrogate and Ilkley –
focusing on corporate, disputes,
property, personal law. Not all law
firms are created equal.

V	2[18]
T	5
P	21
TS	134
WP	no

V = Vacancies / **T** = Trainees / **P** = Partners / **TS** = Total Staff / **WP** = Work Placement

Lee Bolton Monier-Williams

1 The Sanctuary, Westminster, London SW1P 3JT
Tel: 020 7222 5381
Web: www.lbmw.com

The firm Lee Bolton Monier-Williams is a long established law firm with modern values, based in the heart of Westminster but with a client base spread across the UK and internationally. We act for companies, individuals and businesses across a wide range of sectors with a particular focus on charities, education, real estate, private client and landed estates, wine and spirits, IP and retail.

Types of work Our private client teams advise individuals and businesses on all wealth management and personal matters from wills, trusts and estates to tax planning and family issues.

Our real estate team deal with all aspects of commercial and residential property including development projects, joint ventures, sales and acquisitions, finance, asset management and property disputes.

Our leading EEC (education, ecclesiastical and charity) team acts for numerous well known charities, schools and institutions across a range of highly complex and important projects.

Our corporate and commercial team advises all kinds of business including start-ups, family companies, schools and well known large corporations on all aspects of the commercial life-cycle from incorporation to M&A, compliance, IP and corporate restructuring.

Our employment team advises businesses and individuals on both contentious and non-contentious employment matters including work place disputes, restrictive covenants, dismissals and TUPE.

Our dispute resolution team advise on a range of range of contentious matters including contract and commercial disputes, property disputes, trust and family disputes and IP disputes

Who should apply We are looking for trainees with a good degree (2.1 or above) in law or non-law subjects, who are highly motivated and have first-class communication skills. We expect our trainees to have a genuine interest in the law and what we do, to be professional, enthusiastic and to have a sense of humour.

Training programme Trainees spend six months in our four main departments – private client, dispute resolution, real estate and education and charity.

From the outset our trainees are given responsibility for their own work and have immediate contact with clients and other senior fee earners. Working alongside a senior lawyer or partner, trainees receive mentoring and support throughout the training contract. Trainees play a pivotal role in small teams where expectations are high.

When and how to apply Before 28 February to begin two years later in September. CV and covering letter to susie.hust@lbmw.com. Vacation placements in the spring and summer break form part of the recruitment process, for exact dates please see website.

Sponsorship Contribution towards cost of LPC – £7,000.

Vacancies	2
Trainees	4
Partners	8
Total staff	45

Training contract deadline
28 February 2018

Apply to
Susie Hust

Starting salary
£26,500

Minimum qualifications
2.1 degree, any subject

Sponsorship
LPC

Offices
London

Lee Bolton Monier-William
Solicitors

LEATHES PRIOR
74 The Close, Norwich NR1 4DR
Tel: 01603 610911
Email: lsmith@leathesprior.co.uk
Apply to: Miss Lauren Smith

Specialising in corporate and commercial, employment, regulatory and defence, dispute resolution, mediation, personal injury, sports, franchising, conveyancing, wills, trusts and probate, family and commercial property.

V	1-4
T	7
P	13
TS	100
WP	yes

LEIGH DAY
Priory House, 25 St John's Lane, London EC1M 4LB
Tel: 020 7650 1200
Email: jobs@leighday.co.uk
Apply to: Ms Vash Arora

Leigh Day is a specialist law firm operating across personal injury, environment, international, human rights, product liability, clinical negligence, employment and discrimination.

V	8-10[19]
T	20
P	44
TS	395
WP	no

LENNONS SOLICITORS LTD
Chess Chambers, 2 Broadway Court, Chesham HP5 1EG
Tel: 01494 773377
Email: recruitment@lennonssolicitors.co.uk
Apply to: Ms Hana Kmotrasova

General practice specialising in commercial/residential property, commercial work, dispute resolution (including personal injury, professional and medical negligence), employment, matrimonial, civil work, and wills and probate.

V	1[18]
T	2
P	4
TS	32
WP	no

LEO ABSE & COHEN
40 Churchill Way, Cardiff CF10 2SS
Tel: 02920 383252
Email: rosemaryd@leoabse.co.uk
Apply to: Ms Hayley Jones

Established in the 1950s. A progressive and expanding law firm in South Wales offering a comprehensive range of legal services with particular emphasis on litigation.

V	0
T	4
P	13
TS	140
WP	no

LEONARD CANNINGS SOLICITORS LLP
First Floor, Oakwood Court, 62a The Avenue, Southampton SO17 1XS
Tel: 023 8023 4433
Email: diana.cannings@leonardcannings.co.uk
Apply to: Ms DM Cannings

Specialist litigation practice concentrating on childcare, family, crime, housing and immigration law.

V	2
T	2
P	3
TS	20
WP	no

LESTER ALDRIDGE LLP
Russell House, Oxford Road, Bournemouth BH8 8EX
Tel: 01202 786161
Email: humanresources@la-law.com
Apply to: Human Resources

Regional firm, with offices in Bournemouth, Southampton and London. Strong commercial and private client departments offering full range of legal services and several niche areas.

V	8
T	16
P	42
TS	309
WP	yes

LESTER MORRILL
27 Park Square West, Leeds LS1 2PL
Tel: 0113 245 8549
Email: info@lmlaw.co.uk
Apply to: Ms M Clancy (HR Dept)

Specialists in crime, clinical negligence, family, inquests, social welfare, JRs and actions against the police. Lexcel and IIP accredited.

V	0
T	1
P	4
TS	38
WP	no

LEWIS SILKIN
5 Chancery Lane, Clifford's Inn, London EC4A 1BL
Tel: 020 7074 8000
Email: train@lewissilkin.com
Apply to: Trainee Recruitment Team

Commercial firm with a friendly informal style which encourages client contact and personal development. Two key focus areas include global employment and creative industries.

V	Up to 6
T	10
P	59
TS	343
WP	yes

V = Vacancies / **T** = Trainees / **P** = Partners / **TS** = Total Staff / **WP** = Work Placement

Linklaters LLP

One Silk Street, London EC2Y 8HQ
Email: graduate.recruitment@linklaters.com
Web: careers.linklaters.com
f linklatersgradsuk 𝕏 linklatersgrads

The firm From a shifting geopolitical landscape to the exponential growth in FinTech, this is a time of unprecedented change. At Linklaters, we're ready. Our people go further to support our clients, with market-leading legal insight and innovation. And we go further for each other, too. We're people you want to work with, generous with our time and ready to help. So no matter what the future holds, with us you'll be one step ahead. Great change is here, and we make sure you're ready.

Types of work Rather than specialise in just one area, we're proud to have best-in-class divisions across the board, in corporate, finance and projects, and dispute resolution. And in practice, they frequently work together to advise clients. As a Linklaters colleague, our breadth of expertise means that, wherever you focus, you'll be involved in the very best work, and benefit from continuous, tailored training from experienced lawyers.

Who should apply Our vision is to be best-in-class, which means winning in our chosen markets. To achieve it, we're looking for people with the right approach. And how you think matters more than what you've specialised in, and where. It's why we recruit a diverse mix of candidates who have studied a wide range of subjects, not just law. If you bring the positive ambition and drive we're looking for, and an enthusiasm for learning, we'll give you the world-class opportunities, training and rewards that you need to succeed.

Training programme The Linklaters training programme offers the knowledge and contacts you need to hit the ground running. Non-law graduates spend a conversion year studying the Graduate Diploma in Law (GDL). And all graduates complete the bespoke, accelerated Legal Practice Course (LPC) before starting training contracts. Then over two years you'll take up four six-month seats (placements) in different practice areas and sometimes abroad, for the breadth and depth of knowledge you need to develop and qualify. And throughout your career, you'll be supported with world-class training, courtesy of the Linklaters Law & Business School.

When and how to apply Full details, including applying for training contracts, vacation schemes and our first-year insight programme, are available at careers.linklaters.com.

Work placements We run vacation schemes and insight programmes. To find out more about these, our training contracts, and how to apply, please visit careers.linklaters.com.

Sponsorship For the GDL and LPC, Linklaters covers all costs and we also offer maintenance grants. You'll find all the details on our website.

Vacancies	110
Trainees	230
Partners	450*
Total staff	5,200*
	* worldwide figures

Work placement yes
(see Insider Report on p83)

Apply
Online

Starting salary
£43,000

Minimum qualifications
2.1 degree

Sponsorship
GDL/LPC

Offices
Abu Dhabi, Amsterdam, Antwerp, Bangkok, Beijing, Berlin, Brussels, Dubai, Düsseldorf, Frankfurt, Hong Kong, Lisbon, London, Luxembourg, Madrid, Milan, Moscow, Munich, New York, Paris, Rome, São Paulo, Seoul, Shanghai, Singapore, Stockholm, Tokyo, Warsaw, Washington DC

Linklaters

Remember to cite *The Training Contract & Pupillage Handbook* on your application form if you apply to this firm.

TRAINING CONTRACT DIRECTORY 385

LIGHTFOOTS LLP
1-3 High Street, Thame, Oxfordshire OX9 2BX
Tel: 01844 212 305
Email: lparke@lightfoots.co.uk
Apply to: Ms Lesley Parke

V	0
T	3
P	9
TS	110
WP	no

LODDERS SOLICITORS LLP
Number 10 Elm Court, Arden Street, Stratford-upon-Avon, Warwickshire CV37 6PA
Tel: 01789 293 259
Email: caroline.gionis@lodders.co.uk
Apply to: Mrs Caroline Gionis

At Lodders, our trainees are given a good level of responsibility and exposure to quality work in a variety of areas during their training programme.

V	3
T	6
P	28
TS	115
WP	yes

LONDON SOLICITORS LLP
Office 1, Heron House, London N17 9NF
Tel: 020 8808 1285
Email: koray@thelondonsolicitors.co.uk
Apply to: Mr Cemal Turk

London Solicitors is a solicitors firm with a difference. We have a strong reputation for conveyancing, civil litigation, immigration, employment and family matters.

V	2
T	0
P	2
TS	10
WP	yes

LUQMANI THOMPSON & PARTNERS
77-79 High Road, Wood Green, London N22 6BB
Tel: 020 8365 7800
Email: enq@luqmanithompson.com
Apply to: Ms Milla Walker

London-based firm specialising in immigration, human rights and public law including civil actions against the immigration service.

V	0
T	2
P	5
TS	9
WP	no

LYONS DAVIDSON
Victoria House, 51 Victoria Street, Bristol BS1 6AD
Tel: 0117 904 6000
Email: trainingcontracts@lyonsdavidson.co.uk
Apply to: Miss Sarah Wright

Lyons Davidson is a national law practice operating from headquarters in Bristol and offices in Solihull, Leeds, Surrey, Plymouth, Cardiff and London.

V	4-6
T	20
P	36
TS	1200
WP	no

M & S SOLICITORS LIMITED
20 Newton Road, Heather, Leicestershire LE67 2RD
Tel: 01530 266000
Email: rhughes@mslaw.co.uk
Apply to: Mr R Hughes

We are a niche commercial law firm practising in a rural location.

V	0
T	0
P	3
TS	10
WP	no

M OLUBI SOLICITORS
Unit 4, 2 Tunstall Road, London SW9 8BN
Tel: 020 7737 3400
Email: info@olubi.com
Apply to: Mr Moses Olubisose

South London busy and fast expanding solicitors require energetic hard working applicants for work experience, caseworkers/paralegals, training contracts, marketing, admin and support workers.

V	4
T	2
P	1
TS	7
WP	yes

MACHINS SOLICITORS LLP
Victoria Street, Luton LU1 2BS
Tel: 0158 251 4000
Email: barbara.coppin@machins.co.uk
Apply to: Ms Barbara Coppin

Machins offer genuine expertise and commercial aptitude across a broad range of business and individual services. Recognised as one of the region's leading commercial firms.

V	3[19]
T	5
P	12
TS	92
WP	no

V = Vacancies / **T** = Trainees / **P** = Partners / **TS** = Total Staff / **WP** = Work Placement

Macfarlanes LLP

20 Cursitor Street, London EC4A 1LT
Tel: 020 7831 9222
Email: gradrec@macfarlanes.com
Web: www.macfarlanes.com
🐦 macfarlanesgrad

The firm Macfarlanes is a leading City law firm with a straightforward, independently-minded approach. The driving force behind the firm is an absolute commitment to delivering the right advice in the right way to our clients. The size of our firm is important. We've kept things simple. We've decided against growth at the expense of quality, against size at the expense of efficiency and agility. So while we're large enough to advise on the most complex matters, we're also small enough to ensure that our people and our work are exceptional, without fail.

Finally, rather than opening offices around the world, we take a 'client first' approach to international work. Our clients get the best advice from the right lawyer – wherever in the world they need it.

Our combination of culture and expertise makes us a formidable force in the legal market. Sustaining our position depends on recruiting and training successive generations of truly exceptional lawyers.

Types of work Our main practice areas are: banking and finance; commercial; competition; corporate and M&A; corporate and regulatory investigations; data privacy; derivatives and trading; employment; financial services; hedge funds; investment management; litigation and dispute resolution; pensions; private client; private equity; real estate; restructuring and insolvency and tax.

Who should apply We believe the strongest firm is achieved by choosing a mix of people reflecting different styles so as to meet the needs that we – and our varied range of clients – will have in the future. We look for a rare combination of intellectual curiosity, character and drive. We are looking for ambitious trainees who will thrive on responsibility and challenge and who are ready to begin their careers on day one. We welcome applications from candidates with either a law or non-law background with a 2.1 degree or above.

Training programme Woven into every aspect of life at the firm is an enduring commitment to the development of trainees. Training begins with the Macfarlanes tailored LPC and a week-long induction course at the start of your training contract. During the two-year training contract you'll be working on real cases, doing real work for real clients. As a trainee you will complete four six-month seats in different practice areas including corporate and M&A, two seats in either private client, litigation, commercial real estate or tax and then a seat in one of our specialised practice areas within corporate. The precise allocation of seats is flexible so that we can offer you as broad as legal training as possible. Support and guidance are, of course, vital and you will find your supervisor and principal a valuable source of information and inspiration.

When and how to apply The closing date for training contract applications beginning September 2020 or March 2021 is 31 July 2018. Applications are to be made online via our website.

Work placements Our vacation schemes are designed to give you a two-week snapshot as life as a trainee. We offer vacation schemes at Easter and two summer vacation schemes. We welcome applications from students who are in at least their penultimate year of a degree from any degree discipline, with a predicted 2.1 or above. Applications are online via our website with a deadline of 31 January 2018. For first-year students, we offer an insight day to provide an overview of a City law firm. Applications and further information is available on our website.

Sponsorship CPE/GDL and LPC fees paid and a maintenance allowance of up to £7,000.

Vacancies	25-30
Trainees	60
Partners	87
Total staff	691

Work placement yes
(see Insider Report on p85)

Training contract deadline
31 July 2018

Apply
Online

Starting salary
£44,000

Minimum qualifications
2.1 degree anticipated or acheived

Sponsorship
GDL/LPC

Offices
London

MACFARLANES

Affiliated with
🝣 aspiringsolicitors

Remember to cite *The Training Contract & Pupillage Handbook* on your application form if you apply to this firm.

Firm	Description	V	T	P	TS	WP
MACKARNESS & LUNT 16 High Street, Petersfield GU32 3JJ **Tel:** 01730 265111 **Email:** clairethompson@macklunt.co.uk **Apply to:** Mrs Claire Thompson	A general practice firm dealing with property, litigation, family probate, wills, LPAs, trusts and other matters.	0	0	2	18	no
MACRAE & CO LLP 59 Lafone Street, London SE1 2LX **Tel:** 020 7378 7716 **Email:** office@macraeco.com **Apply to:** Mr JA Turnball	Commercial firm with predominantly international clientele.	0	0	3	7	no
MAGRATH LLP 66-67 Newman Street, London W1T 3EQ **Tel:** 020 7495 3003 **Email:** ben.sheldrick@magrath.co.uk **Apply to:** Mr Ben Sheldrick	Central London niche firm specialising in corporate immigration, employment, entertainment, dispute resolution and corporate commercial.	2[18]	5	8	65	no
MAJOR & CO 51 Quarry Street, Guildford, Surrey GU1 3UA **Tel:** 01483 455 771 **Email:** d_major@majorlaw.co.uk **Apply to:** Mr David Major	A friendly and efficient firm dealing with a wide range of private client and small-medium business work.	0	1	1	8	yes
MAKIN DIXON SOLICITORS Wool Exchange, 10 Hustlegate, Bradford, West Yorkshire BD1 1RE **Tel:** 01274 747747 **Email:** enquiries@makindixon.co.uk **Apply to:** Ms J Campbell	We are a team of specialist solicitors focused entirely on family law. We are an ever expanding firm with 10 offices, including offices in Bradford, Skipton, Halifax and Keighley, covering all aspects of family law.	0	6	2	70	no
MAKKA SOLICITORS LTD 44 Upper Tooting Road, London SW17 7PD **Tel:** 020 8767 9090 **Email:** makkaltd@hotmail.com **Apply to:** Mr F Chaudhary	Our main aim is to help the community and we are looking for like minded staff who wish to do the same.	1	1	3	8	yes
MAKWANA SOLICITORS Devonshire House, 582 Honeypot Lane, Stanmore, Middlesex HA7 1JS **Tel:** 020 8732 5458 **Email:** info@makwanas.co.uk **Apply to:** Miss S Makwana	The firm is a mixed private practice dealing in all types of criminal defence, family and civil litigation work.	1	0	1	2	yes
MALCOLM C FOY & CO LTD 51 Hallgate, Doncaster DN1 3PB **Tel:** 01302 340005 **Email:** info@malcolmcfoy.co.uk **Apply to:** Mrs A Pashley	General practice with offices in Doncaster and Rotherham. No criminal work undertaken. Specialising in commercial and civil litigation, matrimonial, personal injury, private client and residential and commercial property conveyancing.	1	4	8	57	yes

V = Vacancies / **T** = Trainees / **P** = Partners / **TS** = Total Staff / **WP** = Work Placement

	MALIK & MALIK 234-236 High Road, Willesden, London NW10 2NX **Tel:** 020 8830 3050 **Email:** malikandmalik@lawyer.com **Apply to:** Mr M Nazeer	Malik & Malik was established on 1 June 1998. The firm deals with the following areas of law: crime; immigration and nationality; landlord and tenant; conveyancing; and personal injury.	V 1 T 4 P 2 TS 15 WP yes

	MALIK LEGAL SOLICITORS LTD 579 Cheetham Hill Road, Manchester M8 9JE **Tel:** 0161 7956217 **Email:** info@maliklegal.co.uk **Apply to:** Mr Maqbool Malik	Three-partner firm, six solicitors, seven support staff, specialising in administrative law, immigration, crime, human rights, judicial review, company law, personal injury and civil law.	V 4 T 2 P 3 TS 14 WP yes

	MALLETTS Market House, 17 Tuesday Market Place, King's Lynn, Norfolk PE30 1JN **Tel:** 01553 777 744 **Email:** info@malletts.com **Apply to:** Mrs Sharon Mallett	Progressive dynamic firm specialising in serious crime, commercial litigation and family. Needs able and enthusiastic candidates.	V 1 T 2 P 3 TS 30 WP yes

	MANDER HADLEY SOLICITORS 1 The Quadrant, Coventry CV1 2DW **Tel:** 024 76631212 **Email:** enquiries@manderhadley.co.uk **Apply to:** Miss Naomi O'Halloran	Located in Coventry and Kenilworth. Specialising in civil and criminal litigation, family, conveyancing, commercial and company, charities, probate, trusts and wills.	V 0 T 0 P 9 TS 45 WP no

	MAPLES TEESDALE LLP 30 King Street, London EC2V 8EE **Tel:** 020 7600 3800 **Email:** enq@maplesteesdale.co.uk **Apply to:** Ms Anastasia Klein	Maples Teesdale are the UK's leading commercial property law specialists, providing innovative, full service and truly partner-led services to UK based and international clients	V 3[19] T 6 P 18 TS 68 WP no

	MARRIOTT HARRISON LLP 11 Staple Inn, London WC1V 7QH **Tel:** 020 7209 2000 **Email:** liz.arscott@marriottharrison.co.uk **Apply to:** Ms Liz Arscott	Leading corporate/media firm based in the City providing specialist services including corporate, banking, restructuring, media, employment, real estate and dispute resolution across various sectors.	V 2-3[19] T 6 P 18 TS 52 WP yes

	MARRONS 1 Meridian South, Meridian Business Park, Leicester LE19 1WY **Tel:** 0116 289 2200 **Email:** louisemee@marrons.net **Apply to:** Mrs Louise Mee	Marrons is a niche planning and property development practice with a national reputation in the development industry for its legal expertise.	V 1 T 2 P 7 TS 30 WP no

	MARTIN CRAY AND CO 177 Edward Street, Brighton BN2 0JB **Tel:** 01273 673226 **Email:** mcray@martincray.co.uk **Apply to:** Mr MW Cray	The firm specialises in personal injury, family, probate, conveyancing and employment.	V 1 T 2 P 2 TS 22 WP yes

V = Vacancies / **T** = Trainees / **P** = Partners / **TS** = Total Staff / **WP** = Work Placement

MARTIN MURRAY & ASSOCIATES 152-156 High Street, Yiewsley, West Drayton UB7 7BE **Tel:** 01895 431332 **Email:** info@mmasolicitors.co.uk **Apply to:** Mr A Cosma	Martin Murray & Associates is a franchised firm and is one of the leading criminal practices in the Thames Valley.	V 0 T 2 P 9 TS 70 WP no
MARTIN SEARLE SOLICITORS 9 Marlborough Place, Brighton BN1 1UB **Tel:** 01273 609911 **Email:** fiona@ms-solicitors.co.uk **Apply to:** Ms Fiona Martin	Niche employment and community care law practice seeking trainee solicitors on a yearly basis. Casework experience and IT skills essential. Recruiting in January.	V 0 T - P 2 TS 15 WP no
MARTIN SHEPHERD SOLICITORS LLP 753 High Road North, Finchley, London N12 8LG **Tel:** 020 8446 4301 **Email:** acd@martinshepherd.co.uk **Apply to:** Ms Antoinette Doyle	A four branch North London general high street practice with a bias towards commercial work.	V 0 T - P 6 TS 34 WP no
MARTIN-KAYE LLP The Foundry, Euston Way, Telford TF3 4LY **Tel:** 01952 272222 **Email:** recruit@martinkaye.co.uk **Apply to:** Mrs Alison Carter	A progressive practice in the expanding new town of Telford dealing with all aspects of commercial, corporate, IP, employment, litigation and property. Agency work undertaken.	V Poss T 1 P 6 TS 60 WP no
MATRIX SOLICITORS Normanton Business Centre, 258 Normanton Road, Derby DE23 6WD **Tel:** 01332 363454 **Apply to:** Mr Shamim Khan	Niche litigation, company/commercial, environmental and energy law and business immigration specialists in the centre of Derby.	V 0 T 0 P 1 TS 7 WP yes
MAURICE TURNOR GARDNER LLP 15th Floor, Milton House, Milton Street, London EC2Y 9BH **Tel:** 020 7786 8710 **Email:** trainees@mtgllp.com **Apply to:** Mrs Sophie Mazzier	Maurice Turnor Gardner is a boutique private client firm with charity, commercial trust, partnerships, trust dispute resolution and real estate teams.	V 1-2[19] T 4 P 10 TS 38 WP yes
MAYO WYNNE BAXTER LLP 20 Gildredge Road, Eastbourne BN21 4RP **Tel:** 01323 745625 **Email:** recruitment@mayowynnebaxter.co.uk **Apply to:** Miss Clare Smith	An ambitious, quality-driven and friendly firm which recruits trainees via a 'paralegal to trainee' initiative, usually commencing in April/May each year.	V 2 T 4 P 31 TS 214 WP no
MCGUIREWOODS LONDON LLP 11 Pilgrim Street, London EC4V 6RN **Tel:** 020 7632 1600 **Email:** lhr@mcguirewoods.com **Apply to:** Mrs Jane Gritt	The London office of a cross border law firm offering a broad spectrum of legal services within international and domestic corporate and private client matters.	V 1 T 2 P 15 TS 61 WP no

V = Vacancies / **T** = Trainees / **P** = Partners / **TS** = Total Staff / **WP** = Work Placement

Mayer Brown International LLP

201 Bishopsgate, London EC2M 3AF
Tel: 020 3130 8622
Email: graduaterecruitment@mayerbrown.com
Web: www.mayerbrownfutures.com
🐦 talk2mayerbrown

The firm Mayer Brown was one of the first law firms to develop a global platform in recognition of the fact that many of its clients increasingly needed integrated, cross-border legal advice. The firm is now one of the world's leading global law firms with offices in major cities across the Americas, Asia, Europe and the Middle East. In Brazil, the firm has an association with Tauil & Chequer Avogados. Through the association, the extensive international expertise of its lawyers and its presence in the leading financial centres around the world, Mayer Brown provides high quality legal advice and client-focused solutions to support many of the world's leading businesses.

Types of work Our lawyers have expertise across a wide range of areas including corporate, finance, real estate, construction, litigation and dispute resolution, employment, pensions, antitrust and competition, insurance and reinsurance, tax, financial services regulatory and intellectual property.

Who should apply We are looking for candidates who not only have a consistently strong academic record including a minimum of a 2.1 degree (predicted or obtained) in any discipline, but also who have a wide range of interests and achievements outside their academic career. Additionally, we would like to see innovative candidates who can demonstrate a drive for results, good verbal and written communication skills, and an ability to analyse, with good judgement and excellent interpersonal skills.

Training programme One of the advantages of joining Mayer Brown are the choices available to you. As a trainee at the firm, you will be able to tailor your training contract across a broad range of seats, including our main practice areas in London (as listed above), and international secondments in either Hong Kong or the US. If you don't want to stray too far, you have the option to gain valuable in-house experience by going on secondment to one of the firm's major clients. While Mayer Brown is a global law firm, our London office remains a tightly knit team with an open and inclusive culture. You will be given significant opportunities to assist on matters which may be multidisciplinary, cross-border, complex and high-profile in nature.

When and how to apply The deadline for training contracts commencing in March/September 2020 is 31 July 2018. However we encourage students to apply for a vacation scheme as this is the main pipeline for our training contracts each year; the deadline is 31 January 2018 for schemes in the spring and summer and we welcome applications from penultimate year, finalists and graduates too. Applications are made online via the website.

Work placements We run three vacation schemes each year; one in the spring and two in the summer. You will gain experience in two key practice areas and be involved in seminars and social events including a trip to our Paris office. Our vacation schemes are the main pipeline for our training contracts each year.

Sponsorship The firm will cover the cost of the GDL and LPC and provide a maintenance grant of £7,000 in London and £6,500 elsewhere. The firm asks all LPC students to complete the LPC at BPP Law School in London.

Vacancies	15
Trainees	30
Partners	86
Total staff	approx 460

Work placement yes
(see Insider Report on p87)

Training contract deadline
31 July 2018

Apply
Online

Starting salary
£42,000

Minimum qualifications
2.1 degree or equivalent and AAB at A level or equivalent

Sponsorship
GDL/LPC

Offices
Bangkok, Beijing, Brasilia, Brussels, Charlotte, Chicago, Dubai, Düsseldorf, Frankfurt, Hanoi, Ho Chi Minh City, Hong Kong, Houston, London, Los Angeles, Mexico City, New York, Palo Alto, Paris, Rio de Janeiro, São Paulo, Shanghai, Singapore, Washington DC

MAYER·BROWN

Affiliated with
🔗 aspiringsolicitors

McDermott Will & Emery UK LLP

110 Bishopsgate, London EC2N 4AY
Tel: 020 7577 6900
Web: www.mwe.com
🐦 mcdermottlaw

The firm McDermott Will & Emery is a leading international law firm with lawyers located across the United States, Europe and Asia, plus the firm further extends its reach through a strategic alliance with MWE China Law Offices in Shanghai.

McDermott Will & Emery's London office, founded in 1998, brings a full-service legal practice to Europe and complements McDermott's capabilities in France, Germany, Italy and Belgium.

The London office is part of an extensive 19 office international network that provides a unique platform from which McDermott offers legal advice to local and international organisations. The London office represents a wide range of clients, including large commercial, industrial and financial corporations, small and medium-sized businesses, trustees and high-net-worth individuals and families. The firm has around 45 lawyers at present in London, the majority are English-qualified.

Types of work Corporate/transactional, private client, international tax, energy, employment, international disputes and resolutions.

Who should apply The firm is looking for the brightest, best and most entrepreneurial trainees. Candidates will need to demonstrate commercial awareness and a genuine understanding of the firm.

Training programme The primary focus is to provide a practical foundation for your career with the firm. You will experience four seats over the two-year period and a deliberately small number of trainees mean that the firm is able to provide a degree of flexibility in tailoring seats to the individual. Trainees get regular support and feedback.

The firm provides a comprehensive range of benefits which includes private medical and dental insurance, life assurance, permanent health insurance, pension, season ticket loan, subsidised gym membership, an employee assistance programme and 25 days' holiday.

When and how to apply Candidates must apply online at www.apply4law.com/mwe by 29 June 2018 to begin a training contract in September 2020.

Sponsorship LPC funding and maintenance grant.

Vacancies	2
Trainees	4
Partners	581*
Total staff	1,072*

*denotes worldwide figure

Training contract deadline
29 June 2018

Apply
Online at
www.apply4law.com/mwe

Starting salary
£43,000

Minimum qualifications
First or high 2.1 degree

Sponsorship
LPC

Offices
Boston, Brussels, Chicago, Dallas, Düsseldorf, Frankfurt, Houston, London, Los Angeles, Miami, Milan, Munich, New York, Orange County, Paris, Seoul, Silicon Valley, Washington DC, strategic alliance with MWE China Law Offices (Shanghai)

McDermott Will & Emery

Remember to cite *The Training Contract & Pupillage Handbook* on your application form if you apply to this firm.

392 THE TRAINING CONTRACT & PUPILLAGE HANDBOOK

MCHALE & COMPANY 19/21 High Street, Altrincham, Cheshire WA14 1QP **Tel:** 0161 928 3848 **Email:** mch@mchaleandco.co.uk **Apply to:** Mrs Philippa Wright	Established and expanding firm offering specialist advice in the areas of conveyancing (commercial and domestic), financial mis-selling, employment, personal injury, private client and commercial litigation.	V 1 T 4 P 5 TS 40 WP no
MCMILLAN WILLIAMS SOLICITORS MW House, 41 Chipstead Valley Road, Coulsdon CR5 2RB **Tel:** 020 3551 8500 **Email:** dawn.fazackerley@mwsolicitors.co.uk **Apply to:** Miss Dawn Fazackerley	MW Solicitors prides itself on its excellent in-house training, which takes talented individuals from paralegals through to trainee solicitors and beyond.	V Varies T 43 P 60 TS 400 WP yes
MEIKLES 8 North Street, Ferryhill, County Durham DL17 8HX **Tel:** 01740 652811 **Email:** lawrence.petterson@meikles-solicitors.co.uk **Apply to:** Mr L Petterson	High street solicitors with five offices long established throughout South Durham. Significant legal aid practice. Specialising in family, particularly children, criminal, mental health and conveyancing.	V 1[19] T 1 P 9 TS 52 WP yes
MEMERY CRYSTAL LLP 44 Southampton Buildings, London WC2A 1AP **Tel:** 020 7242 5905 **Email:** hseaward@memerycrystal.com **Apply to:** Mrs Helen Seaward	A full-service independent firm specialising in corporate, employment, tax, litigation, IP, property and property litigation. Known for its international sectors including natural resources and retail.	V 4 T 8 P 25 TS 118 WP no
METCALFE COPEMAN & PETTEFAR 28-32 King Street, Kings Lynn PE30 1HQ **Tel:** 01553 778102 **Email:** alison.muir@mcp-law.co.uk **Apply to:** Miss Alison Muir	A firm with four offices which undertakes some specialist commercial work as well as its general practice, which includes legal aid work.	V 1[18] T 4 P 15 TS 120 WP no
METCALFES SOLICITORS 46-48 Queen Square, Bristol BS1 4LY **Tel:** 011 7929 0451 **Email:** info@metcalfes.co.uk **Apply to:** Mrs Sian Frampton	Commercial practice providing quality, cost effective, partner led service to medium sized businesses, together with niche clinical negligence, claimant personal injury and private client practice.	V 0 T 2 P 6 TS 55 WP no
MFG SOLICITORS LLP Adam House, Birmingham Road, Kidderminster, Worcestershire DY10 2SH **Tel:** 01562 820 181 **Email:** denise.clarke@mfgsolicitors.com **Apply to:** Mrs Denise Clarke	Specialising: family, property, wills/probate, litigation. Niche expertise: tax, agriculture, company commercial and employment. On the Law Society's family/children panels and personal injury trust panel.	V 2-4[19] T 6 P 30 TS 140 WP no
MIAN & CO The Citadel, 190 Corporation Street, Birmingham B4 6QD **Tel:** 0121 684 8000 **Email:** mians@btinternet.com **Apply to:** Mrs T S Mian	Long-established criminal defence solicitors practice. Offices based directly opposite Birmingham magistrates court. Mainly legally aided work undertaken.	V 0 T 2 P 2 TS 9 WP no

V = Vacancies / **T** = Trainees / **P** = Partners / **TS** = Total Staff / **WP** = Work Placement

MICHELMORES LLP
Woodwater House, Pynes Hill, Exeter EX2 5WR
Tel: 01392 688688
Email: gradrecruitment@michelmores.com
Apply to: Ms Gabby Essame

Michelmores is an ambitious, top 100 law firm, with offices in Exeter, Bristol and London.

V	8
T	14
P	64
TS	450
WP	yes

MIDDLETON & UPSALL LLP
94 East Street, Warminster BA12 9BG
Tel: 01985 214 444
Email: swhite@mulaw.co.uk
Apply to: Mr Charles Goodbody

V	0
T	1
P	2
TS	25
WP	no

MIDDLETON SOLICITORS
Granite House, 8-10 Stanley Street, Liverpool
L1 6AF
Tel: 0151 236 5599
Email: reception@middletonsolicitors.co.uk
Apply to: Mr Alan Middleton

We are a young city centre based practice. We specialise in various areas of law including sports law, private client, commercial and personal injury.

V	1[18]
T	1
P	3
TS	25
WP	yes

MIDDLEWEEKS
Swan Building, 20 Swan Street, Manchester
M4 5JW
Tel: 0161 839 7255
Apply to: Barbara Cohen

A Manchester litigation practice which specialises in criminal litigation and which is highly regarded in that field, particularly in the area of white collar crime.

V	0
T	2
P	2
TS	19
WP	yes

MILBANK TWEED HADLEY & MCCLOY
10 Gresham Street, London EC2V 7JD
Tel: 020 7615 3000
Email: lnrecruiting@milbank.com
Apply to: Mr Robert Girvan, Manager of Professional Delvopment & Legal Recruiting

International firm headquartered in New York with offices in Europe, the US, Asia and South America, advising government entities, corporations and financial institutions.

V	5
T	9
P	23
TS	165
WP	yes

MILBURNS SOLICITORS LIMITED
3-5 Main Street, Cockermouth, Cumbria C13 9LE
Tel: 01900 67363
Email: lstorr@milburnssolicitors.co.uk
Apply to: Mrs Louise Storr

Eight-partner, four-office firm with large client base in West Cumbria. LEXCEL accredited with LSC quality marks in conveyancing and family.

V	1[18]
T	2
P	8
TS	50
WP	yes

MILLAN SOLICITORS
1368 Leeds Road, Bradford, West Yorkshire
BD3 8ND
Tel: 01274 660 111
Email: millansolicitors@gmail.com
Apply to: Miss GK Millan

Millan Solicitors is a family firm with family values. We are a young, dynamic, expanding firm specialising in civil litigation, immigration and personal injury work.

V	0
T	1
P	1
TS	2
WP	yes

MILLER EVANS & CO
1st Floor, Pepper Street, London E14 9RP
Tel: 020 7987 2515
Email: askus@me-solicitors.co.uk
Apply to: Ms Charlotte Miller

We are a small forward-thinking highly-respected practice at Canary Wharf dealing mainly with property and private client – but also commercial and family.

V	0
T	1
P	2
TS	9
WP	no

V = Vacancies / **T** = Trainees / **P** = Partners / **TS** = Total Staff / **WP** = Work Placement

Mills & Co

Milburn House, Dean Street, Newcastle upon Tyne NE1 1LE
Tel: 0191 233 2222
Email: recruitment@mills-co.com
Web: www.mills-co.com

The firm Mills & Co Solicitors Limited specialises exclusively in shipping and international trade. Based in Newcastle upon Tyne, and currently with a team of 24 lawyers we are the largest specialist in our fields outside London. Newcastle has strong historical roots in shipping and has long been the UK's 'second city' for shipping law and our work is conducted before the same London-based courts and tribunals as the London firms specialising in the same fields. Within shipping and international trade globally, we are ranked alongside the leading London law firms and are compared favourably by clients and legal directories. For academically gifted lawyers wanting to combine the intelletual stimulation of working in some of the most interesting and varied areas of international commercial law with the quality of life advantages of the North East, our traineeships provide a unique opportunity.

Types of work We are a full-service firm in our specialist fields. In shipping we have a significant presence in both 'dry' work (essentially law of contract type work involving all types of contracts used for hiring and insuring ships, carrying cargoes, building and financing new ships, and buying, selling, financing and repairing second-hand ships), as well as 'wet' work (essentially law of tort type work involving collisions between one ship and another ship as well as between ships and other structures, groundings, as well as specialists contracts concerning salvage, towage and other services provided to ships in distress). In international trade we are involved in drafting, advising on and litigating contracts in relation to the international sale of goods.

Who should apply We aim to provide work to the highest standards in the UK and therefore seek trainees who combine high academic achievement (AAB at A level and 2.1 at university level) with an outgoing personality and an international outlook. Languages are an advantage as our lawyers travel to visit the leading shipping markets globally. We are committed to providing the best training possible with the aim that our trainees will stay with us upon qualification and ultimately become partners in the firm. In return we are seeking a genuine interest in shipping law and a clear commitment to remaining in the North East.

Training programme We operate a three-seat system each of about eight months in shipping litigation (shipping contract/tort disputes), commercial (a non-contentious seat including ship sale and purchase, shipbuilding, ship repair and ship finance) and commercial litigation (commodity sale contract disputes). In each seat the trainee sits with a partner specialising in the relevant field. We have a roughly one-to-one ratio between partners and non-partners which allows us to provide detailed supervision of trainees and junior lawyers. Trainees can expect to receive work from most of the partners during their traineeships as we do not operate in teams and aim to ensure that trainees sample all areas of the firm's work.

When and how to apply Apply via our website www.mills-co.com before 29 July 2018 for training contracts commencing in 2020.

Work placements We offer one-week vacation schemes in Spring and Summer 2018 ahead of our 29 July 2018 deadline for 2020 traineeships.

Sponsorship We will pay your GDL and LPC fees.

Vacancies	1
Trainees	2
Partners	12
Total staff	33

Work placement yes

Training contract deadline
29 July 2018

Apply to
See website

Starting salary
£26,500

Minimum qualifications
AAB at A level, 2.1 degree

Sponsorship
GDL/LPC

Offices
Newcastle upon Tyne

MILLS & Co.
— SOLICITORS —

Remember to cite *The Training Contract & Pupillage Handbook* on your application form if you apply to this firm.

Mills & Reeve LLP

Botanic House, 100 Hills Road, Cambridge CB2 1PH
Tel: 01223 222336
Email: graduate.recruitment@mills-reeve.com
Web: www.mills-reeve.com
🐦 millsandreeve

The firm Mills & Reeve is a major UK law firm and among the 50 largest UK law firms. Our business model is straightforward – the highest quality advice, outstanding client service and value for money. Our highly collaborative culture underpins this model and has created our strong ambition to grow. Increased scale and focus have enabled us to achieve leading positions in our work for substantial and high growth businesses and individuals as well as in the health, higher education and further education sectors, real estate and insurance across the UK.

Our commercial clients include global and UK based businesses, FTSE and AIM listed organisations, private companies and start-ups. We work with firms across the globe (including fellow members of the SCG Legal, a worldwide network of leading law firms) to support our clients' international requirements.

For the 14th year running Mills & Reeve has been listed in *The Sunday Times* Top 100 Best Companies to Work For, which recognises that we put people at the centre of our business.

Types of work Mills & Reeve's services are delivered through firm-wide core groups: corporate and commercial, employment, family, insurance disputes, private client, projects and construction, real estate and regulatory, public and commercial disputes. Further specialist sector teams focus on: charities, education, food and agribusiness, government, health, sport, technology and life sciences.

Who should apply We welcome applications from penultimate-year and final-year law students, final-year non-law students and graduates. Candidates should already have or expect a 2.1 degree or equivalent from either a law or non-law background. You'll have a good balance between academic ability, interpersonal skills, drafting skills, common sense, commercial awareness, confidence and a professional attitude. We look for candidates who have the potential to develop into our solicitors of the future.

Training programme Trainees complete six four-month seats and work alongside a partner or principal associate. Movement between offices is encouraged and supported with an accommodation allowance. Training is supported by a full induction, in-house training programme developed by our team of professional support lawyers and the professional skills course (PSC).

When and how to apply Apply online. Closing dates are 31 July 2018 for training contracts commencing September 2020 and 31 January 2018 for summer placements in 2018.

Work placements Our award-winning summer placement scheme allows you to get a taste of Mills & Reeve and the legal profession before applying for a training contract. We offer two weeks' work experience at one of our offices in Birmingham, Cambridge, Manchester and Norwich. Online applications for two-week placements during the summer must be received by 31 January 2018.

Sponsorship Mills & Reeve will fund the GDL and LPC course fees for future trainees. There is also a maintenance grant during the GDL and LPC.

Vacancies	18
Trainees	39
Partners	117
Total staff	800

Work placement yes
(see Insider Report on p89)

Training contract deadline
31 July 2018

Apply
Online

Starting salary
£26,000

Minimum qualifications
2.1 degree, any discipline

Sponsorship
GDL/LPC

Offices
Birmingham, Cambridge, Leeds, London, Manchester, Norwich

MILLS & REEVE
Achieve more. Together.

Remember to cite *The Training Contract & Pupillage Handbook* on your application form if you apply to this firm.

396 THE TRAINING CONTRACT & PUPILLAGE HANDBOOK

Mishcon de Reya LLP

Africa House, 70 Kingsway, London WC2B 6AH
Tel: 020 3321 7000
Email: trainee.recruitment@mishcon.com
Web: www.mishcongraduates.com
f mishcon 𝕏 mishcongrads

The firm Based in London with an office in New York, Mishcon de Reya services an international community of clients and provides advice in situations where the constraints of geography often do not apply. The work we undertake is cross-border, multi-jurisdictional and complex. Our clients are dynamic and sophisticated and we reflect that in our belief in challenging the conventional or accepted ways of working. We fiercely guard our clients' interests, recognising the significant nexus between business affairs and personal affairs. Building strong personal connections with our clients and their businesses is important to us. It is for these reasons we say 'It's business. But it's personal'.

Mishcon de Reya has grown rapidly in recent years, showing more than 100% revenue growth since 2010. A central role is played by the academy, the firm's in-house place of learning, development and new thinking, the active and innovative social impact strategy and various diversity initiatives are reflected in its top 25 place in *The Sunday Times* Best Companies to Work For list of 2017.

Types of work We are organised internally into six different departments: corporate, employment, dispute resolution, family, Mishcon private and real estate. The firm also has a number of specialist groups including competition, finance and banking, fraud, immigration, international arbitration, IP and art.

Who should apply Applications are welcome from penultimate-year law and final-year non-law undergraduate students as well as other graduates wishing to commence a training contract in two years' time. The firm recruits from a wide range of universities. Our trainees are typically high-achieving and intelligent individuals with good interpersonal skills and outgoing personalities. Strength of character and ability to think laterally are also important.

Training programme Trainees have the opportunity to gain experience, skills and knowledge from across the firm in four six-month seats involving both contentious and non-contentious work. Because of the relatively few training contracts offered, trainees can be exposed to high-quality work with lots of responsibility early on. Trainees are supported with a wide ranging training and development programme in addition to the Professional Skills Course. Trainee performance is monitored closely and trainees can expect to receive regular feedback in addition to mid-seat and end-of-seat appraisals.

When and how to apply Applicants should submit an online application for vacation schemes via our trainee recruitment website: www.mishcongraduates.com. Applications close 15 January 2018. Applicants will be considered for a training contract once they have completed a vacation scheme.

Work placements We run three vacation schemes, one over Easter and two in July. Our schemes have been designed to provide individuals with an insight into the role of a trainee, our culture and our people. As well as being paid on the vacation scheme, those not living within commuting distance of London will be provided with free accommodation. We run a fun vacation scheme with an informative workshop programme covering all practice areas of the firm, combined with individual and group work sessions.

Sponsorship The firm provides full LPC and GDL funding, and a maintenance grant of £6,000 payable in the GDL and LPC year.

Vacancies	12-15
Trainees	29
Partners	115
Total staff	772

Work placement yes

Training contract deadline
15 January 2018

Apply to
Charlotte Lynch,
Graduate & Lateral
Recruitment Manager

Starting salary
£40,000

Minimum qualifications
2.1 degree or higher

Sponsorship
GDL/LPC

Offices
London, associated
office in New York

Mishcon de Reya

MILLS CHODY LLP
226-228 Kenton Road, Kenton, Harrow, Middlesex
HA3 8BZ
Tel: 020 8909 0400
Email: info@millschody.com
Apply to: Mr Shinder Johal

A well-established high street firm specialising predominantly in property, family law, private client and litigation.

V	1-2
T	1
P	5
TS	20
WP	no

MILNE MOSER
100 Highgate, Kendal, Cumbria LA9 4HE
Tel: 01539 729786
Email: solicitors@milnemoser.co.uk
Apply to: Mr D J Emmett

An old-established but progressive general practice and estate agency undertaking all types of contentious and non-contentious work.

V	0
T	0
P	6
TS	27
WP	no

MINCOFFS SOLICITORS LLP
5 Osborne Terrace, Jesmond, Newcastle upon
Tyne NE2 1SQ
Tel: 0191 281 6151
Email: info@mincoffs.co.uk
Apply to: Ms Michelle Dodds

Mincoffs Solicitors, one of the northeast's major law firms providing a first class legal service to commercial and private clients across the UK.

V	1[19]
T	2
P	9
TS	70
WP	yes

MINSTER LAW SOLICITORS
Alexander House, Hospital Fields Road, York
YO10 4DZ
Tel: 0345 356 3000
Email: training.contracts@minsterlaw.co.uk
Apply to: Mrs Amy Thirtle

Minster Law is full service consumer law firm, with a specialism in personal injury. We offer a range of legal services including private client, employment and civil litigation.

V	5
T	10
P	0
TS	830
WP	yes

MLP LAW LLP
7 Market Street, Altrincham, Cheshire WA14 1QE
Tel: 0161 926 9969
Email: lesleys@mlplaw.co.uk
Apply to: Mrs Lesley Sullivan

Applications are invited from self motivated lawyers of partnership potential. This dynamic and highly accredited practice offers outstanding hands-on training and structured career progression.

V	3[19]
T	2
P	6
TS	22
WP	yes

MOHAMMED & CO
St John's House, 42 St John's Place, Preston
PR1 3XX
Tel: 01772 888700
Apply to: Mr Hanif Mohammed

V	0
T	2
P	1
TS	13
WP	yes

MONRO WRIGHT & WASBROUGH LLP
7-8 Great James Street, London WC1N 3DF
Tel: 020 7404 7001
Email: contact@mww-llp.com
Apply to: Mr Nicholas Barlow

Long established private client firm situated beside Gray's Inn, specialising in litigation, taxation, trusts/estates, charities, commercial and residential property.

V	2[19]
T	3
P	9
TS	35
WP	no

MOORE BLATCH LLP
Gateway House, Tollgate, Chandlers Ford
SO53 3TG
Tel: 023 8071 8000
Email: recruitment@mooreblatch.com
Apply to: Graduate Recruitment

One of the South's leading full-service law firms advising businesses and private clients. Nearly 300 staff based in London, Lymington, Richmond and Southampton.

V	3[19]
T	6
P	42
TS	270
WP	no

V = Vacancies / **T** = Trainees / **P** = Partners / **TS** = Total Staff / **WP** = Work Placement

Morgan, Lewis & Bockius UK LLP

Condor House, 5-10 St Paul's Churchyard, London EC4M 8AL
Tel: 020 3201 5000
Email: londontrainingprogramme@morganlewis.com
Web: www.morganlewis.com

The firm With 30 offices across North America, Asia, Europe and the Middle East, Morgan Lewis provides comprehensive corporate, transactional, regulatory and litigation services to clients of all sizes across all major industries. The firm's regulatory and industry focused practices help clients address legal, government and policy challenges. Founded in 1873, Morgan Lewis comprises more than 2,200 legal professionals.

Types of work Morgan Lewis's London office offers a wide range of business and commercial services, including: competition; corporate; debt and equity capital markets; finance and restructuring; labour and employment including employment litigation and immigration advice; private investment fund formation and operation; structured transactions; tax planning and structuring; international commercial dispute, arbitration, insurance recovery, and white collar matters. Morgan Lewis is also strong in various business sectors, including life sciences, financial services, energy and technology, where the firm's leading regulatory and commercial lawyers provide a real insight into their industries.

Who should apply Morgan Lewis is seeking candidates with a consistently strong academic record, who would respond with confidence to opportunities to work on challenging assignments across a wide variety of areas. Candidates should be able to demonstrate strong interpersonal, communication and client service skills and analytical ability, as well as a proven ability to work effectively both independently and within a team.

Training programme Morgan Lewis's London training programme is led by an experienced training principal. Our partners and trainee supervisors also have broad experience of working with trainees. Following a full induction to the firm, our programme will provide you with consistently high-quality, challenging assignments, working directly with senior lawyers across a range of practices and industry groups on complex and frequently cross-border matters. Through this hands-on and varied experience, you can expect to build a thorough understanding of the firm's business and of working with international, high-profile clients. Over two years you will complete four six-month seats with the opportunity to gain experience in at least three distinct areas of law. International secondment opportunities to our Brussels, Dubai, Moscow and Singapore offices may also be available. In addition to formal appraisals, the office environment allows regular contact with, and feedback from, the training principal, supervisors and other lawyers. Trainees will have the opportunity to actively participate in all in-house associate training sessions, and to take part in pro bono work and business development activities.

When and how to apply Candidates should apply for a training contract by completing the firm's online application form which is available on our website www.morganlewis.com. Applications will be accepted from October 2017 for training contracts to commence in 2020. The closing date for applications is 31 July 2018.

Work placements Morgan Lewis offers a limited number of placements during the summer each year. The aim of our placement scheme is to provide candidates the opportunity to gain an insight into life as a trainee at the firm. To apply for a place on our summer programme applicants should complete the firm's online application form. The closing date for applications is 31 January 2018.

Sponsorship We will sponsor students through the GDL and LPC. A maintenance grant of £8,000 will also be provided.

Vacancies	6-8
Trainees	12
Partners	34
Total staff	100

Work placement yes

Training contract deadline
31 July 2018

Apply
Online at
www.morganlewis.com

Starting salary
£45,000

Minimum qualifications
High 2.1 degree plus AAB at A level

Sponsorship
GDL/LPC

Offices
Almaty, Astana, Beijing, Boston, Brussels, Chicago, Century City, Dallas, Dubai, Frankfurt, Hartford, Hong Kong, Houston, London, Los Angeles, Miami, Moscow, New York, Orange County, Paris, Philadelphia, Pittsburgh, Princeton, San Francisco, Shanghai, Silicon Valley, Singapore Tokyo, Washington DC, Wilmington

Morgan Lewis

Morrison & Foerster (UK) LLP

CityPoint, One Ropemaker Street, London EC2Y 9AW
Tel: 020 7920 4000
Email: lmccall@mofo.com
Web: www.mofo.com
f mofollp 𝕏 mofo_londongrad

The firm Morrison & Foerster is a leading global firm with over 1,000 lawyers in key technology and finance centres in the US, Europe and Asia. In Europe we have a team of 120 lawyers in our strategic hubs of London, Berlin and Brussels. We work alongside our colleagues in the US and Asia, drawing on cultural, jurisdictional and market knowledge to deliver the best advice and client service with a global approach. Dynamic technology companies, significant financial investors and financial institutions, leading consumer product companies and other market leaders come to MoFo for our expertise, knowledge, advice, commerciality, transaction support and individually tailored client service. We handle some of the world's largest cross-border transactions and resolve some of the biggest disputes across multiple jurisdictions. Our firm was built on, and continues to succeed, because of the talent of our lawyers and their innovative approach in the practice of law. We practise in a collegial environment where we value teamwork and diverse perspectives and operate as one firm. As our nickname suggests, we take our work seriously but we don't take ourselves too seriously.

Types of work Bankruptcy and restructuring, capital markets, corporate/M&A, data privacy, employment, equity derivatives, financial transactions, funds, investigations, litigation, outsourcing, tax and technology transactions.

Who should apply We're looking for people who are intellectually curious, focused and highly motivated. We want applications from students who can demonstrate a genuine interest in law, who enjoy building relationships and value collaboration. Diversity is deeply engrained in MoFo's culture. We recognise that generating the best ideas requires diverse perspectives and want our future trainees to share this philosophy.

Training programme We offer our trainees significant responsibility and the support and training you need to excel in your work. The training period consists of four six-month seats with the potential for joining one of our Asian offices for one seat. There's an active mentoring programme as well as a formal review process four times per year.

When and how to apply Apply via our online application form at careers.mofo.com/law-students. We have two vacancies for our 2018 and 2019 training schemes and four vacancies for 2020. The closing date for 2018 and 2019 is 30 November 2017. The closing date for 2020 is 7 January 2018.

Work placements In 2018 we will be running one vacation scheme at Easter and two in the summer. Our Easter vacation scheme runs for one week and each summer vacation scheme runs for two weeks. Our vacation schemes provide prospective trainees a chance to learn about Morrison & Foerster behind the scenes and to consider whether they want to become a future trainee and an ambassador for our firm. Through our work assignments you'll gain a really good picture of just how much responsibility we give our trainees. You'll also get to know our London-based partners, associates and staff. We treat our vacation scheme as an extended interview and it is the sole method of selecting our future trainees.

Sponsorship We pay full GDL and LPC course fees at The University of Law for our future trainees. We also offer an £8,000 maintenance grant during the GDL and LPC. If students have already completed the GDL or LPC prior to securing a training contract with us we offer 50% reimbursement of fees.

Vacancies	5
Trainees	8
Partners	19
Total staff	85

Work placement yes

Training contract deadline
7 January 2018

Apply
Online at
careers.mofo.com/law-students

Starting salary
£46,000

Minimum qualifications
2.1 degree

Sponsorship
GDL/LPC

Offices
Beijing, Berlin, Brussels, Denver, Hong Kong, London, Los Angeles, New York, Northern Virginia, Palo Alto, San Diego, San Francisco, Shanghai, Singapore, Tokyo, Washington DC

MORRISON FOERSTER

MOOSA-DUKE SOLICITORS 11, De Montfort St, Leicester LE1 7GE **Tel:** 0116 254 7456 **Email:** mduke@moosaduke.com **Apply to:** Mrs M Duke	Niche practice specialising in clinical negligence only. LSC franchise for clinical negligence. Law Society clinical negligence panel.	V 1[18] T 2 P 2 TS 11 WP yes
MORGAN JONES & PETT Grey Friars House, 18-20 Prince of Wales Road, Norwich NR1 1LB **Tel:** 01603 877000 **Email:** davidpett@m-j-p.co.uk **Apply to:** Mr DR Pett	Specialist personal injury and clinical negligence firm. Also family and conveyancing departments. Offices in Norwich.	V 0 T 1 P 3 TS 23 WP no
MORRISH SOLICITORS LLP Oxford House, Oxford Row, Leeds LS1 3BE **Tel:** 0113 245 0733 **Email:** paul.scholey@morrishsolicitors.com **Apply to:** Mr Paul Scholey	City centre location close to law courts. Most types of legal work undertaken with particular specialisation in personal injury. Not recruiting trainees at present.	V 0 T 4 P 15 TS 90 WP no
MORRISONS SOLICITORS LLP Clarendon House, Clarendon Road, Redhill RH1 1FB **Tel:** 01737 854 500 **Email:** hr@morrlaw.com **Apply to:** Miss Michela James	A Morrisons Solicitors trainee solicitor benefits from working in a firm with more than 200 years of accumulated knowledge and expertise across some of the most important sectors of UK law.	V 2-4[19] T 4 P 13 TS 140 WP no
MORTONS 110-112 High Street West, Sunderland SR1 1TX **Tel:** 0191 514 4323 **Email:** mortons@mortons-solicitors.com **Apply to:** The Practice Manager	Please apply to the Practice Manager in own handwriting and enclosing a full CV.	V 0 T 1 P 6 TS 35 WP no
MOSS & CO 17 Lower Clapton Road, London E5 0NS **Tel:** 020 8986 8336 **Email:** narinder.moss@mosslaw.co.uk **Apply to:** Mrs Narinder Moss	A specialist legal aid firm for crime, housing and actions against the police, as well as welfare benefits. Police station accreditation an advantage.	V 1[18] T 2 P 2 TS 10 WP yes
MOWLL & MOWLL Trafalgar House Gordon Road, Whitfield, Dover, Kent CT16 3PN **Tel:** 01304 873344 **Email:** enquiries@mowll.co.uk **Apply to:** Mrs Valerie Scott	Established 130 years in Dover dealing with commercial property, company law, probate, conveyancing, family and civil litigation including employment.	V 0 T 0 P 4 TS 17 WP no
MUCKLE LLP Time Central, 32 Gallowgate, Newcastle upon Tyne NE1 4BF **Tel:** 0191 211 7879 **Email:** alison.appleby@muckle-llp.com **Apply to:** Alison Appleby	Muckle LLP is a highly successful commercial law firm in Newcastle, focussed around being the number one law firm in the North East for business.	V 3-5 T 9 P 30 TS 137 WP yes

V = Vacancies / **T** = Trainees / **P** = Partners / **TS** = Total Staff / **WP** = Work Placement

MULLIS & PEAKE 8-10 Eastern Road, Romford, Essex RM1 3PJ **Tel:** 01708 762326 **Email:** martyntrenery@mplaw.co.uk **Apply to:** Mr Martyn Trenerry	We specialise in commercial work for business including company, employment and licensing. Private client includes litigation, accident claim, trust and probate, and advice to the elderly.	V Poss[18] T 2 P 7 TS 56 WP no
MURRELL ASSOCIATES LIMITED 14 High Cross, Truro, Cornwall TR1 2AJ **Tel:** 01872 226 990 **Email:** info@murrellassociates.co.uk **Apply to:** Mr Chris Wills	Murrell Associates is a specialist team of corporate/commercial lawyers, providing commercial legal services to businesses in the South West and beyond.	V 0 T 0 P 3 TS 16 WP yes
MUSA PATELS 71-73 Bradford Road, Dewsbury WF13 2EG **Tel:** 01924 437800 **Email:** info@musapatels.co.uk **Apply to:** Mr Musa Patel	General practice specialising in criminal law, immigration law, residential and commercial conveyancing.	V 0 T 0 P 2 TS 16 WP no
MUSTOE SHORTER 6-8 Frederick Place, Weymouth DT4 8HQ **Tel:** 01305 752700 **Apply to:** The Staff Partner	Small company with the latest technology with offices in Dorchester and Weymouth dealing with most types of high street business.	V 0 T 3 P 7 TS 50 WP no
MYERSON SOLICITORS LLP Grosvenor House, 20 Barrington Road, Altrincham WA14 1HB **Tel:** 0161 941 4000 **Email:** vacancies@myerson.co.uk **Apply to:** Miss Jordanna Reynolds	A leading independent law firm based in South Manchester, representing businesses and individuals in Manchester, Cheshire, the UK, EU and beyond. We offer an accessible, high-quality and better value alternative to regional and national firms.	V 0 T 6 P 19 TS 81 WP yes
NANDY & CO 62 Woodgrange Road, Forest Gate, London E7 0QH **Tel:** 020 8536 1800 **Apply to:** Ms Nanda Welivitgodage		V 0 T 0 P - TS - WP no
NAPTHENS 7 Winckley Square, Preston PR1 3JD **Tel:** 01772 888444 **Email:** human.resources@napthens.co.uk **Apply to:** Ms Nicola Mason	Departments in commercial property, residential property, family, wills and estate planning, corporate, litigation, employment, rural and licensing. Offices in Preston, Blackburn, Blackpool, Southport and Cumbria.	V 2-4[19] T 7 P 27 TS 227 WP no
NASH & CO SOLICITORS LLP Beaumont House, Beaumont Park, Plymouth PL4 9BD **Tel:** 01752 664444 **Email:** law@nash.co.uk **Apply to:** Mr Jon Loney	A leading Plymouth commercial and private client law firm specialising in all main areas of legal practice.	V 0 T 0 P 12 TS 72 WP no

V = Vacancies / **T** = Trainees / **P** = Partners / **TS** = Total Staff / **WP** = Work Placement

Firm	Description	V	T	P	TS	WP
NELSONS Pennine House, 8 Stanford Street, Nottingham NG1 7BQ **Tel:** 0115 958 6262 **Email:** careers@nelsonslaw.co.uk **Apply to:** HR Department	Nelsons is one of the largest law firms in the East Midlands, providing a full range of legal services to the corporate and private sectors.	0	6	48	193	no
NEWCASTLE UNDER LYME BOROUGH COUNCIL Civic Offices, Merrial Street, Newcastle, Staffordshire ST5 2AG **Tel:** 01782 717717 **Email:** paul.washington@newcastle-staffs.gov.uk **Apply to:** Mr Paul R Washington	Local authority.	0	0	-	2	no
NEXUS SOLICITORS Carlton House, 16-18 Albert Square, Manchester M2 5PE **Tel:** 0161 819 4900 **Email:** cpugh@nexussolicitors.co.uk **Apply to:** Mr Christopher Pugh	We provide commercial legal services and business advice to SME's, plcs and high net worth individuals. Nexus is a commercial practice established in July 2000.	0	1	9	45	no
NOBLE SOLICITORS 26-28 Stuart Street, Luton, Bedfordshire LU1 2SW **Tel:** 01582 544370 **Apply to:** Mr Gareth Cotton	We are a busy criminal and mental health specilaist practice covering the Bedfordshire and north Hertfordshire area.	0	0	3	40	yes
NOCKOLDS Market Square, Bishops Stortford CM23 3UZ **Tel:** 01279 755777 **Email:** hrdept@nockolds.co.uk **Apply to:** Mrs Sue Stevenson	General practice undertaking all types of legal work for a wide variety of private and commercial clients.	3[19]	5	13	140	yes
NORTH YORKSHIRE COUNTY COUNCIL County Hall, Northallerton, North Yorkshire DL7 8AD **Tel:** 0845 872 7374 **Email:** legal.services@northyorks.gov.uk **Apply to:** Mrs Pauline Smurthwaite	Provides legal advice to North Yorkshire County Council and other public bodies, expertise in all areas of public sector law. We have the Lexcel standard.	0	2	0	43	yes
OBASEKI Unit 1, 222 Kingsland Road, London E2 8AX **Tel:** 020 7739 7549 **Email:** solicitors@legalpaal.com **Apply to:** Ms Jennifer Obaseki	We provide expert advice on property, immigration, family, employment, criminal, commercial and civil law. We offer private service and legal aid.	1[19]	2	3	11	yes
OGLETHORPE STURTON & GILLIBRAND 16 Castle Park, Lancaster LA1 1YG **Tel:** 01524 846846 **Email:** dlgillibrand@osg.co.uk **Apply to:** Mr David Gillibrand	A well-established firm in serving the business and rural community based in North Lancashire and the South Lakes.	1-2	3	8	46	no

V = Vacancies / **T** = Trainees / **P** = Partners / **TS** = Total Staff / **WP** = Work Placement

Norton Rose Fulbright LLP

3 More London Riverside, London SE1 2AQ
Tel: 020 7444 2113
Email: graduate.recruitment@nortonrosefulbright.com
Web: www.nortonrosefulbrightgraduates.com
f nortonrosefulbrightgraduatesuk **𝕐** nlawgrad

The firm Norton Rose Fulbright is a global legal firm. We provide the world's pre-eminent corporations and financial institutions with a full business law service. We have more than 4,000 lawyers and legal staff in over 50 cities across Europe, the United States, Canada, Latin America, Asia, Australia, Africa, the Middle East and Central Asia.

Types of work Recognised for our industry focus, we are strong across all the key industry sectors: financial institutions; energy; infrastructure, mining and commodities; transport; technology and innovation; as well as life sciences and healthcare. Wherever we are, we operate in accordance with our global business principles of quality, unity and integrity. We aim to provide the highest possible standard of legal service in each of our offices and to maintain that level of quality at every point of contact.

Training programme There's no progress more vital than what you'll experience on our training contracts. Over two years – broken into four six-month seats – you'll hit all kinds of firsts with us, big and small. You'll explore new areas, for instance. Each seat will take you through different sectors and practice areas, with at least one seat in each of corporate, banking and litigation. One of your seats will almost certainly be on secondment too – your first encounter with working in a new country, or maybe six months spent working in a client office. As you move from one milestone to the next, you'll have a sizeable team at your back. A partner mentor to turn to and to learn from. A trainee buddy to teach you the ropes. And the whole trainee development team to keep you on track from day to day.

When and how to apply We offer up to 45 training contracts each year across two intakes. For the March and September 2020 intakes law and non-law penultimate years, finalists, graduates should apply from 1 October 2017 to 15 July 2018.

Work placements Finding the place you want to spend your career is a moment you'll always remember, and that's exactly the kind of insight we offer on our vacation schemes. Whether you're with us for one week or two, we pack a lot into these three schemes. You'll do real work, for real clients. You'll network with colleagues. You'll present group projects on legal issues. It's a lot of new ground to cover, but if you want to understand what it's really like to work here, nothing else comes close. Pay for the week is £350, and on top of that, you'll leave us knowing for sure that you're on the right path.

Everyone remembers the first day they walked through the doors of their future firm. For many of our lawyers, that happens on our open days and first step programmes. First step caters to first-year undergraduates, while our open days are designed for undergraduates, graduates and career changers of all degree subjects. Either way, it's the opportunity to step through our doors, make a first impression, and use our packed schedule of interactive sessions to discover whether law is right for you.

Sponsorship We cover the cost of all tuition fees for the GDL and LPC as well as providing maintenance grants; £8,000 for the GDL and £7,000 for the LPC.

Vacancies	Up to 45
Trainees	106
Partners	1,180
Total staff	7,100

Work placement yes

Training contract deadline
15 July 2018

Apply
Online via
www.nortonrosefulbright
graduates.com

Starting salary
£44,000

Minimum qualifications
AAB at A level and
2.1 degree or equivalent

Sponsorship
GDL/LPC

Offices
Almaty, Amsterdam, Athens, Austin, Bahrain, Bangkok, Beijing, Bogotá, Brisbane, Brussels, Bujumbura**, Calgary, Cape Town, Caracas, Casablanca, Dallas, Dar es Salaam, Denver, Dubai, Durban, Frankfurt, Hamburg, Harare**, Hong Kong, Houston, Jakarta* Johannesburg, Kampala**, London, Los Angeles, Luxembourg, Melbourne, Mexico City, Milan, Monaco, Minneapolis, Montréal,Moscow, Munich, NewYork, Ottawa, Paris, Perth, Piraeus, Pittsburgh-Southpointe, Port Moresby, Quebec, Riyadh*, Rio de Janerio,San Antonio, San Francisco, Shanghai, Singapore, St Louis, Sydney, Tokyo, Toronto, Warsaw, Washington DC

*Associate offices
**Alliance offices

NORTON ROSE FULBRIGHT

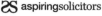
Remember to cite *The Training Contract & Pupillage Handbook* on your application form if you apply to this firm.

404 THE TRAINING CONTRACT & PUPILLAGE HANDBOOK

Orrick, Herrington & Sutcliffe (UK) LLP

107 Cheapside, London EC2V 6DN
Tel: 020 7862 4600
Email: recruitlondon@orrick.com
Web: www.orrick.com/london/gradrecruitment
f orrick 🐦 orrick

The firm Orrick is a leading international law firm with more than 1,100 lawyers in 25 offices located throughout North America, Europe and Asia. Orrick has earned a global reputation advising both established and emerging companies, banks and international financial institutions. Much of Orrick's client work involves cross-border transactions in the tech, finance and energy sectors, as well as dispute resolution and regulatory investigations. At Orrick you will benefit from its core values of collegiality, integrity, excellence, enthusiasm and respect for individuality.

Who should apply If you set your standards high, have a strong work ethic and are a bright, talented graduate of any discipline looking for a firm offering a broad-based training contract, then Orrick could be for you. Applicants should have at least three A-level passes at grades A and B and a 2.1 degree.

Training programme Orrick is a firm for those looking for a high level of responsibility from day one. We value team players and reward collaboration over competition. We aim to give individuals the opportunity to flourish in a lively and supportive work environment and encourage interaction among lawyers across international offices at every level of experience within the firm. We support learning through a steadfast focus on training and a mentoring programme that will provide trainees with the right foundation for building their legal career and for working with clients. A genuine open door policy means trainees work closely with partners and of counsel as well as associates to gain practical experience in research, drafting, procedural and client-related skills.

Our two-year training programme is made up of six four-month seats with regular appraisals throughout. Our dedicated trainee partner oversees the supervision and management of our trainees. There are regular training sessions on legal and soft skills to enhance your development as a lawyer. Our extensive training programme is provided by in-house experts, clients and specialist professionals. Trainees undertake the Professional Skills Course during their induction programme. In 2017, 100% of the trainees who qualified with us in August stayed on with us as associates.

When and how to apply Our training contract and open day applications will open from 11 October 2017, and you can apply online via our website. Our training contract applications will close on 29 June 2018. We will be holding open days in the spring of 2018. Applications for these will close on 9 February 2018.

Work placements We will be holding open days in the spring of 2018 which provide a good opportunity to see the London office of a US law firm in action. Applicants spend the day learning more about the firm and the work on offer in the London office as well as participating in a business game designed to give a flavour of the work of a City lawyer. Further details can be found on our website.

Sponsorship GDL and LPC fees paid plus £7,000 maintenance.

Vacancies	6-8
Trainees	12
Partners	30
Total staff	160

(Figures for London office)

Training contract deadline
29 June 2018

Apply
Online

Starting salary
£40,000 (2017)

Minimum qualifications
As and Bs at A level plus 2.1 degree, any discipline

Sponsorship
GDL/LPC

Offices
Beijing, Brussels, Düsseldorf, Geneva, Hong Kong, Houston, London, Los Angeles, Milan, Moscow, Munich, New York, Orange County, Paris, Portland, Rome, Sacramento, San Francisco, Seattle, Shanghai, Silicon Valley, Taipei, Tokyo, Washington DC, Wheeling (GOC)

orrick

Osborne Clarke LLP

One London Wall, London EC2Y 5EB
Tel: 0117 917 3484
Email: trainee.recruitment@osborneclarke.com
Web: www.joinoc.com
f osborneclarketrainee 🐦 oc_trainee

The firm Osborne Clarke is an award-winning multinational law firm. We've grown rapidly, with 19 global offices and we're proud to say that our influence and impact can now be applied almost anywhere. The core sectors we work in all thrive on innovation; digital business, energy, financial services, life sciences, real estate, recruitment and transport. Our sector teams include lawyers from all legal disciplines, effortlessly blending expertise, insight and enthusiasm. Crucially, we think sector first, organising ourselves around the current affairs and future challenges of the industries we serve, rather than traditional legal practice areas. It helps keep us one step ahead. Like any private practice, legal expertise is at the heart of everything we do. But what makes us distinctive? For a start, you can expect to get involved in truly fascinating work. The variety of our deals and the diversity of our clients provide an exciting and immersive commercial framework. This is a firm where fresh ideas (and the confidence and conviction to see them through) are highly prized, and we're never afraid to take a view. It is also firm with a coherent commercial vision, with a clear direction, supported by a compelling sense of purpose and identity. Put simply, we're going places. And you can put our positive, can-do attitude down to sustained success, in terms of both profile and performance. Finally, there's our culture. When we asked our recent recruits what attracted them to us, they used words like 'friendly', 'inclusive', 'open' and 'fun'. To our clients we are 'approachable', 'proactive', 'understanding' and 'formidable'.

Types of work Main areas of expertise include; banking and finance, business regulation, commercial, corporate, employment and benefits, litigation, pensions, projects, real estate, restructuring and insolvency and tax.

Who should apply? We are looking for candidates who can: communicate effectively; think commercially and practically; solve problems creatively; build effective relationships; and demonstrate initiative. Foreign language skills are also an advantage.

Training programme Our high profile clients expect us to be brilliant, so we put a lot of effort into helping our people be the best they can throughout their careers – not just at the start of it. We foster the brightest and the best, with class-leading training and development programmes, and a unique climate of learning and discovery for everyone. We place value on individuals and respect their needs, motivations and choices. Our workplaces are designed to promote collaboration, often featuring open plan structures that make it easy to fit-in, mix and get involved. You'll also find flexible and imaginative approaches to everyone's work/life needs, with a connected infrastructure that is adaptive and tailored to bringing out the best in people. As a trainee, you'll complete four seats: corporate or banking, real estate or tax, litigation, and one other. In each seat, a senior lawyer will supervise your day-to-day progress and give you regular feedback, so you know how you're doing. They're there to help you up your game. Every three months, you'll have a formal progress review to help you track your development. Our trainees get lots of responsibility. And they find that it's what differentiates their training contracts from others.

Work placements Each of our vacation scheme placements runs for two weeks over the summer and offers a great opportunity for candidates to really get to know the firm. The placement follows a structured programme which allows candidates to spend time in two different departments and get involved in real client work. Beyond work there are plenty of social events organised by our trainees.

Vacancies	20
Trainees	40
Partners	213
Total staff	1,370

Work placement yes
(see Insider Report on p91)

Apply
Online via
www.joinoc.com

Starting salary
Bristol – £34,750
London and Thames
Valley – £40,000

Minimum qualifications
2.1 degree, any discipline

Sponsorship
GDL/LPC

Offices
Amsterdam, Barcelona, Brescia, Bristol, Brussels, Cologne, Hamburg, London, Madrid, Milan, Munich, New York, Padua, Paris, Reading, Rome, San Francisco, Silicon Valley

Remember to cite *The Training Contract & Pupillage Handbook* on your application form if you apply to this firm.

OLDHAM MARSH PAGE FLAVELL White House, 19 High Street, Melton Mowbray, Leicester LE13 0TZ **Tel:** 01664 563162 **Apply to:** Mr Neil Pidgeon	General market town practice including financial services, personal injury, matrimonial, crime. Legal aid franchise.	**V** **T** **P** **TS** **WP**	Poss 0 3 30 no
O'MELVENY Warwick Court, 5 Paternoster Square, London EC4M 7DX **Tel:** 020 7088 0000 **Email:** graduate-recruitment@omm.com **Apply to:** Mrs Natalie Beacroft	O'Melveny is an international law firm with over 750 lawyers working across 15 offices in the US, Europe and Asia.	**V** **T** **P** **TS** **WP**	Up to 3 6 7 50 yes
O'NEILL PATIENT SOLICITORS LLP Chester House, 2 Chester Road, Hazel Grove, Stockport, Cheshire SK7 5NT **Tel:** 0844 576 2121 **Email:** enqs@oneillpatient.co.uk **Apply to:** Mr Steven Thomas	An established and successful firm enjoying an enviable reputation for both private client and company/commercial work which also specialises in volume conveyancing and remortgage work.	**V** **T** **P** **TS** **WP**	0 0 10 240 no
OSBORNES SOLICITORS LLP Livery House, 7-9 Pratt Street, London NW1 0AE **Tel:** 020 7485 8811 **Email:** sandrahillard@osbornes.net **Apply to:** Mrs Sandra Hillard	A firm which undertakes all aspects of general practice, carried out to a high professional standard.	**V** **T** **P** **TS** **WP**	4 7 18 108 yes
OSMOND & OSMOND 55/57 Temple Chambers, Temple Avenue, London EC4Y OHP **Tel:** 020 7583 3434 **Email:** p.flaherty@osmondandosmond.co.uk **Apply to:** Mr Paul Flaherty	Work placements – submit CV together with covering letter to Mr Flaherty.	**V** **T** **P** **TS** **WP**	1[18] 2 2 8 yes
OURY CLARK 10 John Street, London WC1N 2EB **Tel:** 020 7067 4300 **Email:** contact@ocsolicitors.com **Apply to:** Ms Juliet Oury	We are a boutique commercial practice specialising in commercial, corporate, commercial property, employment, litigation and business immigration law. Advising all types of businesses.	**V** **T** **P** **TS** **WP**	1 2 6 22 no
OVER TAYLOR BIGGS 4 Cranmere Court, Lustleigh Close, Exeter EX2 8PW **Tel:** 01392 823 811 **Email:** richard.biggs@otb.uk.com **Apply to:** Mr Christopher Over	We are a dynamic commercial practice with an emphasis on property, corporate and litigation services.	**V** **T** **P** **TS** **WP**	1 1 5 20 no
OWEN WHITE Senate House, 62-70 Bath Road, Slough SL1 3SR **Tel:** 01753 876800 **Email:** russell.ford@owenwhite.com **Apply to:** Mr Russell Ford	We are a top rated regional law firm with specialisms in social housing, real estate, franchising and employment, and have a high trainee retention rate.	**V** **T** **P** **TS** **WP**	2 5 6 40 no

V = Vacancies / **T** = Trainees / **P** = Partners / **TS** = Total Staff / **WP** = Work Placement

OWEN WHITE AND CATLIN 74 Church Road, Ashford, Middlesex TW15 2TP **Tel:** 01784 254188 **Apply to:** Mrs JD Williamson	One of the largest practices covering all aspects of legal work in West London. Progressive and expanding firm and provides a wealth of opportunity for trainees.	**V** 3 **T** 0 **P** 11 **TS** 130 **WP** no
OZORAN TURKAN 203 Green Lanes, Islington, London N16 9DJ **Tel:** 020 7354 0802 **Email:** info@ozoranturkan.com **Apply to:** Ms D Ozoran	Small high street firm; two partners covering family, crime, immigration, conveyancing, wills and probate.	**V** 2[18] **T** 2 **P** 2 **TS** 10 **WP** yes
PAINTERS 29 Church Street, Kidderminster DY10 2AU **Tel:** 01562 822295 **Email:** cdh@painters-solicitors.co.uk **Apply to:** Mr Charles Hobbs	High street practice doing contentious and non-contentious work, commercial and private client, criminal and family, legal aid contracts.	**V** 0 **T** 0 **P** 9 **TS** 50 **WP** no
PALMERS 19 Town Square, Basildon, Essex SS14 1BD **Tel:** 01268 240000 **Email:** recruitment@palmerslaw.co.uk **Apply to:** Mrs Gina Newman	Palmers Solicitors is an established law firm in Essex covering the whole spectrum of legal advice for commercial and private clients from its three offices.	**V** 0 **T** 1 **P** 8 **TS** 90 **WP** yes
PARAGON LAW LIMITED Finelook Studios, 7B Broad Street, Nottingham NG1 3AJ **Tel:** 0115 964 4123 **Email:** hruk@paragonlaw.co.uk **Apply to:** Miss Marie Stafford	Multiple award winning niche immigration law firm, recognised as a leader in its field of practice by the *Legal 500* and *Chambers & Partners*.	**V** 0 **T** 2 **P** 2 **TS** 30 **WP** yes
PARDOES SOLICITORS LLP West Quay House, Northgate, Bridgwater TA6 3EU **Tel:** 01278 457891 **Email:** hr@pardoes.co.uk **Apply to:** HR Department	Serving the South West, our offices in Bridgwater, Taunton, Yeovil, Dorchester and Bridport provide a broad range of legal services (personal and commercial).	**V** 1[19] **T** 1 **P** 8 **TS** 76 **WP** no
PARIS SMITH LLP 1 London Road, Southampton SO15 2AE **Tel:** 023 80482482 **Email:** sarah.giles@parissmith.co.uk **Apply to:** Mrs Sarah Giles	Large regional firm, based in Southampton and Winchester. Established practice with various specialist areas. Recognised as leaders in the South by *Legal 500* and *Chambers*.	**V** 4 **T** 8 **P** 37 **TS** 161 **WP** yes
PARK WOODFINE HEALD MELLOWS LLP 1 Lurke Street, Bedford MK40 3TN **Tel:** 01234 400000 **Email:** admin@pwhmllp.com **Apply to:** The Managing Partner	General firm covering commercial, family, civil litigation, conveyancing, probate and wills, commercial, family, commercial mediation and employment. Well established with three branch offices.	**V** 0 **T** 1 **P** 7 **TS** 60 **WP** no

V = Vacancies / **T** = Trainees / **P** = Partners / **TS** = Total Staff / **WP** = Work Placement

Paul Hastings

8th Floor, Ten Bishops Square, London E1 6EG
Tel: 020 3023 5100
Email: yvettecroucher@paulhastings.com
Web: www.paulhastings.com
f paulhastingsllp ✔ paul_hastings

The firm With lawyers serving clients from 21 worldwide offices, Paul Hastings provides a wide range of services across Europe, America and Asia. Through a collaborative approach, entrepreneurial spirit and firm commitment to client service, the legal professionals of Paul Hastings deliver innovative solutions to many of the world's top financial institutions and *Fortune 500* companies.

Types of work Paul Hastings' London office focuses on corporate and real estate finance transactions, leveraged finance, M&A, restructuring, capital markets and securitisation, funds, litigation, payment systems and financial services, employment and tax. The London office has particular experience in multi-jurisdictional European transactions, working together with our offices in Frankfurt, Milan, Paris and Brussels.

Who should apply We seek undergraduates and postgraduates from both law and non-law backgrounds who combine intellectual ability with enthusiasm, creativity and a demonstrable ability to thrive in a challenging environment.

Training programme Our two-year training programme provides experience in four practice areas, including the possibility of a secondment to a client.

When and how to apply Online application through Paul Hastings website www.paulhastings.com. Please apply by 31 July 2018 for training contracts commencing in September 2020.

Work placements Ad hoc work placements offered on application to the London office.

Sponsorship GDL and LPC fees and maintenance offered to successful applicants.

Vacancies	6
Trainees	12
Partners	27
Total staff	150
Work placement	yes

Training contract deadline
31 July 2018

Apply
Online

Starting salary
£45,000

Minimum qualifications
2.1 degree

Sponsorship
LPC/GDL and maintenance grant

Offices
Atlanta, Beijing, Brussels, Chicago, Frankfurt, Hong Kong, Houston, London, Los Angeles, Milan, New York, Orange Country, Palo Alto, Paris, San Diego, San Francisco, São Paulo, Seoul, Shanghai, Tokyo, Washington DC

PAUL
HASTINGS

Remember to cite *The Training Contract & Pupillage Handbook* on your application form if you apply to this firm.

TRAINING CONTRACT DIRECTORY **409**

Payne Hicks Beach

10 New Square, Lincoln's Inn, London WC2A 3QG
Tel: 020 7465 4300
Email: recruitment@phb.co.uk
Web: www.phb.co.uk

The firm Payne Hicks Beach is a medium size London law firm with a global reach, a 300 year history at the same location in Lincoln's Inn and a thoroughly 21st century approach to client service. The firm provides solution-led advice and legal services to domestic and international private and commercial clients including individuals, families, businesses and trustees. Much of the firm's work has an international element building on strong links with the USA, Canada, Scandinavia, the Middle East and Far East, the main offshore centres, Switzerland and other European countries. Work is regularly handled in French, Italian, German, Danish and Arabic. The firm consistently 'punches above its weight' in the complexity of the clients it serves and matters it handles, and specialist advisers work in close-knit teams to deliver a seamless service across all its practice areas. Trainees invariably feel part of the team from the moment they arrive.

Types of work The firm's reputation has been built on family and private client work as one of the small number of firms in the UK who provide these services at the highest level. Its commanding position in these areas is complemented by an excellent reputation for contentious trusts and dispute resolution, privacy and media law, company and commercial law, employment, residential and commercial property and citizenship and immigration work. Despite their position in the market, Payne Hicks Beach's lawyers pride themselves on the confidentiality and discretion with which they conduct their work, not least because the firm's clients include many household names, as a result of which the firm is one of London's best kept secrets.

Who should apply Applicants for training contracts should have an excellent academic record (an upper second class degree is a minimum requirement), a high degree of drive and determination, and will need to demonstrate, by reference to their experience or otherwise, an ability to analyse problems accurately, to be creative in finding practical commercial solutions, and communicating these clearly, as well as a flair for building relationships with colleagues and clients alike.

Training programme Trainees usually spend six months in each of four specialist departments, with their preferences being taken into account in this rotation so far as possible. There is only one trainee per department at any one time, so he or she plays a very important role, receiving a high level of responsibility, with real work and supervised client contact from the outset. Trainees are subject to regular assessment, with mid seat reviews and end of seat appraisals, and engage in the required Professional Skills and induction courses, as well as a formal in-house training programme. However, with the firm's team outlook and open door policy they also have constant access to help and support from partners and associates who are acknowledged experts in their fields.

When and how to apply Applications are made online via the firm's online application system AllHires (accessed via the firm's website). This includes a requirement for a formal letter of application, submitted online.

Work placements Due to the confidential nature of the work, and the high profile of the firm's clients, as a matter of policy neither work placements nor summer schemes are offered.

Sponsorship Payne Hicks Beach offers full GDL and LPC funding, and a maintenance grant each year of study. BPP Law School is the firm's preferred provider.

Vacancies	2
Trainees	5
Partners	30
Total staff	146

Training contract deadline
31 July 2018

Apply
Online

Starting salary
Competitive

Minimum qualifications
2.1 degree

Sponsorship
GDL/LPC

Offices
London

PAYNE|HICKS|BEACH

Remember to cite *The Training Contract & Pupillage Handbook* on your application form if you apply to this firm.

(410) THE TRAINING CONTRACT & PUPILLAGE HANDBOOK

PARKER BULLEN LLP 45 Castle Street, Salisbury SP10 3SS **Tel:** 017 2241 2000 **Email:** charles.frank@parkerbullen.com **Apply to:** Mr Charles Frank	Premier law firm based in Salisbury and Andover. Rapidly growing, dynamic and innovative, offering experience in legal services for both individuals and businesses.	V 2[19] T 2 P 7 TS 61 WP yes
PARKER RHODES HICKMOTTS 14 & 22 Moorgate Street, Rotherham, South Yorkshire S60 2DA **Tel:** 01709 511100 **Email:** info@prhsolicitors.co.uk **Apply to:** Mrs Fiona Shinner	A general practice high street firm based in Rotherham.	V 0 T 3 P 3 TS 49 WP no
PATCHELL DAVIES 183 High Street, Blackwood, Gwent NP12 1ZF **Tel:** 01495 287 128 **Email:** law@patchelldavies.co.uk **Apply to:** Mr H Patchell	Single office high street practice established 1977 established private client, conveyancing, commercial, family and litigation base.	V 0 T 0 P 2 TS 7 WP no
PATTERSONS SOLICITORS 31 Harrison Road, Halifax, West Yorkshire HX1 2AF **Tel:** 01422 353555 **Email:** pattersonssolicitors@googlemail.com **Apply to:** Mr Brent J Patterson	Firm specialising in legal aid work: crime, benefits, debt, education, housing. Some personal injury.	V 0 T 0 P 1 TS 7 WP no
PAUL ROBINSON SOLICITORS LLP The Old Bank, 470/474 London Road, Westcliff SS0 9LD **Tel:** 01702 338338 **Email:** ablack@paulrobinson.co.uk **Apply to:** The Partnership Secretary	Established 1983. General practice undertaking all areas of law. Investor in people. Lexcel. CQS.	V 1 T 2 P 9 TS 85 WP no
PEACOCK & CO 94 High Street, Wimbledon Village, London SW19 5EG **Tel:** 020 8944 5290 **Email:** kim@peacock-law.co.uk **Apply to:** Ms Kim Peacock	General practice with offices in the heart of Wimbledon Village and Epsom Surrey.	V 1 T 1 P 8 TS 30 WP no
PEARSON HINCHLIFFE LLP Albion House, 31 Queen Street, Oldham OL1 1RD **Tel:** 0161 785 3500 **Email:** joanne.ormston@phsolicitors.co.uk **Apply to:** Ms Joanne Ormston		V 2[18] T 2 P 8 TS 49 WP no
PEMBERTON GREENISH LLP 45 Cadogan Gardens, London SW3 2AQ **Tel:** 020 7591 3333 **Email:** law@pglaw.co.uk **Apply to:** Mrs Debbi Jentas	Pemberton Greenish LLP is a central London law firm specialising in real estate, private wealth and corporate.	V 0 T 5 P 16 TS 87 WP no

V = Vacancies / **T** = Trainees / **P** = Partners / **TS** = Total Staff / **WP** = Work Placement

PENNINGTONS MANCHES LLP 125 Wood Street, London EC2V 7AW **Tel:** 020 7457 3000 **Email:** traineepost@penningtons.co.uk **Apply to:** Ms Helen Lewis	Offices in London, Basingstoke, Cambridge, Guildford, Oxford, Reading and San Francisco. Broad practice with business services, real estate and private individuals divisions and focus on sectors.	**V** 12-14 **T** 25 **P** 110 **TS** 600 **WP** yes
PETER BROWN & CO SOLICITORS LLP 1st Floor, Comer House, 19 Station Road, New Barnet, Hertfordshire EN5 1QJ **Tel:** 020 8447 3277 **Email:** info@peterbrown-solicitors.com **Apply to:** Ms Vicky Gower	We are based in New Barnet and specialise in commercial and residential property. Nearly all our work is from established clients or recommendations.	**V** 1 **T** 0 **P** 6 **TS** 20 **WP** no
PETERS & PETERS 15 Fetter Lane, London EC4A 1BW **Tel:** 020 7822 7777 **Email:** jbeckwith@petersandpeters.com **Apply to:** Ms Julie Beckwith	Recognised as market leader in business crime, international and domestic commercial fraud, encompassing commercial/civil litigation, criminal cartels, extradition, economic sanctions and regulatory work.	**V** 2 **T** 2 **P** 10 **TS** 75 **WP** yes
PHILCOX GRAY LTD 73-75 Newington Causeway, London SE1 6BD **Tel:** 020 3207 2074 **Email:** postroom@philcoxgray.co.uk **Apply to:** Ms Margaret Sullivan	High street social welfare practice with specialists in child law, family, housing and mediation.	**V** 0 **T** 1 **P** - **TS** 18 **WP** yes
PHILLIPS 6 Wood Street, Mansfield, Nottinghamshire NG18 1QA **Tel:** 01623 658556 **Apply to:** Mr Mark Marriott	Growing practice with contracts in criminal and family law. Aims to serve working class people with high quality and a smile.	**V** 0-1 **T** 2 **P** 2 **TS** 9 **WP** no
PICKERINGS SOLICITORS Etchell House, Etchell Court, Bonehill Road, Tamworth, Staffs B78 3HQ **Tel:** 01827 317070 **Email:** recruitment@pickerings-solicitors.com **Apply to:** Ms Sue Hatton	Specialist advice for businesses and individuals throughout the Midlands. LEXCEL & CQS and in the *Legal 500* of leading law firms.	**V** 1 **T** 1 **P** 4 **TS** 33 **WP** no
PICTONS SOLICITORS LLP 28 Dunstable Road, Luton, Bedfordshire LU1 1DY **Tel:** 01582 878538 **Email:** info@pictons.co.uk **Apply to:** HR Department	With offices in Luton, Millton Keynes and Tring, applications for training contracts are invited 1 April to 31 July two years in advance.	**V** 0 **T** 3 **P** 5 **TS** 50 **WP** no
PINSENT MASONS LLP 30 Crown Place, London EC2A 4ES **Tel:** 0141 567 8776 **Email:** graduate@pinsentmasons.com **Apply to:** Graduate Recruitment	Pinsent Masons is a global 100 law firm, specialising particularly in the energy, infrastructure, financial services, real estate and advanced manufacturing and technology sectors.	**V** 72 **T** 141 **P** 420 **TS** 3000 **WP** yes

V = Vacancies / **T** = Trainees / **P** = Partners / **TS** = Total Staff / **WP** = Work Placement

PITMANS LLP The Anchorage, 34 Bridge Street, Reading RG1 2LU **Tel:** 0345 222 9222 **Email:** psmith@pitmans.com **Apply to:** Mr Phil Smith	Commerical practice primarily serving large and medium-sized corporate clients in property, dispute resolution, commercial, corporate, pensions, employment and niche areas.	V 8 T 16 P 40 TS 210 WP no
PJE SOLICITORS 115 Broadway, Treforest, Pontypridd, Rhondda Cynon Taff CF37 1BE **Tel:** 01443 408647 **Email:** info@pjesolicitors.co.uk **Apply to:** Mr Mark David Leyshon	Well-established firm. Strong litigation, employment, matrimonial and conveyancing client base. Aim to expand. 20 minutes from Cardiff. General practice serving valleys and city.	V 0 T 1 P 2 TS 10 WP no
PLEXUS LAW 30-36 Monument Street, London EC3R 8NB **Tel:** 0844 245 4000 **Email:** recruitment@parabisresourcing.co.uk **Apply to:** Mr Jonathan Kay	Highly regarded specialist litigation practice and ABS, providing innovative solutions to the insurance, travel and other related industries. Recently merged with specialist insurance firm Greenwoods.	V 0 T 50 P 117 TS 1800 WP no
POPE & CO 71 High Street, Sittingbourne ME10 4AW **Tel:** 01795 474 004 **Email:** admin@popeandco.co.uk **Apply to:** Mr Daniel Milan	Two-partner practice engaging in full range of legal services including family, crime, litigation, conveyancing and probate.	V 0 T 1 P 2 TS 12 WP yes
PORTER DODSON Central House, Church Street, Yeovil, Somerset BA20 1HH **Tel:** 01935 424581 **Email:** info@porterdodson.co.uk **Apply to:** Ms Deborah Carrington	Expanding general practice working in specialist teams covering commercial (contentious and non-contentious) litigation, private client and property. Five offices in Somerset and Dorset.	V Poss T 3 P 22 TS 120 WP no
PORTNER 7/10 Chandos Street, London W1G 9DQ **Tel:** 020 7616 5300 **Email:** info@portner.co.uk **Apply to:** Mr Mitchell Griver	Deals primarily with complex and interesting work providing a personalised service to substantial clients. Niche is commercial property.	V 1 T 1 P 4 TS 29 WP no
POTHECARY WITHAM WELD 70 St George's Square, London SW1V 3RD **Tel:** 020 7821 8211 **Email:** traineeapplication@pwwsolicitors.co.uk **Apply to:** Training Administrator	Main areas are charities and individuals. Work covered includes company and commercial, residential and business property, trusts, wills, probate, civil litigation, employment and education.	V 1[18] T 2 P 4 TS 28 WP no
POWELL & CO Verbruggen's House, No 1 Street, Royal Arsenal Riverside, London SE18 6GH **Tel:** 020 8854 9131 **Email:** ruthpowell@powell-solicitors.co.uk **Apply to:** Ms Ruth Powell	Small, but highly regarded niche clinical negligence firm. We also have PI, family and housing. Law Society panel members, LSC franchise.	V 0 T 1 P 2 TS 14 WP no

V = Vacancies / **T** = Trainees / **P** = Partners / **TS** = Total Staff / **WP** = Work Placement

PwC

1 Embankment Place, London WC2N 6DX
Tel: 0808 100 1500
Web: www.pwc.com/uk/work-in-legal
f pwccareersuk **✇** pwc_uk_careers

The firm Our client facing legal practice is an exciting place to launch your legal career. With more than 3,200 lawyers across more than 90 countries, we have one of the most geographically extensive legal services network in the world. Because of the way our business is structured, we're able to provide our clients rounded solutions, incorporating multi-disciplinary advice from our wider PwC business areas. It's a unique training environment and by harnessing the collective expertise of more than 19,000 employees across the wider PwC firm in the UK, we can give you an unrivalled, ready-made network on your first day. You'll feel respected and encouraged to be the best you can be – thanks to the quality of our legal training, plus the daily exposure to the highest standards of work, and broad business skills.

Types of work The practice groups you could work in include mergers and acquisitions, banking, commercial litigation, commercial fraud, corporate structuring, cyber security, employment, intellectual property and information technology, pensions, real estate and tax litigation. You may also complete a seat in Dubai or on one our many client secondment.

Who should apply We generally recruit two years in advance for trainee solicitors and focus on penultimate-year law students and final-year non-law students. You'll need to be on track for a 2.1 or above and have a keen interest in business law.

Training programme This is a training contract like no other. As well as legal expertise, you'll build strong business advisory skills – invaluable in a world where business and legal issues are increasingly intertwined. You'll quickly gain practical, hands-on experience and lateral thinking skills as part of teams generating creative ways to tackle complex problems. You'll take the core and elective modules of the Professional Skills Course between your second and fourth seats. And we'll broaden your abilities with extensive internal training in business development and networking, management and interpersonal skills.

When and how to apply Join us – we'll help you reach your full potential. Please note we mainly recruit trainees through our summer vacation schemes. The next available scheme is Summer 2018. All successful applicants from the 2018 scheme will be offered a training contract to join in 2018 or more usually 2019. Apply by 26 January 2018.

Work placements Our three-week paid summer vacation scheme is a great way to find out how we work and see for yourself how distinctive we are in the legal, gaining valuable legal work experience during your time with us. You'll be paid a competitive salary. You'll have the opportunity to join client meetings and calls, conduct research, practise legal drafting, join our seminar and training programme and work directly alongside our lawyers. The scheme is our principal route towards securing a training contract with us.

Sponsorship Trainees can apply for a scholarship award to help with the costs of the Graduate Diploma and the Legal Practice Course provided they haven't yet taken these courses. If successful, you'll receive the total cost of the tuition and examination fees plus a significant contribution towards living expenses.

Vacancies	25
Trainees	25
Partners	35
Total staff	320+

Work placement   yes

Apply
Online via
www.pwc.com/uk/work-in-legal

Starting salary
£39,000

Minimum qualifications
2.1 honours degree in any degree discipline

Sponsorship
GDL/LPC

Offices
London

POWELL SPENCER & PARTNERS
290 Kilburn High Road, London NW6 2DD
Tel: 020 7604 5600
Email: patriciaemmanuel@psplaw.co.uk
Apply to: Ms Patricia Emmanuel

We are a legal aid practice specialising in crime, family law, personal injury, clinical negligence and immigration. Not currently recruiting.

V	0
T	1
P	2
TS	44
WP	no

PREMIER SOLICITORS LLP
Premier House, Lurke Street, Bedford MK40 3HU
Tel: 01234 358080
Email: info@premiersolicitors.co.uk
Apply to: The Recruitment Partner

Main areas are wills, probate, trusts, tax planning, Court of Protection, commercial property, conveyancing, litigation, company commercial, immigration, family, employment and notary services.

V	10
T	10
P	6
TS	80
WP	yes

PRETTYS
Elm House, 25 Elm Street, Ipswich IP1 2AD
Tel: 014 7323 2121
Email: lbloomfield@prettys.co.uk
Apply to: Miss Lisa Bloomfield

One of the largest practices in East Anglia, Prettys has a substantial commercial division, and an established private client base.

V	3-4
T	8
P	6
TS	75
WP	yes

PUNCH ROBSON
35 Albert Road, Albert Road, Middlesbrough TS1 1NU
Tel: 01642 230700
Email: mhealy@punchrobson.co.uk
Apply to: Mrs M Healy

We are an ambitious, good quality firm acting for many local commercial property and private clients. We also have family and mental health specialist practitioners.

V	1-2[18]
T	2
P	7
TS	53
WP	yes

QUALITY SOLICITORS J A HUGHES
Centenary House, King Square, Barry Vale of Glamorgan CF62 8HB
Tel: 01446 411000
Email: timhackett@jahughes.com
Apply to: Mr TG Hackett

We are a high street practice founded in 1888. A forward looking five partner firm, covering a wide spectrum of law.

V	1
T	6
P	6
TS	30
WP	yes

QUALITY SOLICITORS JOHN BARKERS
2 Town Hall Street, Grimsby DN31 1HN
Tel: 01472 268888
Apply to: Ms Kerry Chinn

General practice, but with emphasis on commercial and commercial property matters. The office is located centrally in Grimsby in its commercial hub.

V	Poss
T	0
P	2
TS	6
WP	yes

QUALITYSOLICITORS BRADBURY ROBERTS & RABY
Wadsworth House, Laneham Street, Scunthorpe, North Lincolnshire DN15 6PB
Tel: 01724 854000
Email: brrlaw@qualitysolicitors.com
Apply to: Miss Clare Appleyard

Medium-sized firm in town centre, handling personal injury, commercial, employment, conveyancing, probate, matrimonial and family. Family legal aid franchise. LEXCEL accredited.

V	1[18]
T	1
P	5
TS	47
WP	no

QUALITYSOLICITORS DAVISONS
Sycamore House, 54 Calthorpe Road, Birmingham B15 1TH
Tel: 0121 685 1234
Email: g.davison@qsdavisons.com
Apply to: Mr G Davison

Practice specialising mainly in conveyancing with family, employment, private client, litigation and commercial work throughout six offices in the West Midlands area.

V	0
T	11
P	7
TS	150
WP	no

V = Vacancies / **T** = Trainees / **P** = Partners / **TS** = Total Staff / **WP** = Work Placement

QUALITYSOLICITORS HOWLETT CLARKE LLP 96 Church Street, Brighton BN1 1UJ **Tel:** 01273 327 272 **Email:** eloisefb@howlettclarke.co.uk **Apply to:** Ms Eloise Freeman-Brown	We are a long-established general practice of over 240 years, providing a full range of legal services to the business community and to private individuals.	V T P TS WP	2^{19} 4 3 45 no
QUALITYSOLICITORS JACKSON CANTER 3rd Floor, Walker House, Exchange Flags, Liverpool L2 3YL **Tel:** 0333 321 4580 **Email:** enquiries@jacksoncanter.co.uk **Apply to:** Ms Amanda Hodgson	A committed and well organised general client and legal aid practice in Liverpool undertaking a wide range of work. Recent recruitment has been internal only.	V T P TS WP	1 2 10 190 no
QUALITYSOLICITORS LARGE & GIBSON Kent House, 49 Kent Road, Portsmouth PO5 3EJ **Tel:** 023 9229 6296 **Email:** reception@largeandgibson.co.uk **Apply to:** Mr Richard Wootton	Criminal, civil litigation, family, commercial and residential conveyancing, company, wills and probate, company, personal injury and employment.	V T P TS WP	0 0 2 20 no
QUALITYSOLICITORS LAWSON & THOMPSON 30 Front Street, Newbiggin-by-the-Sea, Northumberland NE64 6PL **Tel:** 01670 856060 **Apply to:** Mr TJR Barker	High street practice with good local client base. Applications invited from ambitious, hardworking individuals with a good sense of humour who are prepared to be team players.	V T P TS WP	0 0 6 30 no
QUALITYSOLICITORS MIRZA 216 Hoe Street, Walthamstow, London E17 3AY **Tel:** 020 8520 4416 **Email:** k.elahi@mirzasolicitors.co.uk **Apply to:** Mr Khalid Elahi		V T P TS WP	2 2 4 18 yes
QUALITYSOLICITORS TRUEMANS Eden House, 38 St Aldates, Oxford OX1 1BN **Tel:** 01865 722 383 **Email:** info@truemans.org.uk **Apply to:** Mr M Trueman	Oxford city centre firm with excellent reputation. Higher court advocacy is a speciality. Full provision of high street services offered.	V T P TS WP	0 1 3 18 no
QUALITYSOLICITORS TURNERLAW Oakfield House, 93 Preston New Road, Blackburn BB2 6AY **Tel:** 01254 688400 **Email:** law@turnerlaw.co.uk **Apply to:** Mr P Garner	General practice including personal injury, family, commercial and crime.	V T P TS WP	0 3 3 25 no
RADCLIFFESLEBRASSEUR 85 Fleet Street, London EC4Y 1AE **Tel:** 020 7222 7040 **Email:** gradrec@rlb-law.com **Apply to:** Mrs Erika Ely	A distinctive law firm with a client-focus approach particularly in the area of growing businesses, healthcare and charities, property investors and developers and private clients.	V T P TS WP	4 8 40 170 no

V = Vacancies / **T** = Trainees / **P** = Partners / **TS** = Total Staff / **WP** = Work Placement

RAI SOLICITORS 19 Stoke Road, Slough SL2 5AP **Tel:** 01753 576 800 **Email:** info@raisolicitors.com **Apply to:** Mr ZS Rai	An established sole practitioner firm providing a wide range of legal services with emphasis on conveyancing, immigration and family law.	V 0 T 1 P - TS 3 WP yes
RAJ LAW SOLICITORS 169 Tooting High Street, Tooting Broadway, London SW17 0SY **Tel:** 020 3133 0000 **Email:** info@rajlaw.co.uk **Apply to:** Mr Raj Boodhoo	We are based in South West London. We provide services in relation to criminal defence, immigration and asylum, civil litigation and family law.	V 0 T 2 P 2 TS 8 WP no
RALLI Jackson House, Sibson Road, Sale M33 7RR **Tel:** 0161 832 6131 **Email:** lisa.harris@ralli.co.uk **Apply to:** Mrs Lisa Harris	Ralli applies law exceptionally across its broad range of specialist practices. It relies on talented people with exceptional skills to achieve this.	V 0 T 1 P 6 TS 55 WP no
RATCLIFFE & BIBBY SOLICITORS 69-71 Church Street, Lancaster LA1 3ET **Tel:** 01524 39039 **Email:** sarah.carr@rblegal.co.uk **Apply to:** Miss S Carr	A three-office firm based in Lancaster, Carnforth and Morecombe provide a wide variety of services including conveyancing, personal injury, employment, family and probate.	V 0 T 2 P 5 TS 45 WP yes
RATNA & CO 169a High Street North, London E6 1JB **Tel:** 020 8470 8818 **Email:** ratna@ratna.co.uk **Apply to:** Mr Majid Shafiq	We are a small firm specialising in immigration, property, family and wills with some employment work.	V Poss T 1 P 2 TS 7 WP no
RAWAL & CO 310 Ballards Lane, North Finchley, London N12 0EY **Tel:** 020 8445 0303 **Email:** solicitors@rawalaw.co.uk **Apply to:** Ms Linda Burchill	Established high street firm specialising in crime, housing, family and welfare benefit welcomes applications from law graduates for traineeship.	V 0 T 1 P 1 TS 7 WP yes
RAWLINS DAVY PLC Rowland House, Hinton Road, Bournemouth BH1 2EG **Tel:** 01202 558844 **Email:** enquiries@rawlinsdavy.com **Apply to:** Mr E John Kennar	Well-established local firm with offices in central Bournemouth, who have in recent years expanded to create a highly focused team of principally general commercial and commercial property lawyers.	V 0 T 2 P 8 TS 45 WP no
RAWLISON BUTLER LLP Griffin House, 135 High Street, Crawley RH10 1DQ **Tel:** 01293 527744 **Email:** info@rawlisonbutler.com **Apply to:** Ms Jo Graver	Leading law firm which delivers a full range of quality commercial services, as well as providing expert guidance to the private client.	V 0 T 1 P 14 TS 74 WP no

V = Vacancies / **T** = Trainees / **P** = Partners / **TS** = Total Staff / **WP** = Work Placement

Reed Smith

The Broadgate Tower, 20 Primrose Street, London EC2A 2RS
Tel: 020 3116 3000
Email: graduate.recruitment@reedsmith.com
Web: www.reedsmith.com
f reedsmithgraduatesuk ♥ reedsmithllp

The firm Reed Smith is a global law firm, with more than 1,800 lawyers in 27 offices throughout Europe, the Middle East, Asia and the United States. Our offices benefit from an international framework, but each one retains key elements of the local business culture. London is currently the largest office with more than 600 people and is based in The Broadgate Tower, which boasts fantastic views of the city.

Types of work We are particularly well known for our work advising leading companies in the areas of financial services, life sciences, health care, energy and natural resources, advertising, technology and media, shipping and real estate. We provide litigation and other dispute resolution services in multijurisdictional and high-stake matters, deliver regulatory counsel, and execute the full range of strategic domestic and cross-border transactions.

Who should apply We are looking for individuals with the drive and potential to become a world-class business lawyer. We want 'players' rather than 'onlookers' with a strong intellect, initiative, the ability to thrive in a challenging profession and the personal qualities to build strong relationships with colleagues and clients.

Training programme Given the range of work undertaken in the London office, trainees get the chance to have a varied training contract and develop a wide range of skills. We offer a four-seat programme, and there are also opportunities for secondments to clients and our overseas offices.

We have developed a new version of the Legal Practice Course (LPC) that fully integrates legal and business learning and leads to a unique Master's qualification, the MA (LPC with Business). Our bespoke programme was the first of its kind and allows students to study commercial and legal aspects in parallel so that they complete the course before entering the training contract with us.

We have vacancies for training contracts commencing in August 2020 and February 2021.

When and how to apply By 30 June 2018, for training contracts commencing in August 2020 and February 2021. Apply online via our website.

Work placements Our summer vacation programme allows delegates to spend two weeks in a department of their choice. In addition to shadowing associates and partners in the team, delegates participate in bespoke training sessions and practical exercises to build their skills and knowledge.

They also enjoy a number of social events arranged for the group. Each year we offer places to applicants who will, on arrival, have completed at least two years of undergraduate study.

Sponsorship We pay for course fees and provide financial assistance for the LPC and GDL.

Vacancies	25
Trainees	50
Partners	681
Total staff	3232

Work placement yes
(see Insider Report on p92)

Training contract deadline
30 June 2018

Apply to
Chloe Muir

Starting salary
£40,000

Minimum qualifications
2.1 degree

Sponsorship
CPE/GDL/LPC

Offices
Abu Dhabi, Astana, Beijing, Century City, Chicago, Dubai, Falls Church, Frankfurt, Hong Kong, Houston, London, Los Angeles, Munich, Miami, New York, Paris, Philadelphia, Piraeus, Pittsburgh, Princeton, Richmond, San Francisco, Shanghai, Silicon Valley, Singapore, Tysons, Washington DC, Wilmington

ReedSmith

Affiliated with

Remember to cite *The Training Contract & Pupillage Handbook* on your application form if you apply to this firm.

418 THE TRAINING CONTRACT & PUPILLAGE HANDBOOK

READ DUNN CONNELL 30, Park Road, Bingley BD23 3NR **Tel:** 01274723858 **Email:** robert@rdcsolicitors.co.uk **Apply to:** Mr Robert Anderson	Offices in Bradford, Bingley and Ilkley. Well-established firm dealing in commercial; employment; matrimonial; dispute resolution and PI; residential and commercial property; trusts; probate; and tax planning.	V 0 T 0 P 4 TS 20 WP no
REENA GHAI SOLICITORS Stable Cottage, 42 High Street, Cranford, Middlesex TW5 9RU **Tel:** 020 8759 9959 **Email:** contact@ghaiandco.com **Apply to:** Ms Reena Ghai	Franchised legal aid department specialising in crime, family and welfare benefits.	V 0-1 T 2 P 1 TS 6 WP no
REES PAGE 8/12 Waterloo Road, Wolverhampton WV1 4BL **Tel:** 01902 577777 **Email:** alund@reespage.co.uk **Apply to:** Mr Andrew Lund	West Midlands practice supplying legal services to corporate and private clients. We are dedicated practitioners with a friendly philosophy to training and trainees.	V 0 T 0 P 8 TS 46 WP no
REST HARROW & CO SOLICITORS 238 Merton Road, London SW19 1EQ **Apply to:** Mr M Ivan-Perera	High street firm providing wide range of legal services with emphasis on commercial law and conveyancing.	V 0 T 1 P 2 TS 3 WP yes
REYNOLDS COLMAN BRADLEY LLP Bury House, Bury Street, London EC3A 5AR **Tel:** 020 7220 4700 **Email:** john.bradley@rcbllp.com **Apply to:** Mr John Bradley	Specialist professional negligence, insurance, commercial and construction litigation practice based in the heart of the city in both London and Bristol.	V 1 T 1 P 3 TS 22 WP yes
RIAZ SOLICITORS 280 Manningham Lane, Bedford BD8 7BU **Tel:** 01274 488110 **Apply to:** Mr M Riaz	We are specialists in criminal defence, personal injury and immigration work.	V 0 T 1 P - TS - WP yes
RIPPON PATEL & FRENCH LLP 37 Harley Street, London W1G 8QG **Tel:** 020 7323 0404 **Email:** rpfsols@aol.com **Apply to:** Mr A Patel		V 1 T 1 P 2 TS 6 WP yes
RIX & KAY SOLICITORS LLP The Courtyard, The Office Village, Uckfield, East Sussex TN22 1SL **Tel:** 01825 744462 **Email:** jennyreardon@rixandkay.co.uk **Apply to:** Ms Jenny Reardon	Rix & Kay Solicitors are a leading practice in the South East with 14 recommendations in the *Legal 500* for its specialist departments.	V 1[18] T 2 P 22 TS 125 WP yes

V = Vacancies / **T** = Trainees / **P** = Partners / **TS** = Total Staff / **WP** = Work Placement

RJR SOLICITORS 18 Melville Street, Ryde, Isle of Wight PO33 2AP **Tel:** 01983 562 201 **Email:** virgil.philpott@rjr.co.uk **Apply to:** Mr Virgil Philpott	High street firm with three offices on the Isle of Wight. Established for over 100 years.	V 0 T 0 P 5 TS 45 WP no
RN WILLIAMS & CO 53 Waterloo Road, Wolverhampton WV1 4QQ **Tel:** 01902 429051 **Email:** cr@rnwilliams.com **Apply to:** Miss Charlotte Richards		V 1[18] T 1 P 3 TS 19 WP no
ROBERT LIZAR 159 Princess Road, Moss Side, Manchester M14 4RE **Tel:** 0161 226 2319 **Email:** rlizar@robertlizar.com **Apply to:** Ms Patricia Graham	Legal aid work in crime, actions against police, family, mental health, civil liberties.	V Poss T 0 P 6 TS 22 WP no
ROBERT MEATON AND CO SOLICITORS Victoria Buildings, Albert Square, 1 Princess Street, Manchester M2 4DF **Tel:** 0845 634 9955 **Email:** info@rmandco.co.uk **Apply to:** Mr Andrew Davies	General commercial practice that undertakes commercial and residential property, PI, employment, debt collection, commerical litigation, financial mis-selling, professional negligence and business matters.	V 1 T 1 P 2 TS 13 WP no
ROBERTS JACKSON SOLICITORS Sandfield House, Water Lane, Wilmslow SK9 5AR **Tel:** 01625546073 **Email:** recruitment@robertsjackson.co.uk **Apply to:** Mrs Sophie Weids	Award-winning niche industrial disease practice offering graduate training scheme for LLB, GDL, LPC and BPTC graduates. Excellent training provided. Training contracts only offered internally.	V 6 T 21 P 9 TS 220 WP yes
ROBINSONS 10-11 St James Court, Derby DE1 1BT **Tel:** 01332 291431 **Email:** rob.styles@robinsons-solicitors.co.uk **Apply to:** Mr Rob Styles	A commercial practice but with some retail elements in Derby and Ilkeston.	V 0 T 0 P 7 TS 61 WP no
ROBSON & CO 147 High Street, Hythe, Kent CT21 5JN **Tel:** 01303 264581 **Email:** post@robson-co.co.uk **Apply to:** Mr Malcolm Dearden	Friendly and supportive small practice dealing in a range of non-contentious and contentious services including family law in pretty Cinque Port Town.	V 0 T 0 P 2 TS 8 WP no
THE ROLAND PARTNERSHIP St Mark's House 52 St Mark's Road, Saltney, Chester CH4 8DQ **Tel:** 01244 659404 **Email:** anne.hall@therolandpartnership.co.uk **Apply to:** Mrs Anne Hall	Specialist solicitors based in Chester, leading firm in medical negligence, serious injury and personal injury, also conveyancing. LSC quality marked.	V 0 T 0 P 2 TS 20 WP no

V = Vacancies / T = Trainees / P = Partners / TS = Total Staff / WP = Work Placement

ROLLITS	Recommended by leading law		
Wilberforce Court, High Street, Hull HU1 1YJ	directories for corporate and	**V**	2-3
Tel: 01482 323239	commercial work, charity law,	**T**	5
Email: ed.jenneson@rollits.com	planning and environmental law,	**P**	21
Apply to: Mr Edward Jenneson	employment, commercial property,	**TS**	118
	intellectual property work and social	**WP**	yes
	housing.		

RONALD FLETCHER BAKER LLP	Application by CV, cover letter and		
77a Baker Street, London W1U 6RF	article (>500 words) on what you	**V**	3
Tel: 020 7613 1402	consider to have been the most	**T**	5
Email: recruitment@rfblegal.co.uk	significant legal development in the	**P**	9
Apply to: Mr Rudi Ramdarshan	last year.	**TS**	40
		WP	no

RONALDSONS	The firm serves the community		
45 Dereham Road, Norwich NR2 4HY	of Norwich and its surrounds by	**V**	1
Tel: 01603 621113	providing family law and residential	**T**	1
Email: mail@ronaldsons.com	conveyancing services.	**P**	1
Apply to: Mr Richard Ronaldson		**TS**	10
		WP	no

ROOKS RIDER	Long-established London firm		
Challoner House, 19 Clerkenwell Close, London	servicing UK and international	**V**	0
EC1R ORR	businesses and private clients	**T**	0
Tel: 020 7689 7000	specialising in tax.	**P**	7
Email: lawyers@rooksrider.co.uk		**TS**	37
Apply to: Ms Lindsey Hemingway		**WP**	no

ROPES & GRAY INTERNATIONAL LLP	The London office of Ropes & Gray		
60 Ludgate Hill, London EC4M 7AW	has a fully integrated team of 30	**V**	5-7
Tel: 020 3201 1500	partners, five counsel, 79 associates	**T**	15
Email: londonhr@ropesgray.com	and 15 trainees, speaking 32	**P**	30
Apply to: Miss Katy McAteer	languages.	**TS**	214
		WP	yes

ROSENBLATT	Based in the City, our practice		
9-13 St Andrew Street, London EC4A 3AF	provides a comprehensive	**V**	0
Tel: 020 7955 0880	commercial law service to UK and	**T**	7
Email: graduaterecruitment@rosenblatt-law.co.uk	overseas businesses.	**P**	22
Apply to: Mr Anthony Field		**TS**	80
		WP	no

ROSLING KING LLP	Commercial firm, successfully		
10 Old Bailey, London EC4M 7NG	competes with large City firms,	**V**	4[19]
Tel: 020 7246 8000	specialising in real estate, banking,	**T**	8
Email: traineerecruitment@rkllp.co.uk	insurance and reinsurance, corporate,	**P**	13
Apply to: Mr James Walton	restructuring and insolvency, dispute	**TS**	85
	resolution, construction, employment	**WP**	no
	and general commercial.		

ROYDS WITHY KING	Fast-growing and ambitious		
5-6 Northumberland Buildings, Queen Square,	composite law firm with offices in	**V**	12
Bath BA1 2JE	Bath, Oxford, London and Wiltshire.	**T**	19
Tel: 01225 425731	We are seeking driven, charismatic	**P**	64
Email: careers@roydswithyking.com	and client-focused trainees across	**TS**	470
Apply to: Miss Claire Fennell	our offices.	**WP**	yes

V = Vacancies / **T** = Trainees / **P** = Partners / **TS** = Total Staff / **WP** = Work Placement

Roythornes Solicitors

Enterprise Way, Pinchbeck, Spalding Lincolnshire PEII 3YR
Tel: 01775 842500
Email: traineerecruitment@roythornes.co.uk
Web: www.roythornes.co.uk
🐦 roythornes

The firm Roythornes is a top 150 law firm with particular strengths in agriculture, property, food and commercial law. The longstanding relationships we form with our clients, sometimes over generations, develop from being trusted advisors and recognised experts in those areas. Based locally, nationally and internationally, our clients include major blue-chip companies, family businesses, private estates and high-net-worth individuals. We operate from four strategically located offices, taking a commercial approach to the work we do. More recently we were delighted to be named as one of the '1000 Companies to Inspire Britain' by the London Stock Exchange.

Types of work With a national reputation we work with an impressive range of clients. Established some 80 years ago, our business was shaped by the work we carried out for farmers and landowners and to this day agriculture remains one of our key sectors. We help farming businesses and the families who own and run them, manage their business and personal matters. National property developers are also key clients of ours. At the other end of the spectrum, we work with well-known food manufacturers and commercial clients whose products appear on the shelves of every major supermarket in the country. Our talented lawyers have an incredible depth of knowledge and regularly appear at the head of league tables in leading law guides such as the *Legal 500*.

Who should apply We are looking for 'big picture thinkers' who want a meaningful career in law – those who want to be involved in exceptional work rather than just run-of-the-mill. You need to have the ambition and drive to make it happen. We are looking for trainees who will care about our clients and want to be part of those longstanding relationships, growing their work through referrals. We set a minimum degree level of 2.1, but just as importantly our ideal candidate should have enthusiasm for the work we do.

Training programme We are a partner-led firm and our trainees experience exceptional learning, development and supervision. Working alongside some of the leading experts in their fields the successful candidates will be exposed to complex, challenging work that will help them mature into the best they can be. We have our own in-house 'agri-academy', regular 'lunch and learn' sessions alongside many courses led by external training providers. We are also growing our mentoring scheme and are fully committed to a blended learning approach.

When and how to apply Applications for 2019 close on 31 January 2018. To apply, take a look at our website under careers and then the 'trainees' section. Here you'll find profiles of some of our current trainees, explaining what it's like to work at Roythornes, and a little about the training they receive and their life outside work. You will also find out about the application process and the key dates of which you need to be aware.

Work placements We run a summer vacation scheme in July for two weeks. Applications for this should be sent to traineerecruitment@roythornes.co.uk by 13 April 2018 for a place in Summer 2018.

Sponsorship For successful applicants, we offer LPC sponsorship of up to £10,000 per annum.

Vacancies	6
Trainees	6
Partners	26
Total staff	187

Work placement yes

Training contract deadline
31 Janaury 2018

Apply
Online

Starting salary
£24,500

Minimum qualifications
2.1 or higher preferred

Sponsorship
LPC

Offices
Spalding, Nottingham, Peterborough, Alconbury

RPC

Tower Bridge House, St Katharine's Way, London E1W 1AA
Tel: 020 3060 6000
Email: manifesto@rpc.co.uk
Web: www.rpc.co.uk/manifesto
🐦 lifeinalawfirm

The firm Leading lawyers. Great clients. And an unrivalled commercial approach to business. At RPC we offer a depth of knowledge and creativity that few firms can rival, and combine this with high quality training programmes that are consistently lauded in the leading directories.

Types of work Banking and finance, commercial litigation, corporate, corporate insurance, competition, construction and projects, corporate finance, dispute resolution, employment, energy/transport/infrastructure, restructuring and insolvency, insurance and reinsurance, intellectual property, IT, media, personal injury, professional negligence, pensions and benefits, real estate, regulatory, tax, technology, outsourcing, international trade and arbitration.

Who should apply Although proven academic ability is important (we require a 2.1 degree or above, not necessarily in law) we value energy, enthusiasm, business sense, commitment and the ability to relate well to others just as highly.

Training programme As a trainee you will receive first rate training in a supportive working environment. You will collaborate closely with a partner and will be given real responsibility as soon as you are ready to handle it. At least six months will be spent in four areas of our practice. We encourage our trainees to express preferences for the areas in which they would like to train. In addition to the Professional Skills Course, we provide a complementary programme of in-house training. When you qualify we hope you will stay with us and we always do our best to place you in the area of law that suits you most.

When and how to apply Apply online at www.rpc.co.uk/manifesto by 13 July 2018 for a 2020 training contract.

Work placements We run summer schemes each year in our London office to enable prospective trainees to spend time with us, getting a feel for the work we do and the unique RPC atmosphere. 12 students at a time spend two weeks with us experiencing the real working life of RPC, supervised by our associates, giving you a fantastic insight into whether a career here is right for you.

During the scheme we expose you to the business side of being a lawyer, including finding out about the importance of client service, marketing and business development and involving you in a 'real-time' group project. There are also opportunities to go to court, assist with research, draft documents, take part in a number of interactive workshops and attend client meetings.

Workshop and insight days – The London spring workshop provides a great snapshot of RPC and what a career in law is really like. Our workshop is open to students in their first year studying law or the penultimate year of a non-law degree. The London insight day is for students wanting to find out more about RPC before submitting a summer scheme or training contract application. Our insight day is open to students in their penultimate or final year studying law or the final year of a non-law degree.

Sponsorship GDL funding: fees paid plus up to £7,000 maintenance LPC funding: fees paid plus up to £7,000 maintenance.

Vacancies	12
Trainees	37
Partners	81
Total staff	760

Work placement yes
(see Insider Report on p93)

Training contract deadline
13 July 2018

Apply
www.rpc.co.uk/manifesto

Starting salary
£38,000

Minimum qualifications
2.1 degree

Sponsorship
GDL/LPC

Offices
London, Bristol, Hong Kong, Singapore

Russell-Cooke LLP

2 Putney Hill, London SW15 6AB
Tel: 020 8789 9111
Email: graduate.recruitment@russell-cooke.co.uk
Web: www.russell-cooke.co.uk
🐦 russellcooke

The firm Russell-Cooke is a top 100 law firm based in London. Our work is diverse, ranging from professional regulation to corporate and commercial, real estate, insolvency, commercial and regulatory litigation, family and children law, employment and immigration, fraud and crime, personal injury and medical negligence, residential property, charities, French property, trust and estates disputes, private client, trusts and tax.

Our expertise is highly rated, with many of our lawyers known as leaders in their fields. We are known as the lawyers' lawyer as a significant amount of our work is received from professional bodies and other lawyers.

Trainees are a fundamental part of our firm. We will give you significant responsibility from the early stages of your career with plenty of client contact. While benefitting from a friendly and professional support network, you will need to be ready to thrive on the challenges that real-life legal work throws at you.

Who should apply In most cases, trainees will need at least two A grades and one B grade at A level (excluding general studies) and an upper second-class degree to be considered. As well as academic grades, intellectual rigour, adaptability and the ability under pressure to handle a diverse range of people and issues efficiently are vital attributes for the role.

Training programme As a trainee, you will be offered four six-month seats covering our core practice areas. You will be given the opportunity to choose from a wide variety of seats during your contract. As we select a small cohort of trainees to join us each year, you will have ample opportunity to manage your own caseload and deal directly with clients. Each of our trainees is assigned a mentor to help guide them through the process; ensuring support is available when needed. As a Russell-Cooke trainee, you can expect to receive in-house and external training to develop your skills and knowledge.

When and how to apply Apply online before 31 July 2018 for training contracts beginning in September 2020. Go to www.russell-cooke.co.uk/trainees.

Sponsorship We provide our trainees with capped sponsorship of up to £10,000 per candidate for LPC fees. We also offer an interest-free loan of up to £5,000 repayable out of a trainee's salary over a two-year period.

Vacancies	9
Trainees	20
Partners	61
Total staff	334

Training contract deadline
31 July 2018

Apply
Online at
www.russell-cooke.co.uk/
trainees

Starting salary
£35,500 plus discretionary
bonus

Minimum qualifications
2.1 degree and AAB grades
at A level (excluding general
studies)

Offices
Central London, Kingston-
upon-Thames, Putney

RUSSELL-COOKE
SOLICITORS

RUSSELL & RUSSELL Churchill House, Wood Street, Bolton BL1 1EE **Tel:** 01204 399299 **Email:** info@russellrussell.co.uk **Apply to:** Mrs Emma Hughes	Long-established firm undertaking criminal, conveyancing, PI, family and probate. Offices in Bolton, Atherton, Bury, Farnworth, Middleton, Horwich and Chester.	**V** 4 **T** 4 **P** 22 **TS** 200 **WP** no
SA LAW Gladstone Place, 36-38 Upper Marlborough Road, St Albans, Hertfordshire AL1 3UU **Tel:** 01727 798000 **Email:** info@salaw.com **Apply to:** Mrs Samantha Walsh	SA Law is one of the most dynamic legal practices in the South East offering specialist commercial services supported by leading private client expertise.	**V** 2[18] **T** 6 **P** 15 **TS** 90 **WP** no
SAMUEL PHILLIPS LAW FIRM Gibb Chambers, 52 Westgate Road, Newcastle upon Tyne NE1 5XU **Tel:** 0191 232 8451 **Email:** jennygoldstein@samuelphillips.co.uk **Apply to:** Ms Jennifer Goldstein	We are a specialist firm offering private client, commercial/civil litigation, family, employment, and commercial and residential property.	**V** 1 **T** 1 **P** 4 **TS** 44 **WP** yes
SAMUELS 18 Alexandra Road, Barnstaple, Devon EX32 8BA **Tel:** 01271 343457 **Email:** mail@samuels-solicitors.co.uk **Apply to:** Mr Jan Samuel	A well-established firm with a strong client base covering most areas of commercial, private client and litigation work.	**V** 1 **T** 0 **P** 3 **TS** 16 **WP** yes
SAS DANIELS LLP 30 Greek Street, Stockport SK3 8AD **Tel:** 0161 475 7676 **Email:** recruitment@sasdaniels.co.uk **Apply to:** Mrs Chris Swerling	During the placement, students get insight into life as a trainee, the firm's vision and values, meet management and work in several work types.	**V** 4[19] **T** 6 **P** 20 **TS** 150 **WP** yes
SAVAS & SAVAGE SOLICITORS LIMITED 20 Stanney Lane, Ellesmere Port CH65 9AD **Tel:** 0151 357 2375 **Email:** sav@savasandsavage.co.uk **Apply to:** Mr Savas Argirou	Four training contracts spread between Ellesmere Port, Heywood and Manchester branches.	**V** 3 **T** 3 **P** 4 **TS** 25 **WP** yes
SB SOLICITORS 228a Whitechapel Road, London, London E1 1BJ **Tel:** 020 7539 1900 **Email:** sb_solicitor@yahoo.co.uk **Apply to:** Mr S Bhuwanee	Growing two-partner practice dealing with housing law, conveyancing (residential and commercial), litigation and construction work.	**V** 0 **T** 0 **P** 2 **TS** 4 **WP** no
SCAIFF LLP 23 Foregate Street, Worcester WR1 1UW **Tel:** 01905 27505 **Email:** mail@scaiff.co.uk **Apply to:** Mrs Dawn Hodgkins	General practice with emphasis on company commercial and litigation particularly personal injury and medical negligence.	**V** 0 **T** 0 **P** 3 **TS** 21 **WP** no

V = Vacancies / **T** = Trainees / **P** = Partners / **TS** = Total Staff / **WP** = Work Placement

SCHILLINGS INTERNATIONAL 41 Bedford Square, London WC1B 3HX **Tel:** 020 7034 9000 **Email:** enquiries@schillings.co.uk **Apply to:** Mrs Lindsey Watts	With over 30 years experience, Schillings assist prominent individuals and businesses wherever they are in the world; whatever their reputation and privacy issues.	V 0 T 0 P 9 TS 62 WP no
SCHOFIELD SWEENEY LLP Church Bank House, Church Bank, Bradford BD1 4DY **Tel:** 01274 306000 **Email:** trainingcontracts@schofieldsweeney.co.uk **Apply to:** Mr Adrian Ballam	An ambitious and progressive commercial law firm with friendly staff that works with a diverse range of businesses, entrepreneurs and public sector organisations.	V 3[19] T 7 P 31 TS 161 WP yes
SCOTT ROWE SOLICITORS Chard Street, Axminster, Devon EX13 5DS **Tel:** 01297 32345 **Email:** kevin.bull@scottrowe.co.uk **Apply to:** Mr Kevin Bull	Well-established West Country firm offering full range of legal services, seeks talented and hardworking trainees. The firm is Lexcel and Investors in People accredited for over 10 years.	V 1[18] T 1 P 3 TS 26 WP no
SEDDONS 5 Portman Square, London W1H 6NT **Tel:** 020 7725 8000 **Email:** trainingcontracts@seddons.co.uk **Apply to:** Mr Simon Jacobs	We advise our UK and international clients on real estate, family law, wealth management, disputes, corporate law, employment and more.	V 2 T 6 P 32 TS 116 WP no
SENTINEL SOLICITORS 204 Seven Sisters Road, Finsbury Park, London N4 3NX **Tel:** 020 7100 3100 **Email:** sajid@sentinelsolicitors.co.uk **Apply to:** Mr Sajid Sheikh	Sentinel Solicitors is an award-winning law firm that specializes in immigration and human rights. It offers training and work placement opportunities to law students.	V 2[18] T 1 P 3 TS 6 WP yes
SERGEANT & COLLINS 25 Oswald Road, Scunthorpe DN15 7PS **Tel:** 01724 864215 **Email:** sergeantcollins@tiscali.co.uk **Apply to:** Mr P Wright	Traditional high street practice dealing with conveyancing, probate, family work, crime and general business matters.	V 0 T 1 P 2 TS 15 WP no
THE SETHI PARTNERSHIP SOLICITORS The Barn House, 38 Meadow Way, Eastcote, Ruislip HA4 8TB **Tel:** 020 8866 6464 **Email:** ritu@sethi.co.uk **Apply to:** Mrs Ritu Sethi	General practice – specialising in property work, crime, matrimonial, litigation, immigration, civil litigation, wills and probate.	V 1 T 1 P 3 TS 25 WP yes
SEWELL MULLINGS LOGIE LLP 7 Dollar Street, Cirencester GL7 2AS **Tel:** 01285 650000 **Email:** jbb@sml-law.co.uk **Apply to:** Mr John Bartholomew	The largest practice in Cirencester providing excellent and varied training. We offer a full range of legal services and have a well established client base.	V 1[19] T 3 P 7 TS 42 WP no

V = Vacancies / **T** = Trainees / **P** = Partners / **TS** = Total Staff / **WP** = Work Placement

SHACKLOCKS LLP St Peters House, Bridge Street, Mansfield NG18 1AL **Tel:** 01623 626141 **Email:** clarem@shacklocks.co.uk **Apply to:** Mrs Clare McShane	Successful applicants will work as paralegals for up to 12 months with the opportunity of a training contract thereafter for the right candidates.	V 2-4[18] T 3 P 7 TS 35 WP no
SHAKESPEARE MARTINEAU LLP One Colmore Square, Birmingham B4 6AA **Tel:** 080 0763 1000 **Email:** training.contracts@shma.co.uk **Apply to:** Mrs Katherine Stocks	A dynamic and passionate law firm that combines a commercial and personal atmosphere. Please apply for training contracts to start in 2019 and 2020.	V 10 T 20 P 130 TS 850 WP no
SHARP YOUNG & PEARCE 6 Weekday Cross, Nottingham NG1 2GF **Tel:** 0115 959 0055 **Email:** jmillward@syplaw.com **Apply to:** Mrs J Millward	General practice based in centre of Nottingham with four branch offices and dealing with all aspects of legal work.	V 0-1 T 1 P 10 TS 65 WP no
SHEARMAN & STERLING (LONDON) LLP 9 Appold Street, London EC2A 2AP **Tel:** 020 7655 5000 **Email:** graduates@shearman.com **Apply to:** Mr Paul Gascoyne	One of New York's oldest firms, our London office, established in 1972, has become a leading practice covering all aspects of international commercial law.	V Approx 17 T 30 P 35 TS 300 WP yes
SHEIKH & CO 208 Seven Sisters Road, London N4 3NX **Tel:** 020 7263 5588 **Apply to:** Mr SA Sheikh	General practice with 80% legal aid work. The firm expanded very rapidly within a year.	V 2 T 4 P 3 TS 35 WP yes
SHERRARDS SOLICITORS LLP 45 Grosvenor Road, St Albans, Hertfordshire AL1 3AW **Tel:** 01727 832830 **Email:** careers@sherrards.com **Apply to:** Mrs Joanne Perry	A progressive firm with a strong bias towards commercial work and litigation, while retaining experienced private client departments.	V 1 T 4 P 15 TS 90 WP no
SHORT RICHARDSON & FORTH LLP 4 Mosley Street, Newcastle-upon-Tyne NE1 1DE **Tel:** 0191 232 0283 **Email:** lb@srflegal.co.uk **Apply to:** Mrs Lisa Berg	We are a commercial law firm based in Newcastle upon Tyne. Practice areas: employment, property, private client, commercial litigation and insolvency, and regulation/financial crime.	V 1 T 1 P 8 TS 23 WP no
SHRANKS Ruskin House, 40/41 Museum Street, London WC1A 1LT **Tel:** 020 7831 6677 **Email:** shrank@shranks.co.uk **Apply to:** Mr Jeremy P Ticktum	Landlord and tenant, commercial property, company/commercial, residential conveyancing, personal injury, employment, general litigation, wills, trusts and probate.	V 0 T 1 P 2 TS 9 WP no

V = Vacancies / **T** = Trainees / **P** = Partners / **TS** = Total Staff / **WP** = Work Placement

Shoosmiths

The Lakes, Bedford Road, Northampton NN4 7SH
Tel: 03700 863679
Email: joinus@shoosmiths.co.uk
Web: www.shoosmiths.co.uk
f shoosmithsgraduates **🐦** shoosmithsgrads

The firm Growing steadily, with offices across the UK, Shoosmiths is a progressive, forward-thinking law firm, with a real spirit of enterprise. We really value our people, giving them the freedom, recognition and support to succeed; while clients find us open, accessible and easy to work with. Recognised recently as The UK Law Firm of the Year at the British Legal Awards, and being the first top 100 law firm to achieve the Investors in People Gold Standard, shows we are committed to providing the top quality service our clients love, and which our people love to deliver. And we accepted the award for the Best Trainer for four years in a row!

Types of work Shoosmiths is a full-service law firm offering you experience in a variety of areas, including commercial, corporate, employment, real estate, intellectual property, banking, planning, and dispute resolution. Through our Access Legal consumer brand, we also offer private client, personal injury, clinical negligence, and conveyancing.

Who should apply You should be open-minded and innovative with a can-do attitude. You'll be trained in a non-hierarchal, open plan environment. As a trainee, you will value a social life outside the office. Work wise, you will care about the quality of service you give to clients, and will want to make a real and direct contribution to the firm's success.

Training programme There is nothing like diving straight in and having a go, and while we would not ask you to do something that you are not comfortable tackling, we expect you to relish the opportunity to get experience of real cases and deals from the start. In our opinion, it is the best way to learn. We allocate no more than one trainee to each team, which means trainees enjoy high levels of involvement with the team, and are given good quality work and contact with clients.

Over two years, you will complete four six-month placements, one of which could be an external secondment to a client's in-house legal team, providing an invaluable insight from the client's perspective. Secondments are seen as a valuable opportunity for relationship building with clients and to help the personal development of our solicitors and trainees. You will see how the in-house legal team interacts with the business and with its external legal advisers, while helping to develop the relationship between the client and Shoosmiths.

Our trainees take an active part in corporate responsibility (CR) from their very first week. They create and drive initiatives of their own, including 'New Friday', a national networking event for young professionals.

When and how to apply Please apply online at www.shoosmiths.co.uk/graduates. Please check our website for locations we are currently recruiting to.

Work placements We offer placements of one week to help you get a real insight into the life of a trainee. Placements provide invaluable experience, allowing you to choose the right firm for you, and can even fast track you to a place on the assessment day for a training contract.

Sponsorship We are happy to offer you financial assistance in relation to your forthcoming GDL and/or LPC. We do not specify a particular provider for your postgraduate studies.

Vacancies	20
Trainees	42
Partners	175
Total staff	1,550

Work placement yes
(see Insider Report on p95)

Training contract deadline
30 June 2018

Apply
Online

Starting salary
£27,000-£28,000

Minimum qualifications
Any degree

Sponsorship
GDL & LPC

Offices
Basingstoke, Belfast, Birmingham, Edinburgh, Leeds, London, Milton Keynes, Manchester, Northampton, Nottingham, Solent, Reading

SH∞SMITHS

Affiliated with

aspiringsolicitors

Remember to cite *The Training Contract & Pupillage Handbook* on your application form if you apply to this firm.

SHULMANS LLP 10 Wellington Place, Leeds LS1 4AP **Tel:** 0113 245 2833 **Email:** training@shulmans.co.uk **Apply to:** Mr Chris Peace	Shulmans LLP is a full service UK 200 corporate law firm based in a single site office in Leeds delivering high quality advice to businesses.	V 3 T 6 P 25 TS 190 WP no
SIDLEY AUSTIN LLP Woolgate Exchange, 25 Basinghall Street, London EC2V 5HA **Tel:** 020 7776 9633 **Email:** graduaterecruitment@sidley.com **Apply to:** Ms Nicole Katz	Sidley Austin LLP is one of the world's largest law firms, with approximately 1,900 lawyers in 20 offices across the globe.	V 12 T 22 P 43 TS 260 WP yes
SILLS & BETTERIDGE LLP 46 Silver Street, LINCOLN LN2 1ED **Tel:** 01522 542211 **Email:** ldavies@sillslegal.co.uk **Apply to:** Miss Leanne Davies	A broadly-based practice acting for a range of private and business clients and taking publicly funded work.	V 219 T 6 P 43 TS 265 WP yes
SILVERBECK RYMER Dempster Building, Atlantic Way, Brunswick Business Park, Liverpool L3 HUU **Tel:** 0151 236 9594 **Apply to:** Ms Diane Taylor	Major player within the insurance litigation sector, acting for claimant and liability claims department. 'Centre of excellence' for catastrophic injuries.	V 0-3 T 3 P 7 TS 218 WP no
SILVERDALE SOLICITORS Silverdale House, 404 Cheetham Hill Road, Manchester M8 9LE **Tel:** 0161 740 0333 **Email:** enquiries@silverdalelaw.co.uk **Apply to:** Mr M J Amin	Broad-based general practice undertaking contentious and non-contentious work. Busy practice with substantial growth over past 12 months including a third office in Manchester city centre.	V 0 T 2 P 4 TS 25 WP yes
SIMKINS LLP Lynton House, 7-12 Tavistock Square, London WC1H 9LT **Tel:** 020 78745600 **Email:** trainingcontractregistrations@simkins.com **Apply to:** Trainee Recruitment	West End commercial law firm providing a wide range of legal services with a particular focus on the media, entertainment, marketing and leisure industries.	V 2 T 4 P 20 TS 45 WP yes
SINTONS LLP The Cube, Barrack Road, Newcastle upon Tyne NE4 6DB **Tel:** 0191 226 7878 **Email:** louise.dack@sintons.co.uk **Apply to:** Mrs Louise Dack	Leading firm with three main practice groups: commercial; private client; and personal injury. Approachable, forward thinking, supportive and committed to continued career development.	V 0 T 5 P 26 TS 200 WP yes
SJP LAW 5 Parliament Street, Hull HU1 2AZ **Tel:** 01482 324591 **Email:** kcu@sjplaw.co.uk **Apply to:** Ms Kirsty Cuckson	Providing a full range of commercial services to medium-sized owner managed businesses; also dealing with complex personal injury/clinical negligence litigation.	V 2 T 4 P 5 TS 50 WP yes

V = Vacancies / **T** = Trainees / **P** = Partners / **TS** = Total Staff / **WP** = Work Placement

Simmons & Simmons

CityPoint, One Ropemaker Street, London EC2Y 9SS
Tel: 020 7628 2020
Email: recruitment@simmons-simmons.com
Web: www.simmons-simmons.com/graduates
f simmonsgraduates ✈ simmonsgrads

The firm Scratch the surface of Simmons & Simmons and you'll discover a leading law firm of over 1,600 colleagues, offering expert legal advice across Europe, the Middle East and Asia. We operate across four key sectors and through a range of services to help clients navigate all kinds of legal challenges, from buying and selling national chain stores to developing new fleets of aircraft. We work in the areas that matter the most to everyone's future, from life sciences to technology, media and telecommunications. So whatever you do, wherever you go, you'll see developments we've been involved in. All you need to do is look, and you'll uncover the world of law.

Who should apply We're looking for perceptive, ambitious future lawyers. You see the finer detail – the intricate legal framework that powers and shapes our everyday – and you've got the drive to be part of it. We are looking for students who are on course for at least a 2.1 in any degree subject. That said, academic performance isn't everything; that's why we look for raw talent and potential throughout our assessment process.

Training programme Our training contracts are offered in both London and Bristol, and either way, you'll spend two years discovering the innovation we're known for. As well as moving through four six-month seats across our sectors, you'll also benefit from the compass programme; our unique and progressive trainee skills academy that offers a combination of practical learning, mentoring and online tools. Our teams will teach you everything they know about the world of law, and you'll find your niche in the process, qualifying into your choice of practice area.

Work placements Get right to the heart of life as a trainee lawyer on our vacation schemes. Over one or two weeks in either Bristol or London, you'll experience the work, the reach and the day-to-day buzz of our international firm. In short, it's the chance for us to get to know each other on a deeper level. That's why it's also the best route to a training contract with us, with many vacation schemers returning as trainees.

Winter vacation scheme (London): A one-week scheme aimed specifically at final-year students and graduates of all disciplines. Applications open 1 October 2017.

Spring insight scheme (London): A two-day workshop for first-year students of all disciplines, as well as penultimate-year non-law students. Applications open 15 January 2018.

Summer vacation scheme (London): A two-week scheme open to penultimate and final-year students and graduates of all disciplines. Applications open 15 October 2017.

Summer vacation scheme (Bristol): A one-week scheme open to penultimate-year law students and final-year students and graduates of all disciplines. Applications open 15 October 2017.

A series of open days are also available in London and Bristol to all students and graduates, running throughout the year.

Sponsorship We will cover your full tuition fees for law school and offer a maintenance grant of £7,000 for the GDL and £7,500 for the LPC.

Vacancies	30+
Trainees	80
Partners	250+
Total staff	1,600+

Work placement yes

Apply
Online at www.simmons-simmons.com/graduates

Starting salary
London
1st year – £42,000
2nd year – £47,000
Bristol
1st year – £37,000
2nd year – £38,000

Minimum qualifications
2.1 degree (or equivalent)

Sponsorship
GDL/LPC

Offices
Amsterdam, Beijing, Bristol, Brussels, Doha, Dubai, Düsseldorf, Frankfurt, Hong Kong, Jeddah*, Lisbon*, London, Luxembourg, Madrid, Milan, Munich, Paris, Riyadh*, Shanghai, Singapore, Tokyo
*Associated offices

Simmons & Simmons

Affiliated with

⊃⊂ aspiringsolicitors

Remember to cite *The Training Contract & Pupillage Handbook* on your application form if you apply to this firm.

430 THE TRAINING CONTRACT & PUPILLAGE HANDBOOK

SKADDEN, ARPS, SLATE, MEAGHER & FLOM (UK) LLP 40 Bank Street, Canary Wharf, London E14 5DS **Tel:** 020 7519 7000 **Email:** graduate.hiring@skadden.com **Apply to:** Mr Aidan Connor	Skadden is an award winning global law firm with 25 international offices and approximately 2,000 lawyers. Voted Best US Law Firm in London (*Legal Business*).	V Approx 10 T 18 P 31 TS 235 WP yes
SLATER & GORDON (UK) LLP 58 Mosley Street, Manchester M3 2BU **Tel:** 0161 3833964 **Email:** recruitment@slatergordon.co.uk **Apply to:** Miss Louise Myers	Slater & Gordon Lawyers is an international, award-winning law firm committed to becoming the largest provider of personal legal services in the UK.	V 53 T 36 P 86 TS 3500 WP no
SLATER GORDON SOLUTIONS LEGAL LTD Slater Gordon Solutions, Dempster Building, Atlantic Way, Brunswick Business Park, Liverpool L3 4UU **Apply to:** Mr Aaron Leigh		V 1 T 10 P 5 TS 1150 WP no
SLAUGHTER AND MAY One Bunhill Row, London EC1Y 8YY **Tel:** 0207 090 4454 **Email:** trainee.recruit@slaughterandmay.com **Apply to:** Mrs Janine Arnold	A leading international law firm whose main activities are in the field of corporate, commercial and financing law.	V 80 T 150 P 115 TS 1100 WP yes
SMITH LLEWELYN PARTNERSHIP 18 Princess Way, Swansea SA1 3LW **Tel:** 01792 464444 **Email:** enquiries@smithllewelyn.com **Apply to:** Mr Julian Thomas	South Wales' leading medical negligence, pharmaceutical product liability and personal injury firm; community legal service franchise in all areas committed to the victim.	V 1 T 2 P 4 TS 40 WP yes
SMITH PARTNERSHIP 4th Floor, Celtic House, Friary Street, Derby DE1 1LS **Tel:** 01332 225 225 **Email:** recruitment@smithpartnership.co.uk **Apply to:** Mr Bally Atwal	Smith Partnership is a young dynamic firm with offices throughout the East Midlands, work areas include commercial, criminal and private client services.	V 4 T 8 P 28 TS 250 WP no
SO LEGAL LIMITED 55 South Street, Eastbourne, East Sussex BN21 4UT **Tel:** 01323 407555 **Email:** jobs@solegal.co.uk **Apply to:** Ms Lisa Jones	This is an opportunity to train within a distinctive law firm. Candidates will have their LPC and a law degree and be local to Sussex.	V 5[19] T 2 P 2 TS 12 WP no
SONN MACMILLAN WALKER 12 Widegate Street, London E1 7HP **Tel:** 020 7377 8889 **Email:** emacmillan@smw-law.co.uk **Apply to:** Mr Euan Macmillan	Specialist criminal defence firm, mainly legal aid work. Members of the Serious Fraud Panel. Applications accepted for work placements all year round.	V 2[19] T 4 P 3 TS 25 WP yes

V = Vacancies / **T** = Trainees / **P** = Partners / **TS** = Total Staff / **WP** = Work Placement

SOOKIAS & SOOKIAS 5th Floor, 15 Brook's Mews, London W1K 4DS **Tel:** 020 7465 8000 **Email:** info@sookias.co.uk **Apply to:** Ms Barbara Lewin	Small West End solicitors specialising in commercial work including immigration, litigation, tax and company matters.	V 0 T 0 P 4 TS 20 WP no
SOUTHERNS Mackenzie House, 68 Bank Parade, Burnley BB11 1UB **Tel:** 01282 422711 **Email:** ncronin@southernslaw.info **Apply to:** Mrs Jan Cook	General high street practice. Offices also in Nelson, Colne and Blackpool.	V 0 T 0 P 6 TS 63 WP no
THE SPEAKEASY 166 Richmond Road, Cardiff CF24 3BX **Tel:** 029 2045 3111 **Email:** info@speakeasy.cymru **Apply to:** Mr Warren Palmer	Not-for-profit legal advice centre providing free legal advice and representation regarding debt, benefits and housing.	V 0 T 0 P - TS 14 WP no
SPEARING WAITE LLP 34 Pocklingtons Walk, Leicester LE1 6BU **Tel:** 0116 262 4225 **Email:** info@spearingwaite.com **Apply to:** Miss Sarah Moore	One of the largest firms in Leicester specialising in commercial property, corporate, intellectual property, dispute resolution, employment and private client.	V 2-4[19] T 6 P 21 TS 98 WP no
SPELTHORNE BOROUGH COUNCIL Council Offices, Knowle Green, Staines TW18 1XB **Tel:** 01784 451 499 **Email:** legal@spelthorne.gov.uk **Apply to:** Mr Michael Graham	Small local government team in a Surrey district council. Procurement, litigation, property, planning and licensing. We welcome summer placements for interesting candidates.	V 0 T 0 P 0 TS 7 WP yes
SPENCE & HORNE 343 Mare Street, Hackney, London E8 1HY **Tel:** 020 8985 2277 **Email:** 202@spencehorne.co.uk **Apply to:** Miss Angela Spence	Small practice specialising in immigration, family, property, housing and probate, offering adivce for family housing with limited advice in some areas of civil litigation and compromise agreements.	V 0 T 0 P 1 TS 4 WP yes
SRI KANTH & CO 557 High Road, Wembley, Middlesex HA0 2DW **Tel:** 020 8795 0648 **Email:** info@srikanthsolicitors.co.uk **Apply to:** Mr S Srikanthalingam		V 2 T 2 P 2 TS 11 WP yes
STEELE RAYMOND LLP Richmond Point, 43 Richmond Hill, Bournemouth BH2 6LR **Tel:** 01202 204510 **Email:** jenniferrogerson@steeleraymond.co.uk **Apply to:** Ms Jennifer Rogerson	A modern and expanding firm with a wide range of clients providing predominantly business and commercial law advice.	V 2-3[18] T 5 P 14 TS 75 WP no

V = Vacancies / **T** = Trainees / **P** = Partners / **TS** = Total Staff / **WP** = Work Placement

Squire Patton Boggs (UK) LLP

7 Devonshire Square, Cutlers Gardens, London EC2M 4YH
Tel: 020 7655 1000
Email: careers@squir.com
Web: www.squirepattonboggs.com
f squirepattonboggscareers 🐦 spb_careers

The firm We are a global law firm with 46 offices in 21 countries. Our team of 2,600 includes more than 1,500 lawyers. Recognised as having one of the broadest global footprints in the legal industry, we provide access to new knowledge, new markets and new expertise.

We support private and public sector clients across extensive global practice areas. Our teams have well-established local and regional positions across North America, Europe, Asia Pacific, the Middle East and Latin America. Collectively, we cover 140 jurisdictions and speak over 40 languages.

In the UK, we operate from offices in Birmingham, Leeds, London and Manchester, working with a diverse mix of global clients. Many of these are among the biggest names and brands in the world: FTSE and *Fortune* 100 companies, emerging and fast-growth businesses, financial institutions, and regional and national governments.

Training programme In the UK, we offer a unique training contract tailored to individual trainee needs. We provide a comprehensive induction programme at an external campus, followed by tailored department training to each seat and tailored skills training through various seminars and workshops.

The programme comprises six four-month seats during the trainee's training contract. The key to the training contract is "involvement and responsibility", which is achieved through the choice and number of seats that can be undertaken during the programme, including secondments to clients and our overseas offices. Trainees benefit from two-tier supervision and challenging work.

When and how to apply Apply online at www.squirepattonboggs.com.

Work placements We run a two-week summer placement scheme and a one-week winter placement scheme that provide students with genuine experience as to what life is like as a trainee solicitor.

Penultimate-year law students, final-year non-law students and all postgraduate students are eligible to apply for the summer placement scheme. Students in their final year or above (law and non-law) are eligible to apply for the winter placement scheme.

All students who are successful in getting onto a placement scheme will automatically be considered for a training contract.

Vacancies	25
Trainees	46
Partners	500
Total staff	2,600
Work placement	yes
Apply	
Online	
Offices	
46 offices across 21 countries	

Stephenson Harwood LLP

1 Finsbury Circus, London EC2M 7SH
Tel: 020 7809 2812
Email: graduate.recruitment@shlegal.com
Web: www.shlegal.com/graduate

The firm Stephenson Harwood is a thriving, international law firm with over 150 partners and more than 900 staff worldwide. We act for a wide range of listed and private companies, institutions and successful entrepreneurs. We also offer a full-range of services in a wide variety of sectors. What's more, when it comes to delivering sound commercial solutions to complex business challenges, we punch well above our weight.

Through our international network of offices and affiliates, we provide clients with quality resources and expert local knowledge in Africa, Europe, the Middle East, Latin America and Asia. Indeed, with around 25% of our people operating out of Seoul, Hong Kong, Beijing, Shanghai and Singapore, our link to Asia is stronger than ever.

Types of work Commercial litigation; corporate; employment and pensions; finance; marine and international trade; and real estate.

Who should apply Firstly we look for a quick intellect. As well as at least a 2.1 in any discipline plus 320 UCAS points or equivalent, you'll need strong analytical skills, sound judgement, imagination and meticulous attention to detail. Also vital are the communication skills to be persuasive and build rapport, plenty of drive and determination, plus a keen interest in business.

Training programme We take just 18 trainees on each year. So you can look forward to a huge amount of individual attention, coaching and mentoring. Your structured programme involves four six-month seats in our contentious and non-contentious practice groups. You can expect on-the-job training complemented by in-house seminars; to share an office with a partner or senior associate; and to benefit from a continuous review of your career development. You could also have the chance to spend one of your six-month seats in Hong Kong, Singapore, Dubai, Paris or Seoul and to take advantage of client secondment opportunities. We'll give you your own caseload and as much responsibility as you can shoulder.

When and how to apply Applications for training contracts commencing 2020 are open from 1 October 2017 until 31 July 2018. Please apply online at www.shlegal.com/graduate.

Work placements We run winter, spring and summer placement schemes each year. Typically you'd spend one or two weeks in our offices, spending time in one or two of our practice groups. Sitting with qualified lawyers and tackling some case work, you'll get a real taste of life at our firm. On your first day, we'll assign you a buddy, a current trainee who'll help you settle in, answer your questions and give you an honest overview of what it's like to work for us. You'll also be able to make the most of an organised programme of interactive sessions, one of which is given by our CEO, Sharon White, plus various social events and talks.

We have eight places on each scheme for both law and non-law students. Find out more at www.shlegal.com/graduate.

Sponsorship We pay fees for GDL and LPC at BPP Law School, London, and offer maintenance awards of up to £6,000 if you're still studying.

Vacancies	18
Trainees	36
Partners	150
Total staff	900

Work placement yes
(see Insider Report on p97)

Training contract deadline
31 July 2018

Apply
Online via
www.shlegal.com/graduate

Starting salary
£40,000

Minimum qualifications
First or 2.1 degree

Sponsorship
GDL/LPC

Offices
London, Hong Kong, Paris, Piraeus, Singapore, Shanghai, Dubai, Beijing, Seoul
Associated offices in:
Bucharest, Jakarta, Guangzhou

**STEPHENSON
HARWOOD**

Affiliated with
aspiringsolicitors

Remember to cite *The Training Contract & Pupillage Handbook* on your application form if you apply to this firm.

434 THE TRAINING CONTRACT & PUPILLAGE HANDBOOK

STEELES LAW LLP
3 The Norwich Business Park, Whiting Road,
Norwich NR4 6DJ
Tel: 01603 598 000
Email: hr@steeleslaw.co.uk
Apply to: Human Resources Department

Full service firm with a modern approach and exceptional work-life balance. Providing trainee solicitors with hands on experience from the start.

V	1-3
T	4
P	8
TS	80
WP	yes

STEPHEN RIMMER LLP
28 Hyde Gardens, Eastbourne BN21 4PX
Tel: 01323 644222
Email: bb@stephenrimmer.com
Apply to: Mr Alan Hobden

V	0
T	6
P	6
TS	74
WP	no

STEPHENS & SON LLP
Rome House, 37-41 Railway Street, Chatham,
Kent ME4 4RP
Tel: 01634 811444
Email: email@stephens-son.co.uk
Apply to: Miss Jacqueline Shicluna

Established firm with reputation for excellence within the Medway Towns. The firm has achieved Lexcel and IIP.

V	0
T	0
P	8
TS	35
WP	no

STEPHENS SCOWN
Curzon House, Southernhay West, Exeter EX1 1RS
Tel: 01392 210700
Email: graduaterecruitment@stephens-scown.co.uk
Apply to: Miss Emma King

We're UK Law Firm of the Year as recognised in the British Legal Awards and have band one *Chambers* rankings across four practice areas.

V	10
T	23
P	55
TS	300
WP	yes

STEPHENSONS
24 Lord Street, Leigh, Lancashire WN7 1AB
Tel: 01942 777777
Apply to: Mrs Janine Turner

North West regional full service practice. Serving small and medium sized businesses, public sector organisations, bulk referrals from banks and insurance companies, private individuals and LSC work.

V	5
T	18
P	26
TS	325
WP	yes

STEVENSDRAKE LIMITED
117-119 High Street, Crawley, West Sussex
RH10 1DD
Tel: 01293 596900
Email: paul.dungate@stevensdrake.com
Apply to: Mr Paul Dungate

Niche commercial practice with strong corporate, property and commercial departments. Also litigation, insolvency and large specialist debt collection section.

V	0
T	1
P	7
TS	45
WP	no

STONE KING
13 Queen Square, Bath BA1 2HJ
Tel: 01225 337599
Email: tassyvincent@stoneking.co.uk
Apply to: Mrs Tassy Vincent

Stone King specialise in charities, employment, personal and business law. Nationally recognised for our work; we train lawyers of the future that make the difference.

V	4
T	8
P	33
TS	197
WP	yes

STONE ROWE BREWER
Stone House, 12/13 Church Street, Twickenham,
Middlesex TW1 3NJ
Tel: 020 8891 6141
Email: info@srb.co.uk
Apply to: Mr John Andrews

General practice covering personal injury, commercial litigation, employment, family and conveyancing. Members of the Personal Injury Panel and the Employment Lawyers Association.

V	1-2
T	4
P	5
TS	50
WP	no

V = Vacancies / **T** = Trainees / **P** = Partners / **TS** = Total Staff / **WP** = Work Placement

Stevens & Bolton LLP

Wey House, Farnham Road, Guildford GU1 4YD
Tel: 01483 302264
Email: traineerecruitment@stevens-bolton.com
Web: www.stevens-bolton.com

The firm Stevens & Bolton LLP is recognised as a leading national law firm, offering a full range of commercial legal services. We are recommended in 24 specialist practice areas by leading legal directories and have received widespread awards recognition. Over the years we have been named and shortlisted for Best Recruiter and Best Trainer – Medium Regional Law Firm at the LawCareers.Net Training & Recruitment Awards. Based in Guildford, our single office approach ensures excellent communication and efficient co-ordination of our resources. We provide legal services both nationally and internationally, with unswerving focus on quality. From the outset, our trainees get first class experience of the business world. We advise a number of the top 100 and other UK FTSE companies, as well as many other substantial international groups, owner managed businesses and SMEs. As such, the work we carry out is both interesting and challenging. We are committed to being a responsible business. We participate in a wide range of charity and community initiatives, and have full regard to the importance of minimising our impact on the environment. We also organise social events over the year and there are a number of sports teams, including netball and football as well as a firm choir.

Who should apply We welcome applications from candidates with either a law or non-law background, with at least 340 UCAS points and at least one A at A level, who have achieved (or expect to achieve) a 2.1 degree or higher (unless there are exceptional circumstances). Essential qualities include: very good communication skills, being a team player, adaptability, being able to manage competing deadlines and projects, drive and ambition, intelligence, attention to detail, business interest and enthusiasm to be a lawyer and to work for Stevens & Bolton.

Training programme Our trainees have genuine responsibility and experience of dealing with clients – and are made to feel part of the team from day one. As a trainee you will have the chance to spend six months in four of the key business areas we specialise in, namely M&A and other corporate work, insolvency and banking/finance, commercial, private wealth and family, real estate, IP, dispute resolution and employment, pensions and immigration. There may also be an opportunity for trainees to undertake a client secondment. We are dedicated to encouraging continuous professional development, delivered in a variety of ways to give our trainees the best chance to become rounded, assured and respected professionals. Training in technical and business skills and early exposure to stimulating work with a variety of clients is instrumental in providing a solid foundation. Our unique combination of factors – supervision when you need it, support from colleagues and the opportunity to embrace early responsibility as soon as you are ready – creates a compelling proposition at the outset of your career.

When and how to apply Applications should be made by completing our online application form available from our website from 1 December to 1 June each year.

Work placements We run two programmes each year in the summer of one-week duration. Applications are accepted between 1 December and 31 January.

Sponsorship We pay the fees for the CPE/GDL and LPC and a maintenance grant for each course of study. Any future trainees who are yet to take their LPC or the GDL are usually required to attend The University of Law Guildford. Please see the firm's website for further details.

Vacancies	5
Trainees	10
Partners	42
Total staff	227

Work placement yes

Training contract deadline
1 June 2018

Apply to
Online via
www.stevens-bolton.com

Starting salary
£33,000

Minimum qualifications
2.1 degree in a law or non-law degree, 340 UCAS points for A levels

Sponsorship
GDL/LPC plus maintenance grant

Offices
Guildford

STEVENS&BOLTON

Sullivan & Cromwell LLP

1 New Fetter Lane, London EC4A 1AN
Tel: 020 7959 8900
Email: traineesolicitors@sullcrom.com
Web: careers.sullcrom.com/uk-trainee-solicitors
🐦 sullcrom

The firm Sullivan & Cromwell provides the highest quality legal advice and representation to clients worldwide. The results we achieve have set us apart for more than 130 years and serve as a model for the modern practice of law. At S&C, there is no such thing as second best. Meritocracy, responsibility and opportunity foster the success of each new employee. S&C has more than 875 lawyers across an international network of 13 offices on four continents. We maintain a unified firm culture worldwide and provide our clients with highly integrated advice on a global basis. The London office, established in 1972, is S&C's largest office excepting its New York City headquarters. There are approximately 80 English, US and dual-qualified lawyers working in the office across a number of practice areas.

Types of work S&C London is perhaps unique in the scale, complexity and significance of the work carried out in an office of its size. Our practice areas include: M&A and private equity; capital markets; finance (credit, leveraged and acquisition); restructuring; project finance; competition law and tax.

Who should apply We seek trainees who have an excellent prior academic record along with strong academic credentials, including a projected or achieved first or upper second class honours degree, or the equivalent. You should possess genuine intellectual curiosity, integrity, strong interpersonal skills, commercial awareness and an ambition to succeed at one of the world's leading law firms. We expect most of our applicants to be penultimate-year law students and final-year non-law students. Graduates and post-graduates are also eligible.

Training programme We offer our trainees the opportunity to do superior work, meet exceptional people and grow in a supportive culture. We aim to distinguish our trainee programme by offering genuine mentoring from partners and senior lawyers who will take a keen interest in your career development.

When and how to apply To apply for the 2018 summer vacation scheme, apply by CV (including a full classification and percentage breakdown of all academic results) and a covering letter. We will be accepting applications for our 2018 summer vacation scheme from 1 November 2017 through 12 January 2018. To apply for a training contract starting in 2020, apply by CV (including a full classification and percentage breakdown of all academic results) and a covering letter. We will be accepting applications for our 2020 trainee intake from 1 May through 13 July 2018.

Work placements Two two-week summer placements. Remuneration £500 per week.

Sponsorship Full sponsorship of GDL and LPC fees, plus a maintenance grant.

Vacancies	4-6
Trainees	10
Partners	21
Total staff	154

Work placement yes
(see Insider Report on p99)

Training contract deadline
13 July 2018

Apply to
traineesolicitors@sullcrom.com

Sponsorship
GDL/LPC

Offices
Beijing, Brussels, Frankfurt, Hong Kong, London, Los Angeles, Melbourne, New York, Palo Alto, Paris, Sydney, Tokyo, Washington DC

SULLIVAN & CROMWELL LLP

STONES SOLICITORS LLP
Linacre House, Southernhay Gardens, Exeter
EX1 1UG
Tel: 01392 666777
Email: anneclark@stones-solicitors.co.uk
Apply to: Mrs Anne Clark

One of the largest firms in Exeter with full range of clients from commercial to private individuals.

V	2[19]
T	4
P	14
TS	100
WP	no

STORRAR COWDRY
25 White Friars, Chester CH1 1NZ
Tel: 01244 400567
Email: all@storrarcowdry.co.uk
Apply to: Mrs D Storrar

City centre general practice with good quality work. No criminal law.

V	0
T	1
P	7
TS	24
WP	no

STOWE FAMILY LAW LLP
8 Fulwood Place, Gray's Inn, London WC1V 6HG
Tel: 020 7421 3300
Email: enquiries@stowefamilylaw.co.uk
Apply to: Ms Morna Bunce

Stowe Family Law is the UK's largest specialist family law firm, with family lawyers and divorce solicitors across 10 UK offices.

V	Varies
T	2
P	20
TS	60
WP	yes

STS SOLICITORS
1st Floor, 159 Brent Street, Hendon, London
NW4 4DH
Tel: 020 7112 8355
Email: info@sts-solicitors.com
Apply to: Mrs Husniye Sera Bazen

V	2
T	0
P	1
TS	5
WP	yes

STUART MILLER SOLICITORS
247 High Road, Wood Green, London N22 8HF
Tel: 020 8888 5225
Email: recruitment@stuartmillersolicitors.co.uk
Apply to: HR Manager

We specialise in defending fraud, cybercrime and criminal cases. Highly commended at the Law Society's Excellence Awards.

V	2[18]
T	0
P	2
TS	32
WP	yes

SURREY LAW CENTRE
Jacobs Yard, Woodlands Road, Guildford, Surrey
GU1 1RL
Tel: 01483 215000
Apply to: Ms Laura Melbourne

We are a law centre that provides clientcentric services to those with domestic abuse, employment, housing or family issues.

V	0
T	2
P	0
TS	9
WP	yes

SWEETMAN BURKE & SINKER
158-160 The Broadway, West Ealing, London
W13 0TL
Tel: 020 8840 2572
Email: reception@sbs-law.co.uk
Apply to: Mr Jonathan Koffman

No vacancies at present.

V	Poss
T	1
P	3
TS	16
WP	yes

SWITALSKIS SOLICITORS LLP
19 Cheapside, Wakefield WF1 2SD
Tel: 01924 882 000
Email: ruth.coneron@switalskis.com
Apply to: Mrs RJ Coneron

V	0
T	4
P	12
TS	250
WP	no

V = Vacancies / **T** = Trainees / **P** = Partners / **TS** = Total Staff / **WP** = Work Placement

SYSTECH SOLICITORS LIMITED Chapter House, 18-20 Crucifix Lane, London SE1 3JW **Tel:** 0151 707 1019 **Email:** jayne.bryson@systech-solicitors.com **Apply to:** Mr R A Farrell	We are a niche practice, providing specialist contentious and non-contentious legal services to global clients across all construction and engineering sectors.	V T P TS WP	0 0 0 25 no
TALBOT & CO 148 High Street, Burton-On-Trent, Staffordshire DE14 1JY **Tel:** 01283 564716 **Email:** tombramall@talbotco.co.uk **Apply to:** Mr TJ Bramall	Long-established *Legal 500* firm with extensive high-quality private client base. Particular expertise in wills, tax, trusts, estates and probate. Also property, litigation, matrimonial and charities.	V T P TS WP	1 1 1 20 yes
TALBOT WALKER LLP 16 Bridge Street, Andover, Hampshire SP10 1BJ **Tel:** 01264 363354 **Email:** employment@talbotwalker.co.uk **Apply to:** Miss Sonia Adlem	Three-member, one-branch litigation firm.	V T P TS WP	1 1 3 18 no
TALLENTS SOLICITORS 3 Middlegate, Newark NG24 1AQ **Tel:** 01636 671881 **Email:** roy.westerby@tallents.co.uk **Apply to:** The Practice Manager	Offices in Newark, Mansfield and Southwell.	V T P TS WP	0 0 5 51 no
TASSELLS 20 West Street, Faversham, Kent ME13 7JF **Tel:** 01795 533337 **Email:** law@tassells-solicitors.co.uk **Apply to:** Mr James Matthews	Broad based general practice, undertaking all the usual non-contentious and contentious work.	V T P TS WP	1 1 7 21 yes
TAYLOR ROSE TTKW 13-15 Moorgate, London EC2R 6AD **Tel:** 020 3450 4444 **Email:** paul.davis@taylor-rose.co.uk	Taylor Rose TTKW is a top 200 independent, multi-disciplined law firm with 250 experts operating from five offices, representing clients from the everyday cases to the most complex issue.	V T P TS WP	1-2 2 13 250 no
TAYLOR VINTERS LLP Merlin Place, Milton Road, Cambridge CB4 0DP **Tel:** 01223 225148 **Email:** recruitment@taylorvinters.com **Apply to:** Mrs Alix Balfe-Skinner	Taylor Vinters is an international law firm supporting the businesses which drive the innovation economy and the entrepreneurs and private wealth that underpin them.	V T P TS WP	6 14 24 170 yes
TAYLOR WALTON LLP 28-44 Alma Street, Luton LU1 2PL **Tel:** 01582 731161 **Email:** jim.wrigglesworth@taylorwalton.co.uk **Apply to:** Mr Jim Wrigglesworth	Progressive and substantial practice, providing specialist advice to commercial and private clients.	V T P TS WP	2 5 27 150 yes

V = Vacancies / **T** = Trainees / **P** = Partners / **TS** = Total Staff / **WP** = Work Placement

Taylor Wessing

5 New Street Square, London EC4A 3TW
Tel: 020 7300 7000
Web: www.taylorwessing.com/graduate
f taylorwessinggraduates 𝕏 taylorwessing

AWARDS 2017
BEST TRAINER
LARGE CITY FIRM

The firm Taylor Wessing is a full-service international law firm, standing at the forefront of the industries of tomorrow. Acting as legal advisors to well-known clients in progressive and cutting-edge sectors, we're a firm for the ground breakers, the smart thinkers and the trail blazers. Our spark, focus and lateral thinking make us exceptional legal advisors, helping our clients to succeed by thinking innovatively about their business issues. Our focus on the industries of tomorrow – technology, media and communications, life sciences, private wealth and energy – means that alongside law students, we also recruit a wide range of students who have studied non-law degrees. Our clients include private and public companies, financial institutions, professional service firms, public sector bodies of both large and medium size and wealthy individuals. Our international presence is also something that we strive to protect as we continue to strengthen our brand globally. We act for 32 of the world's 50 leading brands and work with clients in the world's most dynamic industries (TMC, private wealth, life sciences and energy).

Types of work Taylor Wessing offers industry-focused advice and in-depth sector experience gained by bringing together internationally-focused lawyers from diverse legal backgrounds including: banking and finance; capital markets; copyright and media law; corporate; commercial agreements; construction and engineering; employment and pensions; EU competition; IT and telecoms; litigation and dispute resolution; patents; planning and environment; private client; projects; real estate; restructuring and corporate recovery; tax; trade marks and designs.

Who should apply We look for team players with a minimum of ABB grades at A level and a 2.1 degree in any discipline. You'll need to be confident and enthusiastic with the communication skills to build vibrant relationships with our clients. You'll have the energy, ambition and creativity to take early responsibility and have a real impact on our business and our clients' business. You'll also be committed to a career in law.

Training programme Our award-winning training (we won LawCareers.Net Best Trainer – Large City Firm 2017) combines our in-house Professional Skills Course with six-month seats in four different practice groups, including one contentious seat and one in our corporate or finance areas. Our programme is recognised for the extent of partner contact available to trainees, and you'll work closely with associates on high-quality work from the outset. Frequent client contact and secondment opportunities to their offices are also offered and regular support and feedback every step of the way will ensure that your career is aligned to the growth and needs of the firm and our clients.

Work placements Our award winning vacation schemes (ranked number 1 in law based on student reviews on rate my placement 2017) are designed for you to experience life as a trainee solicitor in a fast-paced and innovative City law firm. You'll spend two weeks in two different practice groups gaining first-hand experience under the supervision of associates and partners. We have 36 places in 2018 and the closing date for applications is 30 January 2018.

First year opportunities: Join us on our first year insight day in April 2018. To be eligible to attend you must be a first-year law student or penultimate non-law student. For more information please visit our website.

Sponsorship GDL and MA (LPC with Business) fees at BPP London sponsored. A maintenance grant is provided.

Vacancies	20
Trainees	45
Partners	400
Total staff	1,800+

Work placement yes

Training contract deadline
30 April 2018

Apply
Online at
www.taylorwessing.com/
graduate

Starting salary
1st year – £40,000
2nd year – £44,000
Post qualification – £63,000

Minimum qualifications
2.1 degree

Sponsorship
GDL/LPC

Offices
Amsterdam, Berlin, Bratislava, Brussels, Budapest, Cambridge, Dubai, Düsseldorf, Eindhoven, Frankfurt, Hamburg, Hanoi, Ho Chi Minh City, Hong Kong, Jakarta, Jeddah, Kiev, London, Munich, New York, Paris, Prague, Riyadh, Seoul, Silicon Valley, Singapore, Vienna, Warsaw Representative offices in Beijing, Brno, Klagenfurt, Shanghai

TaylorWessing

Affiliated with
as aspiringsolicitors

TEACHER STERN LLP 37-41 Bedford Row, London WC1R 4JH **Tel:** 020 7242 3191 **Email:** recruitment@teacherstern.com **Apply to:** Mr James Baker	Long-established commercial practice with a focus on transactional and contentious property, general commercial litigation,commercial and corporate work, employment and private client.	V 4 T 9 P 31 TS 121 WP yes
TEES LAW Tees House, 95 London Road, Bishop's Stortford CM23 3GW **Tel:** 0800 0131165 **Email:** letitia.glaister@teeslaw.com **Apply to:** Miss Letty Glaister	Important regional practice offering a full range of legal services to clients from individuals to public companies, encompassing private clients, agricultural, insurance and commercial concerns.	V 3 T 6 P 20 TS 240 WP yes
TEMPLE HEELIS LLP 1 Kent View, Kendal, Cumbria LA9 4DZ **Tel:** 01539 723757 **Email:** lwilliams@templeheelis.co.uk **Apply to:** Mr John Osborne	A progressive provincial practice specialising in civil litigation, including personal injury, wills, tax planning, probate, employment, family and conveyancing.	V 0 T 1 P 6 TS 30 WP no
TERRELLS LLP 61 Lincoln Road, Peterborough PE1 2SE **Tel:** 01733 896 789 **Email:** enquiries@terrells.co.uk **Apply to:** Mr Roger Terrell	Modern high street firm practice (no crime) specialising in family law. Accredited with LEXCEL and Investors in People quality marks.	V 1 T 3 P 2 TS 18 WP no
TERRY JONES SOLICITORS Abbey House, Abbey Foregate, Shrewsbury SY2 6BH **Tel:** 01743 285888 **Email:** recruitment@terry-jones.co.uk **Apply to:** Mr Anthony Iles	We are Lexcel accredited, progressive and pride ourselves in providing professional, practical and cost effective advice and assistance.	V Poss T 9 P 4 TS 120 WP no
THACKRAY WILLIAMS LLP Kings House, 32-40 Widmore Road, Bromley BR1 1RY **Tel:** 020 8290 0440 **Email:** jane.macleod@thackraywilliams.com **Apply to:** Ms Jane MacLeod	The largest firm in the Bromley and North Kent region. A vibrant and progressive general practice with a growing commercial side.	V 3[19] T 6 P 18 TS 150 WP no
THALIWAL & CO SOLICITORS 298 Welford Road, Leicester LE2 6EG **Tel:** 0116 274 5252 **Email:** enquiries@thaliwalsolicitors.co.uk **Apply to:** Mr R Thaliwal	Our mental health law team advise and represent clients in mental health review tribunals, hospital managers meetings and our specialist immigration law team provides advice and assistance in both the East and West Midlands.	V 0 T 0 P 1 TS 11 WP yes
THOMPSON SMITH AND PUXON Stable 6, Stable Road, Colchester CO2 7GL **Tel:** 01206 574431 **Email:** info@tsplegal.com **Apply to:** Mr Richard Porter	Commercial, private client and family work, with niche practices in personal injury and clinical negligence.	V Poss T 1 P 11 TS 75 WP no

V = Vacancies / **T** = Trainees / **P** = Partners / **TS** = Total Staff / **WP** = Work Placement

Thomas Cooper LLP

Ibex House, 42-47 Minories, London EC3N 1HA
Tel: 020 7481 8851
Email: recruitment@thomascooperlaw.com
Web: www.thomascooperlaw.com
f thomascooperlawllp **🐦** thomascooperllp

The firm Thomas Cooper LLP was funded in 1825 and specialises in international maritime, trade and finance law. We take a pragmatic approach, providing clear advice that helps clients navigate through the complexity of international commerce. We regularly advise on all aspects of maritime law from high profile casualties and major maritime losses to fatal accident and personal injury claims. We also represent our clients' interests in day to day commercial disputes arising under shipping contracts.

Who should apply We do not require our trainees to have a specific knowledge of maritime law, but we do expect solid academics, a willingness and intellectual flexibility to solve practical as well as legal problems and the enthusiasm and personality to succeed in an established, fast paced and professional market. We have a reputation for punching above our weight. Our trainee retention rate is one of the best in the legal sector.

Training programme We are recognised as a leading international law firm and have overseas offices in Paris, Piraeus, Singapore, Madrid and São Paulo. We also provide training seats in a few of our overseas offices. Many of the trainees who have undertaken international seats have enjoyed the experience and we support you every step of the way, assisting you with a place to live, an interesting and challenging workload and the excitement of living and working in a new jurisdiction. Similarly in London training at Thomas Cooper means training as part of a team. We seek to retain all successful candidates and expect trainees to work with senior members of staff and partners as well as with associates and other trainees.

Thomas Cooper LLP's training is hands-on from day one. Each of your seats will be overseen by a partner or senior solicitor. Throughout your qualifying period you will be allocated a supervising partner who will oversee your assessments and act as a point of reference as you move through the firm. You will be expected to interact professionally with our clients, counsel, experts and others and to contribute to the substantive and practical requirements of each case. We are specialist litigators and deal with a variety of commercial arbitration disputes as well as general litigation. Maritime law can be challenging both academically and practically and the type of roles you will be involved in may include: drafting instructions to counsel, assisting in taking witness statements, reviewing disclosure and collating evidence, obtaining further information, and providing advice to clients and to others on the running of the case, and the next step that needs to be taken. You will assist the lead partner by taking a note of conferences with experts and counsel, participating in mediations and preparing cases for arbitration or court.

When and how to apply If you have any questions or would like further information please contact us: recruitment@thomascooperlaw.com. For full details of our application process please visit www.thomascooperlaw.com/careers.

Vacancies	Up to 3
Trainees	8
Partners	28
Total staff	96
Work placement	no

Apply
Online

Starting salary
1st year – £34,000
2nd year – £37,500
(based on 2016 salaries)

Minimum qualifications
2.1 degree

Offices
London, Madrid, Paris, Piraeus, São Paulo Singapore

Thomson Snell & Passmore LLP

3 Lonsdale Gardens, Tunbridge Wells, Kent TN1 1NX
Tel: 01892 510000
Email: recruitment@ts-p.co.uk
Web: www.ts-p.co.uk

The firm Thomson Snell & Passmore has a reputation for providing high quality, intelligent advice. We provide a comprehensive legal service and build long-term relationships by encouraging a culture of respect, understanding and excellence. It's a common sense approach that's surprisingly uncommon.

Our offices are located in the centre of Tunbridge Wells and in the Thames Gateway. The firm attracts clients both locally, nationally, and internationally.

Types of work We possess a strength and depth of expertise that only a handful of firms in the South East can claim. You will work with a wide range of clients, local and national. Our services are: corporate and commercial; employment; commercial property; dispute resolution; private client; family; residential conveyancing; clinical negligence; and personal injury.

Who should apply We appoint people on the basis of intellectual ability, commercial acumen, enthusiasm, drive, initiative, and strong interpersonal and team-working skills.

Training programme Thomson Snell & Passmore has a reputation for offering excellent training and opportunities. Trainee solicitors are the firm's future assistants, associates and partners. We find out what your personal and professional aspirations are and provide you with the development opportunities you need to achieve them.

A comprehensive induction programme will help you adjust to your career in business and law. We do our very best to allocate seats in your preferred practice areas. Each of the four six-month seats will give you a thorough grounding and exposure to a variety of areas of law. You will have a dedicated trainee supervisor, regular coaching and three-monthly reviews that give you the opportunity to talk through your progress, development needs and future path. Our commitment to bespoke training and development will enable you to move your career in the direction you want it to go.

When and how to apply Apply by 31 July 2018 to begin September 2020. Applicants should apply by the firm's own application form available via our website. A 2.1 degree in any discipline is the minimum required.

Work placements Our structured and inspiring programme will give you a flavour of what to expect from a career in the law and help you make choices for the future.

The firm offers two placements over the Easter period and eight placements over the summer period. Applicants should apply by the firm's own application form available via the website.

Sponsorship Grant and interest-free loan available for the LPC.

Vacancies	6
Trainees	12
Partners	39
Total staff	230

Work placement yes

Training contract deadline
31 July 2018

Apply
Online

Starting salary
Competitive market rate for a South East regional firm

Minimum qualifications
2.1 degree, any discipline

Sponsorship
LPC

Offices
Tunbridge Wells,
Thames Gateway

Thomson Snell & Passmore

Remember to cite *The Training Contract & Pupillage Handbook* on your application form if you apply to this firm.

443 THE TRAINING CONTRACT & PUPILLAGE HANDBOOK   TRAINING CONTRACT DIRECTORY **443**

Thrings

6 Drakes Meadow, Penny Lane, Swindon SN3 3LL
Tel: 01793 410800
Email: recruitment@thrings.com
Web: www.thrings.com
f thringslaw 🐦 thringslaw

The firm As one of the UK's top 100 law firms with offices in London, Bristol, Swindon and Bath, Thrings' strategic growth over the past five years has provided a platform to build on the commercial focus of the firm and to offer the complete service for businesses and their owners.

Types of work Thrings offers specialist advice in sectors such as aerospace and defence, agriculture, energy and waste, innovation and technology, and financial services from partner-led teams whose expertise matches that found in much larger City firms.

Who should apply You're bright and pro-active, with a real commercial awareness. You're enthusiastic, dedicated and able to think independently. You hold a minimum 2.1 with paralegal experience (ideally one year), have either completed the LPC or have a place confirmed, have completed a GDL/CPE (if applicable). We are open to applicants with 2.2 degree if you have paralegaling experience. You grasp facts well and work out solutions quickly. You're sitting here nodding your head, agreeing as you read this? We want to hear from you.

Training programme We operate a structured two-year training contract split into four six-month seats. You can expect to gain experience within at least three different practice areas, with a balance of contentious and non-contentious work types. You are likely to work in a number of our offices, which means you'll benefit from working in different environments, with different colleagues, in different locations. There is also the opportunity to sit within the personal injury team, Novum Law, which is a sister company of Thrings LLP.

You will gain hands-on experience and early responsibility, opportunities to work with a diverse client base, a dedicated supervisor, you'll have regular appraisal feedback and be given the opportunity to attend training courses. There are regular office organised social events and the firm offers a competitive salary and benefits package.

When and how to apply Apply via our website wwww.thrings.com for training contracts in 2019.

Vacancies	10
Trainees	13
Partners	60
Total staff	337

Training contract deadline
2 June 2018

Apply
Online

Starting salary
£26,000

Minimum qualifications
2.1 degree

Offices
Swindon, Bath, Bristol, London, Southampton

THRINGS
SOLICITORS

THOMPSONS SOLICITORS Congress House, Great Russell Street, London WC1B 3LW **Tel:** 020 7290 0000 **Email:** enquiries@thompsons.law.co.uk **Apply to:** The HR Department	Thompsons Solicitors is the most experienced trade union, employment rights and claimant personal injury practice in the UK.	V 0 T 0 P 50 TS 888 WP no
THOMSON WEBB & CORFIELD 16 Union Road, Cambridge CB2 1HE **Tel:** 01223 578086 **Email:** pcarr@twclaw.co.uk **Apply to:** Ms Pippa Carr	Progressive Cambridge firm with expanding commercial and corporate teams, handling private and public company clients. Private client departments, including trusts, family and crime.	V 1[18] T 2 P 9 TS 39 WP no
THORNE SEGAR LTD 3 Bancks Street, Minehead, Somerset TA24 5DE **Tel:** 01643 703234 **Email:** clare.cash-davis@thornesegar.co.uk **Apply to:** Ms Clare Cash-Davis	A progressive company with a clearly planned future, specialising in private client, family and residential conveyance work.	V 1 T 0 P 2 TS 27 WP yes
THORPE & CO 17 Valley Bridge Parade, Scarborough YO11 2JX **Tel:** 01723 364321 **Email:** info@thorpeandco.com **Apply to:** The Recruitment Contact	General practice with three offices including domestic conveyancing, probate, family, personal injury and criminal work.	V 1 T 1 P 8 TS 55 WP no
TILLY BAILEY & IRVINE LLP York Chambers, York Road, Hartlepool TS26 9DP **Tel:** 01429 264101 **Email:** ntaylor@tbilaw.co.uk **Apply to:** Mr Neil Taylor	Tilly Bailey & Irvine is one of the UK's longest established law firms with offices in Hartlepool, Wynyard, Barnard Castle and Stockton.	V TBC[18] T 1 P 13 TS 146 WP no
TIM JOHNSON / LAW 117 Temple Chambers, 3-7 Temple Avenue, London EC4Y 0HP **Tel:** 020 7036 9120 **Email:** recruitment@timjohnson-law.co.uk **Apply to:** Mr Tim Johnson	Tim Johnson / Law is a niche firm of solicitors based in the City of London specialising in UK employment and international labour law.	V 0 T 1 P 1 TS 4 WP yes
TINKLIN SPRINGALL 9-11 Rectory Road, Beckenham BR3 1JB **Tel:** 020 8402 7222 **Email:** ics@tinklinspringall.co.uk **Apply to:** Mr Ian Springall	Training covers conveyancing, litigation, probate and general matters.	V 2[18] T 4 P 7 TS 50 WP no
TINN CRIDDLE & CO 6 High Street, Alford, Lincolnshire LN13 9DX **Tel:** 01507 462882 **Apply to:** Mr Geoffrey Allen	Small, three-office, country practice.	V 0 T 1 P 4 TS 10 WP no

V = Vacancies / **T** = Trainees / **P** = Partners / **TS** = Total Staff / **WP** = Work Placement

TINSDILLS Hays House, 25 Albion Street, Hanley, Stoke on Trent ST1 1QF **Tel:** 01782 262031 **Email:** lawyers@tinsdills.co.uk **Apply to:** Mrs Jane Massey	The firm has four offices located in North Staffordshire and South Cheshire. The firm is innovative and proactive acting for private, corporate and institutional clients.	**V** TBC[18] **T** 9 **P** 11 **TS** 97 **WP** no	
TLT LLP One Redcliff Street, Bristol BS1 6TP **Tel:** 0333 006 0703 **Email:** graduate@TLTsolicitors.com **Apply to:** Ms Gemma Cowley	Described by industry commentators as 'the firm to watch', TLT remains one of the fastest growing law firms in the UK.	**V** Up to 15 **T** 35 **P** 115 **TS** 1020 **WP** yes	
TMJ LAW SOLICITORS 5 Notre Dame Mews, Northampton NN1 2BG **Tel:** 01604 608111 **Email:** infotmj@googlemail.com **Apply to:** Mr T J Synnott	An established but young and dynamic firm providing company and commercial expertise to a diversity of corporate and private clients using the latest IT solutions.	**V** 2 **T** 2 **P** 2 **TS** 12 **WP** yes	
TMJ LEGAL SERVICES LTD Foster House, 99 Raby Road, Hartlepool TS24 8DT **Tel:** 01429 235616 **Email:** legal@tmjlegal.co.uk **Apply to:** Mr Kl Morgan	General practice specialising in private client, personal injury and matrimonial/children work.	**V** Poss **T** 1 **P** 3 **TS** 35 **WP** yes	
TOLLERS SOLICITORS 1 Waterside Way, Bedford Road, Northampton NN4 7XD **Tel:** 01604 258558 **Email:** sarah.finlayson@tollers.co.uk **Apply to:** Mrs Sarah Finlayson	A Midlands based multi-niche practice providing you with both personal and business legal services. An established law firm with a progressive and modern outlook.	**V** 4 **T** 4 **P** 19 **TS** 138 **WP** no	
TOUSSAINTS First Floor, 150 Soho Road, Birmingham B21 9LN **Tel:** 0121 523 5050 **Apply to:** Miss Mary Toussaint	Busy high street office undertaking residential, commercial property, litigation, civil, crime and family work.	**V** 0 **T** 0 **P** 1 **TS** 1 **WP** yes	
TOZERS LLP Broadwalk House, Southernhay West, Exeter, Devon EX1 1UA **Tel:** 01392 207020 **Email:** enquiries@tozers.co.uk **Apply to:** Mrs Fiona Grafton-Smith	One of the oldest and largest firms in Devon, we act for clients locally and nationally in a range of specialisations at our three offices.	**V** Poss **T** 2 **P** 20 **TS** 120 **WP** yes	
TRANTERS 29/31 Middle Hillgate, Stockport, Cheshire SK1 3AY **Tel:** 0161 480 9999 **Email:** web@freeclaim.co.uk **Apply to:** Graduate Recruitment	LAB franchised with specialist solicitors dealing with crime and accident claims with offices in South Manchester, Stockport and East Manchester.	**V** 4 **T** 4 **P** 6 **TS** 100 **WP** yes	

V = Vacancies / **T** = Trainees / **P** = Partners / **TS** = Total Staff / **WP** = Work Placement

Travers Smith LLP

10 Snow Hill, London EC1A 2AL
Tel: 020 7295 3000
Email: graduate.recruitment@traverssmith.com
Web: www.traverssmith.com
f traverssmithgraduates **🐦** traverssmith

The firm Travers Smith is an award-winning independent City law firm with a reputation for enterprising thinking and uncompromising quality in all of its chosen fields, and a focus on advising clients on international matters. Competing directly with the largest City firms, we attract top-quality work but still offer a professional yet relaxed working environment providing the best of both worlds. It is this environment that has led to one of the highest staff retention rates in the City. A very high proportion of our work has an international dimension and we accompany our clients to every corner of the globe. To do that, we have developed close ties with carefully chosen quality overseas independent law firms who share our specialist strengths and very demanding standards. Travers Smith is defined by its independence, unique culture, deep commercial insight, progressive thinking and incomparable client experience. Above all else, Travers Smith is a collaborative firm. We treat people with respect, allowing them to conduct business in the most effective way for clients. This has led to a climate of shared knowledge and goals, supported by a friendly, engaging team spirit.

Types of work The main areas of our practice are commercial (including IP and IT), competition, corporate, employment, employee incentives, dispute resolution, finance, financial services and markets, operational risk and environment, pensions, real estate, restructuring and insolvency, and tax.

Who should apply We'll give you responsibility from day one – you will quickly find yourself on the phone to clients, in meetings and handling your own work with all the guidance you need. As such the firm looks for people who can combine academic excellence with plain common sense; who are determined, articulate and able to think on their feet, and who take their work but not themselves seriously. A law degree is not a necessity – around half the trainees who joined last year came from a non-law background.

Training programme The firm's comprehensive training programme ensures that trainees experience a broad range of work. All trainee solicitors sit with partners and associates, which ensures a refreshing lack of hierarchy. It also means that trainees receive individual and extensive training from experienced lawyers, and can look forward to client contact, and the responsibility that goes with it, from day one.

During the two-year training contract, trainees spend six months in our corporate department and another six months in either the dispute resolution or the employment departments. The firm offers you a choice for your other two seats in two of our other specialist departments. Trainees may also have the opportunity to spend six months in the firm's Paris office.

When and how to apply Apply online through cvMail via our website at www.traverssmith.com for a training contract commencing in either September 2020 or March 2021. Applications open on 1 October 2017 and the deadline is 31 July 2018.

Work placements We offer three summer schemes of two weeks each commencing 18 June, 2 July and 16 July 2018. We also offer a winter scheme of two weeks (places allocated on a rolling basis).

Sponsorship We pay GDL and LPC fees plus a maintenance grant.

Vacancies	25
Trainees	50
Partners	77
Total staff	604

Work placement yes

Training contract deadline
31 July 2018

Apply
Online at
www.traverssmith.com

Starting salary
£43,500

Minimum qualifications
2.1 degree and AAB at
A level

Sponsorship
GDL/LPC

Offices
London, Paris and close ties
with carefully chosen quality
overseas independent law
firms

TRAVERS SMITH

Affiliated with
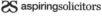

TRETHOWANS LLP London Road, Salisbury, Wiltshire SP1 3HP **Tel:** 023 8032 1000 **Email:** recruitment@trethowans.com **Apply to:** Mrs Kate Ellis	A leading law firm based in the south, advising businesses and individual clients throughout the UK with a team of over 210 people including 35 partners.	V T P TS WP	3-4 6 35 214 yes
TROWERS & HAMLINS LLP 3 Bunhill Row, London EC1Y 8YZ **Tel:** 020 7423 8312 **Email:** avithlani@trowers.com **Apply to:** Mr Anup Vithlani	From nine offices across the UK, Middle East and Far East, we offer a comprehensive and joined-up service to clients across the globe.	V T P TS WP	23 46 161 903 yes
TV EDWARDS SOLICITORS 35-37 Mile End Road, London E1 4TP **Tel:** 020 3440 8000 **Email:** enquiries@tvedwards.com **Apply to:** Ms Christine Woolfenden	With offices across London. T V Edwards LLP is a leading predominantly publicly-funded firm offering an extensive range of legal services.	V T P TS WP	0 9 13 120 yes
TWM SOLICITORS LLP 65 Woodbridge Road, Guildford, Surrey GU1 4RD **Tel:** 01483 752700 **Email:** jobs@twmsolicitors.com **Apply to:** Miss Rita Hilla	A growing and ambitious regional practice seeking trainees with motivation and energy, who can demonstrate a genuine commitment to a career in law.	V T P TS WP	0 8 32 200 no
VEALE WASBROUGH VIZARDS LLP Narrow Quay House, Narrow Quay, Bristol BS1 4QA **Tel:** 0117 925 2020 **Email:** careers@vwv.co.uk **Apply to:** Mrs Ellen Marsh	We act nationally for clients in education and charities, healthcare, private wealth, family-owned business and public sectors. We also offer a dedicated service to individuals.	V T P TS WP	8-10 18 72 411 yes
VINCENT SYKES 4 West Street, Oundle, Peterborough PE8 4EF **Tel:** 01832 272971 **Email:** danielb@vincentsykes.co.uk **Apply to:** Mr Daniel Berry	Solicitors in small town of Oundle, near Peterborough. Undertake general work with a bias to non-contentious work.	V T P TS WP	0 1 1 6 no
VINCENT SYKES & HIGHAM LLP Montague House, 1 Chancery Lane, Thrapston, Northamptonshire NN14 4LN **Tel:** 01832 732 161 **Email:** rhona.rowland@vshlaw.co.uk **Apply to:** Mrs Rhona Rowland	Well-established East Midlands firm, specialists in company/commercial work.	V T P TS WP	0 1 4 26 no
VODAFONE GROUP SERVICES Vodafone House, The Connection, Newbury, Berkshire RG14 2FN **Tel:** 01635 33251 **Email:** legaltraining@vodafone.com **Apply to:** Mr Nick Woodrow	Vodafone is the world's leading mobile telecommunications community. Vodafone's Group legal function (based in Newbury, Paddington, Luxembourg and Dusseldorf) supports Vodafone's global initiatives.	V T P TS WP	0 2 0 110 yes

V = Vacancies / **T** = Trainees / **P** = Partners / **TS** = Total Staff / **WP** = Work Placement

Vinson & Elkins RLLP

20 Fenchurch Street, 24th Floor, London EC3M 3BY
Tel: 020 7065 6000
Web: www.velaw.com
🐦 vecareers

The firm Vinson & Elkins is a leading US-based international law firm with more than 650 lawyers located in 16 cities across the globe. Over four decades ago, we became one of the first US law firms to establish a practice in London. Since then, we have built a dynamic office, undertaking work that has gained the respect of clients around the world. Over the years, V&E has amassed a wealth of experience working on projects for clients in almost every country on the map. We are accustomed to working not only in well-defined markets, but also in less familiar and more challenging environments, under developing local regimes or those with evolving communications and infrastructure. We know how to adapt to local customs, cultures and laws, enabling us to handle matters quickly and effectively. We work in tandem with our clients, travelling wherever and whenever we are needed. We know what it takes to make deals work and to win cases. This knowledge enables us to offer creative solutions for our clients engaged in leading-edge projects around the world.

Types of work Our clients are predominantly in the energy, finance and infrastructure sectors and the London office specialises in M&A, private equity, construction, project development and finance, international arbitration and litigation, corporate and structured finance and tax.

Who should apply We are looking to recruit ambitious individuals with exceptional academic results, sound commercial awareness and rounded personalities. The ability to think laterally and creatively is essential, as is a need for common sense and a willingness to take the initiative.

Training programme The firm operates a non-rotational training system and trainees work in all practice areas throughout their two years. The training is designed to provide variety, flexibility and responsibility from the start. V&E won the LawCareers.Net 'Best Recruiter – US Firm in the City' in 2017 and 'Best Trainer – Medium City Firm' award in 2010. V&E has been nominated five previous times, having also won in 2006. While being based in London our trainees can expect to undertake overseas secondments and international travel during the course of their two years.

When and how to apply The deadline for applications is 31 July 2018 to begin training in 2020. Applications should be made by way of our online application form, available from our website. Please note, we give preference to those students who have previously completed a summer vacation placement with us.

Work placements We view vacation placements as an important part of our recruitment process and have been nominated on multiple occasions in the category 'Best Work Placement Scheme – City Firm' and 'Best Recruiter – US Firm in the City' (and won this category in 2017). For Summer 2018 placements apply by 31 January 2018. Applications should be made by way of our application form, available from our website. We are hosting an open day at our London office on 21 March 2018 for first-year law degree students or non-law students in their penultimate year. Applications can be made by emailing graduaterecruitment@velaw.com before 9 February 2018. Please include your name, contact details and your current stage of education. Please also confirm that you have achieved our minimum academic requirements of at least AAB at A level or equivalent. Open day places will be filled on a first-come first-served basis.

Sponsorship LPC and GDL fees paid plus a maintenance grant of up to £8,000.

Vacancies	4
Trainees	8
Partners	15
Total staff	79

Work placement yes
(see Insider Report on p100)

Training contract deadline
31 July 2018

Apply to
Sarah Stockley

Starting salary
1st year – £50,000
2nd year – £55,000
NQ salary – £120,000

Minimum qualifications
2.1 degree, AAB at A level
(or equivalent)

Sponsorship
GDL/LPC

Offices
Austin, Beijing, Dallas, Dubai, Hong Kong, Houston, London, Moscow, New York, Palo Alto, Richmond, Riyadh, San Francisco, Taipei, Tokyo, Washington DC

Vinson&Elkins RLLP

Remember to cite *The Training Contract & Pupillage Handbook* on your application form if you apply to this firm.

VYMAN SOLICITORS LTD
Vyman House, 104 College Road, Harrow,
Middlesex HA1 1BQ
Tel: 020 8427 9080
Email: anup.vyas@vyman.co.uk
Apply to: Mr Anup Vyas

Niche commercial practice which provides proactive legal advice and support to its commercial clientele ranging from pharmaceutical and property companies to bar and restaurant businesses.

V	2
T	1
P	4
TS	24
WP	yes

W BROOK & CO
2a Doncaster Road, Goldthorpe, Rotherham,
South Yorks S63 9HQ
Tel: 01709 898697
Email: wbrook@walterbrook.wanadoo.co.uk
Apply to: Mr W Brook

General practice including crime, family law/care, personal injury, domestic conveyancing. Franchised firm.

V	1[18]
T	1
P	2
TS	20
WP	no

W H MATTHEWS & CO
11-13 Grove Road, Sutton, Surrey SM1 1DS
Tel: 020 8642 6677
Email: sutton@whmatthews.com
Apply to: Mr Charles Howard

General practice although very strong private client base. Established in 1881. Seven out of the twleve partners were trainees with the firm.

V	0
T	1
P	12
TS	49
WP	no

WAINWRIGHT & CUMMINS
413A Brixton Road, London SW9 7DG
Tel: 020 7737 9330
Email: ajw@wainwrightcummins.co.uk
Apply to: Mr AJ Wainwright

We look for individuals with a commitment to working in the publically funded area and who have practical experience of working with similar firms.

V	0
T	4
P	4
TS	35
WP	yes

WAKE SMITH SOLICITORS
No1 Velocity, 2 Tenter Street, Sheffield S1 4BY
Tel: 011 4266 6660
Email: jo.barnett@wake-smith.com
Apply to: Mrs Jo Barnett

General practice serving both commercial and private clients.

V	1[19]
T	2
P	19
TS	105
WP	yes

WALL JAMES CHAPPELL
15-23 Hagley Road, Stourbridge, West Midlands
DY8 1QW
Tel: 01384 371 622
Email: post@wjclaw.co.uk
Apply to: Mrs S Griffiths

Well-established West Midlands firm offering full range of legal services, seeks talented and hard working trainee.

V	1
T	2
P	7
TS	35
WP	no

WALLACE LLP
One Portland Place, London W1B 1PN
Tel: 020 7636 4422
Email: trainees@wallace.co.uk
Apply to: Mrs Tricia Davenport

A commercial law practice respected for its reassuringly straightforward approach. We are a progressive and innovative firm with a portfolio of domestic and international clients.

V	0
T	0
P	18
TS	60
WP	no

WALLACE ROBINSON & MORGAN
4 Drury Lane, Solihull B91 3BD
Tel: 0121 705 7571
Email: enquiries@wallacerobinson.co.uk
Apply to: Mr R P Hughes

The firm does not currently have any training contract positions available.

V	1-2
T	2
P	6
TS	40
WP	no

V = Vacancies / **T** = Trainees / **P** = Partners / **TS** = Total Staff / **WP** = Work Placement

Walker Morris LLP

Kings Court, 12 King Street, Leeds LS1 2HL
Tel: 0113 283 2500
Email: hellograduates@walkermorris.co.uk
Web: www.graduate.walkermorris.co.uk
🐦 wmgraduate

The firm Walker Morris LLP are a large, commercial practice based in Leeds. We are a well respected law firm and one of the highest recruiters of trainee solicitors in Leeds with fantastic retention rates. 45% of our partners trained with the firm.

Types of work Company commercial; corporate; intellectual property and trademarks; energy, infrastructure and government; projects; renewables and energy; corporate tax; commercial real estate; planning and environmental; CDR; insolvency; sports; employment; construction; regulatory services.

We offer a full range of services to commercial clients, both nationally and internationally.

Who should apply Second-year law students and final-year non-law students with excellent A-level grades and ideally a 2.1 degree. Applications are also welcome from candidates who are currently on or have completed the GDL/LPC. We are looking for bright, commercially minded and practical individuals who can get on with clients and team members. They must show a sense of humour and fun when the pressure is on and adopt a commonsense approach to clients' problems.

Training programme Our two-year training programme incorporates six four-month seats with the opportunity to choose your seats in the second year. Trainees sit in an office with either a partner or an associate and receive a formal appraisal at the end of each seat. We provide a structured induction programme in your first week. The Professional Skills Course is provided and IT training/workshops are also given. Formal training including lectures, workshops, seminars, and skills programmes. There is also potential for secondments outside the firm.

When and how to apply We are recruiting 15 trainees for our 2020 intake. The closing date is 31 July 2018 and applicants should complete our online application form.

Work placements We offer a one-week structured vacation scheme. Schemes take place in April and June, with 48 places available. The closing date is 31 December 2017 and applicants should complete our online application form.

Sponsorship We will pay LPC and GDL fees plus £5,000 maintenance fees to students who we have offered a training contract. We are in partnership with BPP Law School – BPP are based in nine city centre locations and you can decide which one you attend.

We offer a £3,000 travel bursary to future trainees. The successful applicants will have demostrated a desire to undertake charitable work and/or develop their commercial skills either in the UK or abroad.

Vacancies	15
Trainees	32
Partners	48
Total staff	450+

Work placement yes
(see Insider Report on p101)

Training contract deadline
31 July 2018

Apply to
Duncan Lole,
Graduate Recruitment
Partner

Starting salary
£27,000

Minimum qualifications
Ideally a 2.1 degree

Sponsorship
GDL/LPC

Offices
Leeds

WALKER MORRIS

Firm	Description	V	T	P	TS	WP
WALLER & HART SOLICITORS LIMITED Hazelberry, 29 Basset Road, Camborne, Cornwall TR14 8SH **Tel:** 01209 714064 **Email:** solicitors@wallerandhart.co.uk **Apply to:** Mr Peter Clive Hart	Our office is based in Camborne, Cornwall (for over 40 years). We provide a wide range of legal services, specialising in commercial and private clients.	0	0	–	14	no
WALTER WILSON RICHMOND 360B Station Road, Harrow, Middlesex HA1 2DE **Tel:** 020 8427 8484 **Email:** wwr@walterwilson.co.uk **Apply to:** Mr VM Manek	Young forward-looking practice offering training in landlord/tenant, residential and commercial conveyancing, civil litigation, family law, employment, legal aid, probate and inheritance disputes.	0	2	1	7	yes
WALTERS & PLASKITT 2 Westport Road, Burslem, Stoke-on-Trent ST6 4AW **Tel:** 01782 819611 **Apply to:** Mr S Leech	General high street practice with an emphasis on crime, family law and litigation. Action against the police, personal injury, legal aid and private clients.	Poss	1	4	60	yes
WANNOP & FOX York Road Chambers, York Road, Bognor Regis PO21 1LT **Tel:** 01243 864001 **Email:** info@wannopfox.com **Apply to:** Mr Chris Gambs	Medium-sized mixed practice, largely private client but with some commercial property and general company/commercial work. Franchise in family and crime. No current vacancies.	0	4	6	52	no
WANSBROUGHS Northgate House, Devizes SN10 1JX **Tel:** 01380 733 300 **Email:** mail@wansbroughs.com **Apply to:** Ms Anna Wensley Stock	Commercial practice conducting work usually associated with larger practices. Areas include commercial, corporate, commercial and private property, complex tax, trusts, estates, family and insurance litigation.	2-3[18]	4	16	90	no
WARD GETHIN ARCHER 10 Tuesday Market Place, King's Lynn PE30 1JT **Tel:** 01553 660033 **Email:** sarah.scott@wardgethinarcher.co.uk **Apply to:** Ms Sarah Scott	Residential and commercial property, private client, employment, civil, personal injury and family. Additional offices in Dereham, Ely, Heacham, Swaffham, Chatteris and Watton.	1[19]	1	16	149	no
WARD HADAWAY Sandgate House, 102 Quayside, Newcastle upon Tyne NE1 3DX **Tel:** 0191 204 4003 **Email:** joinus@wardhadaway.com **Apply to:** Graduate Recruitment Team	Ward Hadaway is a full service commercial law firm with offices in Newcastle, Leeds and Manchester. We are a Northern law firm for national business.	10	24	85	450	yes
WARNER GOODMAN LLP Portland Chambers, 66 West Street, Fareham PO16 0JR **Tel:** 01329 288121 **Email:** recruitment@warnergoodman.co.uk **Apply to:** Ms Angela Dobson	A well-established medium-sized regional firm. Offices in Southampton, Fareham and Portsmouth. Legal aid franchise; member of specialist panels.	2-4	7	17	160	no

V = Vacancies / **T** = Trainees / **P** = Partners / **TS** = Total Staff / **WP** = Work Placement

Watson Farley & Williams LLP

15 Appold Street, London EC2A 2HB
Tel: 020 7814 8000
Email: uktrainees@wfw.com
Web: www.wfw.com/trainee

The firm WFW was founded in 1982 in the City of London. It has since grown rapidly to over 150 partners with a total staff of over 700. We are a distinctive law firm with a leading market position in international finance and investment, maritime and energy. We also specialise in natural resources, transport, real estate and technology. We have offices in London, New York, Paris, Hamburg, Munich, Frankfurt, Rome, Milan, Madrid, Athens, Singapore, Bangkok, Hong Kong and Dubai. The firm is able to provide an integrated, multi-jurisdictional service between offices and worldwide through an extensive network of specialist correspondence lawyers. In each of our offices our lawyers have expertise in the laws of the local jurisdiction and a knowledge and understanding of local business customs and culture.

Types of work The firm is divided into five practice groups: corporate, finance, energy and projects, litigation and real estate. The groups and our offices work together to support our international client base.

Who should apply Each year we recruit 18 trainees. Although there is no typical WFW trainee, there are certain qualifications, skills and traits that we look for. You will need a 2.1 or above – or predicted if you haven't yet graduated. We also ask for at least ABB from A-level results, or their equivalent, if you have taken other qualifications. As well as academic achievement, we particularly value applicants with clear initiative, drive and commercial awareness.

Training programme Our two-year training contract differs from many other firms. With us you will gain valuable insight from six four-month seats, one overseas in either Paris, Singapore, Athens, Bangkok, Hamburg or Dubai. In each you'll join a team led by a partner and see complex and high value transactions first hand. Your training contract will be hands-on, with as much experience of clients and real, high-profile work as possible. You'll also benefit from plenty of exposure to senior lawyers, many acknowledged leaders in their field. The firm has a reputation for challenging work. Yours will be no exception as we believe that only total immersion can provide you with the experience you require. We give you early responsibility but we also offer plenty of support and feedback.

When and how to apply All applications for training contracts should be made via our website www.wfw.com/trainee before 27 July 2018.

Work placements Our vacation scheme is the best way to familiarise yourself with WFW. The two-week placements are at our London office. They give us a chance to get to know you, and you a chance to experience the firm in more depth.

To appreciate first-hand the kind of work trainees undertake day to day, you will work with solicitors in one of our core practice groups for the whole period. To complement this focus on one area, you will also participate in a variety of training and social events designed to give you a general overview of the firm.

Applications must be received before 26 January 2018.

Sponsorship Full payment of fees for the GDL and LPC as applicable depending on the point of offer. We also provide a maintenance grant of £6,500/£5,500 depending on location.

Vacancies	18
Trainees	36
Partners	152
Total staff	700+

Work placement yes
(see Insider Report on p103)

Training contract deadline
27 July 2018

Apply
Online at
www.wfw.com/trainee

Starting salary
£43,000

Minimum qualifications
ABB at A level or equivalent
and 2.1 degree any
discipline

Sponsorship
GDL/LPC

Offices
London, New York,
Paris, Hamburg, Munich,
Frankfurt, Rome,
Milan, Madrid, Athens,
Singapore, Bangkok,
Hong Kong, Dubai

WATSON FARLEY
&
WILLIAMS

WARNERS SOLICITORS
Bank House, Bank Street, Tonbridge TN9 1BL
Tel: 01732 770660
Email: recruitment@warners-solicitors.co.uk
Apply to: Mrs Sally Hardwick

Warners is a modern and innovative law firm built on a strong heritage, providing expert advice to both businesses and individuals.

V	2[19]
T	2
P	22
TS	111
WP	no

WATKINS SOLICITORS
192 North Street, Bedminster, Bristol BS3 1JF
Tel: 0117 939 0350
Email: bw@watkinssolicitors.co.uk
Apply to: Ms BJ Watkins

Progressive law firm specialising in family, education, wills, probate and public law. Firm offers informal, unpaid work experience of two weeks – waiting list for placement.

V	0
T	2
P	3
TS	32
WP	yes

WATSON BURTON LLP
1 St James' Gate, Newcastle NE99 1YQ
Tel: 0191 244 4444
Email: graduates@watsonburton.com
Apply to: Miss Claire Pringle

Watson Burton is a leading law firm with a well-earned reputation for helping our clients succeed and providing first-class legal advice.

V	3[19]
T	10
P	14
TS	110
WP	yes

WATSON LEGAL
Office B, The Dutch Barn, Main Road, Ford End CM3 1LN
Tel: 01279 466910
Email: recruitment@watson-legal.com
Apply to: Ms Sarah Watson

We believe in delivering a strong client-focused service. We pride ourselves on our professional, friendly and conciliatory approach. We provide a different approach to training, with truly hands on experience in a supportive working environment.

V	1[18]
T	0
P	1
TS	2
WP	yes

WATSON WATSON SOLICITORS
Mercury House, Shrewsbury Business Park, Shrewsbury, Shropshire SY2 6LG
Tel: 01743 770 400
Email: jenny@watsonwatson.com
Apply to: Ms Jenny Watson

Watson Watson solicitors – niche firm based in Shrewsbury, Shropshire with a nationwide client base. Our core areas are corporate, commercial, property and tax law.

V	2
T	5
P	2
TS	20
WP	yes

WEDLAKE BELL LLP
71 Queen Victoria Street, London EC4V 4AY
Tel: 020 7395 3000
Email: recruitment@wedlakebell.com
Apply to: Graduate Recruitment Department

Wedlake Bell provides a full service to UK and international corporate and private clients.

V	6
T	12
P	59
TS	250
WP	yes

WEIGHTMANS LLP
100 Old Hall Street, Liverpool L3 9QJ
Tel: 0345 073 9900
Email: graduate.recruitment@weightmans.com
Apply to: Mr James See

Weightmans is a top 50 national law firm with offices in Birmingham, Dartford, Glasgow, Knutsford, Leeds, Leicester, Liverpool, London and Manchester.

V	Up to 18
T	33
P	187
TS	1306
WP	yes

WEIL, GOTSHAL & MANGES (LONDON) LLP
110 Fetter Lane, London EC4A 1AY
Tel: 020 7903 1000
Email: graduate.recruitment@weil.com
Apply to: Mrs Lisa Powell

International law firm, with over 1,200 lawyers worldwide and a reputation for providing first-class US and European legal advice.

V	15
T	26
P	33
TS	297
WP	yes

V = Vacancies / **T** = Trainees / **P** = Partners / **TS** = Total Staff / **WP** = Work Placement

WELLERS LAW GROUP LLP
Tenison House, Tweedy Road, Bromley BR1 3NF
Tel: 020 8464 4242
Email: hr@wellerslawgroup.com
Apply to: Ms Deena Bowman

Registered office Bromley. Additional offices, London, East Horsley and Great Bookham, Surrey, Sevenoaks. Commercial and private client firm with additional specialites of charity law and parish and town councils. Established over 100 years.

V	1[19]
T	1
P	3
TS	85
WP	no

WENDY HOPKINS FAMILY LAW PRACTICE
13 Windsor Place, Cardiff CF10 3BY
Tel: 029 2034 2233
Email: enquiries@wendyhopkins.co.uk
Apply to: Miss SE Wyburn

The first and largest purely family law firm in Wales, with expanding offices in Cardiff. Private family work, mainly high-value cases.

V	1
T	1
P	4
TS	27
WP	no

WH DARBYSHIRE & SON
252 Lytham Road, Blackpool FY1 6EX
Tel: 01253 346646
Apply to: Miss Lynn S Williams

Two offices, 252 Lytham Road Blackpool and 51 Commonside, Ansdell. Main areas of expertise, personal injury, benefits, probate, domestic, commercial conveyancing, crime and matrimonial. Legal aid franchise.

V	0
T	1
P	5
TS	13
WP	no

WH LAW LTD
Priory House, 2 Priory Road, Dudley, West Midlands DY1 1HH
Tel: 0845 1265900
Email: mrogers@whlaw.co.uk
Apply to: Mr M Rogers

Progressive firm committed to providing a quality legal service specialising in employment, health and safety, environment, PI and clinical negligence. No current vacancies.

V	0
T	1
P	3
TS	10
WP	no

WHITE & CO
51 Alexandra Street, Southend-on-Sea SS1 1BW
Tel: 01702 340340
Email: alison@whitesolicitors.co.uk
Apply to: Miss AM White

Niche family law/wills and probate practice providing advice and representation in both publicly and privately funded work including public law care proceedings.

V	1[18]
T	
P	2
TS	12
WP	yes

WHITEHEAD MONCKTON
72 King Street, Maidstone ME14 1BL
Tel: 01622 698000
Email: joanneforbes@whitehead-monckton.co.uk
Apply to: Mrs Joanne Forbes

Whitehead Monckton is one of the largest law firms in Kent, with offices in Canterbury, Maidstone, Tenterden and London. Providing a comprehensive range of services.

V	Varies[19]
T	2
P	10
TS	118
WP	no

WHITWORTH & GREEN SOLICITORS LTD
241 Church Street, Blackpool FY1 3PB
Tel: 01253 294582
Email: info@wgsolicitors.co.uk
Apply to: The Practice Manager

We are a young, energetic, high street practice with four offices. We have a strong reputation for crime, civil litigation, commercial and family.

V	4
T	2
P	2
TS	16
WP	yes

THE WILKES PARTNERSHIP
41 Church Street, Birmingham B3 2RT
Tel: 0121 710 5916
Email: khackett@wilkes.co.uk
Apply to: Mrs Kate Hackett

One of the leading second tier firms in Birmingham offering a full range of corporate support services continuing to expand in all areas.

V	4
T	8
P	18
TS	160
WP	no

V = Vacancies / **T** = Trainees / **P** = Partners / **TS** = Total Staff / **WP** = Work Placement

White & Case

5 Old Broad Street, London EC2N 1DW
Tel: 020 7532 2899
Email: londontrainee@whitecase.com
Web: www.whitecasetrainee.com
f whitecase 🐦 whitecase

The firm White & Case is a global law firm with nearly 2,000 lawyers worldwide. We've built an enviable network of 41 offices in 29 countries. That investment is the foundation for our client work in 159 countries today. Many White & Case clients are multinational organisations with complex needs that require the involvement of multiple offices. As part of our training contract, we offer every trainee a guaranteed six-month overseas seat.

Types of work In London, our key areas of work include: banking, financial restructuring and insolvency; capital markets (including regulatory compliance, high yield and securitisation); dispute resolution (including antitrust, commercial litigation, intellectual property, international arbitration, trade, white collar and construction and engineering); energy, infrastructure, project and asset finance (EIPAF); corporate (including M&A, private equity, employment, compensation and benefits, investment funds, real estate and tax).

Who should apply White & Case is looking to recruit ambitious trainees who have a desire to gain hands-on practical experience from day one and a willingness to take charge of their own career. They should have an understanding of international commercial issues and an interest in working on big-ticket, cross-border work. We recruit both law and non-law students and owing to the nature of our work, language skills are of interest. Applicants will be welcomed for their individuality, their ability to contribute to the cutting-edge work we do and the energy with which they approach the job at hand. They should have achieved, or be on track to achieve, a high 2.1, have a positive and friendly attitude, be enthusiastic and work well in teams.

Training programme The training contract consists of four six-month seats, one of which is guaranteed to be spent in one of our overseas offices, including Abu Dhabi, Beijing, Dubai, Frankfurt, Hong Kong, Moscow, New York, Paris, Prague, Singapore, Stockholm and Tokyo. The remaining three seats can be spent in any one of the firm's practice groups in London. Receiving a high level of partner and senior associate contact from day one, our trainees can be confident that they will receive high-quality, stimulating and rewarding work. Trainees work in small, focused teams, so their colleagues trust them to perform tasks accurately and efficiently. White & Case is a "high-stretch, high-support" workplace that celebrates individual excellence and team success. We actively encourage our trainees to take early responsibility, and there is a strong emphasis on practical training, with plenty of support and feedback. Alongside the training contract, our trainees are encouraged to get involved in all aspects of our globally-renowned pro bono programme, often working directly with clients and even managing small matters. White & Case recruits and develops trainee solicitors with the aim of retaining them on qualification.

When and how to apply Apply online at www.whitecasetrainee.com by 5 November 2017 for our winter vacation scheme and by 31 January 2018 for our spring and summer vacation schemes. Apply for a training contract by 31 July 2018. We hold open days on 9 November 2017 and 29 November 2017, and also a first-year, two-day insight scheme on 16-17 May 2018. Please visit our website for more information.

Work placements A vacation scheme provides a great way to experience first-hand what life is like as a White & Case trainee. Playing an active part in the life of the London office you will receive real work from a dedicated supervisor, attend interactive, informative sessions and be given plenty of opportunities to network at social events.

Vacancies	50
Trainees	75
Partners	101
Total staff	828 (London)
Work placement	yes

Training contract deadline
31 July 2018

Apply to
Christina Churchman,
Graduate Resourcing &
Development Manager

Starting salary
1st year – £46,000
2nd year – £50,000

Minimum qualifications
2.1 degree and AAB

Sponsorship
GDL/LPC

Offices
Abu Dhabi, Astana, Beijing, Berlin, Boston, Bratislava, Brussels, Cairo, Doha, Dubai, Düsseldorf, Frankfurt, Geneva, Hamburg, Helsinki, Hong Kong, Istanbul, Jakarta*, Johannesburg, London, Los Angeles, Madrid, Melbourne, Mexico City, Miami, Milan, Moscow, New York, Paris, Prague, Riyadh*, São Paulo, Seoul, Silicon Valley, Shanghai, Singapore, Stockholm, Sydney, Tokyo, Warsaw, Washington DC.
*Associated firm

WHITE & CASE

WILKIN CHAPMAN LLP
Cartergate House, 26 Chantry Lane, Grimsby
DN31 2LJ
Tel: 01472 262626
Email: angela.english@wilkinchapman.co.uk
Apply to: Mrs Angela English

Leading Lincolnshire and East Yorkshire law firm offering a wide range of legal services to private, corporate and publicly-funded clients.

V	4
T	11
P	42
TS	360
WP	yes

WILKINSON & BUTLER
Peppercorn House, 8 Huntingdon Street, St Neots
PE19 1BH
Tel: 01480 219229
Apply to: Mr Dawson

An old-established market town general practice handling all types of matters for private clients, commercial clients and legal aid.

V	0
T	0
P	4
TS	20
WP	no

WILKINSON WOODWARD LIMITED
11 Fountain Street, Halifax HX1 1LU
Tel: 01422 339600
Email: msc@wilkinsonwoodward.co.uk
Apply to: Mrs Maureen Cawthorn

General practice with legal aid franchises. Clients vary from large companies to private individuals.

V	1-2
T	2
P	8
TS	92
WP	no

WILLANS LLP
28 Imperial Square, Cheltenham GL50 1RH
Tel: 01242 514000
Email: law@willans.co.uk
Apply to: Ms Bridget Redmond

Practice dealing with all types of commercial and private client work, except crime, from town centre offices.

V	0
T	0
P	14
TS	70
WP	no

WILLS CHANDLER
76 Bounty Road, Basingstoke, Hampshire
RG21 3BZ
Tel: 01256 322911
Apply to: Mr A Dodson

Typical high street firm undertaking a mix of work including matrimonial, litigation, probate and conveyancing. Old fashioned service, but modern systems.

V	1
T	1
P	3
TS	14
WP	no

WILSON & BIRD
Ideal House, Exchange Street, Aylesbury
HP20 1QY
Tel: 01296 436766
Apply to: Mrs J Majek

High street mixed practice. Private client. Varied workload and experience.

V	1
T	0
P	1
TS	6
WP	no

WILSON BROWNE SOLICITORS
4 Grange Park Court, Roman Way, Northampton
NN4 5EA
Tel: 01604 876697
Email: enquiries@wilsonbrowne.co.uk
Apply to: Mr John Whitehouse

General practice with offices in Northamptonshire and Leicester offering a wide range of client services including company/ commercial, residential conveyancing, private client, civil litigation and family.

V	0
T	4
P	16
TS	118
WP	no

WILSON SOLICITORS LLP
697 High Road, Tottenham, London N17 8AD
Tel: 020 8808 7535
Email: info@wilsonllp.co.uk
Apply to: Mr Matthew Davies

Large legal aid practice specialising in crime, immigration/refugee law, public law, and family law. Trainee solicitors usually start as caseworkers or paralegals.

V	5
T	15
P	12
TS	70
WP	no

V = Vacancies / **T** = Trainees / **P** = Partners / **TS** = Total Staff / **WP** = Work Placement

Wilsons Solicitors LLP

Alexandra House, St Johns Street, Salisbury, Wiltshire SP1 2SB
Tel: 01722 412412
Email: jo.ratcliffe@wilsonslaw.com
Web: www.wilsonslaw.com
🐦 wilsonslawcom

The firm Ranked as one of the top private client and charity law firms in the country, our almost 300-year heritage, combined with lawyers who are recognised leaders in their fields, enables Wilsons to provide a unique combination of skills and experience to our clients. Our lawyers are dedicated to ensuring a detailed understanding of their clients' interests and a seamless working relationship across the different specialities of the practice.

Types of work Private client: We act for clients with business interests, landed and inherited wealth, foreign domiciliaries, UK and offshore trustees and non-resident individuals with links to the UK. Services include tax planning, estate and succession planning, asset structuring, UK and offshore trust information and advice, wills and trusts and estate administration and probates and intestacies valued at up to £50m. Family: The team's expertise ranges from pre-nuptial agreements and civil partnerships to divorce, children's arrangements and surrogacy law. Charity: Wilsons has one of the most highly ranked teams in the UK. We advise on the complete range of legal needs and have a particular specialism in contentious and non-contentious legacy work. The constitutional and governance team has considerable expertise in advising military charities and the charitable care sector. Agriculture: Wilsons' rural team has a practice centred on the needs of rural business and landowners. These include complex sales and purchases, development options for landowners, grants and diversification advice and property litigation, including landlord and tenant, partnership matters, boundary, title and rights of way disputes. Commercial: The commercial team specialises in employment, commercial property and corporate work. Corporate work focuses on commercial tax and asset planning, transactions and refinancing. Property: Our clients have substantial commercial, agricultural and residential property interests and the firm advises on purchasing, letting and sales. Litigation and dispute resolution: Wilsons has one of the largest teams outside London. We advise clients on a wide range of contentious matters to provide an efficient and effective means of dispute resolution. In addition to its expertise in agricultural and probate disputes, the firm has specialists who can advise on all aspects of commercial dispute claims and reputation management.

Who should apply We aim to employ the highest quality people; our reputation relies on this. We look for applicants with a 2.1 degree. We place considerable emphasis on teamwork and applicants must be able to demonstrate effective verbal and written communication skills.

Training programme The number of solicitors that have trained, qualified and remained with us is a testament to our trainee programme. If you show willingness and aptitude you will be given responsibility from an early stage.

When and how to apply The deadline for applications for a training contract is 30 June 2018 to commence a training contract in September 2020. Application forms can be obtained from our website.

Work placement Each year in June/July we run a work placement scheme in Salisbury for second-year law students or third-year non-law students onwards. There are five places available on our placement scheme. We make a contribution towards costs. The closing date for applications for a placement in 2018 is 31 March 2018.

Sponsorship We provide an interest-free loan of up to £4,500 for the LPC. Further details are available on application.

Vacancies	4
Trainees	8
Partners	29
Total staff	157

Work placement yes

Training contract deadline
30 June 2018

Apply to
Mrs Jo Ratcliffe

Starting salary
Above market rate

Offices
London, Salisbury

Winckworth Sherwood

Minerva House, 5 Montague Close, London SE1 9BB
Tel: 020 7593 5000
Email: trainees@wslaw.co.uk
Web: www.traineehub.wslaw.co.uk
f winckworthsherwood 🐦 ws_law

The firm Winckworth Sherwood LLP is a dynamic law firm providing a wide range of legal services to a diverse range of businesses, not-for-profit organisations and private individuals.

Types of work Corporate and commercial: We advise on corporate, mergers and acquisitions, partnerships and JVs, commercial arrangements, outsourcing and procurement, corporate finance and capital markets, funds and IP, IT contracts and data protection.
Employment and partnership: We provide contentious and non-contentious advice covering financial, insurance, retail, hotel, media, publishing, real estate and educational establishments. We also advise senior executives and on partnership disputes, as well as specialist non-contentious partnership advice.
Infrastructure projects: We specialise in private legislation promoting projects of major strategic importance. We also advise central and local government bodies, developers and operators on infrastructure planning, development, constructions, procurement, structuring and finance.
Not for profit: We advise a large number of educational and affordable housing operators, charitable and religious organisations and cultural and leisure service providers, delivering a full range of legal expertise.
Private wealth and tax: We advise high-net worth individuals, families, senior executives, private trustees and executors on a full range of private legal matters, including complex residential property solutions, tax and succession issues, pre-marital advice, divorce and family.
Real estate and planning: We work for some of the leading national residential and commercial developers, national house builders, investors and fund managers. This includes commercial real estate and regeneration, planning, development, corporate finance, funds, tax, construction, asset management and property litigation capability.

Who should apply We require a strong academic record both at school and university, but we also look for attributes which demonstrate the potential for making a positive contribution to the firm such as drive and enthusiasm, resilience, team working and excellent communications skills and an analytical and logical approach.

Training programme As a trainee you will rotate though four departments in six-month placements or seats. The purpose of each seat is to give you a solid grounding in that area of the law. We encourage substantial client contact from the start and you will be involved in all phases of a matter. As a trainee you will usually sit with a partner or senior solicitor and may be given the opportunity to manage your own files, subject to suitable supervision. We have a well developed in-house continuing educational programme. As well as legal training, we also provide business skills such as presentation skills, time management and networking.

When and how to apply Apply online at www.traineehub.wslaw.co.uk by 30 June 2018 for a 2020 training contract.

Work placements As part of the trainee recruitment process our summer placement programme runs every year for two weeks in July. Applications should be made online between November and February of each year. We also have a trainee open day in July (as an alternative to the work placement) for potential trainees which forms part of the interview process.

Sponsorship With some conditions, we provide financial assistance for course fees for trainees attending the Legal Practice Course.

Vacancies	8
Trainees	14
Partners	58
Total staff	328

Work placement yes

Training contract deadline
30 June 2018

Apply
Online

Minimum qualifications
2.1 degree

Sponsorship
LPC

Offices
London, Oxford, Manchester

Remember to cite *The Training Contract & Pupillage Handbook* on your application form if you apply to this firm.

Winston & Strawn London LLP

CityPoint, One Ropemaker Street, London EC2Y 9AW
Tel: 020 7011 8700
Email: trainingapplication@winston.com
Web: www.winston.com
🐦 winstonlaw

The firm For more than 160 years, Winston & Strawn LLP has served as a trusted adviser and advocate for clients across virtually every industry. In that time, the firm has built a law practice with tremendous breadth and global reach. We are proud of the many accolades we have received over the years – a tribute to our lawyers' creativity, flexibility, depth of experience, and commitment.

Winston's London office serves high-profile, multinational clients on a distinctly international level. When it comes to our employees, our goal is to maximise individual potential with professional development opportunities, emphasise the firm's culture, and contribute positively to the community. Winston has more than 900 attorneys in a number of practice areas across 17 offices.

Types of work Winston's London office provides high-quality legal services in a diverse range of areas including cross-border M&A and finance, project and transportation finance, private equity and venture capital, tax, litigation, international arbitration, contentious regulatory, privacy and data security, and EU antitrust/competition services.

Who should apply We seek well-rounded, commercially aware, imaginative people with a genuine intellectual curiosity and with strong academics (including an expected or achieved first or upper second class honours degree) who will work hard for our clients, interact well with others in a close-knit team, and make meaningful contributions to our continued growth and success in London, as well as globally. We seek ambitious individuals looking to build a long term career at the firm and want all of our trainees to stay with the firm upon qualification and continue to develop as associates with a view to ultimately become a partner.

Training programme Our trainees are asked to carry out real legal work from day one, interact directly with clients, and contribute to all aspects of firm life. Trainees have our full attention and support throughout their training contract and sit with a partner or a senior associate for each of the four seats.

When and how to apply To secure a training contract you should first apply for our summer vacation scheme. To apply for the 2018 summer vacation scheme (which normally takes place in July each year), please apply by CV and a covering letter. We will be accepting applications from 15 October 2017 to 15 January 2018. Please note that due to the success of our recent summer vacation scheme we are only able to offer training contracts from September 2020 onwards. Please include a full classification and percentage breakdown of all academic results in your CV.

Work placements A two-week summer placement. Remuneration £400 per week.

Sponsorship Full sponsorship of GDL and LPC fees, plus a maintenance grant (not retrospective).

Vacancies	4
Trainees	5
Partners	16
Total staff	58

Work placement yes

Apply
Online

Minimum qualifications
2.1 degree

Sponsorship
GDL/LPC

Offices
Brussels, Charlotte, Chicago, Dallas, Dubai, Hong Kong, Houston, London, Los Angeles, Moscow, New York, Newark, Paris, San Francisco, Shanghai, Silicon Valley, Washington DC

Remember to cite *The Training Contract & Pupillage Handbook* on your application form if you apply to this firm.

Withers LLP

16 Old Bailey, London EC4M 7EG
Tel: 020 7597 6000
Email: recruitment@withersworldwide.com
Web: www.withersworldwide.com
f withersworld **🐦** withersrecruits

The firm Withers LLP is an international law firm dedicated to the business, personal and philanthropic interests of successful people, their families, their businesses and their advisers. Our mission is to offer a truly integrated legal service to people with sophisticated global wealth, management and business needs. The firm has been recognised for its great working environment having been consistently listed in *The Sunday Times* 100 Best Companies To Work For (2012-2016). In 2015 the firm won 'Best Training for vacation scheme and training contract' at the AllAboutLaw awards. Furthermore, the firm won LawCareers.Net's 'Best Training Principal' award in 2014, 2015 and 2017.

Types of work The wealth of today's high-net worth individuals has increased in multiples and many are institutions in their own right. Our global expertise ensures our ability to respond to these changing legal needs and offer integrated solutions to the international legal and tax needs of our clients. With 167 partners and over 1,000 people we have unparalleled expertise in commercial and tax law, trusts, estate planning, litigation, IP, charities, employment, reputation management, family law and other legal issues facing high-net worth individuals.

Withers' reputation in commercial law along with its status as the largest private client team in Europe sets it apart from other City firms. Work is often international due to the complexity of our client base which includes some of the wealthiest global citizens. We have acted for 51% of the UK *Sunday Times* 'Rich List' and a significant number from the US '*Forbes*' and Asian '*Hurun*' rich lists. Trainees who speak a relevant language may have the opportunity to complete a seat in one of our offices abroad.

Who should apply Each year we look for a diverse mix of trainees who are excited by the prospect of working with leaders in their field (who are often in the public eye as spokespersons for the profession). Trainees should have a high degree of determination, great attention to detail and be able to demonstrate business acumen and entrepreneurial flair.

Training programme Trainees spend six months in four different departments. Teams are small (files are typically handled by one senior fee earner and a trainee) so the client will know your name. Buddy and mentor systems as well as on the job training ensure trainees are fully supported from the outset.

When and how to apply Apply online by 31 July 2018 to begin training in September 2020. Interviews usually take place between May and August.

Work placements We run two-week placements at Easter and over the summer in London. Apply online by 31 January 2018 for places in 2018.

Sponsorship Fees plus £5,000 maintenance for both the GDL and LPC are paid.

Vacancies	11
Trainees	22
Partners	167
Total staff	1,100

Work placement yes
(see Insider Report on p105)

Training contract deadline
31 July 2018

Apply
Online

Starting salary
1st year – £37,000
2nd year – £40,000

Minimum qualifications
2.1 degree, AAB at A level

Sponsorship
GDL/LPC

Offices
London, Milan, Geneva, Padua, San Francisco, New York, New Haven (Connecticut), Greenwich (USA), Hong Kong, The British Virgin Islands (BVI), Singapore, Sydney, San Francisco, Rancho Santa Fe, Los Angeles, San Diego, Tokyo (Withers Japan, Zeirishi Houjin)

withersworldwide

Affiliated with

ZS aspiringsolicitors

Firm	Description	V	T	P	TS	WP
WILSONS SOLICITORS Ease House, 52 High Street, Oxford OX33 1 XT **Tel:** 01865 874 497 **Email:** wilsonsolicitor@btconnect.com **Apply to:** Mr Howard Wilson	We are a legal aid firm in civil and crime with an emphasis on advocacy.	2	2	1	5	yes
WLL SOLICITORS Berkeley Square House, Berkeley Square, London W1J 6BD **Tel:** 020 7887 1959 **Email:** info@wllsolicitors.com **Apply to:** The Practice Manager	Niche litigation practice specialising in bankruptcy. Applicants must be highly motivated, relish a high level of responsibility, be team players, have initiative and a 2.1 degree, preferably in law.	2	1	1	7	yes
WOODFINES LLP 352 Silbury Boulevard, Milton Keynes MK9 2AF **Tel:** 01908 202150 **Email:** jegan@woodfines.co.uk **Apply to:** Mr John Egan	A dynamic and expanding regional practice offering a comprehensive range of legal services. We see recruitment and training as the core of our development plan.	3^{19}	6	20	152	yes
WORTLEY BYERS LLP Cathedral Place, Brentwood CM14 4ES **Tel:** 01277 268368 **Email:** aelliss@wortleybyers.co.uk **Apply to:** Mrs Anne Elliss	Wortley Byers is based in Brentwood, Essex. Specialist areas include business law, taxation, employment and litigation, intellectual property law, insolvancy, commercial property and planning.	0	0	11	60	no
WRIGHT HASSALL LLP Olympus Avenue, Leamington Spa CV34 6BF **Tel:** 01926 886688 **Email:** humanresources@wrighthassall.co.uk **Apply to:** Human Resources Team	A leading full service commercial law firm, the largest in Warwickshire, with all the services that you would expect from a city or global firm.	4	8	35	280	yes
WRIGLEY CLAYDON 29-33 Union Street, Oldham OL1 1HH **Tel:** 0161 624 6811 **Email:** john.mann@wrigleyclaydon.com **Apply to:** Mr John Mann	Medium general practice.	1	0	5	26	no
WRIGLEYS SOLICITORS LLP 19 Cookridge Street, Leeds LS2 3AG **Tel:** 0113 244 6100 **Email:** sue.greaves@wrigleys.co.uk **Apply to:** Miss Sue Greaves	A specialist firm which concentrates on the financial affairs, property and assets of private individuals, charities, foundations, trustees and pension schemes.	2	4	21	193	no
YORKLAW LTD T/AS BURN & COMPANY Ebor House, LondonEbor Business Park, Millfield Lane, Nether Poppleton, York YO26 6QY **Tel:** 01904 655442 **Email:** enquiries@burn-company.co.uk **Apply to:** Mr Michael Creamer		0	0	5	20	no

V = Vacancies / **T** = Trainees / **P** = Partners / **TS** = Total Staff / **WP** = Work Placement

YOUNG & PEARCE 58 Talbot Street, Nottingham NG1 5GL **Tel:** 0115 959 8888 **Apply to:** Mr Richard Bates	Modern offices set in the centre of Nottingham. Fully computerised. Niche licensing and commercial, crime, family, civil litigation, BSI and legal aid franchise.	V 1 T 1 P 8 TS 33 WP yes
ZYDA LAW 60 Cygnet Court, Timothy's Bridge Road, Stratford-upon-Avon CV37 9NW **Tel:** 01789 413 949 **Email:** secretary@zydalaw.com **Apply to:** S Secretary	Recruiting one trainee solicitor for an award-winning, boutique planning and environmental law firm with expertise in energy and infrastructure development.	V 1 T 2 P 1 TS 5 WP yes

V = Vacancies / **T** = Trainees / **P** = Partners / **TS** = Total Staff / **WP** = Work Placement

*Law*Careers.Net™

Delivering your future in law

LCN Weekly is packed with news, profiles, opinion and advice about becoming a lawyer, and delivered to your inbox for free every Tuesday.

Don't miss out on this essential source of information!

Subscribe to LCN Weekly at
www.lawcareers.net/mylcn/

Barristers

The Bar Council

The Bar Council represents barristers in England and Wales. It promotes the Bar's high-quality specialist advocacy and advisory services in support of fair access to justice for all; the highest standards of ethics, equality and diversity across the profession; and the development of business opportunities for barristers at home and abroad.

The Bar Council represents the interests of the Bar on all matters relating to the profession. It is also the Approved Regulator of the Bar of England and Wales, discharging its regulatory functions through the independent Bar Standards Board (BSB) (see page 469).

In its representative capacity, the Bar Council has been at the forefront of many initiatives to defend the rule of law and promote access to justice, and to support the legal services sector and equality and diversity in the profession. The Bar Council engages constructively with government, Parliament and other stakeholders in the legal services sector to defend, maintain and support a system of justice of which we can all be proud.

The profession

A strong and independent Bar exists to serve the public and it is essential to the effective administration of justice. As specialist, independent advocates, barristers help people to uphold their legal rights and obligations, acting often on behalf of the most vulnerable members of society. The Bar makes a vital contribution to the efficient operation of criminal, family and civil courts. It provides a pool from which a significant proportion of the judiciary is drawn, on whose independence the rule of law and our democratic way of life depend.

There are approximately 16,000 members of the Bar of England and Wales, the majority of whom operate independently under the 'cab rank' rule, which requires barristers to accept instructions in any field in which they practise on being offered a proper fee. This duty exists regardless of the barrister's views of the client or the case. The cab rank rule, which governs only barristers, is regarded as a fundamental element of the rule of law in this country. It accounts, at least in part, for the high regard in which the Bar of England and Wales is held both at home and abroad.

Many self-employed barristers are now trained to take direct public access work, which means members of the public, businesses and other organisations can go directly to a barrister for legal services and not, as has traditionally been the case, via a solicitor.

Of the self-employed Bar, nearly half routinely undertake publicly funded work, whether prosecuting or defending in the criminal courts or appearing in children and family cases. Many barristers are involved in pro bono work as members of the Bar Pro Bono Unit or the Free Representation Unit (see page 65). Others give freely of their time to support Bar Council initiatives to improve social mobility in the profession, give careers advice in schools, or help shape Bar Council policy.

Approximately 3,000 barristers are employed. Employed barristers practise in-house within a wide range of organisations and sectors, varying from business and government to social and health services. Examples of employers include the Crown Prosecution Service, the Armed Forces, the Medicines and Healthcare Products Regulatory Authority and the Investment Management Association.

Entry to the Bar

The Bar Council is strongly committed to ensuring that the Bar continues to become a more diverse and socially representative profession. It reaches out to as wide a range of people as possible, working with everyone from school students to mature entrants in order to provide accurate, reliable and helpful information about a career at the Bar. The Bar Council works with numerous organisations which share a common interest in achieving this aim, from the Inns of Court, the circuits and specialist Bar associations to carefully selected charities such as the Social Mobility Foundation and the Citizenship Foundation. The annual Bar Mock Trials competition, produced with the Citizenship Foundation, reaches 2,000 students a year, giving them access to valuable coaching from practising barristers and the opportunity to compete in teams with schools from across the country.

As well as attending law fairs at universities with a high proportion of students from low economic backgrounds, the Bar Council runs the Pupillage Fair, which is the largest in the country with over 50 chambers participating and a range of workshops and CV clinics for aspiring barristers. The Bar Council also manages the Pupillage Gateway to ensure that the application process for this vital stage of entry to the profession is fair and transparent.

Each year over 600 barristers participate in various outreach programmes organised by the Bar Council. These programmes, which include the Bar Placement Weeks in London, Birmingham, Manchester, Bristol and Leeds for Year 12 and 13 students to experience life as a barrister, are designed to encourage sixth formers in state schools throughout England and Wales to consider a career at the Bar. The Bar Council also has an e-mentoring scheme which pairs barristers with students who meet social mobility criteria and who are interested in joining the Bar.

Young Bar
Students, pupils and junior barristers will be particularly interested in the work of the Bar Council's Young Barristers' Committee (YBC), which represents and promotes the interests of barristers of up to seven years' call. The YBC is actively engaged with the development of Bar Council policy and promotes and supports young barristers through its annual workshop and the Young Bar Hub and Toolkit. The Bar Council also provides a Pupillage Helpline and Pupillage Supervisor Network to support young barristers and promote good practice.

Career development
The Bar Council offers a wide range of training courses to support barristers throughout their careers, including a mentoring service for barristers seeking to become silks (Queen's Counsel), and mentoring for barristers returning to work following a break for parental leave. The Bar Council also runs a variety of events and conferences to encourage continued professional development throughout a barrister's career at the Bar.

International opportunities
The International Committee of the Bar Council promotes the Bar overseas and facilitates introductions and networking opportunities at a wide variety of events. It has also sought to encourage and assist barristers, as well as chambers, to think of international work as an increasingly important source of instruction.

Services
The Services department of the Bar Council provides support and resources to help its members and those who work with them. These services cover all aspects of life at the Bar including Debt Recovery Panels, the Direct Access Portal and the Bar's own escrow service, BARCO. This is in addition to managing the Bar's voluntary fee, the Bar Representation Fee which can be paid by all members of the Bar including students. It provides access to a wide range of affinity services (including

accountancy, financial planning, insurance and healthcare) at commercially attractive rates. It also arranges accredited training courses throughout the country, seminars and lectures in conjunction with the various committees and policy teams, as well as an Employed Bar Awards ceremony, Pupillage Fair and a combined Annual and Young Bar conference. For those considering a career at the Bar, the department manages an extensive careers programme for students and operates the Pupillage Gateway, an online portal providing a flexible and cost-effective way for chambers and authorised training organisations to advertise pupillages and manage applications.

Supporting barristers
The Bar Council provides three helplines for barristers: the Ethical Enquiries Line, the Equality and Diversity Helpline, and the Pupils Helpline. The Ethical Enquiries Line provides guidance on ethical problems that barristers may face in the course of their work and is managed by a specially trained team. The Equality and Diversity Helpline advises barristers (including pupils), clerks and practice managers on regulatory and statutory equality duties, as well as on best practice. The Pupils Helpline gives confidential advice and support to members of the Bar who are currently undertaking pupillage.

The Bar Council is undertaking an increasing amount of work to promote wellbeing in the profession and has recently set up a wellbeing portal to provide online resources and sign-posting for members of the Bar and those who work with them to get help, advice and guidance on their wellbeing.

Well briefed
The Bar Council works closely with the Inns of Court, circuits and specialist Bar associations to provide support and guidance to all barristers, including professional guidance and regulatory

updates on issues such as money laundering and data protection. In addition to the information provided on the Bar Council's website (www.barcouncil.org.uk), the Bar Council provides fortnightly updates about the work it is doing on behalf of the Bar through its fortnightly e-newsletter, BarTalk. To subscribe to BarTalk, email BarTalk@ BarCouncil.org.uk.

Representing the Bar
The Bar Council makes representations on matters affecting the administration of justice to government, Parliament, the institutions of the European Union, international legal organisations and other stakeholders. Where appropriate, the Bar Council considers and develops proposals for law reform, and regularly communicates its views to government and others.

Much of the Bar Council's representative work and many of its initiatives are only possible because its members pay the voluntary Bar Representation Fee (BRF) of £100 a year to fund these vital services. The Bar Council website provides more detail on the BRF and information on much of the work listed above.

This information is supplied by the Bar Council.

The Bar Standards Board

The Bar Standards Board (BSB) regulates barristers and specialised legal services businesses in England and Wales in the public interest. It is responsible for:

- setting the education and training requirements for becoming a barrister;
- setting continuing training requirements to ensure that barristers' skills are maintained throughout their careers;
- setting standards of conduct for barristers;
- authorising organisations that focus on advocacy, litigation and specialist legal advice;
- monitoring the service provided by barristers and the organisations it authorises to assure quality; and
- handling complaints against barristers and the organisations that it authorises, and taking disciplinary or other action where appropriate.

Qualifying as a barrister in England and Wales

Anyone considering training to become a barrister should be aware that the BSB is in the process of changing the way in which barristers must train and qualify. For up-to-date information on when any changes will come into effect, please visit the BSB website.

Here the BSB explains the current education and training system and how it is likely to change in the future.

In 2016 the BSB published the Professional Statement for Barristers to make clear what we believe the outcomes of training for the Bar should be. This describes the knowledge, skills and attributes that all barristers should have on their first day of practice. The Professional Statement applies to all newly qualified barristers whether they qualify via the current training arrangements or via those that may apply in the future.

The Professional Statement for Barristers is available on the BSB's website at www.

barstandardsboard.org.uk/qualifying-as-a-barrister/future-bar-training/professional-statement.

Current training requirements

Since 2006 the BSB has overseen the three stages that must be completed to qualify as a barrister, as well as the process of transferring to the Bar from practice abroad or as a solicitor in practice in England and Wales.

The three stages of training are termed academic, vocational and pupillage.

Academic stage
Either an undergraduate law degree (2:2 minimum) or an undergraduate degree in another subject (2:2 minimum) and the one-year conversion course Common Professional Examination/Graduate Diploma in Law (CPE/GDL).

Vocational stage
The Bar Professional Training Course (BPTC), which can be completed full time over one year, or part time over two.

One of the requirements for entry to the BPTC is a pass on the Bar Course Aptitude Test (BCAT). The BCAT tests students' critical thinking skills and the result of the test gives an indication of the likelihood of success on the BPTC.

Another requirement for entry to the BPTC is joining one of the four Inns of Court. Students must undertake qualifying sessions, provided by the Inns, in order to be called to the Bar by their Inn on successful completion of the BPTC. The four Inns have their own websites, where information on activities that they offer can be found.

Pupillage
Pupillage is the final stage in qualifying for practice at the Bar, during which practical training under the supervision of an

experienced barrister is gained. It is a one-year training period spent in an approved training organisation (ie, a barristers' chambers or another approved legal environment). It is divided into two parts: a non-practising six months (known as the 'first six') and six months in which the pupil can offer reserved legal services with provisional authorisation (known as the 'second six').

Pupillage providers must advertise all pupillage vacancies on www.pupillagegateway.com, which is a service provided by the Bar Council. The Pupillage Gateway offers a common timetable for the application process. Through a financial award or earnings, all pupils must receive no less than £1,000 per month from their training organisation, plus reasonable travel expenses where applicable.

More information on the three current stages of qualification is available at www.barstandardsboard.org.uk/qualifying-as-a-barrister/current-requirements.

Future ways to qualify as a barrister
In March 2017 the BSB decided that it will authorise a limited number of future training routes for prospective students to qualify as barristers. The future system for training for the Bar will retain the three elements of training that have proved successful in the past: academic, vocational and work-based learning. However, changes are planned, especially to the vocational stage.

The aim of the new approach, once the changes have been made, is to encourage an independent, strong, diverse and effective legal profession both now and in future. New barristers need to be able to meet the needs of consumers in a fast-changing market for legal services and to promote access to justice and compliance with the rule of law. The new approach is designed to provide students embarking on a career at the Bar with greater flexibility, accessibility and affordability while maintaining the high standards expected of barristers.

One of the priorities for the change programme – known as Future Bar Training (FBT) – is to ensure that nobody is disadvantaged as a result of any changes made to how barristers will qualify either now or in the future. The BSB is committed to making sure that there is a robust transition process.

To read more about the FBT Programme, visit www.barstandardsboard.org.uk/qualifying-as-a-barrister/future-bar-training. To stay up to date with changes and the FBT programme, follow the BSB on Twitter @barstandards.

This information is supplied by the BSB.

The Young Barristers' Committee

The Young Barristers' Committee (YBC) was established in 1954. Its main terms of reference are to advise the representative committees of the Bar Council on all matters of particular concern to young barristers; to liaise with the BSB on such matters as necessary; and to take such steps as seem likely to promote the interests of the Young Bar having regard to the interests of the Bar as a whole. Although it started as an "experiment for a period of one year in the first instance", it continues to flourish as one of the Bar Council's principal representative committees. The breadth of the work that it covers is surpassed only by the Bar Council itself.

The definition of a 'young barrister' was changed last year to someone in their first seven years of practice (rather than seven years post-call) to ensure that there is adequate support and representation for those starting out in the profession.

What do we do?
The aim of the YBC is to represent the Young Bar and also to ensure that adequate support and provision is made for young barristers. We do this through making representations both internally in the Bar Council and externally to government, the judiciary, the Bar Standards Board (BSB), the Inns and others involved in training and regulating barristers, and those with whom barristers may interact in their working lives. This work includes responding to consultation papers that are issued by various organisations and through attending meetings and providing the invaluable perspective of the Young Bar. Some of our members are elected, while others are co-opted to ensure that our membership is diverse and includes representatives from each of the circuits and from all areas of practice.

Young Bar Hub
The main source of information for young barristers, provided by the YBC, is the Young Bar Hub at www.youngbarhub.com. The site contains the Young Bar Toolkit: an online information resource with advice and guidance on practice management, finances and wellbeing. There is information for self-employed and employed barristers and pupils. The site also houses the Young Bar Blog, which includes a 'day in the life' series with snapshots of the experiences and 'typical days' of members of the committee. There are also articles and information about forthcoming events and activities that the YBC is hosting or supporting.

We have a dedicated Twitter account @YoungBarristers to ensure that up-to-date information on training, events and other issues of interest to young barristers is available.

Court reform
The YBC has been heavily involved in the Bar Council's work on court reform. This includes the "online court" proposed in Lord Justice Briggs' Review of the Civil Courts and Lord Justice Jackson's proposals for fixed recoverable costs in certain civil claims. The YBC has contributed to Bar Council responses to the relevant consultations and attended meetings at the Ministry of Justice and with the senior judiciary in order to ensure that the Young Bar's voice is heard. We have made clear the potential access to justice issues arising out of such proposals, as well as highlighting the potential adverse effects on young barristers.

Remuneration
The cuts to legal aid brought in by the Legal Aid, Sentencing and Punishment of Offenders Act 2012 reduced the availability of public funding for almost all civil and family work. The impact of the act, plus the increase of court fees in the civil courts and the employment tribunal, has disproportionately affected the work available to those at the junior end of the Bar. There has also been an increase in the number of paid "McKenzie

Friends", particularly in the family courts. The YBC has contributed towards the Bar Council's policy work in highlighting these issues, and responding to the judicial consultation on paid McKenzie Friends.

Remuneration for criminal work is also an area which has received intense focus. In this regard, the YBC submitted its own response to the Ministry of Justice's consultation on the proposed new Advocates Graduated Fee Scheme for remuneration in the Crown Court. A YBC working group is also looking into remuneration for magistrates' court work, exploring ways to make sure that young barristers are paid and paid on time. This has involved meeting with the Legal Aid Agency and solicitors' representatives.

Education and training

The YBC's work on education and training involves responding to consultations sent out by the BSB and in particular the Future Training for the Bar project. The YBC remains closely involved in the debate as to whether there should be an alternative to the BPTC.

The YBC's executive has also led on the redesign of the Bar Council's e-Mentoring scheme for non-traditional applicants to the Bar. She has worked with leading charities, including the Citizenship Foundation and Social Mobility Foundation, to design a safe online mentoring platform to allow those from non-traditional backgrounds to link up with barristers. The majority of the mentors are young barristers.

The YBC was also involved in Bar Placement Week, where 60 students from around the country come to London to experience a week of working with barristers, and receive advocacy training and talks from those in practice.

Wellbeing at the Bar

The YBC has continued to be closely involved with the Bar Council's Wellbeing at the Bar Working Group, who have developed a series of online resources to help barristers manage their wellbeing; support others in chambers; and provide guidance and assistance to those supporting someone in difficulties. The Wellbeing at the Bar website is a fantastic resource on such matters and a student section will be added soon. There are also dedicated pages on wellbeing within the Young Bar Toolkit and there was a wellbeing session at the Young Bar workshop, speaking of which....

Young Bar half-Day workshop

This year the YBC held its second annual Half-Day Workshop, entitled The Specialist Advocate. The workshop was designed to focus on practical training in advocacy and practice development issues in criminal, civil, family and employed practice. Our keynote speaker was Sir Brian Leveson, president of the Queen's Bench Division. The plenary Q&A session entitled "Everything you wanted to know about advocacy but were too afraid to ask" also saw a panel of judges of all levels answer young barristers' questions in relation to advocacy. The panel, made up of Mr Justice Foskett, Mrs Justice Andrews, HHJ Nicholas Hilliard QC, Registrar Briggs and DJ Tan-Ikram were questioned on a range of topics from skeleton arguments to stubborn judges!

Young Bar Conference and Annual Conference

For the third year running the Young Bar Conference will take place with the Annual Conference on Saturday 4 November. This allows young barristers to get the best of both worlds: dedicated Young Bar sessions to address issues pertinent to young barristers, and a chance to network with other barristers from all parts of the profession. The theme for this year's conferences is "One Bar: strengths, opportunities and challenges". Pupils and students are welcome to attend, and can do so at a heavily reduced rate.

International work
Building on the YBC's previous international work, we have continued to be involved with the European Young Bar Association and have maintained contacts with the American Bar Association's Young Lawyers Division, the International Bar Association and the International Association of Young Lawyers (AIJA).

This includes co-hosting International Weekend in September, and welcoming young lawyers from Europe, America and across the globe to London for a series of networking and educational events. We have been heavily involved with hosting visiting Chinese and Korean lawyers on the Bar Council's training schemes. The YBC also administers the Bar Council's International Grant programme, which provides financial support for young barristers who attend international events to boost their international practice.

Contact us
If there is anything on which you would like further guidance or support, please do have a look at www.youngbarhub.com or contact our policy analyst, Onyeka Onyekwelu, on 020 7611 1323 or at YBC@barcouncil.org.uk.

Duncan McCombe is chair of the YBC for 2017 and a barrister at Maitland Chambers.

Becoming a barrister

Barristers provide a specialist service in litigation and advocacy, and undertake advisory work. They prepare and present cases for trial, taking on a wide range of cases and clients (but often specialising in one practice area). Barristers also provide an independent advisory service on legal disputes or problems. Most legislation can be interpreted in numerous ways and barristers advise on how it may pertain to a particular case.

Generally, barristers work in private practice and are self-employed. However, they do not operate entirely in isolation: most of them pool their resources to form a 'set' of chambers, which enables them to share many of the costs involved in running a business. Each member of a set is known as a 'tenant' and has a say in the way in which the set is organised.

Pupillage

Pupillage is essentially an apprenticeship whereby pupils observe a set at work and then practise under supervision. It is the final stage of training to be a barrister, where you put into practice everything you have learnt so far. Although you will be 'called to the Bar' on passing the Bar Professional Training Course (BPTC), pupillage is essential for all those wishing to go into practice.

Structure

Pupillage usually takes a year to complete, with the year divided into two six-month periods known as 'sixes'. Each six is spent in a set of chambers (although a small number of places are available in companies and other institutions), under the guidance and supervision of a 'pupil supervisor' – a junior barrister of at least five years' experience. It is not unheard of for each six to be spent in different chambers and/or with a different pupil supervisor.

Content

To qualify as a barrister, pupils are required by the Bar Council to obtain sufficient practical experience of advocacy, conferences and negotiation, as well as legal research and the preparation of drafts and opinions.

The first six is spent shadowing and assisting the pupil supervisor. This involves attending court and case conferences, undertaking research, doing background reading and drafting documents. Thus, a pupil gains insight into how a case is prepared and argued, how a competent practitioner responds to developments as they occur and how pre-arranged tactics can be changed.

The second six sees a pupil take his or her first steps as a professional practitioner. Pupils are permitted to undertake their own cases for clients, under supervision. Inevitably, much of this work involves straightforward cases, but there is always the chance that an important or groundbreaking case may arise.

How to apply

The online application system for pupillages is the Pupillage Gateway (www.pupillagegateway.com).. Most chambers are part of the centralised system (Pupillage Gateway providers), but some are not (non-Pupillage Gateway providers). Available pupillages at both types of chambers are listed on the system, but non-members will have varying deadlines and methods of application, and you will have to check chambers' individual websites for details.

The Pupillage Gateway opens for applications in January (previously, it was open to view from March and open for applications during April). Following consultation, the Bar Council decided to move the application window from April to January so that candidates receive pupillage offers earlier – meaning that candidates will know whether they have secured pupillage before deciding to pay the expensive fees to enrol on the BPTC.

As a rule of thumb, you should apply for pupillage at least a year before you wish to start – that is, in January 2018 for a pupillage beginning in 2019. You can apply to up to 12 Gateway chambers (but as many non-Gateway chambers as you like). There is no longer a clearing function. Pupillage offers via the centralised system are made during May.

Tenancy

On satisfactory completion of pupillage, a pupil will ideally be offered a tenancy at the set in which he or she has trained. However, a quick comparison of the figures concerning the ratio of pupillages to tenancies reveals that this does not necessarily happen. Inevitably, chambers cannot expand indefinitely and sometimes even the most gifted pupil is turned away. In such cases, pupils must work hard to secure a tenancy by any means possible (eg, by undertaking a third or even fourth six or, as a last resort, becoming a 'squatter' (a non-member who uses a set as a base)).

Career timetable: barristers

First-year law and second-year non-law students

The key to this year is thinking ahead. Focus on getting top grades, do your homework on the Bar and get involved in activities that will look good on your CV (mooting and debating are essential, but examples such as Duke of Edinburgh awards or captaining a sports team are also great).

Research and apply for work experience (be it a mini-pupillage or a non-formal placement) in chambers for your summer holiday. Try to arrange a few stints in different chambers to get an overview of the various work areas, unless you are unusually keen to specialise in one particular work area. For an alternative way to pick up much-needed experience, see our "Free Representation Unit" section. Remember that without work experience, any application for pupillage is unlikely to be taken seriously. Work experience will not only give you a stronger CV, but should also help you to decide whether the Bar really is for you.

Join one of the four Inns of Court, which are non-academic societies that provide activities and support for barristers, pupils and students. You must join an Inn before 31 May of the year in which you intend to commence the Bar Professional Training Course (BPTC), but it is a case of the earlier, the better in terms of getting involved with the activities and using the facilities (eg, library and common rooms).

Second-year law and final-year non-law students

Autumn term, winter holidays and spring term

Attend relevant careers events, including careers fairs, presentations and talks, and pupillage fairs. Look into funding possibilities for postgraduate training (eg, local education authority grants and inn scholarships). Keep applying for mini-pupillages.

Non-law degree students will need to apply for a place on the conversion course, known as the Graduate Diploma in Law (GDL). If you intend to study full time, you should apply through the Central Applications Board (www.lawcabs.ac.uk) from September onwards in your final year at university. There is no closing date for applications; rather, applications are dealt with as they are submitted and institutions are notified weekly of new submissions. Applications for part-time courses must be made directly to the provider.

Summer holidays

Find out about pupillage applications. Look at the different BPTC providers and check their application details. Gain further work experience.

Final-year law and GDL students

Autumn term

Hot on the heels of your mini-pupillages, start making applications for pupillage. Finalise your funding options and be clear about the closing dates for funding applications. For more on funding, see "Financing the vocational courses".

The BPTC is a highly expensive course which does not open up any other career options than the Bar itself, so it is sensible to secure pupillage before deciding to enrol. The centralised BPTC application system – the Bar Student Application Service – usually opens in early December and stays open until the start of the academic year the following September. Find out more and apply at www.barsas.com.

Spring term

Attend pupillage fairs, including the Bar Council's Pupillage Fair on 21 October 2017 and the National Pupillage Fair on 25 November2017.

Applications for pupillage are made through

the centralised Pupillage Gateway (www. pupillagegateway.com). This is the system formerly known as OLPAS. Most chambers are part of the centralised system (Pupillage Gateway providers), but some are not (non-Pupillage Gateway providers). Available pupillages at both types of chambers are listed on the system, but non-members will have varying deadlines and methods of application, and you will have to check chambers' individual websites for details.

The Pupillage Gateway opens for applications in January (previously, it was open to view from March and open for applications during April). As a rule of thumb, you should apply for pupillage at least a year before you wish to start – that is, in January 2018 for a pupillage beginning in 2019. You can apply to up to 12 portal chambers (and as many non-portal chambers as you like). For more on how to apply, see "Becoming a barrister".

Summer term

Pupillage offers via the centralised system will be made during April/May. If necessary, obtain a 'certificate of academic standing' from the Bar Standards Board (BSB).

BPTC

If you were unsuccessful in your pupillage applications last year, apply again this year, in the same way as above.

Once you have successfully completed the BPTC, you will have to undertake 12 qualifying sessions (previously known as 'dining') before being called to the Bar by your inn.

Pupillage

Pupillage is one year spent in an authorised training organisation (either a barristers' chambers or another approved legal environment), usually split into two six-month periods referred to as 'sixes'.

First six

Without practising, you will observe and assist your pupil supervisor and other barristers in chambers. The intention is that you share your supervisor's daily professional life.

Second six

During these six months, you will be entitled to supply legal services and exercise rights of audience as a barrister. You may have cases and your own clients, which you will represent in court. This is when you start to build up your reputation as a barrister. At the end of the second six, you must submit a certificate to the BSB certifying that the second six has been satisfactorily completed. Provided that certain training conditions are met, you will be granted a full qualification certificate. Congratulations – you're a barrister!

Clerks

Budding barristers: take heed! Clerks are the people who can make or break your career, furnish you with work or leave you twiddling your thumbs. You need them on your side. They wield formidable power and are an important source of knowledge and support.

The barrister-clerk relationship is as old as the profession itself and is an integral part of the whole process. Broadly speaking, the job of a clerk is to run the day-to-day business of chambers and organise barristers' caseloads. At the junior end of the job, a clerk will prepare papers, carry documents to and from court and perform other administrative tasks. As a clerk becomes more senior, he or she will manage diaries, liaise between solicitors, clients and barristers, and bring business into the chambers.

Declan Redmond is CEO/director of clerking at Keating Chambers, joining them in 2014. Previously, he was senior clerk and chief executive at Wilberforce Chambers. He has held many senior positions in the Institute of Barristers' Clerks (IBC), including chairman from 2005 to 2008, and currently serves as the body's vice president. With these credentials, it makes sense to listen to what he has to say.

Declan was encouraged to become a clerk by the husband of his college student liaison officer, who was himself a clerk. Declan joined Wilberforce in 1982 and stayed there for 31 years, becoming first junior in 1992, then deputy senior clerk in 1996, senior clerk and chief executive in 1998. Now at Keating, he has risen to the position of CEO and director of clerking.

Declan outlines what his role entails: "These days, I do much more strategic work, which means that I develop and implement business plans that have been agreed with members of chambers. Operations-wise, I have overall responsibility for all the clerks and administration staff (including the finance and administration manager, marketing manager, receptionist and housekeepers). Importantly, I also manage client relationships, which involves a lot of marketing. There is no typical day, which I really like. There are so many different things that can happen – if an important injunction comes in, it can change the way you work during that day. One phone call can change everything. But it's that variety which keeps you going."

❝ As clerks, we build the practice of a new tenant up from nothing, calling on our own contacts and those of chambers that have built up over the years ❞

The IBC was set up to protect clerks within the profession and to facilitate the exchange of views. Declan says: "It allows us all to get together and find out what's happening in the different sections of the Bar (eg, criminal and chancery). In addition, the Bar Council needs to know what the clerks are thinking, so representatives are often invited to join Bar Council committees." The IBC is also concerned with the education and professional development of its members – it has been involved in developing both the BTEC Advanced Award in Chambers Administration for junior clerks and the two-year ILM Level 5 Diploma in Leadership and Management for more senior clerks.

In terms of clerking, Declan has one very clear message for wannabe barristers: "As clerks, we build the practice of a new tenant up from nothing, calling on our own contacts and those of chambers that have built up over the years. Managing client relations is key to the job – the way that a clerk answers the phone, offering a quality service to solicitors and professional clients alike, is vital. If it all works in tandem and you've got a good clerks team with a good reputation, that will bring work in. We go out to solicitors' offices (even as far as the Cayman Islands, sometimes!) – particularly so when we have a new tenant starting. That person has no contacts, so we go out and talk about the junior end of chambers. We're basically saying, 'Look, this wonderful new person has started,' and asking the solicitor to trust us to recommend the right person for the job. Of course, you hope that after a short while, the new tenant will build his or her own practice. It's always a bit annoying if you've made an introduction and then you don't hear from that client again – that's when you have to start asking questions!"

And it's not just introductions to clients – the clerks also act as a bridge between new tenants and QCs: "Although senior members of chambers may know you as a pupil, they don't really know how good you are when you start. We provide that link. If a QC wants a junior brought in, they will trust the clerk's judgement to suggest the right person." Clerks also negotiate client fees, with senior clerks dealing with the more complicated trials, "although we will bring junior clerks in early to help negotiate, as there's nothing like experience".

Declan kindly explains the oft-mentioned 'cab rank rule': "When you go to get a cab from a taxi rank, provided that certain conditions are met (ie, you are going to pay and the destination is agreed on), that cab has to take you. In the world of barristers, if a solicitor phones up and asks for a particular barrister, and that person is available and certain conditions are met (eg, the pay is adequate and the specialism matches), then the barrister should take the case."

One feature of the job that Declan particularly enjoys is guiding someone's career from the very beginning: "You are dealing with over 60 barristers who are all specialists, all highly intelligent, all highly trained, and your job is to help them go from being an unknown to being the top QC in the country (hopefully!). That is the goal as a clerk – you start with a promising pupil, take them as a new tenant, grow them into a QC and, ultimately, maybe get them to the bench. You have nearly as much invested in their career progression as the barrister. Clerks are very much part of the organisation; there's no sense of 'us and them' any more (or there shouldn't be!). It's gone from being something of a gentlemen's club to a fully fledged professional business now."

Declan has some final advice for pupils and new tenants: "Seek the advice of the clerks. We are always happy to help. For example, we hold a lunch for the mini-pupils and keep in touch with pupils before and during pupillage. Once a person is a tenant, we have regular six-monthly reviews to discuss how things are going. Fantastic academics are not everything; if you don't know how to talk to clients or can't deal with staff, you're not going to succeed. A senior clerk will have seen 30 or 40 people come through chambers and will have a wealth of knowledge to share. Don't forget – they are the people who will be running your business for the next 20 to 30 years."

Types of chambers

There are many different kinds of chambers and where you train has a significant influence on your career, as the style, size and clientele of each will vary. Consider the following broad categories to establish which type of set might best match your career goals and working style.

Central London
Commercial sets
Just as the solicitors' profession has a 'magic circle' of law firms, so too does London's commercial Bar. While the precise composition of this elite group may be up for debate, Brick Court Chambers, Essex Court Chambers, One Essex Court, Fountain Court and Blackstone Chambers would all qualify for inclusion. What is beyond doubt is that there are many highly successful barristers' chambers in Central London – a large proportion of them concentrated in and around the four Inns of Court.

Barristers tend to be very familiar with their peers and rivals, as they regularly compete with them for work or square off across the courtroom. Even within a specialist area, sets will have a particular reputation, or their size and style will mark them out from others. A good example is construction law, which has two acknowledged frontrunners: Keating Chambers and Atkin Chambers. Keating is bigger and probably acts for construction companies more often in disputes. Atkin is smaller; its reputation is more closely associated with representing parties in dispute with construction companies, and some suggest that it has more of an academic bent than Keating.

There are multiple areas of specialisation, even within the commercial Bar itself: commercial contract disputes, banking and finance, shipping and international trade, tax, intellectual property, professional negligence ... the list goes on. Some of the top commercial sets pay pupils handsomely (a few of them up to £60,000) and usually allow some funds to be accessed during law school. Your academic and other credentials will need to be impeccable to pass muster here: look at the biographies of junior members of a set for guidance on what its recruiters are looking for.

For a profile of a barrister who is part of a commercial set, see Adam Smith of Maitland Chambers in the "Property" chapter, p522.

Public law sets
Public law can take many forms, from conflicts over EU legislation to planning appeals, from individuals' entitlement to community care to international extradition. While the same is also true of the commercial Bar, it sometimes surprises pupils how little time they spend in court compared to their peers in common law or crime sets. Check each set's website to see what its pupillage programme entails and the size of the pupillage award; the best will match the awards of the top commercial sets.

For a profile of a barrister who is part of a public law set, see Jennifer MacLeod of Brick Court Chambers in the "Public" chapter, p524.

Common law sets
If you are seeking a wide-ranging pupillage with ample court time and a chance to earn your own fees during the second six, then the common law Bar will suit you well. You can cut your advocacy teeth on simple 'infant settlements' (approving a compensation award to a minor); 'winders' (securing a winding-up order in an insolvency case); charging orders and fast-track personal injury claims. Personal injury is a staple at common law sets, but beyond this you will be exposed to a multitude of legal problems, including some small commercial disputes and possibly even criminal cases. Confidence, flexibility and an all-zone Oyster card are essential. Your schedule will become unpredictable and you must be ready at all times to charm and impress the instructing

solicitors who send you work during the early years of your career. Pupillage awards vary hugely; however, the very top players will match those paid by commercial sets.

For a profile of a barrister who is part of a common law set, see Muhammed Haque of Crown Office Chambers in the "Common law" chapter, p492.

Crime sets
Motoring offences, juvenile misdemeanours, gruesome murders, child abuse, terrorism, white-collar fraud, regulatory breaches – London's crime sets handle just about every kind of violation you might imagine. Check on the orientation and reputation of the sets you are hoping to apply to, and look at the biographies of juniors and seniors. Some, for example, specialise in terrorism and extradition; others are boosting their regulatory practices, perhaps in specific sectors such as sport, professional discipline or health and safety. Pupillage involves a baptism of fire, early advocacy and court visits across the capital and beyond. Those motivated primarily by money should look elsewhere.

Regional Bar: supersets and beyond
Just over half of all chambers in England and Wales are located outside London, and just over one-third of all barristers in private practice work from within them. The main concentrations are in larger cities such as Birmingham, Manchester, Bristol, Leeds and Liverpool. Speak to any regional barrister and they will extol the virtues of a tight-knit professional community in which barristers know not only instructing solicitors, but also medical professionals, social workers and

senior police officers. While it is true that London has a magnetic pull on high-value cases, you will find commercial work in larger cities, where some sets have worked hard to compete with their peers in the capital – not least in relation to pricing. All shades of legal practice can be found in the regions, although sets and individual barristers are less likely to specialise to quite the same degree as in the capital. You may earn less in the regions; however, factor in the cost of living and a regional pupillage could make financial sense. Pupillage awards range from £12,000 to £30,000.

The Birmingham Bar is home to the barrister superset. Here, two chambers in particular – No5 and St Philips – have reshaped the market by drawing together barristers from many of the smaller sets. No5, with more than 250 barristers, also has 'annexes' in London and Bristol.

Public sector pupillages
Both the Crown Prosecution Service (CPS) and the Government Legal Service (GLS) offer pupillages leading to permanent roles with fixed salaries, holiday and sickness pay, pensions and all the usual employment protection rights. The CPS has lately tried to keep more of its prosecution advocacy in-house, as opposed to sending briefs to barristers in local chambers. Meanwhile, the GLS offers a rich training programme and a remarkably interesting career path that takes its lawyers from one government department to another over the course of a single career. The GLS is highly recommended for those who love politics, law and the idea of becoming a civil servant as well as an officer of the court.

Reality check: Competition for pupillage is fierce, so over and above getting exemplary grades, you need to show a commitment to joining the Bar. Mooting at university and doing mini-pupillages at chambers which interest you is a great way to demonstrate that you're keen as well as learning more about the different types of atmosphere in different sets.

Bar practice areas

Admiralty and shipping

Shipping law is one of the oldest and most developed branches of commercial law. It falls into two areas: 'dry' shipping involves contractual issues, such as bill of lading and charterparty disputes, whereas 'wet' shipping involves disputes over the ship itself (eg, collision and salvage). Although the shipping industry is by its nature international, London remains the pre-eminent venue for dispute resolution.

Robert Thomas QC gained experience of both the solicitors' and barristers' professions through various placements and mini-pupillages, before deciding which to pursue. "What ultimately attracted me to the Bar was advocacy – the chance to argue on my feet and make decisions," he explains. "I was also drawn by the independence that comes with the role."

After graduating from the University of Cambridge, Robert completed pupillage at what was then known as 2 Essex Court – now Quadrant Chambers. Still at Quadrant and a home-grown QC, Robert has developed a thriving practice in which shipping law forms an important part: "Traditionally, commercial work was always shipping, insurance and commodities, and those three elements – the international sale, transport and insuring of goods – are still a mainstay of much commercial work at the Bar, although there are so many more aspects to take into account these days. Quadrant has been preeminent in those areas for as long as I can remember, and like all junior barristers starting out, expertise and access to the set's client base was passed down to me by my senior colleagues. As I think most barristers will tell you, there is always a degree of chance in how your practice develops, as much depends firstly on the chambers you join and then which clients you really get on with, and who uses you again. I'm lucky enough to be instructed by several mainstream, high-quality firms who choose to come back to me."

'Wet work'

Many different types of case fall under the shipping umbrella. "The variety is huge," says Robert. "You get everything from 'wet work' – which in shipping means work related to collisions and salvage, and now makes up just a very small part of maritime cases – to disputes about damaged cargo; contractual disputes arising out of charterparty agreements for the hiring of ships; and cases resulting from piracy. For an example of the latter, I'm currently working on a case in which a vessel was hijacked and later released by pirates, which has created very interesting legal consequences."

Disputes in the offshore oil and gas industry also come under Robert's shipping portfolio. And if the variety within this area still does not seem enough, high-end cases can extend far beyond shipping matters. "A good example of that diversity is a long-running case that I was involved in a couple of years ago, in which the main issues were of much wider importance and had very little to do with shipping at all," explains Robert. "We were trying to lift the corporate veil – to get behind the corporate structure of a shipping company to the person pulling the strings behind the scenes. The case involved a former Soviet republic and the layers that an individual had put in place to shield himself from the limelight while making a lot of money. Another case, *Prest v Petrodel*, went to the Supreme Court raising the same issues and just got in front of us in the queue, so unfortunately we did not have the chance to fight our corner in court – and the Supreme Court came to the wrong answer from our point of view. Nonetheless, it shows how issues much broader than disputes purely concerned with shipping can arise."

The variety is one of the most appealing aspects of the job. "The disputes in which I act are very rarely the same and that also goes for the people with whom I work," says Robert. "In shipping, there are almost never bland

For more chambers that work in this practice area, please use the "Pupillage index" starting on p531.

Name: **Robert Thomas QC**
Chambers: **Quadrant Chambers**
University: **University of Cambridge**
Undergraduate degree: **Law**

clients – there is usually an interesting story behind each one. And the fact that this area is so international in scope means that you work with people from all over the world. In fact, our only UK-based clients are usually insurers – only one or two of the big commodity houses base themselves in the United Kingdom and all the other players are foreign. This leads to an interesting range of viewpoints, as people with different backgrounds and experiences are bound to see things differently."

66 The disputes in which I act are very rarely the same and that also goes for the people with whom I work – in shipping, there are almost never bland clients 99

However, there is no doubt that life at the Bar is hard work. "Anyone entering the profession should be aware that there will be periods where you really have to roll your sleeves up," warns Robert. "However, this balances out, as during quieter periods you don't need to hang around chambers when you don't need to, because you are your own boss."

Plain sailing?
While Brexit has certainly rocked the boat for the UK economy, Robert does not predict adverse consequences for the shipping Bar: "I think London's pre-eminence in shipping law is unlikely to be affected by Brexit. The only area that I see being immediately affected is the jurisdictional rules – also known as the Brussels Regulations – which are part of European legislation that has long-since superseded common law in most respects. It seems to me that the regulations will have to be put aside now that Britain is to no longer be part of the European Union. However, most of our client base is not based in the European Union either – as an example, we frequently

work with Turkish, Chinese and Russian organisations. This means that that we roll with the global markets. Volatility breeds disputes, as you can imagine when people are making a lot of money one minute and losing a lot of money the next, so the uncertainty around the world at the moment means that the commercial Bar is not a bad place to be."

To be successful in this area of law, Robert is keen to emphasise the importance of strong analytical skills. "Most disputes turn on one or two key issues and it is vital to be able to cut through everything else to identify them," he explains. "You also need to approach matters with an open mind, especially considering the international client base – everyone probably comes to things with a few preconceptions, but it is important to be able to put those aside and deal with the facts on the ground as you find them. Good communication skills are also crucial – it sounds obvious, but being able to clearly convey what can be complex and difficult ideas is a real talent. Bear in mind that you will often have to communicate ideas to lawyers and clients in other countries, who are not from the same legal tradition as you. There is a tightrope between not talking down to people and explaining things clearly so that they can understand the issues of the case and why you think that their case is a good or bad one. This also transfers to court – you have to be aware of your audience; if the judge is not receptive to your point, you need to put it in a different way or gracefully move on, instead of ploughing on regardless."

Finally, Robert advises that determination and perseverance will help those harbouring ambitions of becoming barristers themselves to succeed: "There are plenty of people saying that the Bar is a very tough place to build a career, but the key for budding barristers is not to be put off. The Bar is a very competitive environment, but in my view it is also an extremely meritocratic profession, which is something that we don't emphasise enough."

Chancery

Chancery work is split into two areas: traditional and commercial. Traditional chancery includes trusts, probate, real property and tax, while commercial chancery covers a wide range of finance and business disputes. Chancery work often has an international dimension, relating to asset tracing, cross-border insolvency and offshore trusts. Chancery barristers present cases before tribunals all the way up to Supreme Court level and draft a wide range of documentation.

As a student of English literature at the University of York, James MacDougald may well have wandered the labyrinthine pathways of *The Waste Land* or *War and Peace* and attempted to interpret the antiquated verse of *The Canterbury Tales*. He could even have struggled through the anarchic ramblings of *Finnegan's Wake* or sought to find a foothold in the footnotes of *Infinite Jest*. Indeed, such heavyweight literary challenges to the intellect would have been fine preparation for life at the chancery Bar.

"It is very cerebral work," he explains. "Trust law, for example, is extremely complex and the doctrines can seem abstract and artificial, although most of them derive from quite basic principles of ownership and obligations of good faith. You spend a lot of time reading and researching case law, both very ancient and very recent, and trying to analyse difficult concepts. These are often exercises in pure thought, like solving a mathematical problem."

Grappling with knotty problems
This is what attracted James to the profession in the first place and is still what he enjoys most about his work at the chancery Bar today. He also points out that chancery is a great testing ground for those keen to grapple with these intellectual challenges early on in their careers.

"One of the good things about practising in this area, I always tell mini-pupils, is that you actually get asked to advise on quite complex matters at an early stage in your career," he explains. "This may be because a trust or estate has little money in it and therefore cannot justify the expense of a senior barrister, but nonetheless there could be some very knotty problems to resolve. It's quite a steep learning curve in that respect."

At Ten Old Square, where barristers specialise in traditional and commercial chancery work, pupils sit with a different supervisor every three months and will discuss cases, research various points of law and help them draft documents and letters – meaning that they are involved in all areas of their supervisor's practice. In their second six, there may well be the opportunity to look after their own cases and, if instructions come in that the clerks feel are appropriate for them to deal with, some pupils could find themselves on their feet in the county court or High Court.

James points out, however, that if young barristers hope to spend lots of time in the courtroom, chancery may not be the best option. "I go to court about once a fortnight on average," he calculates. "You do get periods where you're in court more often, but chancery work tends to be a lot more advice based."

> **❝ One of the good things about practising in this area is that you actually get asked to advise on quite complex matters at an early stage in your career ❞**

In another word of warning, he also reveals that a "traditional chancery" practice can involve quite a lot of complex tax law: "I think

For more chambers that work in this practice area, please use the "Pupillage index" starting on p531.

Name: **James MacDougald**
Chambers: **Ten Old Square**
University: **University of York**
Undergraduate degree: **English literature**

applicants should be aware – particularly if they want a "private client" trusts and inheritance practice – that a very big part of that is advising on capital taxes. The tax law is an entirely statutory code, albeit one that is interpreted by judges. Practising in tax involves close, attentive reading of the statutes and, although it doesn't dominate every case, it's nearly always a factor in trust and estate problems. If you find that a real turn-off, you may want to think twice about working in these areas."

Skills to get you through

Those who relish the prospect of getting to grips with the legislative fine print will need a lively analytical mind and impeccable attention to detail. Professional confidence is also vital because, as we have heard, young chancery barristers will need to stand behind their advice from an early stage. Indeed, this is a quality that James considers crucial throughout a barrister's career: "There's an awful lot of work that involves you giving advice for which you will ultimately have to take responsibility. At first, that can be quite a startling realisation: when you first qualify and suddenly realise that the buck stops with you. In the early years it can be hard to believe that senior, experienced solicitors really want your advice, but they do, so you need to have confidence in your view."

While James agrees that the traditional routes of preparing for the Bar, such as mooting and pro bono work, are always a good idea and provide invaluable advocacy experience, he suggests that it is also vital to get a proper handle on what chancery work actually involves. This can be gained, he suggests, by watching hearings in the High Court's Chancery Division (most courts are open to the public) and through the careful selection of mini-pupillages.

"With mini-pupillages, it's not about sheer volume," he advises. "Once you've worked out what you are interested in, do perhaps one or two more in that area to satisfy yourself. At the stage of applying for pupillage, your academic background cannot be changed, so the best preparation is to make sure your know exactly what interests you and why, have a detailed grasp of the sort of work that goes on in that area and be able to demonstrate that interest."

Furthermore, at interview it is important to show your familiarity with the chambers you are applying to. "You should research not just the chambers' overall prospectus, but the individual barristers' profiles as well," he suggests. "In the end, we're not a firm; we're just an association of self-employed individuals and we all have different practices that share common themes. Looking at what individuals do will give you a better idea of the work the group does overall. Most chambers will set out their stall quite broadly, but when you scratch the surface you'll see that the practices of individuals can be quite different in different sets."

Civil

Civil law involves relations between persons and organisations. It encompasses a very broad range of legal issues, including those relating to contract, tort, probate and trusts. More specifically, civil law covers disputes that range from employment to professional negligence, and from education to property.

Bear with us here, but Jonathan McDonagh says that his main reason for not studying law was because he knew he was going to be a lawyer: "I was given good advice by a teacher that I should study something I was interested in and enjoyed at undergraduate level, because I could convert to law later. In fact, history gives you exactly the skills you need as a lawyer – there is a lot of detailed reading and written advocacy in my sort of law, and history is as good as anything to train you for that. There are about 50:50 law to non-law graduates in chambers, including mathematicians, a classicist and even a marine biologist."

Jonathan explains why he was equally certain that the Bar was the place for him: "It's all about temperament. I've got lots of friends who are solicitors, and for many of them the idea of self-employment comes with too many unnecessary risks. For me, I like the flexibility and freedom that it offers. There is also a different sort of responsibility, where you have the challenge of being the person up there in court – the buck stops with you."

Pupillage at Serle Court, while "not a walk in the park", offered a great mix of work and broad training: "You are thrown in at the deep end and it is a massively steep learning curve. However, you have a real sense that people want you to succeed, so you're challenged, but in a supportive environment. You're also given really good internal advocacy training before you're let loose in court!"

Breadth and depth
Like most barristers at Serle, today Jonathan enjoys a diverse caseload, although it leans more towards the commercial chancery end of things and includes trusts, fraud, property and insolvency work. "The trusts work commonly centres on assets being argued over by private clients, institutions or charities," he explains. "I also do quite a bit of property work, including landlord and tenant, and big-ticket commercial matters. Fraud is another substantial area, covering deceit and misrepresentation, as well as trusts and equity. It is usually centred on trying to get someone's money back rather than putting someone in jail."

Another feature of Jonathan's work is its international flavour, with clients currently located in the Gambia, Dubai, Sweden and India. "It is very rare that I get a substantial case that doesn't involve several jurisdictions, including disputes that are in fact happening overseas – I often have clients in offshore jurisdictions such as the Caribbean, Jersey or Dubai," he continues. "Even cases that are being heard in London have some international aspect, such as where the assets are held or the involvement of a foreign party." This variety keeps things lively: "I couldn't do the same sort of case day in, day out. There are a lot of backgrounds and personalities involved that make things interesting; you have opportunities to travel and there are always new problems to solve. Each case has its own facts and you need to think about which bits of trust, tort or contract law you need to combine to solve the problems that arise."

Nizam of Hyderabad v NatWest
One of the most intricate and historically complex cases that Jonathan is handling at the moment involves a dispute between the former UK high commissioner of Pakistan and NatWest over £1 million (now worth around £35 million) that was transferred from the nizam – or monarch – of Hyderabad to the high commissioner in 1948. Jonathan explains the background and where things stand nearly 70 years on: "Hyderabad was in the process of

For more chambers that work in this practice area, please use the "Pupillage index" starting on p531.

Name: **Jonathan McDonagh**
Chambers: **Serle Court**
University: **University of Oxford**
Undergraduate degree: **History and politics**

being annexed by India, and the money was taken from the nizam's bank account without authorisation. It was litigated in the 1950s when the nizam sued Pakistan, but Pakistan pleaded sovereign immunity and the House of Lords upheld that. The case was frozen until 2013, when Pakistan sued to reclaim the money. I act for the grandson of the nizam, who is claiming the sum as a beneficiary of a trust settled by his grandfather, while both Pakistan and India claim it as theirs. It is being heard in the Chancery Division and is essentially a trusts dispute as to who is the rightful beneficial owner of the money. With elements of public international law and sovereign immunity, it's a good example of how I have to adapt my core area to whatever is thrown up by a particular case. This is definitely one of the more interesting ones."

Whatever the brief, flexibility and pragmatism are crucial skills to draw on when preparing for a hearing or trial, says Jonathan: "Sometimes you have to give up on your social life for a while as the demands of a case take priority. If you've got 10 lever arch files to read, you've just got to do it, and if that means you have to cancel dinner plans, then so be it. It all balances out eventually, though – for example, you can take holidays when you want to. There are short-term sacrifices, but everyone accepts that."

He also issues a warning about financial planning: "The thing I hadn't grasped was the difficulty caused by people not paying you in a timely manner. We are paid very well at the commercial chancery Bar, especially when compared to the criminal and family Bars, which have been badly hit by the public funding cuts, but it can be erratic – you can go for months without being paid anything. You need to be astute and plan for that like any other self-employed job; don't spend the money before it has been banked!"

The good news for chancery barristers and other lawyers is that in an economic downturn, such as that which the United Kingdom is facing post-Brexit, more fraud is discovered and individuals are often more motivated to enforce their contractual rights. "The sort of law I do can hit a peak in a recession – we are somewhat countercyclical – so from that perspective I do not think our industry has much to be afraid of in terms of the uncertainty surrounding Brexit." However, change is afoot in terms of new time restrictions on chancery trials: "We are looking at what the full implications of fixed-term trials will be. The courts have traditionally been indulgent over time, which is not sustainable given the court's workload these days. Now that there is the new 'guillotine' system, advocates will be required to take a different approach and be more focused." He urges students to use their year at Bar school wisely to "master the Civil Procedural Rules – it will be the best use of your time and it's genuinely important; if you do, you will have a massive head start in practice".

Sound advice
Jonathan's golden rule for budding barristers is to "go and see it; don't just read about it. Take yourself off to the county court or High Court, and do mini-pupillages and vacation schemes," he elaborates. "There is no substitute for going and sitting with people and talking to them about what they do every day. That's how you get a true feel and understanding for how practice is different from the study of law."

And it all helps you to convince recruiters that you are really hungry for a career in law: "The truth is that top academic grades are taken for granted, so the thing you have to convey is why you want to do the job and that you've got the determination to get through the training and cope with the inevitable knockbacks. It will be different for each person to work out how to get that across, but bear in mind that everyone's application form will be stellar. Think about what you're going to say in the interview room that will make you stand out and make the other barristers really want you as a member of their chambers."

Commercial

The commercial Bar covers a broad range of practice areas, including banking and financial services, sale of goods and shipping, insolvency, professional negligence and civil fraud, insurance/reinsurance and oil and gas law. Barristers also handle matters for commercial clients that overlap with discrete areas of law such as employment, intellectual property and competition. Although advocacy is an important skill for commercial barristers, there is also a heavy emphasis throughout pupillage on developing a full understanding of commercial law principles and honing one's drafting skills.

With luck and hard work, aspiring commercial barristers will have the chance to participate in high-profile disputes involving oligarchs or the collapse of big business and see news of their cases splashed over the financial press. However, commercial barrister Rajesh Pillai stresses the importance for junior barristers of balancing such opportunities against the need to earn their stripes in their own, smaller matters. "It's still the case that you will do small trials – small insurance actions, fights with utility providers, disputed bills – on your own in the county court," he explains. "It's exciting running your own case, and it's a very important training ground. This is where you develop the habit of making strategic decisions yourself and being at the sharp end of the law."

Nor is the work of a commercial junior removed from the stuff of everyday life. As Rajesh points out: "Everyday legal problems are not the widely reported one-offs, such as the super-injunctions or claims against big banks. They can be about relatively small debts, personal investment advice, fights with utility providers, disputes about the quality of work undertaken – these are the aspects of the law which most people see."

Any doubt that this is a worthwhile apprenticeship can be laid to rest with a glance at Rajesh's own career trajectory. An established figure on the international arbitration circuit, from Paris to Singapore, Rajesh also recently acted as part of the counsel team before the Supreme Court in Eclipse Film Partners, No 35, appearing for one aspect of the case as sole advocate. The case involved Her Majesty's Revenue and Customs taking on a tax avoidance scheme used by various high-profile individuals and the team successfully had the various appeals dismissed. "Commercial law can sometimes be a case of pushing around money between rich people and this can seem unwholesome," Rajesh says wryly. "But in this case the result ended up saving UK taxpayers £1 billion."

❝ Written skills are imperative – in particular the ability to distil complex ideas and present them simply ❞

Little acorns

An analytical mind and the ability to articulate and argue clearly and succinctly are vital to success at the commercial Bar. Not every aspect of the job is glamorous: starting out, you can expect a lot of document analysis and drafting of court documents. "Written skills are imperative – in particular the ability to distil complex ideas and present them simply. It was a crucial aspect of my pupillage," he recalls. "This is something you can practise – work on it and polish it. As a junior, your input to a case will be of most worth here."

Prospective commercial barristers also need to develop a business brain and to understand the commercial implications of every matter. In terms of practical steps, Rajesh advises keeping a weather eye on current affairs, particularly issues where commerce, law and politics intersect. "When I was studying in New York and then as an intern at the WTO

For more chambers that work in this practice area, please use the "Pupillage index" starting on p531.

Name: **Rajesh Pillai**
Chambers: **3 Verulam Buildings**
University: **University of Oxford**
Undergraduate degree: **English**

Appellate Body in Geneva, I really got an insight into how the WTO can affect trading standards, which in turn may impact government policy," he explains. "Look at the whole debate over plain packaging for cigarettes: this is politics, state welfare and law all colliding."

Commercial barristers have strong earning potential and pupillages are highly sought after. So, prospective legal eagles need to ensure that their marks are as good as possible because when it comes to getting a pupillage, they will be competing against the best. In order to emphasise commitment, having some moots or advocacy experience on your CV can help to demonstrate your level of interest, while mini-pupillages can give you a feel for the different types of work on offer – the more you can do, the better. "Even if you go somewhere and you don't like it, that teaches you something," Rajesh points out. "You need to understand where your own interests lie. You need to know why a particular area of practice is interesting to you and why you want to do it."

Interesting times
The Bar has changed substantially during Rajesh's career and, given the recent political upheaval, further transformations are inevitable. He explains that at the top sets everything has shifted onto a bigger scale, which affects the mix of work that juniors can expect. For instance, the counsel teams for some parties to the *Berezovsky* litigation involved two silks and three to four juniors; the upcoming *RBS Rights Issue* case is due to take six months and has involved up to 13 barristers from 3 Verulam Buildings alone. This alters things in two main ways for juniors: "It means that on a big case you're less likely to be making your own decisions and seeing things through from start to finish," Rajesh says. "It also means that you're less likely to be involved in developing strategy."

This is why he is so keen to emphasise the importance when starting out of mixing led work on these big cases with a few lower-value hearings, which might include banking, insolvency and small insurance matters, and which are typically heard at county courts. "It gives you the chance to read up on law and articulate your own arguments," he explains. "It's also good to be in front of different tribunals, it teaches you about the rough and tumble of court life." Aspiring commercial barristers should consider which sets will assist them in getting a variety of opportunities.

In terms of further changes down the road, Rajesh believes that the limitation on funding for courts and the judiciary is definitely an issue, especially for the commercial sector. Separately, solicitors are trying to do a lot more themselves, with bigger firms looking to use solicitor advocates in certain instances.

That said, in addition to court work, international arbitration is on the rise, meaning that commercial barristers can expect to spend a lot more time travelling and broadening their exposure to different tribunals and systems of law. Rajesh recalls a recent Indian arbitration in which he was instructed, which involved a number of witnesses and various accusations of fraud and deceit. "The Dubai-based team actively sought out an English counsel team to handle that side of things," he says, "because the English Bar has a reputation for excellence as advocates – on paper, in oral argument and cross-examination."

Whether this is for you comes down to the fine line between feeling the pressure and thriving on it. "You do have to enjoy it," Rajesh says. "When you're being asked questions by a judge and you have your opponent waiting to trip you up – if you concentrate on the pressure you're under, you'd be a bit of a wreck. But if you relish the challenge, and are prepared to put in the hours learning your craft, the commercial Bar could well be the place for you."

Common law

The common law Bar remains an attractive option for those who believe that variety is the spice of life. Typically, common law chambers are multi-disciplinary and are divided into practice groups so that members can develop and maintain specialisations. Areas of practice can include actions against the police, employment disputes, discrimination law, landlord and tenant, personal injury, professional negligence, family law and criminal law.

Although Muhammed Haque QC gave some initial consideration to a career in the solicitors' profession after graduating from university, he realised that "my heart always lay at the Bar". His mind made up, Muhammed completed a postgraduate law conversion – his original degree being in engineering, economics and management – and progressed onto Bar school before gaining a pupillage at Atkin Chambers.

Atkin specialises in construction law, so pupillage there was a "natural segue" from Muhammed's degree and from there his career has gone from strength to strength. Now a Silk – a barrister awarded the prestigious appointment of Queen's Counsel – Muhammed is a specialist in commercial and common law litigation. "I have a mixed, broad practice which is based solidly around the principles of contract and tort," he explains. "I work on commercial disputes ranging from the straightforward to the very high value, which involve the interpretation of contractual terms and the deconstruction of the factual matrices which surround the formation of a contract. Tortious liability cases are often professional negligence cases and they involve going right back to the first principles you learn at university."

Advisory work and conferences now take up a lot of Muhammed's time – the amount of court work he does has lessened since taking Silk. "I'm now in court once a month or so, whereas it used to be around three times a month on average," he explains. "A lot of preparation and research precedes each appearance. For each day in court, I spend about a week preparing."

Master of your fate

The most appealing aspect of the Bar for Muhammed personally is "without any doubt at all, the independence that it gives you. I enjoy being, by and large, the master of my own time and that I work without a boss. There is no one telling me how to manage my case in terms of strategy or tactics – all of that is my own. Every barrister has a different approach and this is one of the main reasons that clients choose to instruct a particular barrister."

In addition to this, the cases themselves are endlessly interesting: "The instructions I receive are for cases which are at the very pinnacle of the legal world and every single case I act on is difficult."

If forced to pinpoint a negative aspect to life as a barrister, Muhammed would highlight the difficulty inherent in building up strong client relationships within the strictly limited timeframes that barristers are often afforded: "It's not a huge downside, but we come into proceedings quite late on, when a lot of the work has already been done by solicitors, and this means that we often don't have sufficient contact with the client at the start in order to find out what they want and what really motivates them – this is something that we instead have to pick up on as we go. This is in contrast to solicitors, who may have spent six months with the client beforehand, during which time they have built up a very good relationship – not being able to do that can be frustrating. A lot of the time, particularly in the case of academic pieces of work, I receive instructions and never actually meet the client."

For more chambers that work in this practice area, please use the "Pupillage index" starting on p531.

Name: **Muhammed Haque QC**
Chambers: **Crown Office Chambers**
University: **University of Oxford**
Undergraduate degree: **Engineering, economics and management**

Muhammed is also one of the many barristers who can't help but worry occasionally over the general uncertainty surrounding work at the Bar: "The thing about our profession is that tomorrow you could be instructed on an amazing piece of work that keeps you busy for six months – or not. Whether you're at one year's call or 20 years in Silk, you're always waiting for the next piece of work to come in and you don't know what it is going to be. This means that you need to be quite a sanguine person and manage your time well."

A changing profession

Taking a step back, Muhammed describes a period of flux in the profession: "The Bar Is going through huge change at the moment. It is largely cost driven and sensibly so, because although it is not quite a race to the bottom, there has been a widespread perception for some years that legal fees are too high. The consequence of that is that people are being squeezed all through the system, which means that with large numbers of meritorious cases, there is simply not the finance to bring them to court. Access to justice may become more and more of an issue over the next couple of years or so. Much will depend on the reforms put in place by Lord Justice Jackson. There is a move toward fixed fees in quite a lot of areas and a wider shift to fixed fees across all areas is almost certainly going to happen now. I support that in principle – I don't think there is anything wrong with parties knowing exactly what they will be liable for at the end of a dispute. There is also nothing wrong with the amount of money eventually recovered being broadly proportionate to the issues involved. The real question is what consequence this will have on the Bar, as much of the solicitors' profession has been working with fixed fees for some years. It will require a large number of barristers to adapt very quickly and for the level at which fixed fees are set to be sufficiently robust."

Muhammed has a couple of good pieces of advice for those with an ambition to succeed as a barrister: "Anyone considering the Bar has to have a determination and belief in their ability to do the job. There will be high points and low points in every junior lawyer's career, but that is part of life and it is important to be realistic about it. Don't forget why you're there and be absolutely resolute in your determination to continue in the profession. The second thing to appreciate is that this career is not all about the law. Being a barrister is a being an adviser, a sounding board – someone who is easy to talk to. Being a great barrister is about understanding the client and what they want from the case, not simply about being able to apply the law to the facts with which you are presented. That is how you are best able to persuade a judge of your client's case – ultimately you are trying to put the judge in your client's shoes and persuade him or her that your client's actions – or inactions – were reasonable. The law is the guide, not the goal."

Finally, Muhammed offers some advice which won't help you win cases, but is nonetheless very important for getting the most out of this career: "Being a barrister can be a lonely profession, but it can also be a sociable profession. I didn't appreciate that a lot of a barrister's time is spent alone, either on the road, in court or in your room in chambers, where you do all your preparation. This means that it is incumbent on you to make the effort to meet other people around chambers and get to know them, and the same goes for court staff and solicitors. But once you appreciate that, you realise that chambers actually has a very social atmosphere and people are always popping in and out of each other's rooms to talk. You get out what you put in."

Competition

Competition and regulatory work involves a mixture of commercial, public and European law. The general competition law prohibitions under EU and domestic law apply to all types of industry, and work in this area also involves a range of sector-specific regulation (eg, in the telecoms, energy and financial services sectors). It also includes merger control under EU law and the Enterprise Act 2002. The work involves a mix of regulatory and court proceedings, with claims for damages for breaches of competition law taking on a higher profile in recent years. Related areas are state aid and the rules on public sector and utility procurement.

Deciding to pursue law at university was more of a "Why not?" than a "That's for me!" moment for Laura Elizabeth John, but a stint as a civil servant confirmed to her that she was on the right path: "My decision to study law was based on no more sophisticated a reason than I was told at school that I'd be a good lawyer and that it meant I could do whatever A levels I wanted! After university, I decided to instead spend 18 months in the civil service, working on putting a bill through Parliament as a policy officer. I realised that I enjoyed law in practice and I reconnected with some of the reasons why I went for it in the first place, so I decided to go back to it." She knew from the outset that the Bar would be a more natural fit: "I preferred the idea of being self-employed. I also like the fact that it is a very meritocratic profession; you do stand or fall on your merits."

Laura competed her pupillage at Monckton, which she describes as being "unqualifiedly positive". The insistence that pupils leave chambers every day at 6:00pm was appreciated, as was the continual assessment process, avoiding stressful pressure points through the year and "allowing us to show how we perform under ordinary conditions, as well as offering a more accurate reflection of what day-to-day practice is like".

High value and multi-party

Although competition law is relatively broad in scope, Laura's work focuses mostly on high-value, multi-party damages claims. "The sorts of issue that arise are often the same as any you would find in any large multi-party litigation – for example, to do with jurisdiction and conflicts of law – as well as more specific issues about whether competition law has been breached," she explains. "Evaluating damages is also very complex, so I work a lot with expert economists and accountants to work out what the world would have looked like if the bad behaviour hadn't occurred. You also become an expert on a really diverse range of issues as you try to get under the skin of a particular industry – for example, I've done cases on lightbulbs, pharmaceutical products and heavy-duty electrical equipment used in power substations. I have had to understand how all those products are manufactured, the supply chain, and the economics of the industries as a whole, in order to work with the witnesses and our experts on the detail of the arguments. That sort of variety is a huge challenge and very stimulating."

Laura goes on to explain what else competition law might encompass: "Many of my colleagues work with the regulators, either at the stage of investigating potential breaches or of handling appeals in the Competition Tribunal or the European courts. There is a whole range of transactional work too; mergers, obviously, but there may also be two companies that want to sign a contract and they need to know whether the terms comply with competition law. Sometimes that sort of work ends up in litigation. For example, I am working on a case about the terms for licensing intellectual property in the telecoms sector, where Company A has sued Company B for infringing its patents, and Company B has alleged that A was in breach of competition law because it had an obligation to give a licence for use on fair, reasonable and non-discriminatory terms."

For more chambers that work in this practice area, please use the "Pupillage index" starting on p531.

Name: **Laura Elizabeth John**
Chambers: **Monckton Chambers**
University: **University of Oxford**
Undergraduate degree: **Law**

French blocking

A fan of the variety offered by the practice area – "I think that's crucial in keeping your interest and motivation in any job" – Laura was privileged to have played a role in the first competition case to be heard by the Supreme Court. Another highlight was a case that went to the Court of Appeal on a procedural point that had been "knocking about for at least 10 years, known as the 'French blocking statute'". She details what occurred: "One of the defendants was resisting disclosure on the basis that it was a French company and French law said that it would commit a criminal offence if it gave disclosure in foreign proceedings. The point went to the Court of Appeal for the first time in our case, and the court confirmed that disclosure is a matter for the English courts and at the discretion of the judge. The judge had exercised his discretion in our favour, which the Court of Appeal upheld, so it was a hands-down win for us and great to get clarity on the point."

As most barristers will tell you, one downside is that your time is no longer entirely your own. "You take on professional and ethical obligations to your clients that you never entirely escape; if someone has an emergency and needs to phone you at 10:00pm, you have to take that call," reflects Laura. "Life outside work can be impacted – which is not to say that you can't have a life, but regularity and predictability are not there in the same way as if you were employed. You regularly have to cancel dinners, drinks and weekends away because matters have to be dealt with in a specific timeframe. It does get easier the more senior you are, but for the first couple of years you have to put your nose to the grindstone and just get on with it."

Justice for all

Laura flags up two recent initiatives which are designed to broaden the scope of who can bring a competition-related action: "The first is a fast-track procedure that aims to move cases through the Competition Appeal Tribunal more quickly and with a costs cap in place. It could be a crucial development, as one of the big problems with competition law claims is cost – getting a case to trial will normally cost millions, if not tens of millions, of pounds, so only the big players can afford to do it. The fast-track procedure should make it more straightforward for smaller players to do something about anti-competitive behaviour." The second is a new procedure to allow for collective actions, similar to those found in the United States: "One feature of competition cases is that the bad behaviour normally occurs at the top of the supply chain – someone overcharges for a small component of a product, with the inflated price being passed down through the supply chain and eventually to the customer at the bottom, who may not even know they've been overcharged. The original overcharger may make millions in illegal profit, but each individual consumer may only have been overcharged pennies and they are unlikely to bring a claim to recover that amount. Collective action is addressing the problem that it is uneconomic for consumers to bring an action, by allowing them to share legal costs."

In Laura's view, the best way to learn more about competition law is to speak to those who are already doing it: "For an area this niche, I don't think you are automatically expected to have studied it – most of us come from a generalist background and then learn on the job. Rather, do a mini-pupillage or come along to drinks evenings at chambers that do this sort of work and talk to the junior barristers." And that applies more generally too: "It is fundamental that you understand the actual job before you apply; the fact that you enjoy studying law and find it interesting is not enough. Practising at the Bar is not like being an academic at all, so you do need to get a feel for the day-to-day job."

Construction

Contentious construction work involves the resolution of disputes by way of litigation, mediation, adjudication or arbitration. **Non-contentious work involves drafting and negotiating contracts and advising on projects, insurance, health and safety, environmental matters and insolvency. Clients range from industry associations, insurers, contractors, architects, engineers, public authorities and government bodies to major companies and partnerships.**

Law was initially more of an academic interest than a burning vocation for Michael Tetstall; it was only when studying at UCL that he finally decided this was where his future lay. Once that decision was made, however, it wasn't hard to decide which branch of the profession to pursue.

"The chance to be an advocate appealed to me," he explains. "That was definitely something that I wanted; but also the chance to spend more time focusing on law rather than the huge volume of work that goes into running a case as a solicitor. Getting into the gritty legal problems – that was probably what I enjoyed most while studying undergraduate law. Then, as I looked at what was involved in the two careers a little bit more, the idea of being self-employed and being able to manage my own practice with a degree of autonomy also seemed attractive."

Michael's first experience of construction law was while working as a legal assistant at a law firm before securing pupillage at Hardwicke. And when two of his three pupil supervisors had construction-focused practices, this reinforced his desire to explore the area further.

Starting in the shadows
As a pupil, Michael's early days were spent shadowing and learning from his supervisors, assisting where possible with research and small pieces of work here and there. As time passed and he became more experienced, he was asked to provide more substantive assistance, such as writing first drafts of documents and preparing research notes. He found this a valuable learning experience which exposed him to some interesting matters.

"I was involved with one of my supervisors on a claim for a demolition contractor against an employer in a big commercial premises," he recalls. "There was a range of claims and both the facts and the law involved contained a high level of interest and complexity. It was great to be involved over an extended period to see it through from its relatively early stages to a conclusion – to experience first hand client conferences, going through the documents and assisting with some of the work for my supervisor. Just to see how a large, complex, multi-party claim comes together and how that is translated into litigation was very useful."

Complexity at all levels
Since taking tenancy, Michael has developed his own practice. He does a significant amount of construction work of his own, alongside acting as a junior to more senior members of chambers on higher-value cases. His practice involves advising clients as well as appearing in court as an advocate. Outside court, he is also frequently instructed as an advocate in alternative dispute resolution processes such as adjudication and mediation.

"Construction law at the Bar is quite varied," he explains. "From small contractor/employer disputes or domestic disputes between homeowners and contractors to the bigger stuff – large contractors with a number of subcontractors below them and a multinational developer as an employer. Ultimately, the sky's the limit with construction claims and the more senior

For more chambers that work in this practice area, please use the "Pupillage index" starting on p531.

Name: **Michael Tetstall**
Chambers: **Hardwicke Chambers**
University: **University College London**
Undergraduate degree: **Law**

you become, the higher the value of the cases you work on and, in theory, the more complex. However, things don't always work like that and you can end up with some low-value matters at the junior end which can still present quite difficult, thorny issues."

> ## ❝ Ultimately, the sky's the limit with construction claims and the more senior you become, the higher the value of the cases you work on and, in theory, the more complex ❞

It is those thorny issues which attracted Michael in the first place and they remain one of the things he enjoys most about the area. "There is a lot of law in it, which I really like," he says. "It doesn't just involve disputes that are entirely decided on the facts; there are a significant number of both factual and legal disputes, and I find that really interesting as a barrister. I also feel that I am constantly learning. You work with experts in a lot of different fields that you may not have come across before and you have to come to understand those fields with their assistance – whether it be different methods for pouring concrete or forensic accountancy. You are working with a diverse team of people and learning a lot as you do so, which is really rewarding."

He suggests that any budding lawyers thinking of practising in the area can get a feel for the sort of work that they might be doing by visiting a hearing at the Technology and Construction Court, a specialist group of courts within the Queen's Bench Division of the High Court of Justice; although he warns that some of the jargon might be a little technical. He also suggests that a number of different chambers (including Hardwicke) publish online construction

newsletters, which provide information in a more accessible form.

Mini adventures
By far the best way to gain experience, he believes, is to do mini-pupillages – not just to bolster a CV, but to understand more about the profession. "Mini-pupillage is really important," he states. "People sometimes think of them purely as a requirement for an application form, but I think it's easy to overlook the fact that at their heart they are about gaining an insight into the law, into different areas of law at a different chambers, and that is a vital aspect. You need to do mini-pupillages for your own benefit, to help you work out what appeals to you, the area in which you want to work and the sort of set in which you'll feel comfortable."

Beyond that, Michael has some advice regarding the level of commitment needed for a career at the Bar: "In terms of overall advice, it is important to be determined and, if you decide that the Bar is for you, to stick at it and show that you have a real, genuine interest in getting there. You should be under no illusion: getting pupillage isn't an easy process and practice at the Bar isn't easy either, so you need to have that genuine desire to do it."

Crime

At the criminal Bar you may be called on to act for either the defence or the prosecution. Specialist criminal law chambers offer expertise in all areas, including child abuse, drug offences, fraud, human rights, mental illness, violent and sexual crime, and white collar crime. As might be expected, criminal barristers spend more time in court than those in almost any other sector of the Bar. The international aspect of criminal law includes human rights, terrorism, war crimes, organised crime, drug trafficking and money laundering. Practitioners in international criminal law regularly appear before foreign tribunals and international courts.

In her own words, Helen Law was "one of those very sad people who at the age of 14 decided I wanted to be a barrister, specifically a criminal barrister", so there was no agonising on a 'what to do with my life' level for her teenaged self, at least. Later, she did a couple of placements at solicitors' firms, but as was fairly clear from the start, they most served to confirm that the Bar was her calling. Although, as Helen points out: "The end point was clear, but the route is always a little unpredictable when you're talking about the Bar."

After graduating in law from the University of Birmingham, doing a master's in public international law and working as a research assistant at the Law Commission for a year, Helen completed the Bar course and secured pupillage – or 'traineeship' as it is termed at this set – at Matrix Chambers, whose barristers cover a wide range of practice areas including crime. "My traineeship was certainly challenging, as you are put under a level of personal scrutiny which I don't think you get in many other job interviews, but I found it utterly fascinating," she recalls of the experience. "My first trainee supervisor was Julian Knowles, who at the time was a junior on a very high-profile murder trial at the Old Bailey. This meant that only a week after I started, I was in court every day for three months – the experience was incredibly interesting and I learnt a lot from day one."

'White collar' crime

In the present, Helen is a successful crime barrister. "I do everything related to criminal justice, which also incorporates criminal law in a public law context – for example, challenging decisions not to prosecute," she explains. "I also perform advisory work during the investigatory stages of criminal cases. For example, in a fraud investigation, I would advise a corporate or individual client about how the case may unfold. And of course I do trial and appellate work, both here and in Strasbourg. The core of my practice is traditionally known as 'white collar' crime, which involves fraud, corruption and money laundering. However, I'm also involved in other areas – I'm currently working on a corruption trial, but am also doing an appeal case concerning drug smuggling and have an immigration offence trial coming up, too."

The workload varies from case to case, particularly in terms of paperwork: "I did a case a few years ago where there were over 100 lever arch files of used and unused evidence, all of which had to be read. In comparison, the case I'm doing at the moment involves fewer than 10 lever arch files of evidence. Reading through the case files is the start of the process with every case – from there you figure out a case strategy which will inform what you do in the months leading up to the trial. There will usually be a lot of preliminary legal research and correspondence, such as disclosure applications. This means that a lot of my work is outside the court room. When a case does finally go to court, I'm often in court for anywhere between one week and three months, as financial crime trials tend to go on longer than some other types of criminal case."

For more chambers that work in this practice area, please use the "Pupillage index" starting on p531.

Name: **Helen Law**
Chambers: **Matrix Chambers**
University: **University of Birmingham**
Undergraduate degree: **Law**

Of all the interesting cases that Helen has worked on so far, one particularly stands out in her memory – partly because it was so nerve wracking: "At five years' call, I prosecuted one of the cases in the parliamentary expenses scandal on my own, which was a daunting, but fantastic experience."

More generally, there are several reasons why Helen enjoys the career of a crime barrister so much. "I'm lucky in that I have a highly varied criminal practice, so no two weeks are the same, and I work in a supportive chambers with some fantastic practitioners in this, and other fields," she explains. "Crime is also a great area to work in for other reasons – it can be intellectually stimulating, but there is also a very human side to the work and you need good people skills to be successful. Your clients will be from all walks of life and they need to be able to trust you. For a period in their lives, you will be a very important person to them because in their mind at least you may be the only thing standing between them and a very unfavourable outcome."

If there is a downside to life at the Bar, it is its unpredictability. Helen admits: "The intensity at which you have to work sometimes is totally out of your control – you can be cruising along, having a normal week when something blows up on a case, and whatever plans you had for the weekend with your family are out the window. But you learn strategies for dealing with it and get better at predicting the types of thing which might blow up."

Cuts and the justice gap
Taking stock of the state of the criminal Bar, Helen identifies one major concern above all others which urgently needs to be addressed: "The most pressing issue is the cuts to legal aid, which have made it incredibly difficult for parts of the justice system to function properly. More people are unrepresented, which slows down the system. Barristers doing legal aid crime have less and less time to spend on each case, as they are having to take on more and more cases to make ends meet. I think if any area should have its standards rigorously maintained, it's crime, as the consequences are so serious. People go to prison, or dangerous people walk, so to lower the standards of the system is totally unacceptable. It is disappointing that the successive cuts to legal aid fail to recognise the importance of that. If the state does not provide for properly funded representation and a fully resourced criminal justice system, the verdicts produced, guilty or innocent, are not reliable. That is damaging not just to defendants, but also and equally to victims and society at large. I say that as someone who has a mixed practice who is fortunate enough not to be financially dependent on criminal legal aid work."

On a similarly sober note, Helen observes how the cuts have unfortunately made life much more difficult for those trying to establish themselves at the Bar: "If you're at the junior end of the criminal Bar in London, it can be difficult to make ends meet and I know people who have quit because of it." That said, if you can make it through those early years, Helen cannot think of a more interesting, challenging and varied way to earn a living.

For those undaunted, Helen has some worthwhile advice for maximising the chances of success: "It is important to understand what criminal practice involves – this is one area of the Bar that is often portrayed on television, but not necessarily accurately. On a personal level, you need to be resilient and have good stamina, as criminal law is not for the faint hearted. Very good interpersonal skills are also essential – you need to be able to talk to people from all backgrounds. So much of what a barrister does rests on understanding people and having some insight into how what you are saying to, for example, a jury, is going to be received."

Employment

A popular misconception is that this area of law is just about employment contracts. In fact, employment lawyers handle a variety of issues, including unfair dismissal, discrimination, redundancy, equal pay and whistleblowing claims, as well as High Court claims arising out of the employment relationship. There has been a big increase in employment law cases in recent years, due to a combination of new European legislation, government policies and employees' increased awareness of their work-related rights.

The unique offerings of the Bar appealed to Kathleen Donnelly from an early age. "I was attracted by the independence and advocacy – the two essentials which define the barrister's role – and the decision was always pretty clear for me," she explains. After her law degree, Kathleen also spent a year working as a research assistant at the Law Commission, and then studied for a master's in law, to get herself into a strong position to obtain pupillage.

After a year of pupillage at another set where she found she was not a particularly good fit, Kathleen completed a 'third six' at Henderson Chambers, where she really found her feet and went on to gain tenancy. "We have a wide range of practice areas at Henderson and junior barristers are encouraged to gain exposure to different kinds of work before gravitating towards the areas that really interest them," she explains. "These also tend to be the areas that a barrister is particularly good at and where they make more effort to build opportunities by attending talks and networking events."

Broad practice
Employment law was one of the areas that got Kathleen hooked as a junior. "I began doing employment work as part of my broader junior practice," she says, "but it really suited me and now around 50% of my practice is comprised of employment work, with the rest made up of significant civil and commercial litigation work."

In her employment practice, Kathleen acts for both companies and individuals at employment tribunals and in the High Court: "The most straightforward type of employment claim is unfair dismissal, and these are the types of case a junior barrister will usually start with. However, my practice now tends to be a mix of whistleblowing, discrimination and employee competition claims." Indeed, Kathleen believes that the introduction of the two-year service requirement for unfair dismissal claims has caused some cases to be presented in more complex ways, as discrimination or whistleblowing cases, which do not have this service requirement. She finds that her employee competition cases are some of the most interesting and exciting, and these are fought in the High Court.

Cross-examination key
Employment is an ideal area for those who love advocacy because outcomes so often rest on cross-examination. "It is almost never simply a dispute over, for example, the interpretation of a contract – in employment cases there is usually a fundamental dispute about the facts, as well as legal argument about what the law is and how it applies to the facts as may be found by the tribunal," Kathleen explains. "Most cases have interesting underlying facts and in order to present the case well, you really have to get to grips with someone else's workplace and experiences." There is a real sense of obligation to do one's best for the client in matters which can be very serious indeed for all those concerned, for example, when there are allegations of sexual harassment. As a barrister, there is a good deal of job satisfaction both for this reason, and also the need to be familiar and able to work with a complex area of law: "I also have to

For more chambers that work in this practice area, please use the "Pupillage index" starting on p531.

Name: **Kathleen Donnelly**
Chambers: **Henderson Chambers**
University: **University of Oxford**
Undergraduate degree: **Law**

keep myself up to date at all times – much employment law derives from Europe and can change very quickly."

If there is a downside to the role, it is its unpredictability. "Cases tend not to be spread evenly throughout the year, so there are times where I have far too much to do, but barristers tend to prefer to be overworked than too quiet" says Kathleen.

The introduction of employment fees pushed through by the Ministry of Justice as part of the government's cost-cutting austerity programme is posing a problem for employment barristers starting out in this field. "I believe that the introduction of employment tribunal fees has restricted access to justice, while I also think that it has negatively impacted on junior barristers starting out in this area because there are fewer straightforward, one-day unfair dismissal cases going before tribunals," Kathleen explains. "This is fine for the established barristers taking on the lengthier discrimination and whistleblowing cases, but the fees have made it harder for junior barristers to get a foothold in this area. The statistics are clear: unless you assume that all the cases that are now not being brought before tribunals were spurious, there are undoubtedly meritorious cases that are now not being heard." Since we interviewed Kathleen, the Supreme Court has in fact ruled that the government's imposition of employment tribunal fees was unlawful.

Open minded on Brexit
A hot topic on everyone's minds, not least employment barristers', is Brexit. However, Kathleen remains open minded. "There will be a period of some uncertainty, but we will have to make further UK employment legislation or use common law to fill the gaps," she argues. "Also, many of the laws that derive from Europe have had very positive effects for individuals and I think

that it would be very hard to take some of those protections away. However, there will be a period of uncertainty, which for lawyers usually means challenge and opportunity."

The proportionality of legal costs is more of an issue in employment tribunal claims than in other civil litigation, because the usual rule of costs following the event does not apply. "In employment cases, normally the successful party does not recover their fees from the other side, so even if someone has a very good claim, it is very important to manage the cost of winning it," explains Kathleen. Some clients instruct barristers on a direct access basis as a way of managing their legal costs, as this can be a way to keep legal costs down.

Forging a career at the Bar is as tough as it has ever been, but Kathleen has some valuable advice for those steeled for the challenge: "To be a barrister, you need resilience because it is almost certainly not going to be an easy route, but remember that lots of barristers who are now enjoying successful careers did not have a straightforward start to their career, so don't give up at the first hurdle. It is also important to know that in this career you need management skills because you are in effect running your own business – you need to manage your own finances and the development of your own practice; it is not enough just to be a good lawyer. If it suits your character, then there are undoubtedly a great many benefits to life as a barrister, and at the employment Bar. I personally also value the real sense of self determination about the way I carry out my work and the direction in which I choose to take my practice. If you are driven to succeed at the Bar and enjoy the challenge of interesting advocacy, then I encourage you to try to establish a practice which includes employment law."

EU and competition

Barristers specialising in this area may appear before the European Court of Justice, the European Court of Human Rights, international tribunals (ICSID, ICC and LCIA), domestic courts and other international tribunals. Matters that may be under dispute include the interpretation of treaties, state responsibility, international investment law, the environment and human rights.

Although he grew up with no family or any other contacts in the law, Brian Kennelly QC nevertheless knew from an early age that he wanted to be a barrister. "When I was young I saw an old black and white film called *Witness for the Prosecution* starring Marlene Dietrich and Charles Laughton – I thought the Charles Laughton character was great and I basically wanted to be him," he recalls. "Later, the self-employed nature of working as a barrister was also really attractive. I liked the idea of being independent."

Brian moved away from his family's home in Ireland to study law at Downing College, Cambridge, followed by a master's in EU law at the *Université libre de Bruxelles*, the French language university situated in the political and administrative centre of the European Union. Emerging from academia with the impressive qualifications mandatory for a career at the Bar, Brian then completed pupillage at Blackstone Chambers, where he is now one of the set's tenants to have been appointed the prestigious title of Queen's Counsel.

Cartel cases
EU law – specifically, competition and sanctions law, forms the majority of Brian's caseload. "The competition law aspect centres mostly on cartels," he explains. "Cases I have worked on include the Vitamins cartel, the LIBOR case and the forex scandal. One way to describe this area would be white collar crime, which involves economics and commercial litigation. It is very interesting to

work in because there is a public law element – for example, in cases such as those involving a breach of prohibition – and an important economics element where my job is to analyse the effect of the alleged crime on competition within the market. Finally, the fact that such cases are usually litigated in commercial damages actions means that they often lead to big commercial trials, which is fascinating and also means that advocacy can make a real difference."

> ❝ **The fact that such cases are usually litigated in commercial damages actions means that they often lead to big commercial trials, which is fascinating and also means that advocacy can make a real difference** ❞

Public law cases are often shorter and are heard in the Administrative Court or the Court of Appeal: "The issues at stake in these cases are fascinating, often involving citizenship, free movement and personal rights. And of course Brexit has potential implications for all these issues – the way in which they will arise and be litigated in the future remains to be seen."

Sanctions cases arise when people have had a travel ban imposed on them or their assets frozen by the European Union, and they want to challenge those sanctions in the European courts. "These cases are really interesting because such asset freezes are imposed as part of EU foreign policy, while the challenges rely on human rights and due process arguments, and often point to human rights violations in the countries which requested the asset freeze," explains Brian. "Clients I'm currently acting for in

For more chambers that work in this practice area, please use the "Pupillage index" starting on p531.

Name: **Brian Kennelly QC**
Chambers: **Blackstone Chambers**
University: **University of Cambridge**
Undergraduate degree: **Law**

that regard include the former president of Egypt, Hosni Mubarak and his family; many members of the former Ukrainian government; the head of the Russian state broadcasting agency; and other prominent individuals who have had their assets frozen by the European Union. In such cases, travel bans have usually been imposed, so I travel to clients' home countries to meet them, find out their story and then put their case to the European court. Essentially, this is challenging EU foreign policy."

Brian now advocates at the pinnacle of the legal system, where international politics and law are intertwined, but the personal highlight of his career involved a smaller case. "The time when I was happiest was when I first appeared as an advocate in the European Court of Justice 10 years ago," he recalls. "In that case I was acting on behalf of Three, which was then a small mobile phone company that was being bullied by its larger competitors, so the case concerned EU telecoms law. While the point of law in question may not seem the most interesting of the cases that I have worked on, to have my first opportunity to plead in the ECJ – which is where I wanted to be and what my whole professional life had been leading up to until that point – was a real privilege and a joy."

Always on the go
Advocacy is certainly the main attraction of life at the Bar in Brian's view: "It is also the hardest part of the job, but the adrenaline rush that comes with it is what distinguishes this career from everything else." If there is a downside, it is the relentless workload that goes into those court appearances: "You can never really stop – you don't have a team to fall back on. You also never really get a proper break because you always have to be available, so although barristers have long holidays, it is not possible to disappear completely – with a family, that can be difficult."

In the near, medium and long term, Brexit is sure to have an effect on cases in this area of law. "I think it is going to make people like me very busy for a few years, but where it will leave us in 10 years' time is a different thing altogether," says Brian. "For the foreseeable future, I think there will be a massive spike in litigation. In the long term, the competition work won't go away, although the EU public law cases may diminish."

For those aspiring to join the profession themselves, Brian has the following advice: "Being realistic, you have to achieve academic success at university, which means working very hard during your studies. The next thing to do is to develop your public speaking and advocacy skills – debating or mooting. That counts for lot in a pupillage application. Finally, you need to consider the sheer hard work that the career demands. You need to have the stamina and determination during the first few years to build up a reputation and a client base, especially if you are coming to the Bar without contacts."

Brian also imparts one final piece of practical knowledge, learned with the clarity of hindsight, which future junior barristers can benefit from – or more likely ignore in their anxiousness to succeed: "In my early years of practice, I could have said 'no' more often. As a junior I never said no to any work as I was insecure and anxious to impress solicitors and clerks. I really did have no holidays at all for a few years. In retrospect, I could have taken a little less work and enjoyed some holiday, and it would have had no effect on my practice in the long run."

Family

Family law barristers deal with all legal matters relating to marriage, separation, divorce and cohabitation, as well as issues relating to children, including contact arrangements, care and placement orders, adoption and surrogacy. Family law also encompasses financial negotiations on divorce, inheritance issues, pre-nuptial agreements and disputes between cohabitants. Some cases involve substantial assets and complex financial arrangements, or high-profile disputes between well-known personalities.

About two years after finishing his degree at Oxford, Andy Campbell had something of an epiphany. "I was working in the City and wasn't really enjoying what I was doing," he recalls. "I wanted to do something more fulfilling and challenging. I don't know if I had developed unrealistic expectations of the level of glamour involved from watching films and television like *Kavanagh QC*, but I thought law might fit the bill."

He set about doing a number of mini-pupillages in different sets to experience different practice areas and quickly identified family law as an area in which he would like to specialise. He focused on Queen Elizabeth Building and a number of other family-led sets when applying for pupillage. "Having done a number of mini-pupillages in different areas, I found family law to be the most interesting and engaging," he explains. "It has a mixture of lots of different types of law to keep you on your toes, but the most important thing is that it's not just retrospective. It isn't simply looking at what has happened in the past; it also looks at what might happen in the future and how you can potentially improve things for people. That really appeals to me and a lot of other people who choose the area."

Tough, but enjoyable
While Andy was justified in his expectation that pupillage would be hard work, he emphasises that it was also very enjoyable. During his first six months he was shadowing other members of chambers – predominantly his pupil supervisor – helping them with the matters on which they were working. However, plenty of support was available if he was ever unsure of how best to proceed. "Everyone's door is always open," he says. "Whether you're a pupil or a leading silk, you can go and speak to anyone and get as much help and support as you need."

The support was still there in his second six, but the stakes were raised slightly as Andy started to take on cases of his own. This is also when he realised that he had made the right choice about his future career. "I was prepared for the first six months, because having done my mini-pupillages I didn't find it too hard to imagine what it would be like to shadow others. But when you get your own cases, you can't really prepare for that and hence it has its own pressure attached. Thankfully, I enjoyed it and that was the acid test. If you do a case, finish it and come back thinking that you want to do another, that's definitely a good sign."

As a tenant, Andy finds his time is reasonably evenly divided between chambers and court. Typically he will be in court two or three days a week, working on a varied caseload encompassing everything from financial matters, sorting out the division of money and other assets on divorce, to cases involving children and residence issues. Of course, those court appearances also produce a lot of paperwork – preparing notes, skeleton arguments, position statements, asset schedules and other related documents. That said, he also points out that there is no such thing as a typical week at the family Bar. "There can be a lot of sitting around and waiting to be called, so that involves speaking to clients – reassuring them and advising them while at court," he says. "Then you also get other

For more chambers that work in this practice area, please use the "Pupillage index" starting on p531.

Name: **Andy Campbell**
Chambers: **Queen Elizabeth Building**
University: **University of Oxford**
Undergraduate degree: **Philosophy, politics and economics**

drafting work: doing witness statements, preparing questionnaires for the other side or analysing bank statements. Every week is different. Some weeks are filled with just one case; others you are sat in chambers doing a witness statement that takes three days; or you might find yourself doing five days in court on five different cases. There is no consistency other than the lack of consistency, really."

> **If you do a case, finish it and come back thinking that you want to do another, that's definitely a good sign**

Complexity from the start

As in other areas, the scale of the cases that a family barrister works on tends to increase as they get more senior. However, there are times when more junior members of chambers – even pupils – can find themselves working on more challenging briefs. "Some of the cases I had when I was a pupil were more complex than a number of the cases I'm doing now," suggests Andy. "The reason is that as a pupil you are the cheapest person in chambers, so if someone wants a barrister but doesn't have a lot of money, a pupil may well be their only option. On the whole, my cases are now more complex; but the most complex cases in pupillage were more difficult than the simplest ones I get now."

The cuts to legal aid made in 2013 are one reason why junior barristers are increasingly a first port of call, and the ramifications do not stop there. Not only have they seen a reduction in the amount of work that reaches the Bar (although Andy suggests that the profession is starting to come to terms with the need to restructure practices to adapt to that loss), but the subsequent increase

in the number of litigants in person has also put a strain on the system – something again which the profession and the government are now trying to accommodate.

"There is a drive to make family law less impenetrable for litigants in person," he explains. "So if somebody goes to court, they are not immediately thrust into a dispute with another lawyer and potentially their former partner. There are now more ways to resolve disputes in a better, more efficient manner – including an increase in alternative dispute resolution. The hope is that more people can come to terms before going to court – not least because of the long delays facing the court system as a result of the fact there are more cases, taking longer to resolve due to the lack of proper representation."

Family barristers need a range of skills depending on the work they are handling at the time. As they may be faced with extremely sensitive situations involving feuding partners or children, the ability to pour oil on troubled waters is paramount. It is also useful to be able to read people and how they might react to different legal approaches in court. Andy further points out that some financial savvy is handy when dealing with matrimonial finance work: "It's definitely useful to have a good head for numbers and to have an understanding of how things which impact on people when they get divorced, like pensions and tax on dividends, work."

Housing/landlord and tenant

Housing/landlord and tenant law embraces all aspects of residential and commercial tenancies and covers issues as diverse as anti-social behaviour, disrepair, human rights, possession claims, succession and assignment. Clients might include local authorities, registered providers of social housing, private landlords and, of course, tenants.

Although he enjoyed the study of history and chemistry at school, Simon Atkinson realised pretty quickly during his undergraduate degree in Melbourne, Australia that the sedentary seclusion of the historian or lab-bound labours of a research chemist would not hold his attention for long outside academia. He still wanted to feed his passion for reading and analytical thinking, but was also keen to flex his argumentation muscles, and the Bar seemed like the perfect place to do so.

A born traveller (his father worked for a multinational oil company and travelled extensively during Simon's youth), the native New Zealander decided that he would rather return to the United Kingdom, where he had spent some of his childhood, to further his legal ambitions. He undertook a two-year law degree at Trinity College, Cambridge.

"The opportunities for practising law in London are very good," he explains. "The quality and diversity of work are second to none. Also, [the Australian state of] Victoria, where I then lived, has a fused profession; realistically you have to spend five or six years as a solicitor before going to the Bar and that really didn't interest me. The prospect of going straight to the Bar when my law degree was over seemed much more appealing, which was another reason for coming over."

Law of the land

A confirmed interest in land law which first emerged during his legal studies, combined with a desire to avoid being pigeonholed into a particular area too early in his career, guided Simon to apply to Wilberforce, as the set undertakes a wide variety of chancery and general commercial work. As his practice has since developed, however, property has featured increasingly prominently, to the point where it "now forms the backbone of my work".

"A large part of that is landlord and tenant work – both commercial and residential," explains Simon. "I really enjoy it, because with property work you get into court more frequently, and you are less commonly led by a QC on cases than in other areas. It's pretty safe to say that there are more opportunities for a young barrister working in property to be given more autonomy – advising, pleading and advocacy – than in many other areas of chancery and commercial law."

At six years' call, Simon now finds himself in court on average once, sometimes twice, a week. The rest of his time is spent drafting papers and skeleton arguments, preparing for and attending conferences, advising, reading and researching points of law, and attending to other paperwork. He also spends quite a bit of his time on the road as many of his court appearances are outside London. "I travel quite a lot for court appearances – property work gets me out into the various county courts across England and Wales. This is because claims are usually heard in the county court nearest to the location of the property in dispute. I enjoy travelling on the train and getting out of chambers for a day!"

"I'm never bored in this job," he adds. "There are cases you enjoy more than others and some more tedious exercises that you have to do. But no two cases are alike. You can go from lots of little cases on all at once, which is basically what I'm doing at the moment, to a period when you're involved in a single big piece of litigation. You go through cycles."

For more chambers that work in this practice area, please use the "Pupillage index" starting on p531.

Name: **Simon Atkinson**
Chambers: **Wilberforce Chambers**
University: **Melbourne University**
Undergraduate degree: **History and chemistry**

Pupil rotation

Pupils at Wilberforce rotate through pupil supervisors every two to three months so that they can experience the different areas of law in which the set practises. Simon points out that it is rare for pupils in the second six months of pupillage to spend much, if any, time on their feet, with the expectation that pupils are there to learn from their supervisors. That said, there is still plenty of live, paper-based work for them to get stuck into.

"I think I was on my feet only perhaps once or twice while I was still a pupil," he recalls, "but you are given a variety of work – both what we call 'dead cases' – cases which your supervisor has previously worked on but are now finished – and live work. In my first week of pupillage I was charged with doing a first draft of an application for specific disclosure in a live matter. There is a great sense of responsibility that is put on you, because you are trusted to get the work right, but you are always given sufficient time to do so. I found that the level of responsibility increases as the year progresses. So even though you may not be on your feet, you will be working on live matters with your pupil supervisor."

Those keen to secure pupillage at a set specialising in landlord and tenant, or property law more generally, should be able to demonstrate an awareness of how recent political and economic developments might affect the area. "Property law, and landlord and tenant law in particular, is readily affected by wider economic issues – for example, the global financial crisis and Brexit. These issues can have a big impact on how the property market is developing," Simon points out. "When I first started out in practice in 2011, commercial leases were coming up for their five or 10-year rent reviews in a very different set of financial circumstances from those in which the leases had been originally agreed. There was therefore a lot of court litigation

– mainly by tenants seeking to prevent their landlords increasing the rents payable under the lease."

He continues: "It is definitely worth prospective members of the property Bar keeping an eye on wider economic, political and social developments, because they have a very real impact on how people deal with their property interests."

As a final piece of advice, Simon warns that when he first came to the Bar he underestimated the sheer amount of hard work involved and the strength needed to deal with it. "You need stamina," he insists. "Obviously, people will tell you that you need to have good academic grades and advocacy skills, both written and oral; this is absolutely true. But it's equally important to be aware that, if you've got a two or three-day trial or you're in court back to back on various matters, you will frequently be working late and getting up early; you'll be thinking about the case for days in advance, potentially; and it is very physically and mentally draining. It is very rewarding, but it is a taxing job. Because you're self-employed, you need to have the drive and determination to put in the hours and the hard work necessary to make sure that you are prepared when you stand up on your feet. So I would say that one of the most underrated strengths at the Bar, particularly in an advocacy-heavy area like landlord and tenant, is stamina."

Human rights

Human rights law is essential for a fair and civilised society where all are protected, including the vulnerable, and is a popular choice for students and practitioners. University law faculties are increasingly offering human rights modules as part of their law degrees and more firms and chambers are boasting specialisms in the field. The introduction of the Human Rights Act 1998 made the European Convention on Human Rights (ECHR) directly enforceable in the national courts.

Philosophy, politics and economics is a popular choice among Oxbridge students, as it provides such a solid grounding for a range of high-end careers. It is no surprise then that human rights barrister Tim Buley studied it while he was at university. Tim was originally attracted to a career as a philosophy academic, but later found that his skills and temperament were well suited to law – particularly the Bar. "I'm very much someone who likes problem solving and I enjoy the academic side of the law," he explains. "On the other hand, I'm quite disorganised, so being a solicitor would never have worked for me."

Porous boundaries
Pupillage soon followed at 4 Breams Buildings, a set which was in merger negotiations with another set, Eldon Chambers, when Tim joined. At the end of pupillage he gained tenancy at the newly formed Landmark Chambers, where he has been a tenant for the last 15 years. In that time he has become a noted human rights barrister alongside other public, planning and environmental law work. "I describe my practice as a general public law practice, of which a significant proportion – possibly as much as half – involves human rights law," he explains. "There is a very porous boundary between general public law and human rights law – for example, if you're doing certain areas such as immigration or parole board cases, most of the cases you encounter will be human rights cases."

Immigration and asylum cases make up a big part of Tim's human rights work. "I act for individuals who are challenging things such as deportation or the government's refusal to recognise their status as refugees," he explains. "Related to that, I also do a lot of work in the field of immigration detention, representing people who claim that they are being unlawfully detained."

Another aspect of Tim's practice is social welfare law, including social security and community care cases. "Clients in this area are often people who are claiming that they do not have enough money to live on, which is often related to their immigration status," he continues. "Discrimination also comes up frequently – many such cases are to do with disability."

Outside immigration, where he generally acts for individuals, Tim's practice is split between representing both sides – claimants and public authorities. For example, he does a lot of general human rights work for the government: "I'm on a few government panels and one of the areas that I'm involved in is prisons, as I frequently advise the Parole Board in relation to Article 5 of the European Convention on Human Rights – the right to liberty."

Many cases involving human rights take the form of judicial review, as this is often the only way to challenge a decision made by a government department such as the Home Office. "As a public lawyer doing judicial review work, you probably have less interaction with clients than other barristers," Tim explains. "I spend two days a week in court on average, but the variation from week to week is huge. In any public law practice – and probably most human rights practices too – although the cases are big, they do not usually run for days or weeks in court. Most hearings last for

For more chambers that work in this practice area, please use the "Pupillage index" starting on p531.

Name: **Tim Buley**
Chambers: **Landmark Chambers**
University: **University of Oxford**
Undergraduate degree: **Philosophy, politics and economics**

between half a day to three days, so I can find myself in court for four days in one week, but on four different cases. I enjoy the variety, but it can be difficult, as it is much harder to prepare multiple cases and keep them all in mind than to just focus on one."

Making a difference
The stakes for many of Tim's clients couldn't be higher. "It is incredibly satisfying to win cases on behalf of people who are requesting asylum or resisting deportation to countries where they would be in danger," he explains. "One case that stands out as an example was when we successfully established that a mentally ill man's immigration detention was in breach of Article 3 of the European Convention on Human Rights, as he wasn't being treated properly at all. I'm also very proud of a social security case in which we established that the government was discriminating against disabled people by not paying them adequate housing benefit. Helping people to access justice and assert their rights in the face of the opposition of the powerful is certainly a big draw of the job. One of the best things about being a barrister is that you get to win cases – nothing is better than winning, especially on behalf of someone for whom the outcome is going to make a real, positive difference."

However, Tim also gets a lot of satisfaction from his work for the government: "It gives you a different perspective and a policy understanding of the way that government works, which is incredibly interesting. I'm lucky in that I am able to do both sides. The variety in what I do is very rewarding, both in terms of the clients, which range from government and commercial bodies to vulnerable individuals, and the actual subject matter that I deal with. I handle lots of immigration and asylum cases, but a few years ago I also worked on a human rights case about a village green, for example – the human rights element was to do with property deprivation."

If you're thinking about this career path, Tim emphasises the need to be aware of what is happening with legal aid. "The legal aid system has suffered big cuts in the last few years and has been reduced gradually ever since I have been in practice," he explains. "This is a big deal for people of limited means who need legal representation, as they are not going to be able to have the same high-quality representation that they would have had before, and in many cases will be unable to access representation at all. This also makes the area less viable for lawyers who need to pay the bills. I don't think the situation is acceptable, but I don't think that it is going to change either."

Not what you see on TV
Tim identifies three key skills that are essential for anyone hoping to be a human rights barrister: "You need really good analytical skills, and clarity of written and verbal expression – it's not so much about making complicated arguments, as making complicated things simple and cutting through to the critical issues. Commitment to your clients and an interest in the work is also important, as it is this that will keep you going."

And Tim also has some more general advice for anyone considering a career at the Bar: "People sometimes have a skewed idea of what human rights work is actually like – many of the things that I find interesting are not what you would tell your friends about at dinner parties. Some barristers have practices involving lengthy factual trials, with extensive cross-examination, others never cross-examine and spend their time making legal submissions only. Some go to court every day, some never go to court at all or settle every case. Some have close contact with their clients, some never meet them. These things vary between different areas of practice. Enjoyment of the nature of the day to day work you are doing is just as important as being interested in the subject matter of the cases. So consider carefully what it is that appeals to you."

Immigration

Immigration lawyers deal with all legal matters relating to immigration and nationality. The work ranges from asylum and human rights claims through applications by family members and students to advising businesses on securing immigration status for their employees. There is a significant and increasing European law element, and many cases raise important human rights issues. The law is rapidly developing, in terms of both statute law and jurisprudence, and procedural timeframes are tight. There is a good deal of overlap with social welfare, mental health, prison law, criminal law and civil actions.

Many people are inspired to follow their future careers by their experiences at university and Michelle Knorr is no exception. Her journey towards the immigration Bar began with a course on international law during her undergraduate degree in politics and international relations at Brown University in the United States.

"It was my first introduction to legal reasoning and legal argument, and I really enjoyed it," she recalls. "It is quite a unique type of activity, not like other forms of study. I was very interested in the subject – we were looking at things like the legality of the war in Iraq, and our tutor was a negotiator for Palestine. He was involved in negotiating peace agreements and was fascinating to listen to. It showed me a side of the law that I thought was really interesting – that's what gave me the idea of pursuing law."

Michelle set about bolstering her academic knowledge of the subject and garnering valuable wider experience before taking the plunge into practice. She completed a master's in international human rights law at the University of Essex and a stint working in international development before doing the GDL at BPP and the BVC at the Inns of Court School of Law. After that, Michelle spent a year as an immigration caseworker at Wilson Solicitors in Tottenham, with the instruction of barristers among her duties.

Pupil life

This experience gave her first-hand insight into what life might be like in chambers – although that didn't mean she wasn't still a little wary of beginning her pupillage. "I was terrified when I started," she admits. "I was having nightmares about having to carry people's bags. You hear so many horror stories about being treated badly and I'm not somebody who has much appreciation for hierarchy, so I think I was a bit nervous about that aspect of it. I knew it was going to be hard work – I was quite up for that – but I was scared of the formality of chambers."

As it turned out, she had nothing to worry about: her colleagues at Doughty Street Chambers were "incredibly supportive" and the cases she was given to handle "fascinating". During the first six months of pupillage, much of the work revolves around the caseload of your pupil supervisor. Pupils may draw up initial draft arguments for them and accompany them to conferences and to court. During the second six, young barristers begin to get on their feet in court. At Doughty Street, pupils are kept busy. "We give them a lot of really interesting work on cutting-edge cases" says Michelle. "Once on your feet, the majority of the court work is crime, which is important because it gets you into the courtroom and trains you to be a good advocate. There are loads of magistrates' court briefs and you are running all over the place. You also continue to work with other members of chambers on their civil briefs, often on very high-profile cases. I did quite a lot of immigration as well, largely because I already had an immigration background. So there were solicitors who were willing to brief me and the immigration team felt that it was safe to brief me on

For more chambers that work in this practice area, please use the "Pupillage index" starting on p531.

Name: **Michelle Knorr**
Chambers: **Doughty Street Chambers**
University: **Brown University**
Undergraduate degree: **Politics and international relations**

immigration cases. Unless you have a background in immigration or your pupil supervisor is an immigration practitioner, you wouldn't do many substantive immigration cases as a pupil, but you might do bail hearings or case management hearings – procedural hearings rather than substantive hearings. You can also do pro bono work for Bail for Immigration Detainees or the Asylum Support Appeals Project."

❝ I really enjoy meeting my clients: they are amazing people from all over the world ❞

Today, the main areas of Michelle's practice include asylum, human rights, deportation, family migration and EU law applications. Other immigration lawyers can specialise in business immigration, but there is quite a lot of crossover, with some covering several different areas. A lot of time is spent in court or at tribunals, and you also do a lot of High Court judicial review work.

"In many areas of civil law, you don't actually get to do a lot of advocacy, but in immigration you do," continues Michelle. "You do a lot of tribunal work. If it's on legal aid, it can be quite badly paid now – there are fixed fees, which are very low – but it's really important work and you can balance it out with other work. As you get more senior, you will spend more time drafting grounds for judicial review or drafting skeleton arguments for the Court of Appeal. So you might spend slightly more time out of court once you are a few years in practice. But at the beginning, you can be in court more often than not."

Location for vocation
Michelle readily admits that most barristers who work in immigration have a vocation for the area, and it is the people whom

she works for and with that make it all worthwhile for her. "Not many people fall into immigration work," she says. "It's not the best-paid area – the real rewards are achieving something for your client and working in a legally complex and challenging specialism. So you definitely have really committed lawyers – people who are, in some respects, activist lawyers – and I really enjoy that. I also really enjoy meeting my clients: they are amazing people from all over the world. They have been through so many experiences, many of which are horrific. You hear stories about their managing to flee across continents; you hear about people who've been exceptionally brave and stood up to dictators. You really meet some very inspiring people, the vast majority of whom I feel quite honoured to represent."

She also acknowledges that because of the close relationships that can develop between immigration barristers and their clients, you have to have to steel yourself for the possibility of defeat – something which can be hard to deal with. "I know a number of people who have left immigration work because they couldn't cope with it," says Michelle. "I'm thinking of one good friend in particular, who just found it too upsetting. She won 99.9% of the cases, but it was the others that she couldn't handle. I think you have to have an attitude whereby you know that you are doing your job the absolute best that you can, and you have to accept that the world is as it is – it is not always fair, and that's why a lot of your clients are in the position they are in the first place."

Intellectual property

IP work can be divided into two main areas: hard and soft intellectual property. 'Hard' intellectual property relates to patents, while 'soft' intellectual property covers trademarks, copyright, design rights and passing off. IP barristers advise on issues that range from commercial exploitation to infringement disputes and agreements that deal either exclusively with IP rights or with IP rights in the wider context of larger commercial transactions.

Science and technology might be an unusual platform from which to embark on a career at the Bar, but that was the case for Chris Hall, who began his career in physics. The switch to the Bar did not come for some time. "After I left university, I worked as a private physics tutor for a couple of years before joining BT as an IT project manager," he explains. "After a while, I found that advocating the technical ideas of others was more enjoyable than doing the programming myself, and I began to earn a reputation as someone who could sell a new project to the bosses." Chris was really getting into the advocacy, and at the same time was missing the aspects of self-employment he had enjoyed as a private tutor: "With advocacy, self-employment, and my science and technology experience, a career at the IP Bar made sense."

Pupillage: "tough, challenging, but rewarding"

Chris secured pupillage at 11 South Square. He is candid about how tough the process really is: "From my own experience and from talking to others at various chambers, pupillage is a uniformly tough experience. You cannot escape the reality that pupillage feels like a year-long interview which you can fail at any moment. If I had one tip, I would emphasise that your supervisor is interested primarily in seeing how you would do things if you were in their shoes. This is likely, for example, to involve you doing a piece of work that your supervisor has already done in the past. That can feel like a waste of time, but of course it isn't because you're trying to prove that you can reach the same standard. Finally, don't lose sight of how brilliant being a barrister is – it is well worth the challenge."

Now a qualified barrister, Chris handles a varied IP caseload. "Most IP barristers start out as general practitioners working across the four key areas – copyright, trademarks, patents and designs," he explains. "It is common for people with science backgrounds to specialise in pharmaceutical or technology patents, but many IP barristers retain wide practices, as the IP Bar is such a specialised area anyway." He also emphasises that IP barristers are regularly involved in many wider cases, such as IT, media or commercial contractual disputes, "where there is an IP angle".

IP law focuses on the granular detail, so Chris's physics background has stood him in good stead. "Most IP sets will tell you that a science, maths or engineering degree is advantageous, if not strictly necessary, because one key skill that IP barristers need is the ability to understand how things work," he explains. This is the case particularly for patents and designs, which usually involve looking at the specific detail of a tangible thing and asking how it works, why it is a certain shape and so on. There are also more specialised niches within IP, so Chris suggests that "you are unlikely to be able to understand complex pharmaceutical patents without some training in chemistry, for example. It is true that a science education lends itself to IP. Nevertheless, a PhD in biochemistry is neither necessary nor sufficient; what really matters is the ability to master new concepts quickly."

Advocacy opportunities

In IP, there are lots of opportunities to go to court. "The IP Bar is unique in that although it is commercial, there are many fixed-cost and low-cost tribunals, affording junior barristers plenty of opportunity to get out there and argue cases. This experience can be difficult to get

For more chambers that work in this practice area, please use the "Pupillage index" starting on p531.

Name: **Chris Hall**
Chambers: **11 South Square**
University: **Imperial College London**
Undergraduate degree: **Physics**

elsewhere at the commercial Bar," Chris explains. "Junior IP practitioners regularly appear in tribunals at the UK Intellectual Property Office, and in the new, bespoke Intellectual Property Enterprise Court."

In terms of litigation, there is an even split between instructions on the side of defendant or claimant. As for where instructions come from, "because IP is quite a small area you regularly see the same faces – there are not that many solicitors who regularly practise in IP, so you build strong relationships with instructing solicitors and there are also many regular clients," Chris continues.

And the cases themselves involve a wide range of products, as Chris outlines: "On my desk I have two snack food products that are sold under very similar names; two scrubbing brushes with similar designs; two letter boxes that function in the same unusual way, and more. One of the satisfying things about IP cases is that a lot of the litigation concerns tangible objects – you can examine them, and see how they work and what they look like."

The job also brings Chris into contact with all kinds of interesting people: "In patent cases, you work with expert witnesses who teach you about very specific areas of technology. This means that in every case you learn something new from a world expert in their field – and you get paid for it! There are some colourful characters too. The first trial I was in concerned the design of caravan covers, and one of the witnesses was an avid caravan enthusiast. In his evidence he described the perils of towing his caravan all over Northwest England in various states of Cumbrian weather with the caravan covers flapping around in the wind and rain. The judge described him as 'engaging and direct'; he was more like a stand-up comedian. In IP, it is more than purely commercial litigation – you regularly get the small family business with a big idea, or sometimes the mad inventor squaring off

against the corporations trying to stop him."

However, these 'David v Goliath' situations don't always end in victory for the underdog. "It is very often the case that when a defendant loses, they lose everything," explains Chris. "It's quite a responsibility for a junior barrister to bear. You see a lot of clients – both claimants and defendants – suffer because of something that perhaps could have been avoided with a bit of legal advice early in the day."

There is much afoot in the wider world of intellectual property and Brexit will undoubtedly have a significant effect, as Chris explains: "A lot of IP law is harmonised across the European Union, and there are many rights which are EU-wide, for example the EU trademark and the EU registered design. The scope and practice involving these rights regularly changes with the jurisprudence emerging from 28 member states. There is also a planned introduction of a unitary patent which will be valid across the European Union. In tandem, the Unified Patent Court is being introduced in 2018 to resolve disputes related to those patents."

No need to rush
Chris has some advice to share for those hoping to achieve the necessary standards. "It is very useful to have some experience in the real world," he begins. "As a junior barrister at the IP Bar, you will often be representing small businesses in relatively low-value cases. The case fits your level of experience, but you will usually be dealing with the person at the top of the small business – the chief executive or sole director. This creates a mismatch in terms of experience, and you have to earn the trust of the client despite your lack of experience. It helps to be able to speak to clients on their level and to demonstrate that you understand their commercial world. This gives clients much more confidence in your ability. So I would positively encourage people to get some experience before coming to the Bar."

Media

Media and entertainment barristers have clients in a variety of sectors, including theatre, film, music, publishing, broadcasting, sport and advertising. They advise and represent clients in court and before other tribunals on matters that might include defamation, privacy and confidentiality, contract disputes, advertising standards, sponsorship, intellectual property and restraint of trade.

The prospect of a life at the Bar proved a powerful draw for budding legal eagle Charlotte Scott: "It sounds clichéd, but I wanted to do advocacy and liked the idea of being in court. The opportunity to explore quite technical areas of law also appealed to me."

After graduating from the University of Cambridge and taking some time out to set up a successful business with a couple of friends, Charlotte gained pupillage at Hogarth Chambers, which is predominantly an IP set. "Hogarth is a really friendly, welcoming set and I was able to explore many different and interesting areas of law within IP, so the pupillage experience was as good as it could be, really," she recalls. "But in general, pupillage is quite a horrible year – the pressure comes from the process – it is essentially a year-long interview. I don't think anyone truly enjoys pupillage and most people are happy to gain tenancy and for it to be over!"

Today, Charlotte specialises in media cases. Her clients are largely in the music industry, so there is a significant overlap with IP in her work. "Cases range from the run of the mill – for example, where premises have failed to take out licences to play music and there is therefore not much of a case to make in their defence – to matters which are much more involved," she explains. "I do a lot of work for the big music collecting societies, many of which have grown more willing to pursue contempt of court proceedings as a form of enforcement action against people who choose not to take out licences."

Rock 'n' roll

Charlotte's clients also include bands of yesteryear for which the bright lights have been replaced by not-so-rock 'n' roll financial wrangling: "I do quite a lot of work to do with the rights issues of disgruntled former band members after a band has split up. Most of the clients I have worked with in this area formed bands in the 1970s and 1980s, and the issue of who owns what, such as the band name, song-writing credits and so on are never clear cut – the band members of course just started making music without thinking about the legal ramifications. It's all brilliant when the band is successful and making money, but when someone wants to leave or there is a falling out, there is usually no legal framework in place and in many cases people are hazy about what happened and what was said, as they were doing a lot of partying at the time!"

The workload varies, but Charlotte gets plenty of opportunities to hone her advocacy skills, especially in the Intellectual Property Enterprise Court (IPEC). "The IPEC has been a great avenue for junior barristers such as myself to gain advocacy experience; as is the Trademarks Registry of the UK Intellectual Property Office. I have also been able to do quite a lot of interim applications and case management conferences in the High Court. Outside of court, my work predominantly involves drafting pleadings, pre-action correspondence, written opinions and giving advice via teleconference or in person."

Holy Grail

Meeting interesting people is guaranteed in Charlotte's line of work. One highlight which really stands out is the first trial she was involved in as a pupil, in which she helped to represent the members of Monty Python. "Even though I was still a pupil, reading through transcripts and just generally sitting in

For more chambers that work in this practice area, please use the "Pupillage index" starting on p531.

Name: **Charlotte Scott**
Chambers: **Hogarth Chambers**
University: **University of Cambridge**
Undergraduate degree: **Law**

and learning, it was a brilliant experience," she recalls. "The Monty Python guys were being sued over the merchandising royalties relating to the film, *Monty Python and the Holy Grail*, and in particular the royalties relating to the stage musical *Spamalot*. Michael Palin, Eric Idle and Terry Jones were all heavily involved, as much of the case rested on what was said and done during the creation of the film. They were in chambers every day for a couple of weeks and we had lunch with them on several occasions, and they were as funny as you would hope they would be!"

❝ The work is interesting, intellectually challenging and it keeps me on my toes ❞

Another milestone was a two-day multitrack trial in the IPEC: "It was almost exactly a year after I had qualified as a barrister and was my first full trial on my own, with cross-examination and so on. It was a moment which really vindicated my career choice; the run-up to the trial had been stressful and I was nervous and worried, but when I got into court I loved it – I knew that everything I had done to get there had been worth it."

Charlotte is enthusiastic about life as a barrister: "I love how the work is so varied and that I don't do the same thing day in, day out. One day I could be being instructed by a big music collecting society, but on another I could be representing the little guy against a big corporation. The work is interesting, intellectually challenging and it keeps me on my toes. The other thing I love is being self-employed. When I was applying for pupillage, I don't think that I appreciated enough just how important a factor this should be to anyone considering a career as a barrister. Being self-employed is both my main cause of stress and my main cause of fun at work – I have to do all

my accounts and tax returns, not to mention all the other admin, which is unpaid and tiresome; but I also have the luxury of being able to work from home when I want and a lot more flexibility and control over my hours."

If there is a downside, it is the solitude involved in much of a barrister's work. "It can be quite a lonely job, but it helps that everyone at Hogarth works with their doors open and people pop in and out to talk to each other, so there is camaraderie; but it's not quite the same as working closely with and bouncing ideas off of a colleague," admits Charlotte.

Running your own business
Charlotte is keen to stress the benefits of having some prior experience outside law for barristers in this area: "Before I came to the Bar, I spent a year setting up a business, which is still running and I'm still involved in. I'm not sure everyone would agree with me on this, but I think that having a commercial mind set is important and it is therefore really beneficial to get some commercial experience before coming to the IP and media Bar. Clients want to know their legal position, but they also want commercially sound advice which tells them how they can achieve their aims."

Finally, Charlotte would advise anyone considering this career path to make sure that they appreciate what being self-employed really means: "It is a stressful job – there is a lot of pressure on you as an individual and while I'm sure that is the case with all professions, it is slightly different when you're self-employed, as the pressure is not coming from your boss, but from having no one but yourself to rely on. You go from being a pupil where there is always someone keeping an eye on you to being out there on your own. Remember that being a barrister is essentially like running your own business, so it is crucial to be commercially proactive and to market yourself, as well as to know the law."

Personal injury

Personal injury (PI) law falls under the law of tort. It involves civil claims brought to obtain compensation for injuries so as to put the injured person back in the position that they would have been in had they not been injured. The subject matter varies considerably, and can range from controversial, high-profile disaster cases through to road traffic accidents and health and safety cases. A related, specialised practice area of PI law is clinical negligence, which involves injuries suffered during medical procedures.

Theo Barclay's passion for the legal profession was first ignited during his studies as a history undergraduate at Oxford. "During my second year I studied some legal history and from that point I thought that becoming a barrister was the way forward – principally because I wanted to be on my feet in court, arguing cases," he recalls. An enjoyable work experience placement with a commercial solicitors' firm failed to change Theo's mind, while a couple of mini-pupillages confirmed that the Bar was where he wanted to be.

After Bar school, Theo completed pupillage at XXIV Old Buildings in Lincoln's Inn before moving to Hailsham Chambers, another commercial set, where he has built up a varied common law practice. "I essentially do a bit of everything," he explains. "Having done a commercial pupillage and then a third six months at Hailsham concentrating mainly on clinical negligence, personal injury and professional negligence matters, I now have a wide variety of different sources of work. It really depends on what comes in at any given moment, but I generally have one or two bigger commercial cases rumbling along in the background, on which I'm a junior, complemented by the day-to-day paperwork of a common lawyer. My favourite part of the job, however, is representing clients in two or three trials a week. The majority of these are personal injury cases."

Advocacy opportunities

Regular court appearances are one of the main draws of PI work, in Theo's view: "That's the brilliant thing about having personal injury as part of your practice – even if you are only two years into your career, you're in court all the time. That has really helped me improve as an advocate. Choosing a practice area that gets you into court is something that I would recommend to everyone. Court advocacy is something that a lot of commercial barristers don't get to do that often, despite being the reason most of us decided to do the job in the first place. There is such a contrast between helping out on a big project and running the show, even on a case which is lower value. It is more interesting on a day-to-day basis when you are in control. As a tennis player might say – the match is 'on your racket'. Personal injury is one of the few areas where you can take the lead in your own cases at only a couple of years' call."

> ## ❝ Choosing a practice area that gets you into court is something that I would recommend to everyone ❞

Some of the most interesting PI cases for barristers at Theo's level of seniority concern fundamental dishonesty: "The general rule is that you cannot as a defendant recover your costs from a claimant, but that rule can be put aside if the claimant has been fundamentally dishonest. However, proving dishonesty in court is very difficult to do, so cases where you think the claimant has been dishonest are an exciting challenge for an advocate. In that situation, it is very important for your client not only to win the case, but also to convince the judge that there has been foul play, and to award the defendant their costs. This requires very careful cross examination in the hostile

For more chambers that work in this practice area, please use the "Pupillage index" starting on p531.

Name: **Theo Barclay**
Chambers: **Hailsham Chambers**
University: **University of Oxford**
Undergraduate degree: **Modern history**

environment that becomes inevitable if you are to accuse someone of lying. Winning these cases is hugely satisfying."

PI work is clearly weighty and consequential in its own right, its suitability for junior barristers honing their advocacy skills notwithstanding. Theo never loses sight of what such cases mean to his clients: "What you're doing matters so much to the people you are representing, whether you are the defendant and are representing a doctor or employer who has been accused of doing something negligent, or you are the claimant and are representing someone who has gone through an awful period in which they have suffered a great deal, and now seeks compensation for substantial losses."

Infinite variety
The unique way of life at the Bar is perhaps the greatest attraction of the job for Theo: "The combination of a university-like way of life – looking things up in the library, thinking hard and meeting tight deadlines – and the intensity of the courtroom is one of the profession's great attractions. The infinite variety is something that I really enjoy. Also, it cannot be overstated how great it is to be in charge of your own time as a self-employed person. Even if you end up working as hard – or harder – than your contemporaries in other professions, there is something wonderful about retaining ultimate control. This does, of course, come with pressure because you have to take responsibility for everything you do. There is a looming nervousness about making a mistake, but that also keeps you invested in the quality of your work."

The Bar – particularly the junior Bar – as we know it is likely to be facing a period of profound change in the near future. "There will be attempts over the next few years to change the costs rules in order to limit the volume of litigation, especially in the PI sector, although the government's intentions have not yet

been fully fleshed out," Theo explains. "It is important to remember that we are working in a market like any other, and any rule changes have a huge impact. It will be important for prospective pupils to keep an eye on the proposals as they develop. The question of online courts is also something that everyone aiming for pupillage needs to consider. If they are introduced in any form, it will fundamentally change the nature of the profession – and therefore the experience of any early-years practitioner. For my part, I think there will be real difficulties in running an online court for PI claims, because so much depends on what an individual says in the witness box – in practice, this can be very different to what has been put in the evidence bundle before."

Nonetheless Theo remains keen to encourage aspiring barristers with the right qualities to pursue their ambitions: "Advocacy lies at the heart of the profession – you need to be someone who likes to stand up and make an unpopular argument under difficult circumstances, before facing tough questions. Academic success is very important as well – you are applying for a job heavily based around research, and the more relevant experience, the better. If you can tick those two boxes there is no reason not to go for it, at which point you will need the third essential quality for getting pupillage – determination. Everyone comes to the Bar through different paths, but there is no barrister who has got there without hard work and a stubborn refusal to give up."

And to that end, Theo signs off with some practical advice: "I would encourage any reader to make full use of the help available at the Inns of Court. When I was starting out, I wish I had educated myself more about what they have to offer. There are so many resources at the Inns to help applicants, including people who can offer invaluable practical advice. It would be remiss not to take every opportunity they offer."

Planning/environment

Planning law regulates the way in which property owners use and develop their property in the interests of the wider community. Local planning authorities are required to follow a legal and policy framework in their decision making. Planning law is often interwoven with other branches of the law, such as environmental, local government and judicial review. Clients might include landowners, developers, local authorities, public and private utilities, government departments, amenity groups and individuals.

In 2012, the year Alexander Greaves was called to the Bar, *Rolling Stone* magazine updated its list of the 500 Greatest Albums of All Time. Nestled at number 258 was the 1968 offering *The Kinks Are The Village Green Preservation Society* – the London band's sixth studio album and one of their most acclaimed works. The album not only cemented a place in music history that year, but also inadvertently held a clue to Alexander's path towards the planning Bar.

"It was not entirely accidental that I ended up in planning law or that I did my pupillage at Frances Taylor Building (FTB)," recalls Alexander. "During my law conversion course, I decided I wanted to go into public law and looked at various different areas. It was then I developed an interest in village green law – a slightly esoteric discipline related to planning law. It was while researching it further that I came across FTB, as they've done quite a lot of work in the area."

He obtained pupillage at FTB and, found that the work he was doing was unlike anything he had experienced during his postgraduate legal education. While he points out that no prior knowledge of the subject is expected of young barristers, the learning curve during his first few months of pupillage was pretty steep.

Three-way split

Pupillage at FTB is split between three supervisors, with pupils spending four months with each and the level of responsibility increasing as experience is gained. "Certainly for the first four months I was pretty much just following my supervisor," recalls Alexander, "accompanying them to inquiries, court, conferences or on site visits. I would also do written work for them in chambers, whether researching points of law or doing first drafts of opinions and skeleton arguments. After the first four months, you are encouraged to start doing more of that sort of work for other members of chambers, which helps broaden your experience. In the second six, you are encouraged take on some work of your own while continuing to do work for other members of chambers."

While much of the work Alexander found himself doing in his own right during this time bore little resemblance to his planning caseload today, it gave him the chance to build confidence dealing with matters on his own and to familiarise himself with the workings of the court. He was also fortunate enough to have the opportunity to act as a junior for another member of chambers on a week-long village green inquiry.

"I'm not sure how many cases I did, but it gives you experience; and although you have the assistance of your supervisors, who are there for guidance if you need it, at the end of the day you are the one on your feet, arguing in court. The nature of the job is such that there isn't a lot of pure planning work at pupil level, although I did do some, so a lot of what I was doing was small county court work, which dropped off once I got tenancy."

Variety is the spice of life

One of the things that Alexander likes most about the planning Bar is that his workload is quite varied and he finds his time split between advisory work, inquiry work and court work. The advisory work consists of

---

For more chambers that work in this practice area, please use the "Pupillage index" starting on p531.

Name: **Alexander Greaves**
Chambers: **Francis Taylor Building**
University: **University of Manchester**
Undergraduate degree: **History**

looking at papers and advising local planning authorities on decisions they may take, advising prospective developers on potential projects or advising people either who want to object to planning permission or who have other queries about land use.

> **❝ From appearing at a planning inquiry to appearing at the High Court, or even in criminal court dealing with prosecutions following enforcement action – flexibility is the key thing ❞**

A planning inquiry is an appeal against a decision of a local planning authority and is presided over by planning inspectors, who make decisions on behalf of the secretary of state. They can vary in length, although Alexander suggests that a rise in the number of informal hearings (which rarely involve barristers) to clear up minor disputes means there are currently fewer one-or-two day inquiries and most last between one and two weeks. These take place up and down the country, depending on where the land to which they relate happens to be. As such, Alexander often finds himself travelling long distances and staying for the duration of the inquiry, and while he very much enjoys the change of scene, he also warns that "they can quite often be in the middle of nowhere".

He also highlights the differences between inquiries and court proceedings: "It is quite different from court advocacy, in that it is common practice to sit down in these inquiries. It is procedurally more informal than a lot of courts and there is not quite such strict adherence to the rules of evidence as in other areas. The only caveat to that would perhaps be for enforcement inquiries where, because

evidence generally relates to evidence of fact, it is given under oath."

Adapt to survive
The difference between court-based planning work, and the more informal environment planning inquiries means that lawyers need to be able to adjust to different tribunals and working conditions. "Being able to adapt to different environments is key," explains Alexander. "From appearing at a planning inquiry to appearing at the High Court, or even in criminal court dealing with prosecutions following enforcement action – flexibility is the key thing."

In addition, Alexander suggests that a general understanding of politics and government policy in the area is very useful and may well be worth cultivating for those attending a pupillage interview at a planning set. "It plays such an important role in the development and application of planning law," he claims. "Policy is so fundamental that having an understanding of current government thinking is vital. National policy and planning practice guidance is available online; you don't need to read through it all, but it's good to have a general understanding of the overriding themes. Quite a lot can be gleaned from the newspapers; affordable housing in London and concerns over fracking are both things that have been in the news quite a lot recently."

"You can also sit in on planning inquiries," he offers. "They happen in council offices up and down the country and are advertised on council websites. Documents are made available to the public either online or at the inquiry venue. It would definitely help you show an interest in planning at interview, where they are interested in why you want to go to a particular chambers, rather than why you just want to be a barrister. It helps to demonstrate that you've looked what that chambers does and show some understanding of the key issues around their areas of specialty."

Professional negligence

Barristers involved in this field deal with claims against professionals such as architects, accountants, solicitors and financial advisers who have allegedly failed to provide services to the level of care and skill which a member of that profession would be expected to demonstrate. Clinical negligence is a type of professional liability that involves disputes between patients and healthcare providers (usually doctors), centring on quality of care. Defendant professionals will usually have indemnity insurance against such claims.

Imran Benson graduated from university with an ongoing passion for law, but was unsure about quite what he wanted to do next. "I wasn't clear enough about the differences between the barrister and solicitor paths, so I embarked on a lot of research," he recalls. "The sound of life at the Bar really interested me, so I applied for a couple of mini-pupillages for a first-hand insight into what being a barrister would be like. I liked the advocacy and the idea of being self-employed, building up my own practice and earning my own money. I thought that if I was going to be working long hours, including some weekends, I might as well be doing it for myself rather than for a firm's partners."

Imran completed pupillage at Hailsham Chambers, where he is now an experienced litigator specialising in professional liability, as well as other forms of commercial and insurance litigation. "Hailsham is very well known for its strong professional negligence practice, among other areas, so I was introduced to this kind of work early on in my career," he explains. "I do a lot of work for insurers, solicitors, accountants and property professionals, and also act for clients of those professionals – banks, businesses and individuals. In a typical professional negligence case, an individual or business will feel that it has been let down by a professional in some way, which will prompt it to launch a claim against that professional. The professional will then contact his or her insurer, who will instruct a solicitor, who will then instruct me to provide legal representation to defend the professional against the claim being brought against them."

However, the seriousness of such disputes does not necessarily mean that they always go to court. "Trials are relatively few and far between – I tend to do four or five a year," explains Imran. "I also attend mediations and do quite a lot of applications and case management conferences, but much of my time is spent on advisory work and pleadings."

Serious allegations

Part of this area's appeal is the chance to work with upstanding professional people for whom the outcome of a case will make a significant difference. "The clients I act for are facing – for them – serious allegations," Imran points out. "Commercial disputes often have a human context. Usually the client will be an experienced professional person who has been told that they have made a serious mistake which has caused someone else loss. Occasionally my client might be dishonest, but most of the time I'm representing people who take their jobs very seriously and are very concerned about the allegation – obviously, if they are named as negligent in a judgment, it will be very difficult for them to continue their careers in the future."

Cases worth £50-60 million involving some of the biggest companies out there have landed on Imran's desk, but one of the highlights of his career so far was much smaller, at least in financial terms: "The case concerned a person who was trying to invest in property and had paid his life savings, around £300,000, to a law firm in order to do this. However, his co-investor took that money out of the firm and stole it, so he was suing the firm on the grounds that it should have had

For more chambers that work in this practice area, please use the "Pupillage index" starting on p531.

Name: **Imran Benson**
Chambers: **Hailsham Chambers**
University: **University of Bristol**
Undergraduate degree: **Law**

better safeguards in place to prevent such a thing happening. The case went to court and I ended up cross-examining one of the partners of the firm, where I had to make serious allegations about his honesty. That was very nerve-racking, but was also very worthwhile – we won in the end and got every penny back for the client. It was very rewarding to help that individual in a serious way, as losing that money would have had a profoundly negative impact on his life."

Rewarding cases and a fully independent lifestyle are key aspects of the Bar's appeal, but the job isn't without its pressures, too. "I'm one of the many barristers who worries that I might run out of work one day. There is always a nervousness and anxiety around that which I don't particularly enjoy," Imran admits. "It would be great to have cases lined up for the next five years so I wouldn't need to think about it, but that is not how the Bar works and it's also part of the fun. I'm always thinking about where my next case is going to come from."

> ❝ **Commercial disputes often have a human context. Usually the client will be an experienced professional person who has been told that they have made a serious mistake which has caused someone else loss** ❞

Changes ahead
Appraising the wider outlook for the Bar, Imran identifies several issues of which anyone considering a career as a barrister should be aware. "In the civil world, the government are thinking about introducing online courts, which may reduce the amount of work available for junior barristers. In

addition fixed fees, if they come in, will also make it harder for junior barristers to earn a living. Nonetheless, I think if you are hard-working, clever and ambitious, you can still make a very respectable life at the Bar."

To succeed, Imran believes that every good barrister must have three key qualities: "Firstly, you need the ability and willingness to work really hard. Secondly, you must be an excellent communicator. And finally, while the ability to express yourself clearly is essential, it is also equally important to be a good listener – you need to be able to take in what your clients are telling you to put together a good case."

And for those seeking pupillage, Imran has this advice: "Think about the sets you would like to work at and look at the profiles of the junior tenants on their websites. You will then be able to see what they have done and compare yourself accordingly to see if that set is appropriate – if you are on a par with those sorts of people in terms of academic and wider achievement, it will be well worth applying."

Finally, Imran again emphasises that being a barrister is about much more than having a sound knowledge and interpretation of the law. "It's also good to have broader interests – in businesses and the markets you might be working in, for example," he observes. "You need to inspire confidence in your clients and make them want to give you work, so wider knowledge and good interpersonal skills are just as important as legal acumen."

Property

Property lawyers act for a variety of domestic and international clients – including property investors and developers, farmers, governments, landowners and public sector bodies – on a wide range of transactions and disputes, involving everything from offices and housing to retail developments and industrial units. The common legal issues arising for commercial property lawyers include acquisitions and disposals of land, investments, landlord and tenant matters, developments and contracts, and environmental law and associated liabilities.

Like his namesake, the father of modern economics, Adam Smith took a measured and well-thought out approach to his future career: "I was always interested in law and had done some work experience at school. I went on to do several mini-pupillages, which definitely encouraged me towards the Bar. I liked the idea of being self-employed, as it would give me more direct control over my career. I also thought that, as a litigation solicitor, it might be frustrating to get to know a case well, and then, potentially, have to refer it on to someone else to provide advice on the key issues. I was also drawn to the day-to-day nature of the work: the advocacy, providing advice on merits and tactics, and preparing pleadings and skeleton arguments – it all appealed."

Pupillage at 9 Old Square offered Adam solid insight into the realities of the profession, especially by virtue of having four separate pupil supervisors, all with different practices: "It was useful to see how my pupil supervisors worked and presented things, and, although it was an intense time, they made it as stress-free as it could be." He joined as a tenant at the end of 2002 and the set merged with Maitland soon thereafter.

Property matters
Today, property is a large part of what Adam's practice is about. He describes a handful of the varied cases he has dealt with recently: "My Gibraltar-based client had provided finance to two BVI companies backed by a number of charges over English properties; the borrowers defaulted, and there was an underlying dispute over the terms of the loan agreements and whether they had been varied. It was a commercial dispute, but the focus of the trial was the alleged release of a major part of the security and whether the client had bound itself to that in return for a part-payment. There were technical points about mortgages and a large amount of disputed evidence. Another involved a wealthy family that owned a large portfolio of commercial and residential properties on a fairly informal basis; they had fallen into disagreement with each other and the ownership of the properties was in dispute – it was in large part a fight over who had said what."

Acting as junior to an eminent silk in the House of Lords was a career highlight for Adam, especially as the case concerned "issues that were of some significance to a lot of property owners; the committee, unsurprisingly, quickly got to the heart of the issues and asked some very probing questions." A notable arbitration relating to a metal-producing business, post-Soviet break-up, also stands out: "Our client had been involved in the management of the business. There had been a management buy-out, with external investment, and the dispute was between the external investor and our client. The ultimate investor was a well-known oligarch with all the financial and political cards in his favour. But we achieved a good result for the client, so that was very satisfying."

Pros and cons of self-employment
Referring back to one of his original reasons for choosing the Bar, Adam cites the freedom of self-employment as one of the best features of the job: "Although it may sometimes be illusory, if a gap in your diary opens up (for example, a case has just settled) and you want to take advantage of that by getting away, you are able to do it –

For more chambers that work in this practice area, please use the "Pupillage index" starting on p531.

Name: **Adam Smith**
Chambers: **Maitland Chambers**
University: **University of Oxford**
Undergraduate degree: **Classics**

there's no checking in with the boss. When you're involved with a case and something needs to be done, obviously that has to happen; but, to a certain extent, when you take a case it's your decision to do so." The ability to make a real difference through your work and the keen intellectual challenges are other draw-cards: "Very many cases throw up interesting problems, so there's nearly always something to think about. It's also satisfying to see what we do having a direct impact – if you win a case for an individual, for whom it has been the last throw of the dice, it's personally very significant."

There is no denying, however, that this career can be all-consuming at times. "That can be good and is part of the excitement of it – we are very invested in it; but, at the same time, your personal life can suffer as a result," he admits. "I've had to work through holidays and frequently cancel plans. There is often a lack of predictability, so that all of a sudden something needs to be done urgently, such as seeking an interim injunction. You can also be under a lot of pressure, particularly close to and during trial. As you get more experienced, you become more comfortable with being in that position and working out how to juggle things."

Adam reflects on how life at the Bar is evolving, both in his own field and elsewhere: "Commercial property work is unlikely to change much in the next few years, other than (in terms of its volume and the nature of disputes and issues which arise) as a result of general economic forces; the biggest upheaval is occurring at the criminal Bar, with major structural changes to publicly funded work. One change that has already occurred generally at the Bar is increased specialism. Less and less you see people with a general common law practice – clients appear to be increasingly keen to be advised and represented by a barrister who is a specialist in the relevant field."

Commitment is key

So what makes for an excellent property barrister? According to Adam, it is broadly the same set of skills you would mark as essential in any civil area of law: "Commitment to the job is essential; the most successful barristers make themselves available to clients and are constantly looking for the best angle to achieve the client's objectives. Analytical ability and knowledge of the law are key. There is often a large amount of information involved, so you need to be able to distil that into the far smaller amount of critically relevant information. You need advocacy skills, both oral and written; a lot of work goes into written as well as oral advocacy. If you can get a judge on your side even before the hearing has started with a good skeleton argument, a significant proportion of the hard work is done. You also need good people skills – the ability to get on with both professional and lay clients, to be pleasant and easy to work with, and to inspire confidence."

Adam suggests that the first steps on the path are to do well in whatever undergraduate degree you have chosen – "proving your analytical ability and ability to sift information is possible in all or nearly all degrees" – and to complete perhaps five or six mini-pupillages in the practice areas that you are interested in. "In addition, you need to show an interest in advocacy, so debating or mooting as a law student, or other public speaking, is particularly important."

His final tips include joining an Inn as soon as you've decided that the Bar is for you, because it is "a great opportunity to meet people, do some mooting and explore funding options through Inn scholarships". He also suggests trying a vacation scheme with a solicitors' firm, as a way of "understanding the day to day work of a litigation solicitor and the pressures that they can work under and demonstrating that you've made a well thought-out decision to join the Bar as opposed to qualifying as a solicitor".

Public

The public law Bar spans the full range of administrative, public and constitutional law. Specific areas within the field include civil liberties and human rights, commercial judicial review, community and healthcare law, disciplinary proceedings and the internal administration of public bodies, education law, housing law, planning law, prison law, and social services and social security law. Public law work has a European influence, with a steady stream of cases being referred to the European Court of Justice for preliminary rulings and other cases raising the issue of the application of the European Convention on Human Rights.

Drawn to the Bar by an early interest in advocacy – "I went into law with a view to becoming a barrister; I never had any intention of becoming a solicitor" – Jennifer MacLeod took some time out after university to see the world, living in the United States and South Africa and working for the UN and various NGOs, before returning to pupillage at Brick Court. She describes her time as a pupil: "It was very challenging, initially because of the difference between learning law at university and practising it; they are a gulf apart. Learning to be an advocate took a huge amount of teaching from my pupil supervisors and I found it quite exhausting! But it was also enjoyable and as you start to see yourself improve, there is a thrilling feeling of being able to do something that you couldn't do six months prior."

Now a barrister of four years' call, Jennifer has a public law practice that is incredibly varied – reflecting the nature of a practice area that "encompasses anything to do with the exercise of state power against individuals, be they corporations or people, and whether a state should be constrained in the exercise of that power, with a variety of human rights and international issues involved". She explains some of the things that attracted her to this field: "If you're at university and interested in the principles of how a state governs, then you will find public law a fascinating area to work in – I certainly do! You are at the edge of politics, law and policy, and part of shaping where things go."

Going public

Jennifer offers examples of the huge variety of both client and subject matter that is a feature of her caseload: "At one point, I was working for a multinational tobacco manufacturer challenging the government's decision to bring in plain packaging; for domestic violence victims in Georgia who were claiming that the state had failed to protect them; for UK welfare beneficiaries who wanted to prove that the government policy of excluding them from certain benefits was unlawful; and for Southern Rail when they were trying to stop the trade unions from striking. I'm currently working for the government on a case against pharmaceutical companies including Pfizer in relation to what's known as 'excessive pricing' of epilepsy drugs. It can be so completely different from one day to the next, you never get bored. And you're also often working on things that you can chat about to anyone – they're important issues in the public domain." She adds that you may find yourself in court less than barristers practising in other areas, "but you're also often working in the public eye, which is both exciting and stressful!"

Reflecting back on one of her seminal career moments, Jennifer says: "I am most proud of my work on the domestic violence case in Georgia, working in collaboration with the European Human Rights Advocacy Centre. We were successful in changing the law completely on domestic violence; the government brought in an entirely new regime, worked with NGOs to develop it and gave compensation to past victims. This relatively small case made a very real practical difference to lots of people's lives."

Both international and domestic work is a feature: "Because my practice entails a lot of

For more chambers that work in this practice area, please use the "Pupillage index" starting on p531.

Name: **Jennifer MacLeod**
Chambers: **Brick Court Chambers**
University: **University of Cambridge**
Undergraduate degree: **Law**

human rights litigation, much of my work is international, but that's not to say that everyone in public law will experience that. For example, I'm also acting for an individual who wants to change the UK law on assisted suicide; which is based in human rights principles but is a domestic public law challenge."

Brexit uncertainty
Public law is one of the practice areas that will be hardest-hit by the United Kingdom's exit from the European Union, relying as it does on EU law principles and the presence of a supranational body. Jennifer elaborates: "In this area, Brexit will have particularly large repercussions because significant areas of public law are based on EU principles, and the way we challenge or constrain what the government can do is often based on EU law. The fact that the state is not supreme in the legal system, because the EU legal system supersedes it, is important. When we lose that, it will have an enormous impact on how you challenge what the state does – or if you can at all. One of the purposes of Brexit was to free the state from such constraints, so the repercussions in this area are enormous."

Also linked to Brexit is the future of human rights laws: "There has been much debate on the extent of human rights protections and whether we need the Human Rights Act; for now, we are all watching closely what will happen."

If an interest in the development of the law is your thing, then public could be your career nirvana. "There is a particular focus on legal, rather than factual, disputes, so you have to have a cerebral interest in that," advises Jennifer. "There is not a huge amount of cross-examination or the drama of performing in front of a jury, so if that's what you're looking for, you might want to think about a different area! Public law is very similar to the mooting you will do at university, so if you've enjoyed that, this could be for you."

In addition, being one of the less traditional areas of law means that public attracts a diverse range of practitioners, as Jennifer explains: "People come from all sorts of background, including other sectors, state schools and a wide range of universities, so you definitely shouldn't be put off because of your background. The most important thing is to be as clear as you can be with your analysis and try to get the best grades you possibly can."

ff If you're interested in the principles of how a state governs, then you will find public law a fascinating area – you're working at the edge of politics, law and policy JJ

Jennifer is keen to pass on some advice about the job that she wished someone had mentioned to her – not that it would have changed her mind about pursuing this is a career, just that to be forewarned is forearmed. "I wish I had been told that it is someone else's job to show that you're doing a bad job, all the time!" she laughs. "It's worth thinking about that before you start; this is not a career free from stress. You are also on a very public stage and things don't always go the way you want. You have to grow a bit of a thick skin."

A final heartening reflection on the nature of the Bar: "One thing I didn't expect was being part of such a great community of people – across chambers and the profession, people are actually in the main very kind and supportive, as well as interesting and smart. I work with amazing colleagues – many of whom have become wonderful friends – and I'm not sure that I expected that. It was a very pleasant surprise."

Revenue

Tax barristers advise and litigate on all aspects of commercial and personal tax issues. Corporate and business tax matters may involve company or group reconstructions, transfer pricing and the use of losses and capital allowances. Tax planning for individuals can encompass capital gains, inheritance and income tax. Typical cases might concern advising on (or acting in disputes concerning) the sale of a family company or the creation and operation of trusts. Barristers also specialise in value added tax and other indirect taxes, including customs duties, excise duties, landfill tax and stamp duties. The work may involve detailed consideration of EU law.

An interest in a highly analytic practice is part of what led Thomas Chacko to a career at the tax Bar: "Tax is a very technical and law-heavy area, both in terms of the legislation and the rapidly evolving caselaw. We focus more on complex statutory interpretation than most other areas of the Bar, so being alert to language is important."

Despite not knowing much about tax when applying for pupillage, Thomas knew he wanted "to do something technical, and to be in court regularly but not all the time, so I applied to sets that did specialist, commercial or chancery work". He found Pump Court a pleasant place to work and was impressed by "the type of work and the atmosphere in chambers". Following a 12-month pupillage, Thomas was happy to be taken on as a tenant. "We are a collegiate set and pop in and out of each other's rooms all the time," he comments. "That's essential, because the law is fast paced and voluminous, and you need to be able to bang on doors and ask questions of the more experienced members of chambers."

Advice heavy

One key feature of the tax Bar is that the balance between litigating and advising is traditionally more heavily weighted towards the latter, as Thomas explains. "As well as my own pieces of advice, I do devilling for senior members, where you basically provide them with a first draft. That's a great chance to gain exposure to more complex areas of law. Some of our advice is given with a view to litigation, while others focus on how to go about something correctly. Because tax law is complicated and it is possible to fall into traps quite easily, a lot of advance planning is required – VAT, for example, is quite counterintuitive."

This is not to say that tax barristers never get the chance to stand up and put their case to a judge. "We certainly do more advice than most, but there is still a fair amount of litigation," Thomas confirms. "You may find yourself as junior or second junior on a big meaty dispute, where you spend months going through documents, drafting and getting everything ready. Litigation has a long lead time, so a matter might be on your desk for nine months before you get to court." The smaller disputes, which are run without a leader, "are no less difficult – things can still be confusing and messy even when there is little money at stake".

Thomas describes a case of his own involving an academic who wanted his pension to be paid out, but first had to prove that he had not been careless in not having paid national insurance on time: "Often it's about creating an impression. I thought he had a good case, but it largely depended on whether we could project the right 'feel': would the judge think that this is a decent person or is he or she just trying it on? I was pleased that we gave the right impression and succeeded."

Furthermore, it's not just about the minutiae of the tax statutes: "Many cases are more about whether a contract existed or whether procedures were followed correctly. A lot of developments in trust law and restitution

For more chambers that work in this practice area, please use the "Pupillage index" starting on p531.

Name: **Thomas Chacko**
Chambers: **Pump Court Tax Chambers**
University: **University of Cambridge**
Undergraduate degree: **Science**

law have come out of tax litigation, because tax is one of the few areas where it might really matter exactly when a right comes into existence, for example." The variety of subject matter is one of the best bits of the job: "You get a new set of papers, open them and have often not come across the area of tax you are asked to advise on. Then, over the next few days, you start to understand what's going on. Tax is so varied – no one "knows" the tax legislation in this country, there's far too much of it – that you are always working through new questions. That can be unnerving at times."

Thomas has noted a definite shift in the contentious landscape. "Everyone is fighting more – both the Revenue and defendants – and the cases go on for longer. Matters used to be argued technically and informally, and there wasn't as much interest in the factual background. That is no longer the case; a few years ago I did a 29-day trial with dozens of files and 15 witnesses that was a real fight over the evidence. It could have been a Commercial Court dispute, but it was being heard in the Tax Tribunal. Even though, by and large, I prefer having a practice where I'm working on papers, I do also like the fact that I'm in court at least once a month – it's an ideal balance."

Be your own boss
Managing that balance is one of the most enjoyable aspects of a barrister's career. "Because you are self-employed, it's your own business and you decide how and when you work," explains Thomas. "There is no one looking over your shoulder. That can be tricky at times, especially when you have three deadlines approaching at the same time." And although it is something you are aware of before you start, the reality of being your own boss can still come as a shock: "I was surprised by how much the way you run things is your own responsibility. No one tells you what to do each day or when to do it. You have to take that on yourself."

Thomas warns that for the specialist Bar in particular, hard graft is required. "You have to put the work in," he cautions. "Bear in mind that there are only around 30 or 40 people each year who go to the commercial and specialist Bar – that's a tiny amount – and thus getting pupillage is extremely competitive. If you are still at university it is worth doing as well as you can academically."

With one eye on your exemplary grades, the other should be on trying to get a sense of what life at the Bar is all about. "Even in really specialist areas such as tax, you are still an advocate, so being able to demonstrate that you have had some general advocacy experience shows that you are genuinely interested in standing on your feet and having an argument," explains Thomas. "We don't expect you to have studied tax before you get here – there is often not the opportunity to do so – but putting some effort into finding out what this career might involve is a good idea."

❝ The law is fast paced and voluminous, and you need to be able to bang on doors and ask questions of the more experienced members of chambers ❞

Pupillage directory

How to use the pupillage index and directory

Barristers' index

These tables are designed to allow you to shortlist sets of chambers by particular criteria. Further information about each set is contained within the pupillage directory.

The tables detail:
- the main location of the set;
- the number of annual pupillages at the set;
- the number of tenants and tenancies offered in the past three years;
- whether mini-pupillages are available;
- whether the set uses the Pupillage Gateway application system; and
- 19 specialisation work areas.

It should be noted that the information has been provided by the chambers themselves and has generally not been verified by us. We do not, therefore, claim that the information is fully accurate and comprehensive, only that it can be used as a starting point for shortlisting appropriate sets. Furthermore, although we have attempted to contact every recruiting chambers, some have not returned information and are therefore absent.

Barristers' directory

The directory contains contact information and a brief practice description for all chambers that have provided information. It is therefore an essential reference guide to chambers that offer pupillages and mini-pupillages.

The basic entry includes an application address, telephone number, email address, the applications procedure (Pupillage Gateway or own system) and a brief description of the set, together with the number of pupillages per year, the number of tenants, the number of new tenants in the last three years and whether the set offers mini-pupillages. Those chambers that have a more detailed directory entry appear in bold in the regional indexes.

These resources should be used in conjunction with the section on the Bar practice areas, which features in-depth interviews with numerous barristers who are keen to pass on their advice about making it in the legal profession.

Pupillage index

Barristers' index

	Location	Pupillages funded	Tenancies in the last three years	Number of tenants	Mini-pupillages offered	Apply through Pupillage Gateway
Albion Chambers	Bristol	0	3	65	✔	✔
Angel Chambers	Swansea	2	1	33	✔	✔
Apex Chambers	Cardiff	2	3	18	✔	✔
Arden Chambers	London	2	5	32	✔	✔
Atkin Chambers	London	2	3	44	✔	
Atlantic Chambers	Liverpool	2	2	56	✔	✔
Bank House Chambers	Sheffield	1	4	40	✔	✔
2 Bedford Row	London	4	4	78	✔	✔
7 Bedford Row	London	2	4	84	✔	
9 Bedford Row	London	2	6	62	✔	✔
25 Bedford Row	London	3	7	70	✔	✔
36 Bedford Row	London	2	3	103	✔	✔
42 Bedford Row	London	2	7	103	✔	✔
29 Bedford Row Chambers	London	2	4	55	✔	✔
Blackstone Chambers	London	4	10	107	✔	✔
4 Breams Buildings	London	4	6	67	✔	✔
One Brick Court	London	Up to 2	2	19	✔	✔
4 Brick Court	London	0	6	36	✔	✔
Brick Court Chambers	London	Normally 4	7	86	✔	✔
Broadway House Chambers	Bradford	1	6	51	✔	✔
Carmelite Chambers	London	2	6	65	✔	
1 Chancery Lane	London	2	2	44	✔	
Charter Chambers	London	0	8	54	✔	
Chartlands Chambers	Northampton	1	2	13	✔	
Citadel Chambers	Birmingham	2	3	56	✔	
Cloisters	London	2	6	51	✔	✔
12 College Place	Southampton	1-2	2	26	✔	✔
Coram Chambers	London	2	4	66	✔	✔
Cornerstone Barristers	London	2	5	50	✔	✔
Cornwall Street Chambers	Birmingham	Up to 2	2	67		
Criminal Defence Solicitors	London	1	2	3	✔	✔
Crown Office Chambers	London	Up to 3	8	98	✔	
One Crown Office Row	London	2	6	73	✔	✔
Crown Office Row Chambers	Brighton	2	3	47	✔	
Crown Prosecution Service	London	30	60	600		
Deans Court Chambers	Manchester	2	7	75	✔	✔
Dere Street Chambers	Newcastle upon Tyne	2	6	90	✔	✔
Devereux	London	2	5	50	✔	✔
Doughty Street Chambers	London	2	5	125	✔	✔
2 Dr Johnson's Buildings	London	Up to 2	5	46	✔	
Three Dr Johnson's Buildings	London	0	1	33	✔	

Chancery	Civil	Commercial	Common	Construction	Crime	Employment	EU	Family	Human rights	IP	Landlord/tenant	Personal injury	Planning	Prof negligence	Public	Revenue	Shipping	TMT
	•	•	•		•	•		•				•			•			
•	•		•		•	•		•			•	•		•				
				•														
	•							•	•		•			•	•			
	•	•		•										•				•
•	•		•		•	•		•			•	•		•	•	•		
•	•		•		•	•		•				•			•			
			•		•			•										
	•	•	•		•	•		•				•		•				
					•													
					•				•									
•	•	•	•		•	•	•	•	•			•		•	•			
	•	•	•			•		•			•	•		•	•			
								•										
	•	•		•	•	•	•	•	•			•	•	•	•		•	•
					•			•										
	•		•					•							•			
•			•			•		•	•			•	•	•	•	•	•	•
	•		•		•	•		•			•	•		•				
•	•	•	•	•	•			•			•	•		•	•			
	•		•		•			•						•				
	•				•			•				•			•			
	•	•	•		•	•		•			•	•	•	•	•			•
•	•		•		•	•					•	•	•					
					•	•												
	•		•			•		•	•		•		•	•	•			•
					•													
	•	•	•		•	•		•			•	•	•	•	•	•		
•	•		•		•	•		•			•	•	•	•	•			
					•													
•	•	•	•		•	•		•			•	•		•	•			
•	•	•	•		•	•		•		•	•	•	•	•	•			
	•	•	•		•	•								•			•	•
	•				•	•	•		•			•	•	•	•			•
	•				•	•		•						•	•			
•	•		•			•		•				•	•		•	•		

Barristers' index

	Location	Pupillages funded	Tenancies in the last three years	Number of tenants	Mini-pupillages offered	Apply through Pupillage Gateway
Drystone chambers	London	2-3	6	85	✔	
East Anglian Chambers	Ipswich	Up to 2	4	43	✔	
Enterprise Chambers	London	1	3	42	✔	✔
Erskine Chambers	London	Up to 2	1	30	✔	
39 Essex Chambers	London	Up to 3	7	128	✔	✔
One Essex Court	London	5	11	98	✔	✔
5 Essex Court	London	Up to 2	3	42	✔	✔
Essex Court Chambers	London	Up to 4	7	90	✔	✔
23 Essex Street	London	1	9	103	✔	
Exchange Chambers	Liverpool	1-2	5	156	✔	
Falcon Chambers	London	Up to 2	5	41	✔	
Farrar's Building	London	2	4	45	✔	✔
Fenners Chambers	Cambridge	Up to 2	2	50	✔	
Field Court Chambers	London	Up to 2	3	60	✔	
187 Fleet Street	London	1-2	8	75	✔	✔
Foundry Chambers	London	2	7	56	✔	✔
Fountain Court Chambers	London	Up to 4	7	81	✔	✔
Francis Taylor Building	London	2	5	56	✔	
1 Garden Court	London	2	5	74	✔	✔
Garden Court Chambers	London	4	27	182	✔	✔
Goldsmith Chambers	London	2	8	73	✔	✔
9 Gough Square	London	1	7	70	✔	
Gough Square Chambers	London	1	2	25	✔	✔
4-5 Gray's Inn Square	London	1	4	33	✔	
1 Gray's Inn Square	London	2	7	73	✔	✔
Gray's Inn Tax Chambers	London	1	1	10	✔	✔
GT Stewart Solicitors	London	1		12		
Guildford Chambers	Guildford	1	5	23	✔	
Guildhall Chambers	Bristol	2	8	87	✔	✔
Hailsham Chambers	London	2	7	50	✔	✔
2 Harcourt Buildings	London	2	6	42	✔	✔
Harcourt Chambers	London	1-2	4	54	✔	✔
Hardwicke	London	2	12	84	✔	✔
1 Hare Court	London	2	5	42	✔	
2 Hare Court	London	2	8	56		✔
3 Hare Court	London	2	4	35	✔	✔
7 Harrington Street Chambers	Liverpool	1	5	90	✔	
Henderson Chambers	London	2	6	49	✔	✔
1 High Pavement	Nottingham	1	2	43	✔	
Hogarth Chambers	London	1	2	21	✔	
Invictus Chambers	London	2	5	19	✔	✔

Chancery	Civil	Commercial	Common	Construction	Crime	Employment	EU	Family	Human rights	IP	Landlord/tenant	Personal injury	Planning	Prof negligence	Public	Revenue	Shipping	TMT
					•													
•	•	•	•		•	•			•		•	•	•	•		•		
•		•									•			•				
•		•												•				
			•	•		•	•				•			•				•
•	•	•				•			•					•		•		•
•	•	•				•	•				•			•	•			•
•	•	•				•	•		•		•			•	•	•	•	•
					•													
•	•	•		•	•	•	•	•	•	•	•	•	•	•		•		
•	•	•			•	•												
•	•	•	•	•	•	•						•		•				•
•	•	•	•		•	•					•	•		•				•
•	•	•	•		•	•			•		•	•		•				•
					•													
					•										•			
		•				•			•		•			•	•			•
		•				•			•		•		•	•	•			
					•													
	•		•		•	•	•		•		•	•	•	•				
	•				•	•			•		•							
	•	•			•	•			•		•		•					
	•	•			•									•				
•	•	•			•	•	•		•	•	•		•	•	•	•	•	•
•	•	•	•		•	•			•		•	•		•	•	•		•
																•		
	•				•	•	•		•		•	•		•				
•	•				•	•			•		•	•		•				
•	•	•			•	•					•	•	•	•				
•	•	•	•								•	•		•				
					•													
•		•		•		•	•				•	•		•				
								•										
					•													
	•	•	•			•	•		•		•			•				
	•				•			•			•							
	•	•	•	•		•					•	•		•	•			•
					•													
•		•								•								•
•	•	•	•		•	•			•	•	•	•			•			•

	Location	Pupillages funded	Tenancies in the last three years	Number of tenants	Mini-pupillages offered	Apply through Pupillage Gateway
Iscoed Chambers	Swansea	1	5	35	✔	✔
One ITL	London	2	4	26	✔	✔
KBG Chambers	Plymouth	1	3	35	✔	
KBW	Leeds	1	4	38	✔	✔
11KBW	London	2-4	6	59	✔	✔
6KBW College Hill	London	2	3	47	✔	
KCH Garden Square Barristers	Nottingham	Up to 2	13	60	✔	
Keating Chambers	London	3	4	65	✔	✔
Kenworthy's Chambers	Manchester	1-2	3	62	✔	
1 King's Bench Walk	London	2	6	55	✔	
2 King's Bench Walk	London	2	4	73	✔	✔
2 King's Bench Walk	London	1	1	10	✔	
4 King's Bench Walk	London	2	4	54	✔	✔
5 King's Bench Walk	London	3	7	48	✔	✔
7 King's Bench Walk	London	Up to 4	6	60	✔	✔
9 King's Bench Walk	London	1	10	26	✔	
12 King's Bench Walk	London	2-3	8	82	✔	✔
Kings Chambers	Manchester	Up to 3	5	112	✔	
Lamb Building	London	Up to 3	8	64	✔	
Landmark Chambers	London	Up to 2	8	85	✔	✔
Lincoln House Chambers	Manchester	1-2	5	67	✔	
Linenhall Chambers	Chester	1	1	70	✔	
Littleton Chambers	London	2	4	57		✔
Maidstone Chambers	Maidstone	1-2	2	15	✔	
Maitland Chambers	London	Up to 3	5	69	✔	
Malins Chambers	London	1	1	6		
Matrix Chambers	London	2	6	90		
1 MCB	London	0	7	47	✔	
Monckton Chambers	London	2	5	58	✔	✔
15 New Bridge Street	London	2	3	46		
New Court Chambers	London	2	4	25	✔	✔
New Park Court Chambers	Leeds	3	3	61	✔	✔
3 New Square	London	1	1	19	✔	✔
4 New Square	London	Up to 2	7	78	✔	
11 New Square	London	1	1	9	✔	
New Square Chambers	London	1	3	41	✔	
8 New Square Intellectual Property	London	Up to 2		28	✔	✔
New Walk Chambers	Leicester	Up to 3	7	22		
No5 Chambers	Birmingham	Up to 3	53	256	✔	
Northampton Chambers	Northampton	1-2	4	14	✔	
Old Court Chambers	Middlesbrough	0-1	1	19		

Chancery	Civil	Commercial	Common	Construction	Crime	Employment	EU	Family	Human rights	IP	Landlord/tenant	Personal injury	Planning	Prof negligence	Public	Revenue	Shipping	TMT
●	●	●	●		●	●		●			●	●	●	●				
					●	●												
	●				●	●		●			●	●		●				
	●	●			●	●		●				●						
	●	●				●	●		●						●			
		●			●	●			●					●	●			
●	●	●	●	●	●	●	●	●	●		●	●	●	●	●			
	●	●		●		●	●							●	●		●	●
●	●	●	●		●	●		●	●	●	●	●	●	●	●	●		
						●												
	●		●		●	●		●			●	●		●				
●	●		●		●	●		●			●			●				
●	●		●			●		●			●	●		●				
					●			●										
	●		●		●									●			●	
	●				●													
	●		●			●					●	●		●				
●	●	●	●	●		●			●		●	●	●	●	●	●		
●	●	●	●		●	●					●	●		●	●	●		
●	●	●	●				●		●		●		●	●	●	●		
	●	●	●		●	●					●	●		●	●			
	●		●		●	●		●			●		●	●				●
●	●	●				●	●				●			●				●
●	●	●				●		●			●	●		●				●
●	●	●	●		●	●		●			●	●		●	●	●		●
	●	●	●	●		●	●		●		●	●		●	●	●		●
	●	●		●				●			●		●	●	●	●		●
								●										
●	●	●	●		●	●	●				●	●		●	●			●
●	●	●	●	●					●			●		●	●			●
●		●								●	●	●		●	●	●	●	
										●								●
●	●	●		●	●	●	●		●		●	●	●	●	●			
●	●	●	●	●	●	●	●	●	●	●	●	●	●	●	●	●		●
	●				●			●										
	●	●	●		●	●		●			●	●	●	●	●			

Barristers' index

	Location	Pupillages funded	Tenancies in the last three years	Number of tenants	Mini-pupillages offered	Apply through Pupillage Gateway
Ten Old Square	London	1	2	26	✔	
15 Old Square	London	1	1	11	✔	
Old Square Chambers	London	2	6	79	✔	✔
Old Square Chambers	Bristol	2	6	79	✔	✔
Oriel Chambers	Liverpool	Up to 2	3	53	✔	
Outer Temple Chambers	London	3	7	89	✔	✔
Five Paper	London	2	3	43	✔	
4 Paper Buildings	London	3	6	79	✔	
5 Paper Buildings	London	2	6	46	✔	✔
9 Park Place	Cardiff	2	6	60	✔	
30 Park Place	Cardiff	1	18	67	✔	✔
Park Square Barristers	Leeds	2	6	125	✔	
Parklane Plowden Chambers	Leeds	Up to 4	6	77	✔	
3PB	London	3	26	170	✔	✔
4 Pump Court	London	2	6	65	✔	
5 Pump Court	London	2	3	57	✔	✔
6 Pump Court	London	0	5	40	✔	✔
Pump Court Chambers	London	2	5	92	✔	✔
1 Pump Court Chambers	London	2	5	75	✔	✔
Pump Court Tax Chambers	London	1-2	2	35	✔	
QEB Hollis Whiteman	London	4	5	66	✔	
Quadrant Chambers	London	3	5	62	✔	✔
Queen Elizabeth Building	London	2	4	33	✔	✔
Queen Square Chambers	Bristol	1	6	39	✔	
Radcliffe Chambers	London	2	3	55	✔	
Three Raymond Buildings	London	Up to 3	6	51		
5RB	London	Up to 2	5	28	✔	✔
Red Lion Chambers	London	3	7	88	✔	
Regency Barristers Chambers	Peterborough	0	1	14		
Selborne Chambers	London	1	3	30	✔	
Serjeants' Inn Chambers	London	0	4	61	✔	✔
Serle Court	London	Up to 3	6	64	✔	
South Square	London	Up to 3	5	44	✔	
11 South Square	London	1	2	17	✔	✔
5 St Andrew's Hill	London	2	6	62	✔	✔
St Ives Chambers	Birmingham	Up to 3	12	37	✔	
9 St John Street Chambers	Manchester	2	7	96	✔	✔
18 St John Street Chambers	Manchester	Up to 4	6	74	✔	
St John's Buildings	Manchester	1	10	156	✔	
St John's Chambers	Bristol	2	7	83	✔	
St Mary's Chambers	Nottingham	2	4	32	✔	✔

Chancery	Civil	Commercial	Common	Construction	Crime	Employment	EU	Family	Human rights	IP	Landlord/tenant	Personal injury	Planning	Prof negligence	Public	Revenue	Shipping	TMT
•		•									•			•		•		
																•		
						•						•	•	•				
						•						•	•	•				
•	•	•	•	•	•	•		•			•	•	•	•				
•	•	•	•		•	•			•		•		•	•				
•	•	•			•	•		•			•			•				
					•			•										
•	•	•	•		•	•		•			•	•	•	•	•			
•	•	•	•		•	•		•			•	•	•	•	•			
•	•	•	•	•	•	•		•			•	•	•	•				
•	•	•	•		•	•		•			•	•		•				
•	•	•	•	•	•	•	•	•		•	•	•	•	•				•
	•	•	•	•	•			•			•	•	•	•				•
	•	•	•		•			•			•	•		•				
	•	•	•		•	•		•			•	•	•	•				
	•	•	•		•	•		•			•	•		•				
	•				•			•			•		•	•				
																•		
					•									•				
		•		•				•						•			•	•
								•										
•	•	•			•	•		•			•	•		•				
•		•						•						•				
						•						•	•	•	•	•		
	•						•				•			•				•
					•													
						•		•			•	•		•				
•	•	•										•		•				
	•				•	•		•						•				
•	•	•												•				
•	•	•												•				
										•								•
	•				•			•										
•	•	•	•		•	•		•	•		•	•	•		•			
•	•	•		•	•	•		•		•	•			•				
•	•	•	•		•	•		•	•		•			•				
	•	•			•	•		•	•		•	•		•	•			
•	•	•	•	•	•	•		•		•	•	•		•	•	•		
								•										

Barristers' index

	Location	Pupillages funded	Tenancies in the last three years	Number of tenants	Mini-pupillages offered	Apply through Pupillage Gateway
St Paul's Chambers	Leeds	0	4	44	✔	
St Philips Chambers	Birmingham	Up to 2	20	175	✔	
Staple Inn Chambers	London	1	5	27	✔	
Three Stone	London	1	3	30	✔	
4 Stone Buildings	London	2	5	36	✔	✔
5 Stone Buildings	London	1	4	33	✔	
9 Stone Buildings	London	1	1	24	✔	
Stone Chambers	London	1	5	26	✔	
Stour Chambers	Canterbury	1	2	16	✔	
Sussex Chambers	Eastbourne	1	1	12	✔	
Tanfield Chambers	London	3	6	65	✔	
Fourteen	London	1	3	34	✔	✔
Temple Court Chambers	London	1	6	18		
Temple Garden Chambers	London	2	6	67	✔	✔
3 Temple Gardens	London	Up to 2	7	52	✔	✔
2TG	London	3-4	7	61	✔	✔
Thomas More Chambers	London	1	4	39	✔	✔
Trinity Chambers	Newcastle upon Tyne	1-2	10	71	✔	✔
Trinity Chambers	Essex	0	4	23	✔	
Unity Street Chambers	Bristol	1	1	13		✔
3 Verulam Buildings	London	Up to 3	6	71	✔	✔
Westgate Chambers	Lewes	Up to 2	3	49	✔	
Wilberforce Chambers	London	2	5	66	✔	
15 Winckley Square	Preston	2	3	46	✔	✔
XXIV Old Buildings	London	3	3	42	✔	

Chancery	Civil	Commercial	Common	Construction	Crime	Employment	EU	Family	Human rights	IP	Landlord/tenant	Personal injury	Planning	Prof negligence	Public	Revenue	Shipping	TMT
•	•	•		•	•	•		•			•	•	•	•	•	•		
•	•	•	•	•	•	•		•			•	•	•	•	•	•		
		•	•		•	•		•			•							
•	•	•									•			•		•		
•		•					•											
•											•			•		•		
•	•	•		•		•					•			•	•	•		
		•				•											•	
	•		•			•		•			•	•		•				
	•	•			•	•		•			•	•		•	•			
	•	•				•		•			•	•						
	•					•		•			•		•					
	•	•	•			•			•		•			•	•			
•	•	•	•	•	•	•		•	•		•	•	•	•	•	•		•
•	•	•	•		•	•		•			•	•	•	•	•	•		
	•					•							•					
•	•		•		•	•		•	•	•	•		•	•	•			
	•	•				•								•				•
•	•	•			•	•		•		•	•	•		•		•		•
	•			•	•			•			•	•		•				
•	•	•		•										•				

Pupillage directory

ALBION CHAMBERS Broad Street, Bristol BS1 1DR **Tel:** 0117 927 2144 **Email:** pupillage@albionchambers.co.uk Apply through Pupillage Gateway	A large, friendly, Western Circuit set with five silks and 60 juniors covering crime, family, employment, PI and other common law areas.

PF 0
T 65
T_{L3Y} 3
MP yes

ANGEL CHAMBERS Ethos Building, Kings Road, Swansea SA1 8AS **Tel:** 01792 464623 **Email:** clerks@angelchambers.co.uk Apply through Pupillage Gateway	Busy common law set specialising in crime, family and civil law.

PF 2
T 33
T_{L3Y} 1
MP yes

APEX CHAMBERS Harlech House, 20 Cathedral Road, Cardiff CF11 9LJ **Tel:** 029 2023 2032 **Email:** clerks@apexchambers.net Apply through Pupillage Gateway	

PF 2
T 18
T_{L3Y} 3
MP yes

ATLANTIC CHAMBERS 4-6 Cook Street, Liverpool L2 9QU **Tel:** 0151 236 4421 **Email:** julie@atlanticchambers.co.uk Apply through Pupillage Gateway	Atlantic Chambers have one 12-month common law pupillage and one chancery pupillage available.

PF 2
T 56
T_{L3Y} 2
MP yes

BANK HOUSE CHAMBERS Old Bank House, 3 Hartshead, Sheffield S1 2EL **Tel:** 0114 275 1223 **Email:** w.digby@bankhousechambers.co.uk Apply through Pupillage Gateway	General common law set specialising in crime, family, civil, employment, personal injury and housing.

PF 1
T 40
T_{L3Y} 4
MP yes

2 BEDFORD ROW Chambers of William Clegg QC, London WC1R 4BU **Tel:** 020 7440 8888 **Email:** loakley@2bedfordrow.co.uk Apply through Pupillage Gateway	Criminal set specialising in general, regulatory crime and fraud. Tenants defend and prosecute at all levels.

PF 4
T 78
T_{L3Y} 4
MP yes

7 BEDFORD ROW Chambers of Collingwood Thompson QC, London WC1R 4BS **Tel:** 020 7242 3555 **Email:** pupillage@7br.co.uk **Apply to:** Helen Compton	A leading common law set practising a mix of civil and criminal work both in London and on the Midland Circuit.

PF 2
T 84
T_{L3Y} 4
MP yes

9 BEDFORD ROW London WC1R 4AZ **Tel:** 020 7489 2727 **Email:** clerks@9bedfordrow.co.uk Apply through Pupillage Gateway	A leading set of chambers specialising in all aspects of criminal law. Applications are only accepted via the Pupillage Gateway.

PF 2
T 62
T_{L3Y} 6
MP yes

PF = Pupillages funded / **T** = Tenants / **T**$_{L3Y}$ = Tenancies in last 3 years / **MP** = Mini-pupillages offered

Arden Chambers

20 Bloomsbury Square, London WC1A 2NS
Tel: 020 7242 4244
Email: pupillage@ardenchambers.com
Web: www.ardenchambers.com
f ardenchambers 🐦 ardenchambers

Description of Chambers Arden Chambers dominates social housing law. We are responsible for all the major publications in this area (eg, *Encyclopedia of Housing Law*; *Journal of Housing Law*; *Housing Law Reports*; *Manual of Housing Law*; *Homelessness and Allocations*) and are habitually ranked as the leading set in both *Chambers & Partners* and the *Legal 500*. Our members are consistently found in the higher courts dealing with social housing cases (both for landlords and occupiers).

We are also active (and very well regarded) in related areas. Local government and public law forms a large part of our practice and, again, we produce some of the leading texts (*Encyclopedia of Local Government Finance*; *Judicial Review*). Many members also have significant landlord and tenant/property/planning law practices. We are particularly well-known for our long-leasehold work, with members responsible for two of the leading works (leasehold disputes; leasehold valuation tribunals). A former member of chambers is now the senior president of the First-tier Tribunal (Property Chamber). Other members are active in both the Housing Law Practitioners Association and the Property Bar Association.

The focus on producing authoritative works stems from our history. We were established by Andrew Arden QC and six other current members in 1993 in order to provide a specialist centre of practice for housing and local government law, based on the publications which Andrew authored or edited.

Areas of work Housing, local government, landlord and tenant, leasehold property, property, planning and public law.

Who should apply Those with an interest in our practice areas who are also prepared to devote part of their professional efforts to maintaining our portfolio of publications.

Pupillage programme We offer two pupillages annually for 12 months. Each pupil is allocated a co-ordinator for the whole period.

When and how to apply Please see the chambers' website regarding applying for pupillage (www.ardenchambers.com).

Mini-pupillages Limited number available during each year. Please apply using the application form on our website (www.ardenchambers.com) and send it to mini.pupillage@ardenchambers.com.

Sponsorship/funding Up to £10,000 award for first six months, guaranteed earnings of £10,000 for second six months, subject to clawback (presently subject to review).

Pupillages funded   2
Tenants   32
Tenancies in last 3 yrs   5

Mini-pupillages   yes

Apply to
Check website for details

Applications contact
Mrs Anita Heartfield

Remuneration for pupillage
Up to £10,000 award in first six, guaranteed earnings of £10,000 for second six, subject to clawback (presently subject to review)

arden
chambers

Remember to cite *The Training Contract & Pupillage Handbook* on your application form if you apply to this chambers.

PUPILLAGE DIRECTORY   545

Atkin Chambers

1 Atkin Building, Gray's Inn, London WC1R 5AT
Tel: 020 7404 0102
Email: clerks@atkinchambers.com
Web: www.atkinchambers.com
🐦 atkinchambers

Description of Chambers Atkin Chambers is a leading commercial set specialising in construction, energy and technology disputes and related professional negligence claims. As well as leading in the domestic field, its barristers have a significant international practice spanning Europe, the Middle East, Asia, Africa and the Caribbean. Chambers is consistently ranked as one of London's leading sets and has one of the highest proportion of *Chambers & Partners* rankings per member of chambers. In their first years of practice, new members may expect earning potential equivalent to peers at the largest commercial sets.

Areas of work Atkin Chambers is a leader in its field: construction and technology law. Its barristers are regularly instructed to advise and act as advocates in relation to some of the largest and most complex international and domestic disputes in their field of expertise. Members of Atkin Chambers have been involved in many of the most high-profile domestic disputes in the fields of construction, technology, power, energy, computers and telecommunications of recent years, both in court and arbitration. Examples include the Shard, Wembley Stadium, Heathrow T5, Crossrail, London Underground as well as major oil and gas and renewable energy projects. Our barristers are also regularly involved in high-value construction, energy and infrastructure projects around the globe and regularly appear at international arbitrations seated in locations such as the Gulf States, Hong Kong and Singapore. Significant opportunities for international travel and practice exist at the junior end of chambers.

Who should apply Applicants for pupillage should have a first-class degree or a good 2.1 degree. Postgraduate qualifications are viewed favourably but are not essential. Applications from non-law graduates are welcomed. Pre-existing knowledge of construction law is not required.

Pupillage programme Atkin Chambers takes recruitment to pupillage and tenancy extremely seriously. The market-leading pupillage award (£72,500 for 2018-2019) reflects this. The pupillage year is highly structured and provides all of the Bar Council's training requirements along with the additional training chambers considers is necessary for successful entry into the high-quality commercial work of its practice. Chambers provides its own advocacy training and assessment in addition to that provided by the Inns of Court. Full and up-to-date details of the structure and goals of chambers' pupillage training programme may be reviewed on our website. Chambers is committed to applying equal opportunities good practice.

When and how to apply Applications for the year starting in October 2019 open on Saturday 30 September 2017 and close at midnight on Wednesday 13 December 2017. Applications should be made by sending a CV and covering letter to pupillage@atkinchambers.com.

Mini-pupillages Up to 10 mini-pupillages are offered each year. Please refer to our website for further details of the mini-pupillage programme and application dates.

Sponsorship/funding Two fully funded pupillages of £72,500 per pupil for 12 months. A drawdown of up to £25,000 is available during the BPTC year.

Pupillages funded	2
Tenants	44
Tenancies in last 3 yrs	3
Mini-pupillages	yes
Apply via website	
Remuneration for pupillage	£72,500
Minimum qualifications	2.1 degree

Atkin Chambers Barristers

Blackstone Chambers

Blackstone House, Temple, London EC4Y 9BW
Tel: 020 7583 1770
Email: pupillage@blackstonechambers.com
Web: www.blackstonechambers.com

Description of Chambers Chambers occupies large and modern premises in the Temple.

Areas of work Blackstone Chambers' formidable strengths lie in its principal areas of practice: commercial, employment, EU, public law, human rights and public international law. The commercial law work includes financial/business law, international trade, conflicts, sport, media and entertainment, intellectual property and professional negligence. Public law incorporates judicial review, acting both for and against central and local government agencies and other regulatory authorities. It also covers all areas affected by the impact of human rights and other aspects of administrative law. All aspects of employment law, including discrimination, are covered by chambers' extensive employment law practice, and chambers' EU work permeates practices across the board. Chambers recognises the increasingly important role which mediation has to play in dispute resolution.

Who should apply Chambers looks for articulate and intelligent applicants who are able to work under pressure and demonstrate high intellectual ability. Successful candidates usually have a 2.1 honours degree at least, although not necessarily in law.

Pupillage programme Chambers offers four 12-month pupillages to those wishing to practise full time at the Bar, normally commencing in September each year. Pupillage is divided into four sections and every effort is made to ensure pupils receive a broad training. The environment is a friendly one; pupils attend an induction week introducing them to the chambers' working environment. Chambers prefers to recruit new tenants from pupils wherever possible. Chambers is a member of the Pupillage Gateway.

When and how to apply Pupillage applications should be made via the Pupillage Gateway. Please refer to the Gateway for dates.

Mini-pupillages Assessed mini-pupillages are an essential part of our pupillage recruitment process and no pupillage will be offered at Blackstone Chambers unless the applicant has undertaken an assessed mini-pupillage. Applications for mini-pupillage are accepted from 1 September 2017 until the Pupillage Gateway opens in 2018. We strongly recommend that applications be made early in our mini-pupillage application window. Applications are preferred in the year before pupillage commences.

Sponsorship/funding Awards of £65,000 per annum are available. A partial draw-down of up to £18,500 is available in the BPTC year. As chambers insists on an assessed mini-pupillage as part of the overall pupillage recruitment process, financial assistance is offered either in respect of out of pocket travelling or accommodation expenses incurred in attending the mini-pupillage, up to a maximum of £250 per pupil.

Pupillages funded	4
Tenants	107
Tenancies in last 3 yrs	10
Mini-pupillages	yes

Apply through Pupillage Gateway

Remuneration for pupillage
£65,000

Minimum qualifications
2.1 degree

Blackstone CHAMBERS

25 BEDFORD ROW 25 Bedford Row, London WC1R 4HD **Tel:** 020 7067 1500 **Email:** clerks@25bedfordrow.com Apply through Pupillage Gateway	We are a leading criminal set specialising in defence work. We pride ourselves on maintaining the highest standards of professionalism, integrity and commitment.	PF 3 T 70 T_{L3Y} 7 MP yes
36 BEDFORD ROW 36 Bedford Row, London WC1R 4JH **Tel:** 020 7421 8000 Apply through Pupillage Gateway	36 Bedford Row will be offering two specialist pupillages: one crime and one civil to begin in October 2018. The pupillages will be offered through Pupillage Gateway.	PF 2 T 103 T_{L3Y} 3 MP yes
42 BEDFORD ROW Bedford Row, London WC1R 4LL **Tel:** 020 7831 0222 **Email:** clerks@42br.com Apply through Pupillage Gateway		PF 2 T 103 T_{L3Y} 7 MP yes
29 BEDFORD ROW CHAMBERS 29 Bedford Row, London WC1R 4HE **Tel:** 020 7404 1044 **Email:** clerks@29br.co.uk Apply through Pupillage Gateway	29BR is best known for matrimonial finance work. However, this reputation masks the reality that it boasts star performers across the range of family law.	PF 2 T 55 T_{L3Y} 4 MP yes
4 BREAMS BUILDINGS Chancery Lane, London EC4A 1HP **Tel:** 020 7092 1900 **Email:** clerks@4bb.co.uk Apply through Pupillage Gateway	4BB is a criminal set. Members prosecute and defend across the whole range of criminal cases, including murder, fraud, terrorist cases, and serious sexual offences.	PF 4 T 67 T_{L3Y} 6 MP yes
ONE BRICK COURT Chambers of Sir Edward Garnier QC, Temple, London EC4Y 9BY **Tel:** 020 7353 8845 **Email:** clerks@onebrickcourt.com Apply through Pupillage Gateway	Leading specialists in media and information law, including defamation, privacy, breach of confidence, data protection, reporting restrictions, contempt, FOI, harassment and other media-related work.	PF Up to 2 T 19 T_{L3Y} 2 MP yes
4 BRICK COURT Ground Floor, Temple, London EC4Y 9AD **Tel:** 020 7832 3200 **Email:** clerks@4bc.co.uk Apply through Pupillage Gateway	Chambers is a leading set in all aspects of family law, with particular regard to child protection issues. Regularly instructed on behalf of local authorities, guardians and parents.	PF 0 T 36 T_{L3Y} 6 MP yes
BRICK COURT CHAMBERS 7-8 Essex Street, London WC2R 3LD **Tel:** 020 7379 3550 **Email:** lyana.peniston@brickcourt.co.uk Apply through Pupillage Gateway	Brick Court Chambers is a leading set with particular expertise in commercial, EU, competition and public law. We normally offer four pupillages each year.	PF Normally 4 T 86 T_{L3Y} 7 MP yes

PF = Pupillages funded / **T** = Tenants / **T_{L3Y}** = Tenancies in last 3 years / **MP** = Mini-pupillages offered

BROADWAY HOUSE CHAMBERS 9 Bank Street, Bradford BD1 1TW **Tel:** 01274 722560 **Email:** cm@broadwayhouse.co.uk Apply through Pupillage Gateway	A progressive common law set of chambers with premises in both the centre of Leeds and Bradford.	PF 1 T 51 TL3Y 6 MP yes
CARMELITE CHAMBERS 9 Carmelite Street, London EC4Y 0DR **Tel:** 020 7936 6300 **Email:** oosullivan@carmelitechambers.co.uk **Apply to:** Miss Orla O'Sullivan	An established set specialising in defence work. Pupils will have the opportunity both to learn and to put that learning into practice as advocates.	PF 2 T 65 TL3Y 6 MP yes
1 CHANCERY LANE 1 Chancery Lane, London WC2A 1LF **Tel:** 020 7092 2900 **Email:** jfensham@1chancerylane.com **Apply to:** Ms Jenny Fensham	Personal injury, professional negligence and clinical negligence practice offering pupils an opportunity to develop wide-ranging litigation skills. Also property, travel and human rights.	PF 2 T 44 TL3Y 2 MP yes
CHARTER CHAMBERS 33 John Street, London WC1N 2AT **Tel:** 020 7618 4400 **Email:** clerks@charterchambers.com	Work: mainly criminal (prosecution and defence), public, prison law, immigration, family, employment. Second six pupils conduct a substantial amount of work in their own right.	PF 0 T 54 TL3Y 8 MP yes
CHARTLANDS CHAMBERS 3 St Giles Terrace, Northampton NN1 2BN **Tel:** 01604 603322 **Email:** enquiries@chartlands-chambers.co.uk **Apply to:** Mr Andrew Davies	Common law chambers. Principal field: family law. Also: immigration and general civil litigation.	PF 1 T 13 TL3Y 2 MP yes
CITADEL CHAMBERS 190 Corporation Street, Birmingham B4 6QD **Tel:** 0121 233 8500 **Email:** clerks@citadelchambers.com **Apply to:** The Pupillage Committee Secretary	Chambers is a large criminal set. Chambers also undertakes some licensing, common law and other specialist work. Pupillages are focused completely on crime.	PF 2 T 56 TL3Y 3 MP yes
CLOISTERS 1 Pump Court, Temple, London EC4Y 7AA **Tel:** 020 7827 4000 **Email:** pupillage@cloisters.com Apply through Pupillage Gateway	Informal, award-winning chambers at the cutting edge of employment, PI, clinical negligence, human rights, public law, commercial, media and sports law.	PF 2 T 51 TL3Y 6 MP yes
12 COLLEGE PLACE Southampton SO15 2FE **Tel:** 023 8032 0320 **Email:** clerks@12cp.co.uk Apply through Pupillage Gateway	A medium-sized, multi-disciplinary set which prides itself on being friendly, approachable and providing a high quality service. Application deadline is noon on 28 February 2018.	PF 1-2 T 26 TL3Y 2 MP yes

PF = Pupillages funded / **T** = Tenants / **TL3Y** = Tenancies in last 3 years / **MP** = Mini-pupillages offered

Crown Office Chambers

2 Crown Office Row, Temple, London EC4Y 7HJ
Tel: 020 7797 8100
Email: clerks@crownofficechambers.com
Web: www.crownofficechambers.com

Description of Chambers Crown Office Chambers is one of the foremost sets of chambers specialising in civil common law work. Formed by the merger of One Paper Buildings and Two Crown Office Row, both long established sets with many leading and highly-regarded practitioners, we are now a set of 98 members, including 23 silks. We have high-calibre teams of counsel in a number of areas of work, ranging from county court disputes to large and complex litigation, and have state-of-the-art facilities.

Areas of work A wide range of common law and commercial work, with particular specialisms in construction, commercial contracts, insurance and reinsurance, personal injury, health and safety, product liability, professional negligence and clinical negligence.

Who should apply The members of Crown Office Chambers pride themselves on their professionalism, an astute and business-orientated awareness of the practical needs of solicitors and clients, combined with an approachable and 'unstuffy' attitude to their work. We look for the same in our pupils, all of whom are regarded as having strong tenancy potential. Pupils are welcomed as an integral part of chambers from the moment they arrive, and are expected to display the motivation, dedication and intelligence which are the hallmarks of a first-class barrister. Academically, we look for a first or upper second-class honours degree (not necessarily in law), and a flair for the oral and written presentation of complex legal arguments. You will be expected to work hard and to show strong commitment to your work, but in a friendly and relaxed chambers environment.

Pupillage programme Pupils sit with two pupil supervisors in their first six months, and one in their second, but are likely to work with a number of different members of chambers practising in different fields of work over the course of the year. They appear in court regularly during their second six, generally handling applications and small trials in the county courts, affording ample opportunity to develop advocacy skills. Chambers also organises a series of advocacy training sessions.

When and how to apply Apply by midnight on 6 February 2018, to begin October 2019 on chambers' application form, downloadable from the chambers' website at www.crownofficechambers.com.

Mini-pupillages Limited number of mini-pupillages available in selected weeks throughout the year. Online form downloadable from chambers' website.

Sponsorship/funding Up to three pupillages offered per year, each with an award of £65,000 (£55,000 plus £10,000 guaranteed earnings in your second six), part of which may be forwarded during the BPTC year.

Pupillages funded	Up to 3
Tenants	98
Tenancies in last 3 yrs	8
Mini-pupillages	yes
Apply via website	
Remuneration for pupillage	£65,000 (£55,000 plus £10,000 guaranteed earnings)
Minimum qualifications	2.1 degree or equivalent

CROWN
OFFICE
CHAMBERS

One Crown Office Row

Temple, London EC4Y 7HH
Tel: 020 7797 7500
Email: mail@1cor.com
Web: www.1cor.com
🐦 1crownofficerow

Description of Chambers This is a long-established and leading civil set of 66 members including 23 silks. We are regularly rated in the top 30 sets in England. Indicators of excellence are the high number of members on the Attorney General's panels, the number of QCs and the high number of former members now in the senior judiciary. We also run the highly acclaimed UK human rights blog: ukhumanrightsblog.com.

Areas of work Our members practise in a wide range of legal specialisms and have been recognised as leading and outstanding practitioners in areas including: clinical negligence; personal injury; professional negligence; professional discipline; inquests; public inquiries; public and administrative law; mediation; human rights; environmental law; costs; employment and equality; immigration and asylum; tax; and cyber. We also have many members with successful practices in multi-party actions, technology and construction and sports law. *Chambers & Partners* has described the set as follows: "Its top-flight performers amass between them an enviable bank of knowledge of medical and regulatory issues, all of which is seasoned with efficient case management and excellent responsiveness. It also proves surprisingly versatile. Experts in environment, personal injury, civil liberties and general public law abound at an outfit that forms a whole that is very much greater than the sum of its parts."

Who should apply Candidates should have a keen interest in the areas of work in which members practise. Academic prowess is important, with a normal requirement of a first or upper second class degree. A sound grounding in legal principle is expected. Chambers retains a strong reputation for the advocacy skills of its members and demonstration of an aptitude for advocacy is helpful. This may be shown in a number of ways, for instance mooting, debating and work in the voluntary legal services sector. Work at the Bar demands high levels of commitment and we look for signs that applicants have that quality by examining, for example, whether they have done mini-pupillages or in some other way established that the Bar, with all its challenges and hurdles, is for them.

Pupillage programme We offer up to two 12-month pupillages. Each pupillage is split between three pupil supervisors. Pupils can expect to gain a wide experience of court and paperwork and have opportunities to help and accompany other members of chambers (including silks) on interesting cases.

When and how to apply Chambers is a member of the centralised pupillage application system, Pupillage Gateway – all details are at www.pupillagegateway.com. Full details of the selection process are at www.1cor.com.

Mini-pupillages We offer places for 15 mini-pupils during June and July each year with applications closing at the end of February. Applications should be addressed to Owain Thomas. We also run an equality and diversity mini-pupillage scheme. Full details are at www.1cor.com/recruitment.

Sponsorship/funding Each pupil receives an annual award of £55,000 paid as a £27,500 grant in the first six months and as £27,500 of guaranteed earnings in the second six. We also fund all necessary training courses for pupils. Pupils may draw down up to 20% of the award in advance to assist in funding their Bar Professional Training Course.

Pupillages funded	2
Tenants	66
Tenancies in last 3 yrs	6
Mini-pupillages	yes

Apply through Pupillage Gateway

Remuneration for pupillage
£55,000

Minimum qualifications
2.1 degree

1 CROWN OFFICE ROW

CORAM CHAMBERS 9-11 Fulwood Place, London WC1V 6HG **Tel:** 020 7092 3700 **Email:** clerks@coramchambers.co.uk Apply through Pupillage Gateway	Members of Coram Chambers act in leading cases in children's disputes in both public and private law and matrimonial finance.	PF 2 T 66 T_{L3Y} 4 MP yes
CORNERSTONE BARRISTERS 2-3 Gray's Inn Square, London WC1R 5JH **Tel:** 020 7242 4986 **Email:** cornerstone@cornerstonebarristers.com Apply through Pupillage Gateway	Cornerstone, a well established, leading set with a friendly, flexible approach, is committed to the care and provision of an excellent legal service to our clients.	PF 2 T 50 T_{L3Y} 5 MP yes
CORNWALL STREET CHAMBERS 85-87 Cornwall Street, Birmingham B3 3BY **Tel:** 0121 233 7500 **Email:** clerks@cornwallstreet.co.uk **Apply to:** Mr Timothy Clarke	Principally crime, family and common law with specialists in other fields. Annexes in Oxford and Shrewsbury.	PF Up to 2 T 67 T_{L3Y} 2 MP no
CRIMINAL DEFENCE SOLICITORS 11-15 St Mary at Hill, Lower Ground, London EC3R 8EE **Tel:** 020 7353 7000 **Email:** pupillagecommittee@criminaldefence.co.uk Apply through Pupillage Gateway	Criminal Defence Solicitors is a friendly and expanding firm. We are a predominantly legal aid practice specialising in criminal law.	PF 1 T 3 T_{L3Y} 2 MP yes
CROWN OFFICE ROW CHAMBERS Blenheim House, 119 Church Street, Brighton BN1 1UD **Tel:** 01273 625625 **Email:** clerks@1cor.com **Apply to:** The Pupillage Committee	A long-established, busy set committed to expansion in Sussex. Up to two 12-month pupillages available each year.	PF 2 T 47 T_{L3Y} 3 MP yes
CROWN PROSECUTION SERVICE CPS CPS HQ - Rose Court, 2 Southwark Bridge, London SE1 9HS **Tel:** 020 3357 0899 **Email:** strategic.resourcing@cps.gsi.gov.uk **Apply to:** Mr Martin McKay-Smith	The CPS offers positions throughout England and Wales for pupil barristers and trainee solicitors. Permanent crown prosecutor opportunities are available upon successful qualification.	PF 30 T 600 T_{L3Y} 60 MP no
DEANS COURT CHAMBERS 24 St John Street, Manchester M3 4DF **Tel:** 0161 214 6000 **Email:** clerks@deanscourt.co.uk Apply through Pupillage Gateway	A leading set of chambers on the Northern Circuit. 11 silks. Excellent facilities. Well-funded pupillages with a view to a tenancy.	PF 2 T 75 T_{L3Y} 7 MP yes
DERE STREET CHAMBERS 33 Broad Chare, Newcastle upon Tyne NE1 3DQ **Tel:** 08443351551 **Email:** clerks@derestreet.co.uk Apply through Pupillage Gateway	A broad-based pupillage with experience of differing areas of chambers' practice. Chambers has premises in both York and Newcastle.	PF 2 T 90 T_{L3Y} 6 MP yes

PF = Pupillages funded / **T** = Tenants / **T**L3Y = Tenancies in last 3 years / **MP** = Mini-pupillages offered

DEVEREUX
Queen Elizabeth Building, Temple, London
EC4Y 9BS
Tel: 020 7353 7534
Email: pupillage@devchambers.co.uk
Apply through Pupillage Gateway

Devereux is one of the UK's top civil and commercial sets leading in commercial, employment, personal injury/clinical negligence, insurance, professional negligence, tax and telecommunications law.

PF	2
T	50
TL3Y	5
MP	yes

DOUGHTY STREET CHAMBERS
53-54 Doughty Street, London WC1N 2LS
Tel: 020 7404 1313
Email: enquiries@doughtystreet.co.uk
Apply through Pupillage Gateway

While at the forefront of many cutting-edge domestic and international human rights cases, we operate across a whole range of different areas of law.

PF	2
T	125
TL3Y	5
MP	yes

2 DR JOHNSON'S BUILDINGS
Temple, London EC4Y 7AY
Tel: 020 7936 2613
Email: pupillage@2drj.com
Apply to: Mr Daniel Benjamin

A medium-sized busy and friendly set. 70% crime, 30% family and civil. Up to two funded 12-month pupillages.

PF	Up to 2
T	46
TL3Y	5
MP	yes

THREE DR JOHNSON'S BUILDINGS
Temple, London EC4Y 7BA
Tel: 020 7353 4854
Email: clerks@3djb.co.uk
Apply to: Ms Lisa Peacock

We are a well established family and civil law set, providing a first-class professional service. Chambers does not plan to offer a pupillage in the forthcoming year.

PF	0
T	33
TL3Y	1
MP	yes

DRYSTONE CHAMBERS
35 Bedford Row, Holborn, London WC1R 4JH
Tel: 020 7404 1881
Email: pupillage@drystone.com
Apply to: The Pupillage Committee

Pupils receive expert training and supervision in general crime, regulatory and extradition law in this leading criminal law set.

PF	2-3
T	85
TL3Y	6
MP	yes

EAST ANGLIAN CHAMBERS
5 Museum Street, Ipswich IP1 1HQ
Tel: 01473 214481
Email: ymay@ealaw.co.uk
Apply to: Mrs Yvonne May

East Anglian Chambers based at three sites, Ipswich, Norwich and Chelmsford, offering a wide range of opportunities.

PF	Up to 2
T	43
TL3Y	4
MP	yes

ERSKINE CHAMBERS
33 Chancery Lane, London WC2A 1EN
Tel: 020 7242 5532
Email: clerks@erskinechambers.com
Apply to: Mr Matthew Parfitt

Erskine Chambers specialises in company law, insolvency and related fields. Our policy is one of expansion and we aim to recruit tenants from our pupils.

PF	Up to 2
T	30
TL3Y	1
MP	yes

39 ESSEX CHAMBERS
81 Chancery Lane, London WC2A 1DD
Tel: 020 7832 1111
Email: clerks@39essex.com
Apply through Pupillage Gateway

Long established civil set with 128 members, including 43 QCs. Chambers has several members on each of the Attorney General's A, B and C panels for civil litigation. Chambers prides itself on its friendly and professional atmosphere.

PF	Up to 3
T	128
TL3Y	7
MP	yes

PF = Pupillages funded / **T** = Tenants / **TL3Y** = Tenancies in last 3 years / **MP** = Mini-pupillages offered

Enterprise Chambers

9 Old Square, Lincoln's Inn, London WC2A 3SR
Tel: 020 7405 9471
Email: london@enterprisechambers.com
Web: www.enterprisechambers.com

Description of Chambers Enterprise Chambers is ranked among the leading sets at the chancery commercial bar. Chambers has a strong bias towards litigation and all of its barristers tend to have a firmly court-centred practice. It is a long-established but forward thinking set, with 29 members in London (former members including Lord Millett, Lord Cross, Lord Justice Balcombe and Mr Justice Mann) and equally thriving branches in Leeds and Newcastle. Chambers values the ability of its members to approach problems in a manner which is both intellectually rigorous and practically grounded and it prides itself on its down-to-earth and client-friendly reputation.

Areas of work Insolvency and company, including: all aspects of the insolvency of companies, partnerships and individuals; directors' duties; fraudulent and wrongful trading and other misconduct; international and cross-border insolvency; and shareholders' disputes. Property, including: both real property law and landlord and tenant practice. The former covers issues arising from the sale of land, land registration, mortgages, easements, adverse possession and property fraud, amongst others. The latter covers issues arising from leases of all types, whether business, agricultural or social housing tenancies. Commercial, including: general contractual disputes and issues arising from the sale of goods, banking, guarantees, consumer credit, business finance, carriage of goods, civil fraud, professional negligence, regulatory matters, and private international law. Equitable remedies, covering: injunctions (including freezing injunctions and search orders), specific performance, and issues arising from constructive trusts, fiduciary duties, fraud and tracing, restitution, estoppel, rectification and rescission.

Who should apply Applications are invited from candidates with a minimum 2.1 degree or equivalent. We seek the best candidates regardless of their background. We always aim to recruit our starter junior tenants from our pupils and have been delighted to maintain a 100% retention rate for our pupils over at least the last eight years, and to then support them in developing thriving junior practices. We therefore look to offer pupillage to those candidates who have the potential to succeed as tenants in chambers.

Pupillage programme Chambers offers one 12-month pupillage in London each year (recruitment for our Leeds and Newcastle branches is conducted separately). Pupils have a minimum of four supervisors and are encouraged to work for other members of chambers to give them the best exposure to all areas of chambers' practice. Our goal is to make pupillage as stimulating and enjoyable as possible and to prepare pupils for a successful practice at the Bar. To that end, pupils in their second six are offered real advocacy experience in court, at an appropriate level, with the support of chambers.

When and how to apply Through the Pupillage Gateway. Further information about the selection process is available on our website.

Mini-pupillages Please see our website to apply for mini-pupillage.

Sponsorship/funding The pupillage award for October 2017 – September 2018 is £55,000. A proportion of the award as agreed with Chambers may be drawndown in advance.

Pupillages funded	1
Tenants	41
Tenancies in last 3 yrs	3
Mini-pupillages	yes

Apply through Pupillage Gateway

Remuneration for pupillage
£55,000 for 2017

Minimum qualifications
2.1 degree or equivalent

Enterprise Chambers
London Leeds Newcastle

Remember to cite *The Training Contract & Pupillage Handbook* on your application form if you apply to this chambers.

ONE ESSEX COURT One Essex Court, Temple, London EC4Y 9AR **Tel:** 020 7583 2000 **Email:** clerks@oeclaw.co.uk Apply through Pupillage Gateway	One Essex Court ordinarily offers four commercial and one intellectual property pupillage.	PF 5 T 98 T_{L3Y} 11 MP yes
5 ESSEX COURT 5 Essex Court, Temple, London EC4Y 9AH **Tel:** 020 7410 2000 **Email:** clerks@5essexcourt.co.uk Apply through Pupillage Gateway	Leading chambers specialising in public law, human rights, police law, personal injury and employment.	PF Up to 2 T 42 T_{L3Y} 3 MP yes
ESSEX COURT CHAMBERS 24 Lincoln's Inn Fields, London WC2A 3EG **Tel:** 020 7813 8000 **Email:** pupillage@essexcourt.net Apply through Pupillage Gateway	Our members offer advisory and advocacy expertise on disputes relating to all aspects of business and commerce, both domestic and international.	PF Up to 4 T 90 T_{L3Y} 7 MP yes
23 ESSEX STREET 23 Essex Street, London WC2R 3AA **Tel:** 020 7413 0353 **Email:** clerks@23es.com **Apply to:** Ms Kate Lumsdon	23 Essex Street is a modern, innovative, approachable set of barristers, with a leading reputation in the fields of crime, fraud and a range of regulatory and disciplinary matters.	PF 1 T 103 T_{L3Y} 9 MP yes
EXCHANGE CHAMBERS One Derby Square, Liverpool L2 9XX **Tel:** 0845 300 7747 **Email:** campbell@exchangechambers.co.uk **Apply to:** Miss Chantal Campbell	Exchange Chambers is a leading set with offices in Manchester, Liverpool and Leeds.	PF 1-2 T 156 T_{L3Y} 5 MP yes
FARRAR'S BUILDING Temple, London EC4Y 7BD **Tel:** 020 7583 9241 **Email:** chambers@farrarsbuilding.co.uk Apply through Pupillage Gateway	Farrar's Building is a leading set of chambers situated in the heart of the Temple, specialising in personal injury, employment, company and commercial work.	PF 2 T 45 T_{L3Y} 4 MP yes
FENNERS CHAMBERS 3 Madingley Road, Cambridge CB3 0EE **Tel:** 01223 368761 **Email:** pupillage@fennerschambers.com **Apply to:** Miss Caroline Allison	Fenners is a common law set offering a varied and well-rounded pupillage affording pupils the opportunity to experience different areas of law prior to specialisation.	PF Up to 2 T 50 T_{L3Y} 2 MP yes
FIELD COURT CHAMBERS 5 Field Court, Gray's Inn, London WC1R 5EF **Tel:** 020 7405 6114 **Email:** pupillage16@fieldcourt.co.uk **Apply to:** The Training and Pupillage Committee	Chambers is an established, highly regarded and friendly set with three broad practice areas: civil, family and public. Members are recommended in UK *Legal 500*.	PF Up to 2 T 60 T_{L3Y} 3 MP yes

PF = Pupillages funded / **T** = Tenants / **T**L3Y = Tenancies in last 3 years / **MP** = Mini-pupillages offered

Falcon Chambers

Falcon Court, London EC4Y 1AA
Tel: 020 7353 2484
Email: pupillage@falcon-chambers.com
Web: www.falcon-chambers.com

Description of Chambers Falcon Chambers are recognised by the legal directories, solicitors and clients as the leading property chambers. Many of the major practitioner texts relating to property law are written by our members. We place a lot of importance on being a friendly, closely integrated group of colleagues. Many former members of chambers have become judges, including Lord Neuberger of Abbotsbury, President of The Supreme Court, Lord Justice Lewison and Mr Justice Morgan.

Areas of work Members of chambers are heavily involved in litigation in the real property, landlord and tenant and property-related fields, including cases involving insolvency, trusts, banking, revenue, professional negligence, environmental and treasury work. We are involved in both contentious and non-contentious work.

Who should apply Applications are welcome from all who have or expect to achieve a 2.1 or first in their degree, including students who have not yet completed a first degree, or non-law students who have not yet completed a GDL. The successful applicant will absorb complex information and identify essential points and practical solutions quickly; communicate clearly, concisely and persuasively, both orally and in writing; and remain calm, objective and confident while working under pressure.

Pupillage programme Our current policy is to offer up to two pupillages each year, each of which is for 12 months. Pupils are allocated to a different pupil supervisor every three months in order to see a range of work and practices. We aim to give our pupils a good grounding in advocacy, in addition to the courses offered by the Inns, by providing structured advocacy training throughout the year. Few of our applicants will have studied our speciality in any depth, and therefore we provide an intensive course in landlord and tenant law at Falcon Chambers usually held in the last week of September.

When and how to apply Falcon Chambers does not receive applications through the Pupillage Gateway. Applications should be made on chambers' application form which is available from the website from the beginning of December 2017 for pupillages starting in October 2019. The closing date is 3 January 2018 and interviews are held in January and February. More details are available on our website.

Mini-pupillages Our mini-pupillages are not assessed, and there is no requirement that you come to chambers on a mini-pupillage before you apply for a pupillage. We do, however, encourage interested candidates to visit us for a few days to experience life at Falcon Chambers. We find that those who do so invariably apply to us for pupillage. The programme lasts for three days (usually Tuesday to Thursday), during which time we try to ensure that you will spend some time in court, sit in on a conference with clients and also sample some paperwork. We hold three mini-pupillage sessions each year, full details along with dates, when to apply and the application form are all available on our website.

Sponsorship/funding Our pupillage award is up to £60,000 per pupil (for those starting in October 2019), of which up to £20,000 is available for drawdown during the BPTC year. In addition, in their second six months, pupils can expect to earn some additional income from their own work. Successful pupils who become junior tenants are usually fully employed doing their own work shortly after being taken on.

Pupillages funded	Up to 2
Tenants	41
Tenancies in last 3 yrs	5
Mini-pupillages	yes
Apply via website	
Remuneration for pupillage	Up to £60,000
Minimum qualifications	2.1 degree

Falcon Chambers

Francis Taylor Building

Inner Temple, London EC4Y 7BY
Tel: 020 7353 8415
Email: clerks@ftbchambers.co.uk
Web: www.ftbchambers.co.uk
🐦 ftb_pupillage

Description of Chambers Francis Taylor Building's (FTB) reputation for excellence is long-standing and we are consistently featured in the legal directories for our expertise and leading role in planning, land valuation, infrastructure, environmental, public law, licensing and regulatory law. Members of chambers undertake specialist advisory work and regularly appear in courts at all levels in this country and abroad, including specialist tribunals and public inquiries. From head of chambers to the most junior tenant, the workload is wide and varied. There are 25 Queen's Counsel in chambers and most junior tenants find themselves working on cases as junior to a silk on a fairly regular basis.

Areas of work As part of our specialist practice, chambers also undertakes work connected with transport and works schemes, utilities, highways, energy, rating, religious liberty and ecclesiastical, heritage and conservation, common land and village greens, education, minerals, statutory nuisance and regulation, health and safety, compulsory purchase and compensation, easements and covenants, mediation, advertisements, employment and consumer law among other areas of related work.

Who should apply Prospective pupils should demonstrate a high intellectual ability and have a degree of at least upper second level. They should have an interest in the fields, in which chambers practises.

Pupillage programme Three pupil supervisors – four months each.

What will you do as a pupil? The first six months – Pupils usually sit in their pupil-supervisors' rooms and experience all aspects of their professional lives. During the first six months pupils read their pupil-supervisors' instructions and papers, research relevant law, attempt their own draft pleadings and opinions for discussion, and attend with them at Court and in conference with solicitors and lay clients. Chambers have an in house training programme for pupils which includes seminars in practice areas and advocacy exercises. The second six months – Pupils are expected to undertake a certain amount of written work for, and attend at court with, other members of chambers as well as their pupil-supervisors. In recent years second-six pupils have also been briefed to appear in a variety of courts and tribunals, including the High Court, County Court and planning inquiries. Pro bono work for FRU, Law For All, the Bar Pro Bono Unit and others is actively encouraged.

What are the prospects of tenancy? Since 2008, chambers has recruited 16 junior tenants. There can, of course, be no guarantee that a new tenant will be recruited from each new year's intake. Chambers recognises its responsibility to those who are not offered a tenancy and does its best to ensure that suitable positions are found elsewhere. In recent years, some of its former pupils have obtained tenancies in other chambers; others have joined major firms of solicitors or worked as lawyers in central and local government.

When and how to apply Apply by 31 January 2018 to begin October 2019. Chambers' application form available on the website or by application to Ms Saira Kabir Sheikh QC.

Mini-pupillages Apply to Mr Charles Streeten.

Sponsorship/funding Two awards of not less than £60,000. A drawdown of up to £15,000 available for BPTC.

Pupillages funded	2
Tenants	56
Tenancies in last 3 yrs	5
Mini-pupillages	yes
Apply via website	
Remuneration for pupillage	Not less than £60,000
Minimum qualifications	2.1 degree

ftb

Francis Taylor Building

187 FLEET STREET 187 Fleet Street, London EC4A 2AT **Tel:** 020 7430 7430 **Email:** chambers@187fleetstreet.com Apply through Pupillage Gateway	A high-profile chambers whose members defend and prosecute in all areas of criminal and regulatory law (especially serious crime and corporate fraud).	PF 1-2 T 75 T_{L3Y} 8 MP yes
FOUNDRY CHAMBERS Quality House, 5-9 Quality Court, Chancery Lane, London WC2A 1HP **Tel:** 020 7400 1800 **Email:** clerks@foundrychambers.com Apply through Pupillage Gateway	Criminal defence and prosecution (inc CPS, SFO, HMRC); fraud and financial regulation; local authority; business regulation; extradition; immigration; professional discipline; and tax litigation.	PF 2 T 56 T_{L3Y} 7 MP yes
FOUNTAIN COURT CHAMBERS Temple, London EC4Y 9DH **Tel:** 020 7583 3335 **Email:** lucy@fountaincourt.co.uk Apply through Pupillage Gateway	A leading set of chambers specialising in commercial work. Up to four pupillages offered through the Pupillage Gateway. Mini-pupillages are available, though not a requirement for 2018 Gateway round.	PF Up to 4 T 81 T_{L3Y} 7 MP yes
1 GARDEN COURT Ground Floor, Temple, London EC4Y 9BJ **Tel:** 020 7797 7900 **Email:** clerks@1gc.com Apply through Pupillage Gateway	1 Garden Court is one of the foremost family law chambers in London and is consistently recognised as a leading specialist in the legal directories.	PF 2 T 74 T_{L3Y} 5 MP yes
GARDEN COURT CHAMBERS 57-60 Lincoln's Inn Fields, London WC2A 3LJ **Tel:** 020 7993 7600 **Email:** info@gclaw.co.uk Apply through Pupillage Gateway	A civil liberties chambers specialising in human rights; family; immigration; crime; housing and civil including employment; gypsy/traveller; inquests; prison; and claims against the police/public authorities.	PF 4 T 182 T_{L3Y} 27 MP yes
GOLDSMITH CHAMBERS Chambers of Anthony Metzer QC, Goldsmith Building, Temple, London EC4Y 7BL **Tel:** 020 7353 6802 **Email:** v.wilson@goldsmithchambers.com Apply through Pupillage Gateway	Argent Chambers has merged with Goldsmith Chambers as of 6 May.	PF 2 T 73 T_{L3Y} 8 MP yes
GOUGH SQUARE CHAMBERS 6-7 Gough Square, London EC4A 3DE **Tel:** 020 7353 0924 **Email:** gsc@goughsq.co.uk Apply through Pupillage Gateway	Gough Square Chambers is a small and friendly set that has developed a leading reputation in consumer, regulatory and financial work.	PF 1 T 25 T_{L3Y} 2 MP yes
4-5 GRAY'S INN SQUARE Gray's Inn, London WC1R 5AH **Tel:** 020 7404 5252 **Email:** clerks@4-5.co.uk	A modern set of chambers that specialises in public law and human rights, planning and environmental law, commercial, sports, intellectual property, education and employment.	PF 1 T 33 T_{L3Y} 4 MP yes

PF = Pupillages funded / **T** = Tenants / T_{L3Y} = Tenancies in last 3 years / **MP** = Mini-pupillages offered

9 Gough Square

The Chambers of Andrew Ritchie QC, 9 Gough Square, London EC4A 3DG
Tel: 020 7832 0500
Email: pupillage@9goughsquare.co.uk
Web: www.9goughsquare.co.uk
🐦 9goughsquare

Description of Chambers 9 Gough Square is a leading common law set of chambers known for its core strengths in advocacy, drafting and advisory work. Clients include solicitors, local government, central government, corporate bodies and individuals. Tenants practise in all areas of work for the first three years after recruitment, which provides enviable advocacy experience and develops an interesting and varied practice.

Areas of work Members of chambers work and specialise in a wide variety of areas. The largest group in chambers practises in personal injury and clinical negligence work and its members are ranked in the leading Bar directories. Members of chambers also represent parties at inquests. There is a strong criminal team with work in fraud, sexual offences and general crime, and a growing regulatory team working with professional bodies and individuals. 9 Gough Square has long been known for its police work, accepting instructions from the Metropolitan Police and other constabularies in a variety of civil and quasi-criminal cases. The family team undertakes public and private law work, regularly appearing in High Court and Court of Appeal cases. Court of Protection work permits cross-over between the family and civil disciplines. The commercial and property team is routinely involved in cases of all levels of complexity, acting for businesses, creditors, debtors, landlords and other individuals. Its members cover the full spectrum of disputes from cases relating to commercial leases and construction contracts to consumer credit and insolvency matters. As a common law set, members of chambers, and particularly junior tenants, frequently encounter and tackle a wide variety of other areas of work, including employment, public and costs work.

Who should apply We look for candidates of high intellectual ability, usually evidenced by at least a 2.1 degree or equivalent, but who can also demonstrate a commitment to the Bar and a flair for advocacy, combined with common sense and sound judgement. If words such as highly-motivated, robust and a real team player apply to you, then we would like to hear from you. 9 Gough Square operates and observes a robust equality and diversity policy. For many years we have been at the forefront of E&D issues at the Bar.

Pupillage programme We offer up to two pupillages of 12 months' duration. All pupillages are funded. We strive to ensure that a pupil sees as broad an array of work as possible, and particularly in our main practice areas. Before a pupil starts on his or her feet, he or she will have sat with a pupil supervisor in each of civil, criminal and family work. The pupillage programme includes regular feedback and assessed exercises.

When and how to apply Deadlines have yet to be set (pending the release of the Bar Council's timetable for 2018) but information will be published on 9 Gough Square's website in good time before the application window opens. It is likely to open in December 2017. Details will be published on the website at www.9goughsquare.co.uk/pupillage.html. The application system is online and applications are only accepted through the dedicated chambers application system. Further information, and a guidance document to accompany the application form, will be uploaded to the website. 9 Gough Square is not a member of the Pupillage Gateway.

Mini-pupillages For further details please see our website at www.9goughsquare.co.uk/mini-pupillage.html.

Pupillages funded   Up to 2
Tenants   70
Tenancies in last 3 yrs   4

Mini-pupillages   yes

Apply via website

Remuneration for pupillage
£50,000

Minimum qualifications
Usually 2.1 or equivalent

1 GRAY'S INN SQUARE Chambers of Stephen Harvey QC, Gray's Inn, London WC1R 5AA **Tel:** 020 7405 0001 **Email:** pupillage@1gis.co.uk Apply through Pupillage Gateway	Chambers is an established common law set with over 70 members inlcuding a number of silks, leading juniors and members of the judiciary.	PF 2 T 73 T$_{L3Y}$ 7 MP yes
GRAY'S INN TAX CHAMBERS 36 Queen Street, London EC4R 1BN **Tel:** 020 7242 2642 **Email:** pupillage@taxbar.com Apply through Pupillage Gateway	A leading set of chambers specialising in revenue law (domestic, European and international). Members undertake all aspects of tax litigation and advice.	PF 1 T 10 T$_{L3Y}$ 1 MP yes
GT STEWART SOLICITORS 21-22 Camberwell Green, London SE5 7AA **Tel:** 020 8299 6000 **Email:** m.krudy@gtstewart.co.uk **Apply to:** Ms Melanie Krudy	GT Stewart is established as one of the leading firms in London for publicly funded work and regularly receives referrals from other firms and agencies.	PF 1 T 12 T$_{L3Y}$ 0 MP no
GUILDFORD CHAMBERS Stoke House, Leapale Lane, Guildford GU1 4LY **Tel:** 01483 539131 **Email:** clerks@guildfordchambers.com **Apply to:** The Pupillage Committee	Family and civil law set serving the South East.	PF 1 T 23 T$_{L3Y}$ 5 MP yes
GUILDHALL CHAMBERS 23 Broad Street, Bristol BS1 2HG **Tel:** 0117 930 9000 **Email:** info@guildhallchambers.co.uk Apply through Pupillage Gateway	Friendly progressive set in the centre of Bristol, situated in two large premises and offering pupils modern IT facilities and thorough training.	PF 2 T 87 T$_{L3Y}$ 8 MP yes
2 HARCOURT BUILDINGS 1st Floor Left, 2 Harcourt Buildings, Temple, London EC4Y 9DB **Tel:** 020 7353 2112 **Email:** clerks@2hb.co.uk Apply through Pupillage Gateway	A leading criminal chambers, defending and prosecuting in London and on the Western and South Eastern Circuits.	PF 2 T 42 T$_{L3Y}$ 6 MP yes
HARCOURT CHAMBERS Temple, London EC4Y 9DB **Tel:** 0844 561 7135 **Email:** clerks@harcourtchambers.law.co.uk Apply through Pupillage Gateway		PF 1-2 T 54 T$_{L3Y}$ 4 MP yes
2 HARE COURT Temple, London EC4Y 7BH **Tel:** 020 7353 5324 **Email:** clerks@2harecourt.com Apply through Pupillage Gateway	We are recognised as a leading criminal set, with an even mix of prosecution and defence work. We offer up to two fully-funded 12-month pupillages per year.	PF 2 T 56 T$_{L3Y}$ 8 MP no

PF = Pupillages funded / **T** = Tenants / **TL3Y** = Tenancies in last 3 years / **MP** = Mini-pupillages offered

Hailsham Chambers

4 Paper Buildings, Ground Floor, Temple, London EC4Y 7EX
Tel: 020 7643 5000
Email: clerks@hailshamchambers.com
Web: www.hailshamchambers.com

Description of Chambers Hailsham Chambers is a long-established set with a distinguished heritage which includes law lords and the UK's current Advocate General to the ECJ. We are proud of our past but are committed to remaining one of the most forward-thinking sets of chambers in London. Members of Hailsham Chambers provide advice and representation in a diverse range of specialities before all levels of courts and tribunals in England and Wales and overseas.

Areas of work Chambers has six main practice areas: professional negligence, medical law, professional disciplinary and regulatory, costs, personal injury and commercial litigation. We have leading practitioners and experts in all these fields and are recognised by the legal directories as a leading set for professional and medical negligence, professional disciplinary and costs disputes. We have strong and long established relationships with all of the leading insurers and national and City firms working in our areas of practice. Our work ethos is to provide the highest possible standards of advocacy, advice and service. This is complemented by the support given by members of Hailsham Chambers to each other within our specialist teams and across chambers.

Who should apply We want motivated and able candidates committed to providing their best and determined to succeed. Usually a minimum 2.1 degree is required but special circumstances will be considered. Hailsham Chambers adheres to and supports the Bar Council's policies on equal opportunity and non-discrimination. That is why we are one of the few sets whose application form involves a problem question: we look to recruit those from any background who sparkle with ability.

Pupillage programme We provide a 12-month period of intensive and high quality training in a relaxed atmosphere. Pupils are likely to spend time with three different pupil supervisors, one for each of the first and second three months, and one for the second six months. The pupil supervisors' respective practices will cover two or more of chambers' areas of specialisation, including clinical disputes or professional negligence in particular. Pupils are encouraged to work with different members of chambers. In the second six months pupils accept instructions and attend court on their own account. Formal and informal feedback is provided and regarded as crucial for the learning process. A mentor is always available to discuss pupillage in the strictest confidence. We provide a thorough advocacy training and assessment programme.

When and how to apply For 12-month pupillage commencing September 2019, please apply through the Pupillage Gateway. In addition, we will be accepting applications through the Pupillage Gateway for one 12-month pupillage commencing September 2018.

Mini-pupillages Hailsham Chambers offers mini-pupillages throughout the year (although vacation periods are best avoided) to those who have started university and can show a real interest in pursuing a legal career. To apply please send a copy of your CV together with a covering letter to Theo Barclay.

Sponsorship/funding We are offering two 12-month pupillages commencing in September 2019. Each of our 12-month pupillages has an award of £50,000 including £5,000 guaranteed earnings. We are also offering one 12-month pupillage funded on the same basis, commencing September 2018.

Pupillages funded	2
Tenants	50
Tenancies in last 3 yrs	7
Mini-pupillages	yes

Apply through Pupillage Gateway

Remuneration for pupillage
£45,000 plus £5,000 guaranteed earnings

Minimum qualifications
2.1 degree

Hardwicke

Lincoln's Inn, London WC2A 3SB
Tel: 020 7242 2523
Email: enquiries@hardwicke.co.uk
Web: www.hardwicke.co.uk
🐦 hardwickelaw

Description of Chambers Hardwicke specialises in commercial, construction, insurance and property law and has expertise in professional negligence, insolvency and personal injury work. We are a successful, innovative set with a reputation for high quality legal expertise, excellent administration and an approachable, business-focused style. This is consistently recognised in *Chambers & Partners* and *Legal 500*.

Who should apply We are looking for candidates of the highest calibre with the potential to become successful barristers. Academic achievement forms a significant part of our considerations, but is not the only criterion. We look at three core skill sets that we think are essential in a good barrister: legal, interpersonal and business/client care skills. When selecting pupils, we are looking for applicants who show the potential to excel in all of these areas.

Pupillage programme We offer two 12-month pupillages each year and recruit with the intention of taking on both pupils if they achieve the standard we require. Our policy is therefore only to offer pupillage to those candidates whom we consider have the potential to join us. We look for pupils with exceptional intellectual ability, excellent communication skills and a genuine interest in our areas of work. You will need to be confident and able to work both on your own and with others, demonstrating not only legal, analytical ability but also commercial good sense. We put a great deal of effort into providing you with the support and training necessary to succeed in an extremely competitive environment. We aim to make you feel part of the team and have an open door policy so as to make our pupils feel they are able to approach any member of chambers for guidance and advice. Our 12-month pupillages are split into three periods of four months. During each period, you will be assigned a pupil supervisor and other members of chambers with whom you will work. You will share the daily professional life of your pupil supervisor, producing pleadings and opinions on their cases, attending conferences and receiving regular feedback. Advocacy is a key component of a Hardwicke pupillage. During your second six months, you can expect to find yourself in court at least once or twice a week. We will provide you with in-house advocacy training, supervised by our members, many of whom are advocacy trainers at the Inns and/or part-time judges. You will also get to know our practice management team and work with them on developing the skills necessary to build a successful practice.

When and how to apply Applications should be made on Hardwicke's own applicaion form which can be downloaded from www.hardwicke.co.uk/recruitment/pupillage. The closing date for applications is in line with the Pupillage Gateway timetable.

Mini-pupillages We offer 12 mini-pupillages per year (three per quarter). Applicants should complete our application form on the recruitment pages of our website. Please visit Hardwicke's website for closing dates and details about eligibility.

Sponsorship/funding We offer two pupillages of £55,000 each: an award of £40,000 and guaranteed earnings of £15,000. Up to £15,000 of the award can be drawn down during the BPTC year. We also fund attendance at the Bar Council's compulsory courses. There is a guaranteed income scheme for first and second year tenants.

Pupillages funded	2
Tenants	84
Tenancies in last 3 yrs	12
Mini-pupillages	yes

Applications contact
Pupillage Committee Secretary

Remuneration for pupillage
£55,000

Hardwicke

1 Hare Court

Temple, London EC4Y 7BE
Tel: 020 7797 7070
Email: clerks@1hc.com
Web: www.1hc.com

Areas of work 1 Hare Court was the first set of chambers to specialise in family law and we now have 12 silks and 30 juniors. The majority of members work in the area of matrimonial finance, while some members of chambers are involved in child law. Former members of chambers include two previous presidents of the Family Division, two Lords Justice of Appeal and four High Court judges of the Family Division. Current members of chambers have acted in almost all the recent important matrimonial finance cases, including *White*, *Miller/McFarlane*, *McCartney*, *Agbaje*, *Radmacher v Granatino*, *Prest*, *Whyatt v Vince* and *Sharland*. Chambers' clients tend to be high-net worth individuals from the worlds of commerce, entertainment, finance and sport.

We expect that applicants will have a strong academic record. 1 Hare Court has a long-standing tradition of contributing to legal works. *Rayden on Divorce*, the principal practitioners' textbook, was renamed *Rayden & Jackson* as a tribute to the former head of chambers Joseph Jackson QC, who edited the work for many years. Members of chambers continue to edit *Rayden & Jackson*, as well as many other leading books, and we regularly contribute articles to the specialist press. Candidates who demonstrate the potential to carry on this strong intellectual tradition will impress.

A pupillage at 1 Hare Court offers training in advocacy, advice and drafting in every aspect of family work, particularly matrimonial finance. Our strong reputation and the quality of training available means that those pupils who are not taken on stand a good prospect of finding a professional opportunity elsewhere, frequently in other specialist chambers.

Who should apply Candidates should be able to show that they have a potential flair for advocacy, presentational and analytical skills and the ability to develop sound judgement, as well as having a strong academic record. Given the emphasis on financial work, some aptitude and interest in commercial/financial matters is desirable. However, chambers' work remains rooted in human problems and a sympathetic but perceptive response to those problems is essential.

When and how to apply We recruit pupils once a year. Applications for pupillages commencing in October 2019 open and close in accordance with the Pupillage Gateway timetable. Applications should be sent with a full CV and handwritten covering letter (marked pupillage application) to the chambers administrator. References may be helpful. Those invited for an interview are likely to be interviewed on a Saturday in June 2018. Chambers is not a member of Pupillage Gateway but keeps to the timetable for the communication and acceptance of offers. For more information see the chambers' website.

Mini-pupillages These are available during term time only. Applicants must be at least at undergraduate level and have some interest in family law. Applications are accepted twice a year and should be sent with a full CV and handwritten covering letter marked for the attention of Tom Harvey. For mini-pupillages between February – July 2018, please apply between 1-31 January 2018. For mini-pupillages between October 2018 – January 2019, please apply between 1-31 July 2018. Ordinarily applications will not be considered outside of these application periods.

Sponsorship/funding Two fully-funded pupillages.

Pupillages funded	2
Tenants	42
Tenancies in last 3 yrs	5
Mini-pupillages	yes
Apply by CV	

Remuneration for pupillage
£35,000 per pupillage plus earnings in second six

Minimum qualifications
2.1 degree

1 HARE COURT

Henderson Chambers

2 Harcourt Buildings, Temple, London EC4Y 9DB
Tel: 020 7583 9020
Email: clerks@hendersonchambers.co.uk
Web: www.hendersonpupillage.co.uk
🐦 hendersonpupils

Description of Chambers Henderson Chambers is a long-established, leading commercial/common law set. It has acknowledged expertise in all of its principal areas of practice, and pupils and members are frequently involved in high-profile commercial and common law litigation.

Areas of work Chambers has unrivalled expertise in product liability (which covers a wide range of commercial work including sale of goods and insurance disputes, multi-party pharmaceutical and medical device claims and regulatory and enforcement proceedings) and is consistently rated as the leading set of chambers in this area. Henderson Chambers is also widely recognised for its health and safety and environment work. We cover all aspects of health and safety litigation and advice, including prosecutions for corporate manslaughter and infringements of health and safety legislation, as well as health and safety policy, management and training. Consistently ranked as one of the leading sets in this field as well as being awarded Health and Safety Chambers of the Year 2014 and Environment Set of the Year 2016, members also provide advice on health and safety and environmental policy, regulatory issues, management and training. Henderson Chambers provide expert counsel to clients across the globe, and are experts at defending environmental damage claims. Over the last few decades, chambers has been involved in many of the major commercial and landmark international group actions.

In addition to this, members of Henderson Chambers are also noted for their expertise and experience in other areas, including: banking and finance, consumer law, personal injury, property law (covering a range of property law from commercial and residential landlord and tenant to real property and property human rights claims), employment law (including restraint of trade and breach of confidence matters; wrongful dismissal and unfair dismissal claims; sex, race and disability discrimination claims; redundancy; transfer of undertakings and EC employment law), regulatory and disciplinary proceedings, public law and judicial review, and technology.

Who should apply We are looking for individuals who can demonstrate a first-class intellect whether via the traditional route of an outstanding higher education record or via proof of success in other professions, in business or in employment. We are a friendly and sociable chambers, and we expect our candidates to be able to show how they have both worked hard and played hard.

Pupillage programme Pupillages are for 12 months, usually with four different pupil supervisors for three months each. Pupils have the opportunity to spend four weeks at an international legal practice in order to experience practice in another jurisdiction first hand. Pupils will attend court regularly during their second six months.

When and how to apply We are part of the Pupillage Gateway and abide by its timetable. Queries about pupillage should be addressed to Helen Ghalem.

Mini-pupillages We offer unassessed mini-pupillages. Applications are by way of an online application form available at www.hendersonpupillage.co.uk.

Sponsorship/funding Chambers offers up to two funded 12-month pupillages a year. Our pupils receive a minimum remuneration of £70,000. This consists of a guaranteed award of £70,000, plus any additional earnings during the second six months.

Pupillages funded	2
Tenants	49
Tenancies in last 3 yrs	6
Mini-pupillages	yes

Apply through Pupillage Gateway

Remuneration for pupillage
£70,000 award plus any additional earnings in the second six

HENDERSON CHAMBERS

3 HARE COURT
Temple, London EC4Y 7BJ
Tel: 020 7415 7800
Email: clerks@3harecourt.com
Apply through Pupillage Gateway

Commercial/common law set which undertakes consitutional, human rights and criminal appeals in the Privy Council. We offer two funded 12-month pupillages each year.

PF	2
T	35
T$_{L3Y}$	4
MP	yes

---

7 HARRINGTON STREET CHAMBERS
7 Harrington Street, Liverpool L2 9YH
Tel: 0151 242 0707
Email: pupillage@7hs.co.uk
Apply to: Mrs Claire Tumilty

PF	1
T	90
T$_{L3Y}$	5
MP	yes

---

1 HIGH PAVEMENT
Lace Market, Nottingham NG1 1HF
Tel: 0115 941 8218
Email: clerks@1highpavement.co.uk
Apply to: Mr Avik Mukherjee

Specialist criminal chambers for the East Midlands.

PF	1
T	43
T$_{L3Y}$	2
MP	yes

HOGARTH CHAMBERS
Lincoln's Inn, 5 New Square, London WC2A 3RJ
Tel: 020 7404 0404
Email: bharrison@hogarthchambers.com
Apply to: Ms Briget Harrison

We are one of the leading intellectual property law sets. Chambers' specialisms include media and entertainment, IT, privacy and chancery law.

PF	1
T	21
T$_{L3Y}$	2
MP	yes

INVICTUS CHAMBERS
1 Mitre Court Buildings, Temple, London EC4Y 7BS
Tel: 03301194300
Email: join@invictuschambers.org
Apply through Pupillage Gateway

PF	2
T	19
T$_{L3Y}$	5
MP	yes

ISCOED CHAMBERS
86 St Helen's Road, Swansea SA1 4BQ
Tel: 01792 652988
Email: clerks@iscoedchambers.co.uk
Apply through Pupillage Gateway

Iscoed Chambers is a long-established common law set based in Swansea.

PF	1
T	35
T$_{L3Y}$	5
MP	yes

ONE ITL
Fleet House, 8-12 New Bridge Street, London EC4V 6AL
Tel: 020 7427 4400
Email: clerks@1itl.com
Apply through Pupillage Gateway

Specialist criminal law chambers prosecuting and defending the full range of criminal work. Also court martial and prison law.

PF	2
T	26
T$_{L3Y}$	4
MP	yes

KBG CHAMBERS
115 North Hill, Plymouth PL4 8JY
Tel: 01752 221551
Email: clerks@kbgchambers.co.uk
Apply to: Mr Thomas Challacombe

General common law set covering all of the West Country, predominantly Devon and Cornwall.

PF	1
T	35
T$_{L3Y}$	3
MP	yes

PF = Pupillages funded / T = Tenants / T$_{L3Y}$ = Tenancies in last 3 years / MP = Mini-pupillages offered

KBW The Engine House, 1 Foundry Square, Leeds LS11 5DL **Tel:** 0113 297 1200 **Email:** clerks@kbwchambers.com Apply through Pupillage Gateway	Applications for pupillage must be made through the Pupillage Gateway.	PF 1 T 38 T$_{L3Y}$ 4 MP yes	

11KBW 11 King's Bench Walk, Temple, London EC4Y 7EQ **Tel:** 020 7632 8500 **Email:** claire.halas@11kbw.com Apply through Pupillage Gateway	This leading employment set also specialises in public and commercial law. Two to four funded pupillages are usually offered each year.	PF 2-4 T 59 T$_{L3Y}$ 6 MP yes	

6KBW COLLEGE HILL 21 College Hill, London EC4R 2RP **Tel:** 020 3301 0910 **Email:** clerks@6kbw.com **Apply to:** Miss Rosalind Earis	Leading set in criminal law and related fields, including public law, extradition, corporate crime and investigations, inquests and regulatory law.	PF 2 T 47 T$_{L3Y}$ 3 MP yes	

KCH GARDEN SQUARE BARRISTERS 1 Oxford Street, Nottingham NG1 5BH **Tel:** 0115 9418851 **Email:** clerks@kchgardensquare.co.uk **Apply to:** Miss Moira Walsh	Family/civil pupillage. Mixed common law set based in Nottingham and Leicester. Innovative and forward thinking. Barmark, *Legal 500* and *Chambers & Partners* rated.	PF Up to 2 T 60 T$_{L3Y}$ 13 MP yes	

KEATING CHAMBERS 15 Essex Street, London WC2R 3AA **Tel:** 020 7544 2600 **Email:** clerks@keatingchambers.com Apply through Pupillage Gateway	Keating Chambers is an award-winning, commercial set specialising in complex domestic and international construction, engineering, energy, international arbitration, procurement, technology and related professional negligence disputes.	PF 3 T 65 T$_{L3Y}$ 4 MP yes	

KENWORTHY'S CHAMBERS Arlington House, Bloom Street, Salford, Manchester M3 6AJ **Tel:** 0161 832 4036 **Email:** maria@kenworthysbarristers.co.uk **Apply to:** Mrs Maria Rushworth	Progressive set with strong emphasis on asylum, civil, commercial, chancery, costs, crime, employment, family, housing, human rights, immigration, personal injury, prison law, police law, judicial review.	PF 1-2 T 62 T$_{L3Y}$ 3 MP yes	

2 KING'S BENCH WALK Ground Floor, Temple, London EC4Y 7DE **Tel:** 020 7353 1746 **Email:** clerks@2kbw.com Apply through Pupillage Gateway	General common-law chambers, primarily based on the Western Circuit. We have chambers in both London and at 3 Guildhall Walk, Portsmouth PO1 2RY.	PF 2 T 73 T$_{L3Y}$ 4 MP yes	

2 KING'S BENCH WALK Chambers of Michael Cogan, Lower Ground Floor, Temple, London EC4Y 7DE **Tel:** 020 7583 0695 **Email:** admin@2kbw.net **Apply to:** Mr Barry Henderson	Multi-racial set. Of particular concern to all practitioners are those areas of law which deal with the liberty and rights of the individual.	PF 1 T 10 T$_{L3Y}$ 1 MP yes	

PF = Pupillages funded / **T** = Tenants / **T**$_{L3Y}$ = Tenancies in last 3 years / **MP** = Mini-pupillages offered

1 King's Bench Walk

Temple, London EC4Y 7DB
Tel: 020 7936 1500
Email: pupillage@1kbw.co.uk
Web: www.1kbw.co.uk
🐦 1kbwchambers

Description of Chambers 1 King's Bench Walk is a leading barristers' chambers in London, specialising in family law, with a pre-eminent reputation both nationally and internationally. We are consistently ranked by the legal directories in the top tier of leading sets for family law. Our barristers have been in most of the groundbreaking cases over the last two decades. 1kbw are market leaders for both matrimonial finance and children. We have a reputation for recruiting the most talented pupils and then providing training and support that is second to none. We proactively try to recruit our tenants from our pupils. In the last decade 17 of the 20 pupils in chambers have been offered tenancy. For that reason, our selection procedure is rigorous.

Who should apply We are looking for outstanding candidates who are confident, articulate, and have the right aptitude for life at the bar. They will be interesting, intelligent and enthusiastic individuals with an interest in the particular specialisms of chambers.

Pupillage programme 1kbw offers two specialist family law pupillages each year. Each pupillage is full time and for 12 months. The first six months (non-practising) are divided between two pupil supervisors, and the second six months (practising period) is spent with a third, each of whom will be a specialist family law practitioner. Chambers also provides 'in-house' advocacy training. We offer each pupil a (tax free) grant of £25,000 which is paid during the first six months. In addition, pupils may retain any income which they earn in the second six months. The reputation of 1kbw is such that our pupils are regularly briefed from the outset.

When and how to apply Our application form can be found on our website in January of each year. 1kbw is no longer within the Pupillage Gateway system although our applications procedure follows the Pupillage Gateway timetable, as approved by the Bar Council and we also make offers according to that timetable. The best candidates will be invited for an interview conducted by a panel representing a cross-section of members of chambers. The top candidates at interview will be shortlisted for a second round of interviews following which offers will be made.

1 King's Bench Walk has a firm commitment to equality and diversity.

Mini-pupillages We consider applications three times a year (in April, September and December), made using the online application form that can be found on our website. There is no interview; mini-pupils are chosen on the strength of their paper applications.

Pupillages funded	2
Tenants	55
Tenancies in last 3 yrs	6
Mini-pupillages	yes
Apply via website	
Remuneration for pupillage	
See website for details	
Minimum qualifications	
2.1 degree	

7 King's Bench Walk

Temple, London EC4Y 7DS
Tel: 020 7910 8300
Email: clerks@7kbw.co.uk
Web: www.7kbw.co.uk

Description of Chambers 7KBW is a top commercial chambers, with a reputation for excellence, intellectual rigour and providing practical, commercial advice. Its members practise across the full breadth of commercial law and are ranked highly in the leading legal directories. Members appear regularly in the Commercial Court, the Court of Appeal, the Supreme Court, the Privy Council and in arbitrations. They also appear in court and arbitrations in a significant number of other jurisdictions including Singapore, Bermuda, the Bahamas, the Cayman Islands, Dubai and Hong Kong.

Areas of work 7KBW's practice areas are exclusively commercial and cover the following: all aspects of insurance and reinsurance, shipping and transport, professional negligence, civil fraud, international trade and commodities, energy, oil and gas, agency, injunctions and arrests, shipbuilding, sale of goods, banking and financial services, aviation, construction and private international law. Most of 7KBW's work has an international dimension.

Who should apply Candidates with strong analytical and intellectual abilities. 7KBW does not typically interview candidates who do not have a first or a good upper second-class degree. 7KBW offers up to four funded pupillages per year.

Pupillage programme Pupils are allocated a pupillage supervisor for the first two to three months and will change pupillage supervisor more frequently thereafter. A large component of pupillage is assisting in the preparation of trials and applications and attending court with the pupil supervisor. It will also involve drafting statements of case, researching the law, advices and attending conferences. Whatever the nature of the pupil supervisor's work, a pupil can expect to be fully involved in it. 7KBW also organises advocacy exercises and pleading seminars for pupils.

When and how to apply Applications should be made via the Pupillage Gateway 2018 season for pupillages commencing in September 2019. Deferred pupillages commencing in September 2020 will also be available but will only be offered in exceptional circumstances.

Mini-pupillages Two-day mini-pupillages are available. Mini-pupillages do not include any formal assessments and completion of a mini-pupillage is not a prerequisite for applying for pupillage, but it is strongly encouraged. For information about how and when to apply, please refer to the website at www.7kbw.co.uk/join-us/mini-pupillage.

Sponsorship/funding Pupillages are fully funded, with awards of £65,000 for 12 months. 7KBW is willing to advance up to £25,000 of the award on an interest-free basis for use during the BPTC year, on condition that any advance will be repaid if the pupil does not pass the BPTC exams or complete his or her pupillage.

Pupillages funded	Up to 4
Tenants	60
Tenancies in last 3 yrs	6
Mini-pupillages	yes

Apply through Pupillage Gateway

Remuneration for pupillage
£65,000

Minimum qualifications
Good 2.1 degree

Remember to cite *The Training Contract & Pupillage Handbook* on your application form if you apply to this chambers.

568 THE TRAINING CONTRACT & PUPILLAGE HANDBOOK

4 KING'S BENCH WALK
Second Floor, Temple, London EC4Y 7DL
Tel: 020 7822 7000
Email: clerks@4kbw.co.uk
Apply through Pupillage Gateway

4KBW is a dedicated common law set situated in Temple, London. Chambers specialises in civil, criminal, family and immigration work.

PF	2
T	54
T$_{L3Y}$	4
MP	yes

5 KING'S BENCH WALK
Chambers of Sarah Forshaw QC & Mark Heywood QC, Temple, London EC4Y 7DN
Tel: 020 7353 5638
Email: clerks@5kbw.co.uk
Apply through Pupillage Gateway

Applications through Pupillage Gateway only.

PF	3
T	48
T$_{L3Y}$	7
MP	yes

9 KING'S BENCH WALK
Chambers of Shabeena Azhar & Jonathan Mole, Temple, London EC4Y 7DX
Tel: 020 7353 9564
Email: pupillage@9kbw.com
Apply to: Mrs Christine Eadie

9 KBW offers one criminal pupillage a year. We always recruit a pupil who we think has what it takes to become a tenant.

PF	1
T	26
T$_{L3Y}$	10
MP	yes

12 KING'S BENCH WALK
Temple, London EC4Y 7EL
Tel: 020 7583 0811
Email: chambers@12kbw.co.uk
Apply through Pupillage Gateway

Chambers covers all contentious civil common law work (except matrimonial). Specialists in personal injury, clinical negligence and employment. Friendly atmosphere.

PF	2-3
T	82
T$_{L3Y}$	8
MP	yes

KINGS CHAMBERS
36 Young Street, Manchester M3 3FT
Tel: 0345 034 3444
Email: clerks@kingschambers.com

One of the largest and most successful sets outside London, specialising in common law, chancery and commercial, and planning and public law.

PF	Up to 3
T	112
T$_{L3Y}$	5
MP	yes

LAMB BUILDING
Temple, London EC4Y 7AS
Tel: 020 7797 7788
Email: clerks@lambbuilding.co.uk
Apply to: The Pupillage Committee

Chambers offers a 12-month pupillage with specified pupillage supervisors and a 'link' junior tenant. Pupillage supervisors are available in crime, family and immigration.

PF	Up to 3
T	64
T$_{L3Y}$	8
MP	yes

LINCOLN HOUSE CHAMBERS
Tower 12, The Avenue North, 18-22 Bridge Street, Manchester M3 3BZ
Tel: 0161 832 5701
Email: pupillage@lincolnhousechambers.com
Apply to: Mr Daniel Thomas

A nationally prominent set of criminal chambers with a fast expanding civil base. Chambers has a modern and progressive approach to all aspects of work.

PF	1-2
T	67
T$_{L3Y}$	5
MP	yes

LINENHALL CHAMBERS
1 Stanley Place, Chester CH1 2LU
Tel: 01244 348 282
Email: clerks@linenhallchambers.co.uk
Apply to: The Pupillage Committee

Busy, large, provincial set undertaking work of a wide description. Members are divided into criminal, civil and family teams (with some overlapping).

PF	1
T	70
T$_{L3Y}$	1
MP	yes

PF = Pupillages funded / **T** = Tenants / **T$_{L3Y}$** = Tenancies in last 3 years / **MP** = Mini-pupillages offered

Landmark Chambers

180 Fleet Street, London EC4A 2HG
Tel: 020 7430 1221
Email: pupillages@landmarkchambers.co.uk
Web: www.landmarkchambers.co.uk
🐦 landmark_lc

Description of Chambers Landmark is ranked as the number one planning and environmental chambers in the UK by the top legal directories. We are consistently regarded as one of the leading sets in our other two main areas of work: property and public.

Members have been involved in some of the most significant cases and inquiries in recent years, including the Supreme Court bedroom tax case, High Speed 2, the third runway for Heathrow and the Supreme Court property case, *Day v Hosebay Ltd*.

Areas of work Landmark is a leading chambers in the UK offering integrated advocacy and advice in the following areas: environmental, international, property, planning, public, rating and valuation.

Pupillage programme Chambers runs a staggered recruitment process. The first phase of recruitment takes place from 1 November onwards (through Landmark's own recruitment portal) and is for candidates who have a particular interest in property law. We accept applications for up to one pupil during this phase. The second phase of the process is for all candidates and takes place between January and May in accordance with Pupillage Gateway. We accept applications for up to two pupillages during this phase.

The pupillage year is divided into four seats of three months each, during which time we offer our pupils experience in all of Chambers' complementary practice areas. We encourage pupils to work for other members and will arrange placements with a silk or senior junior on more complex cases. This allows our pupils to see a wide variety of work and take advantage of Landmark's unique position as a leading specialist set with significant cross-over between its private and public law practices.

Pupils receive regular feedback from their supervisors, as well as undertaking formal feedback sessions with the pupillage committee after three and six months. During the year there are four formal assessments (three written and one oral) and pupils receive feedback on their performance in each of them.

When and how to apply Applications made through Landmark Chambers' recruitment portal and Pupillage Gateway.

Mini-pupillages We operate three mini-pupillage seasons per year. The first (February-March) is aimed at first and second-year law undergraduates and those who are considering a career change. During the second two intakes (May-June and October-November) preference is given to third-year law undergraduates and those undertaking the GDL or BPTC.

Chambers offers all mini-pupils reimbursement of £100 for travel and lunch expenses. Additionally, Landmark operates a discretionary accommodation funding scheme for students visiting from outside London.

For further details about pupillage, mini-pupillage, Landmark's open evenings and property moot competition, please visit: www.landmarkchambers.co.uk/recruitment.

Pupillages funded	Up to 2
Tenants	85
Tenancies in last 3 yrs	8
Mini-pupillages	yes

Apply to
Landmark Chambers' recruitment portal and Pupillage Gateway

Remuneration for pupillage
£65,000, of which £25,000 may be taken as an early drawdown

Littleton Chambers

3 King's Bench Walk North, London EC4Y 7HR
Tel: 020 7797 8600
Email: fschneider@littletonchambers.co.uk
Web: www.littletonchambers.com
🐦 littleton1

Description of Chambers Littleton is acknowledged as being a top-class set in each of its main practice areas. Its success is based upon both the desire to maintain high professional standards and a willingness to embrace change. It prides itself on the skills of its tenants, not only as advocates and advisers on the law, but also for their analytical and practical skills.

Areas of work Littleton Chambers specialises in commercial litigation, employment law, professional negligence, sports law, mediation and arbitration.

Who should apply Applications are invited from candidates with a minimum 2.1 degree or equivalent. Littleton takes a considerable amount of care in choosing our pupils and prefers to recruit its tenants from persons who have completed a full 12-month pupillage with chambers. We endeavour to take on pupils who not only have excellent academic skills, but who show a flair for advocacy, have the ability to understand practical commercial issues, and importantly, have the interpersonal skills to provide the qualities that are expected of the modern-day Bar. We operate an equal opportunities policy which is designed to support diversity in our pupillage recruitment process.

Pupillage programme Chambers generally offers pupillage to two people each year. During the 12-month pupillage, you will have the benefit of four pupil supervisors in succession. Your pupil supervisors will provide support and guidance to you throughout, ensuring that you understand not only the nuts and bolts of a barrister's work, but also the ethical constraints which are such a distinctive feature of chambers' professional life. After six months pupillage you will be entitled to take on your own work. Your pupil supervisor will provide assistance in the preparation of briefs to ensure that your client receives the best possible service from you.

When and how to apply Littleton is a member of the Pupillage Gateway. Offers are made in accordance with their timetable and where appropriate, in the academic year before bar finals.

Mini-pupillages An assessed mini-pupillage forms part of our pupillage application process and mini-pupillages are not offered outside of this process.

Sponsorship/funding We believe that fair remuneration is important. Our pupils receive a £67,500 pupillage award and they keep all second six earnings. It is possible to draw down some of this funding during the year of bar finals.

Pupillages funded	2
Tenants	57
Tenancies in last 3 yrs	4

Apply through Pupillage Gateway

Remuneration for pupillage
£67,500

Minimum qualifications
2.1 degree

LITTLETON

Maitland Chambers

7 Stone Buildings, Lincoln's Inn, London WC2A 3SZ
Tel: 020 7406 1200
Email: pupillage@maitlandchambers.com
Web: www.maitlandchambers.com

Description of Chambers We are a leading set of chambers in commercial chancery litigation ranked at the top of our field in the legal directories. Our appeal to you at the start of your career is the combination of the high-quality instructions we receive, the breadth of our work (from major international litigation to domestic contractual and property disputes) and the volume of advocacy that we do. The majority of our work is done in London, though we frequently advise and appear for clients in other parts of the UK; and much of our work has an international aspect, involving acting for clients and appearing in court overseas.

Areas of work We undertake a full range of commercial chancery work, which is essentially concerned with business, finance and property. Our core areas of practice include commercial litigation, banking, financial services and regulation, civil fraud, insolvency and restructuring, media law, pensions, professional negligence, real property, charity law, trusts and tax. Most of what we do is concerned with dispute resolution (advising, drafting court documents and appearing as advocates); but we also do some non-contentious work in the private client field.

Who should apply Our typical recruit has a first class mind and a sense of commercial practicality, and will enjoy and be stimulated by the challenge of oral and written advocacy. Academically we look for a first or 2.1 degree. You must have an aptitude for and general enjoyment of complex legal argument (demonstrated by mooting). Not all of our barristers have law degrees: of our ten most junior tenants, the majority read subjects other than law and we recognise that training in other academic disciplines can be a good preparation for a legal career. We encourage applications from people from all sections of society, regardless of gender, race, disability, sexual orientation, religion, belief or age.

Pupillage programme We offer up to three 12-month pupillages. You will sit with different barristers during your time in chambers and so have the opportunity to see a wide range of practices; however, you will spend your first three months with one supervisor, so that you can find your feet and establish a point of contact. At regular intervals during your pupillage you will participate in advocacy exercises that take the form of mock hearings, which are prepared in advance from a set of papers, just as in practice. Senior members of chambers act as the tribunal, probing your argument during the 'hearing' and then providing detailed feedback afterwards. There is no limit to the number of tenancy offers we can make in each year; as a general rule, if you are of the requisite standard, you will be offered tenancy.

When and how to apply Chambers is not a member of the Pupillage Gateway. Visit our website from October 2017 for details of how and when to apply.

Mini-pupillages Applications are considered three times a year; please see our website for current deadlines and details of how to apply.

Sponsorship/funding A pupillage award (£65,000 for pupillage starting in October 2019) is offered to all pupils in chambers. Up to £20,000 of the award may be drawn down in advance for BPTC fees or during the BPTC year. We operate a cashflow assistance scheme during the early stages of practice.

Pupillages funded	Up to 3
Tenants	69
Tenancies in last 3 yrs	5
Mini-pupillages	yes

Applications contact
Ms Valerie Piper

Remuneration for pupillage
£65,000

Minimum qualifications
2.1 degree

Matrix Chambers

Griffin Building, Gray's Inn, London WC1R 5LN
Tel: 020 7404 3447
Email: matrix@matrixlaw.co.uk
Web: www.matrixlaw.co.uk
🐦 matrixchambers

Description of Chambers Matrix was set up in 2000 in response to the changing face of the legal landscape at that time. We wanted to achieve a different working model from the traditional English barristers' chambers and, at the time of our establishment, we were labelled "the future of the Bar". We are proud of our record of innovation and our reputation as a professional and approachable set. Our actions are guided by our core values, which outline our principles as an organisation and govern how we work. We operate within a modern environment where diversity, accessibility and client care are widely championed.

Areas of work Our members have expertise in a range of practice areas within the UK and internationally. We have a multi-disciplinary approach with several members recognised as leading practitioners in *Chambers & Partners* and *Legal 500*. Matrix acts for private and public clients and has particular expertise in 29 international and domestic areas of law including commercial, competition, crime, data protection, defamation, discrimination, education, employment, environmental, extradition, fraud, freedom of information, human rights, immigration nationality and asylum, international arbitration, local government, public and administrative law, media, mutual assistance, prison, social welfare, and sports law. Matrix has a strong international presence, acting in more than 114 countries for governments, international corporations, legal firms and individuals. We have an office in Geneva and a dedicated brand for our international work, known as 'Matrix International'.

Who should apply Matrix welcomes applications from exceptional candidates from all backgrounds. For further details, please see our traineeship brochure on the 'recruitment' page of our website.

Pupillage programme Matrix offers up to two traineeships, both starting 1 October for 12 months. The 12-month training period is split roughly into quarters. The training committee tends to choose who will supervise in the first quarter while trainees are finding their feet, but trainees are consulted throughout on which areas of law they would be interested in covering. It is expected that trainees will experience the wide range of work covered at Matrix with seats in varied practice areas throughout the year. There is a scheduled programme of training that takes place throughout the year and includes internal and external training, written and advocacy exercises and secondments. Matrix trainees do not generally take on oral advocacy in their own right until the last quarter.

When and how to apply Please check our website for information on how to apply for a traineeship.

Mini-pupillages We do not currently offer mini-pupillages, but for up-to-date information, details on opportunities available and how to apply please visit the 'recruitment' section of our website at www.matrixlaw.co.uk/recruitment.

Sponsorship/funding Matrix offers up to two 12-month training places each year with an award of £40,000 and an additional £10,000 contribution during the BPTC year for applicants who are yet to undertake Bar finals. Any applicants who have already completed the BPTC year will still be entitled to the additional £10,000 contribution in the year prior to commencing traineeship.

Pupillages funded	2
Tenants	90
Tenancies in last 3 yrs	6

Apply to
Check website for application details

Remuneration for pupillage
£40,000 with an additional £10,000 contribution during the BPTC year

Monckton Chambers

1-2 Raymond Buildings, Gray's Inn, London WC1R 5NR
Tel: 020 7405 7211
Email: chambers@monckton.com
Web: www.monckton.com
🐦 moncktonlaw

Description of Chambers Monckton Chambers specialises in public and commercial law and the interface between the two.

Areas of work We are recognised as a leading set within our specialisms, which include: competition and regulatory; public; sports; tax; and technology, media and communications. Our work is carried out in areas of the law that are rapidly growing and fast moving. It is exceptionally demanding, but also highly rewarding. We are the fastest growing set in the Bar Top 30 (revenues grew by 34% in 2015/16).

Who should apply We are looking for candidates of the highest intellectual calibre. Most successful candidates for pupillage will have a first class honours degree (although it need not be in law) or a graduate degree in law.

We do not, however, expect candidates to have any experience or expertise in the specialised areas in which we practice, merely an interest and enthusiasm for the work that we do. We welcome applications from candidates who have degrees in subjects other than law and are taking (or have taken) the GDL.

It is not only intellectual skills that we are looking for; we are seeking candidates with the personal skills to win the trust of clients and judges alike. Monckton Chambers is a dynamic place to work. Members actively engage in speaking at conferences and seminars, in London and internationally, and in contributing to a variety of publications, ranging from our own marketing materials, to specialist journals and practitioner texts. We are looking for junior tenants who will bring real energy to chambers.

When and how to apply Monckton Chambers is a member of the Bar Council Pupillage Gateway and all applications should be made in accordance with that scheme. We invite applications from pupils in the year preceding the October in which pupillage is due to start. We are, however, in exceptional circumstances willing to consider applications for deferral.

Mini-pupillages We operate a mini-pupillage scheme. This is intended for people who are in their final year at, or have already graduated from, university, and who are interested in our areas of legal practice. Details of how to apply can be found on our website.

Pupillages funded	2
Tenants	58
Tenancies in last 3 yrs	5
Mini-pupillages	yes

Applications contact
Claire Bowers

Remuneration for pupillage
£65,000 for 12 months

Remember to cite *The Training Contract & Pupillage Handbook* on your application form if you apply to this chambers.

574 THE TRAINING CONTRACT & PUPILLAGE HANDBOOK

MAIDSTONE CHAMBERS 51 Earl Street, Maidstone ME14 1PD **Tel:** 01622 688592 **Email:** clerks@maidstonechambers.co.uk **Apply to:** Ms Alexia Zimbler	Friendly set looking to develop future tenants for an expanding workload. Most of our work is in Kent plus occasionally in London, Essex and Sussex.	PF 1-2 T 15 T~L3Y~ 2 MP yes	

MALINS CHAMBERS 115 Temple Chambers, 3-7 Temple Avenue, London EC4Y ODA **Email:** malins@btinternet.com **Apply to:** Mr Julian Malins QC	We are a small set specialising in international work. We take one pupil a year which we advertise the vacancy on the Bar Council website.	PF 1 T 6 T~L3Y~ 1 MP no

1 MCB Third Floor, 15 New Bridge Street, London EC4V 6AU **Tel:** 020 7452 8900 **Email:** clerks@1mcb.com	Chambers has expanded from its radical beginnings to a progressive and friendly set. Strong specialist teams in criminal defence, housing, immigration, family and employment.	PF 0 T 47 T~L3Y~ 7 MP yes

15 NEW BRIDGE STREET 15 New Bridge Street, London EC4V 6AU **Tel:** 020 7842 1900 **Email:** clerks@15nbs.com **Apply to:** Ms Keeley Holland	15 New Bridge Street offers expert representation in criminal, regulatory and immigration law. We combine the highest standards of service with an approachable manner.	PF 2 T 46 T~L3Y~ 3 MP no

NEW COURT CHAMBERS Temple, London EC4Y 9BE **Tel:** 020 7583 5123 **Email:** pupillages@newcourtchambers.com Apply through Pupillage Gateway	Specialist family set dealing with children and finance, public and private. Members represent local authorities, parents, children and extended family members. Friendly atmosphere.	PF 2 T 25 T~L3Y~ 4 MP yes

NEW PARK COURT CHAMBERS 16 Park Place, Leeds LS1 2SJ **Tel:** 0113 243 3277 **Email:** clerks@npc-l.co.uk Apply through Pupillage Gateway	One of the most prestigious sets outside London, based in Leeds and Newcastle. Specialising in serious crime, regulatory law, professional misconduct, civil, and family work.	PF 3 T 61 T~L3Y~ 3 MP yes

3 NEW SQUARE Lincoln's Inn, London WC2A 3RS **Tel:** 020 7405 1111 **Email:** clerks@3newsquare.co.uk Apply through Pupillage Gateway	A specialist intellectual property chambers which is regularly recommended as a leading set for patent, trademark, copyright, media and entertainment law.	PF 1 T 19 T~L3Y~ 1 MP yes

11 NEW SQUARE First Floor, 11 New Square, Lincoln's Inn, London WC2A 3QB **Tel:** 020 7242 4017 **Email:** john.moore@11newsquare.com **Apply to:** The Pupillage Secretary	This leading set is the longest-established specialist tax chambers. Members are at the forefront of high-profile cases and advise on all aspects of revenue law.	PF 1 T 9 T~L3Y~ 1 MP yes

PF = Pupillages funded / **T** = Tenants / **T~L3Y~** = Tenancies in last 3 years / **MP** = Mini-pupillages offered

4 New Square

Lincoln's Inn, London WC2A 3RJ
Tel: 020 7822 2000
Email: pupillage@4newsquare. com
Web: www.4newsquare.com
🐦 4newsquare

Description of Chambers 4 New Square is a leading commercial and civil set of barristers comprising of 78 members, of whom 22 are Queen's Counsel. Its members are recognised as leading practitioners in a wide range of fields including commercial law, professional liability, international arbitration, insurance and reinsurance, commercial chancery, construction and engineering, public law, financial services, costs and sports law.

In recent years individual members of 4 New Square have consistently been included as leading practitioners in the two main legal directories (*Legal 500* and *Chambers & Partners*) and 4 New Square has been named as the top set for professional negligence at the *Chambers UK* Bar Awards. *Jackson & Powell on Professional Liability* (the main text in this area) is written and edited by current and former members of chambers.

Chambers attracts a large amount of junior advocacy work which reflects the emphasis on developing pupils and junior tenants into experienced advocates to equip them for a successful career at the Bar.

When and how to apply 4 New Square is not part of the Pupillage Gateway scheme. Pupillage applications should be made in accordance with the details on our website www.4newsquare.com.

Mini-pupillages We strongly encourage students to apply for a mini-pupillage with us as we believe that they allow prospective applicants to get a real understanding of the work done in chambers. Mini-pupils also have the opportunity to meet members of chambers and get a feel for the working environment.

Mini-pupillages last for two days and, save in exceptional circumstances, take place in specific weeks in April, July, November and December of each year. Mini-pupillages do not involve formal assessment but we do record feedback on your likely suitability for pupillage in chambers. Mini-pupillage application details can be found on our website www.4newsquare.com.

Sponsorship/funding The total annual award is £65,000, comprising a £55,000 award (of which £5,000 is paid immediately upon acceptance of the offer and a further £15,000 can be drawn down during the BPTC year) and guaranteed earnings in the second six months of £10,000. Pupils are allowed to keep any earnings from their second six months, including any earned in excess of the £10,000 guarantee. New tenants have a guaranteed income of £240,000 (net of chambers' expenses), in addition to their pupillage awards, over the first three years of practice.

Pupillages funded   Up to 2
Tenants   78
Tenancies in last 3 yrs   7

Mini-pupillages   yes

Applications contact
Ms Ella Igbiaye

Remuneration for pupillage
£65,000

Minimum qualifications
Good 2.1 degree

NEW SQUARE

New Square Chambers

Lincoln's Inn, London WC2A 3SW
Tel: 020 7419 8000
Email: pupillage@newsquarechambers.co.uk
Web: www.newsquarechambers.co.uk
🐦 newsqchambers

Description of Chambers New Square Chambers offers a concentration of experience in chancery and commercial work and related international matters. We have 41 members, seven silks and 34 juniors.

Areas of work New Square Chambers undertakes a full range of commercial and chancery work including: charities; civil fraud; company law (including directors' disqualification proceedings and shareholders' disputes); highways and rights of way; housing; insolvency; intellectual property; landlord and tenant; partnership law; pensions; probate, administration of estates, wills and intestacy and family provision; professional negligence; property law; revenue; trusts; settlements and taxation. A considerable amount of our work has an international element. Several members of chambers have established practices in overseas jurisdictions, including Antigua, the Bahamas, Bermuda, the British Virgin Islands, the Caymans, the Channel Islands, Gibraltar, Hong Kong and Singapore, and before the Privy Council. Our members' international practices span the full range of chambers' work, including trusts, land, insolvency and public law, in litigious and non-contentious contexts. The editors of *Lewin on Trusts*, *Theobald on Wills*, *Shareholders' Rights*, *Williams Mortimer and Sunnucks – Executors Administrators and Probate*, and the *Law of Freedom of Information* are all members of chambers.

Pupillage programme At New Square Chambers, we aim to recruit bright and enthusiastic pupils with a proven academic background. Consequently, applicants will usually have a first or good upper second degree, although this need not be in law. Despite our size we are an informal and friendly set, and encourage our pupils to take an active part in the life of chambers. Pupils undertake four seats of three months, each with a different pupil supervisor, in order to experience the full range of chambers' work. In addition, pupils are given the opportunity to learn something of the practices of other members of chambers during their pupillage.

When and how to apply Chambers offers one 12-month pupillage, terminable after six months on either side, which carries with it an award of £65,000. Chambers is not a member of the Pupillage Gateway and applications for pupillage commencing in 2019 should be made on our application form which is available at www.newsquarechambers.co.uk. The closing date is 19 January 2018. Applications should be submitted via email in accordance with chambers' pupillage policy which may also be found on our website.

Mini-pupillages A limited number of mini-pupillages are available, usually lasting for three days. Applicants must have at least completed the second year of their law degree or, if they are not yet studying law, the third year of their degree. As with pupillage applicants, we require applicants for minipupillage to be of at least a high 2.1 or first-class standard. Applications may only be made by email to minipupillage@newsquarechambers.co.uk between 1 August and 30 September in any given year and must be made in the manner prescribed in our mini-pupillage policy which can be found in Appendix I to the chambers' Pupillage Policy (2003). Applications not made in the prescribed manner may not receive a response. Please refer to our website for further details or telephone Ms Kira King or Mr Jon Colclough in chambers on 020 7419 8000.

Pupillages funded	1
Tenants	41
Tenancies in last 3 yrs	3
Mini-pupillages	yes

Applications contact
Ms Charlotte Ford

Remuneration for pupillage
£65,000 for 12 months

Minimum qualifications
2.1 degree

8 NEW SQUARE INTELLECTUAL PROPERTY 8 New Square, Lincoln's Inn, London WC2A 3QP **Tel:** 020 7405 4321 **Email:** clerks@8newsquare.co.uk Apply through Pupillage Gateway	The largest specialist intellectual property, media and IT chambers in the UK, covering a broad range of work from technical patent to high profile media.	PF Up to 2 T 28 T_L3Y 0 MP yes
NEW WALK CHAMBERS 27 New Walk, Leicester LE1 6TE **Tel:** 0116 255 9144 **Email:** clerks@newwalkchambers.co.uk **Apply to:** The Management Committee	Chambers continues to enjoy a strong work base coupled with expertise in its specialist areas.	PF Up to 3 T 22 T_L3Y 7 MP no
NO5 CHAMBERS Steelhouse Lane, Birmingham B4 6DR **Tel:** 0845 210 5555 **Email:** pupillage2016@no5.com **Apply to:** Ms Shirley Titmarsh	One of the largest and most dynamic sets of chambers in the country offering unparalled training opportunities to succesful pupillage candidates.	PF Up to 3 T 256 T_L3Y 53 MP yes
NORTHAMPTON CHAMBERS 22 Albion Place, Northampton NN1 1UD **Tel:** 01604 636271 **Email:** clerks@northampton-chambers.co.uk **Apply to:** The Pupillage Committee	Small, well-established, friendly set. Mainly criminal and family work for local solicitors. Good quality work for junior tenants.	PF 1-2 T 14 T_L3Y 4 MP yes
OLD COURT CHAMBERS Newham House, 96-98 Borough Road, Middlesbrough TS12HJ **Tel:** 01642 23 25 23 **Email:** clerks@oldcourtchambers.net **Apply to:** Mr Stephen Constantine		PF 0-1 T 19 T_L3Y 1 MP no
15 OLD SQUARE Lincoln's Inn, London WC2A 3UE **Tel:** 020 7242 2744 **Email:** taxchambers@15oldsquare.co.uk **Apply to:** Ms Amanda Hardy QC	Chambers specialises in revenue law.	PF 1 T 11 T_L3Y 1 MP yes
ORIEL CHAMBERS 14 Water Street, Liverpool L2 8TD **Tel:** 0151 236 7191 **Email:** clerks@orielchambers.co.uk **Apply to:** Ms Tina Moss	We are a prominent, busy, friendly set who offer the successful applicant an excellent grounding in all of chambers' practice areas.	PF Up to 2 T 53 T_L3Y 3 MP yes
OUTER TEMPLE CHAMBERS 222 Strand, London WC2R 1BA **Tel:** 020 7353 6381 **Email:** pupillage@outertemple.com Apply through Pupillage Gateway	Friendly, progressive mixed common-law chambers, offering up to three twelve month pupillages (Sep 2019) - with an award of £60,000. IIP-accredited.	PF 3 T 89 T_L3Y 7 MP yes

PF = Pupillages funded / **T** = Tenants / **T**_L3Y = Tenancies in last 3 years / **MP** = Mini-pupillages offered

XXIV Old Buildings

24 Old Buildings, Lincoln's Inn, London WC2A 3UP
Tel: 020 7691 2424
Email: clerks@xxiv.co.uk
Web: www.xxiv.co.uk
🐦 xxivbarristers

Description of Chambers XXIV Old Buildings is a leading commercial chancery chambers of 42 members with broad domestic expertise and pre-eminence in international work.

Areas of work The barristers at XXIV Old Buildings specialise in a variety of commercial chancery areas with a particular emphasis on trusts and estates and commercial litigation. Areas in which members regularly take instructions include arbitration; aviation; charities; civil fraud, asset tracing and recovery; company; construction; financial services; insolvency; international and offshore; partnership; pensions; professional negligence; real estate litigation and trusts, probate and estates. XXIV Old Buildings is known for its pre-eminence in international and offshore work, both contentious and advisory. With offices in both London and Geneva, the barristers at XXIV Old Buildings regularly appear in courts and tribunals in offshore centres including the British Virgin Islands, the Cayman Islands, Bermuda, Jersey, the Isle of Man, the DIFC, the Bahamas, Gibraltar, Hong Kong and Malaysia. Several barristers are called not only to the Bar of England and Wales but are also members of the Bar of the Eastern Caribbean as well as the Jersey Bar and the Bar of Northern Ireland.

Who should apply Each year we are looking for up to three pupils with a first or 2.1 degree, though not necessarily in law, who have an enthusiasm for the type of work we do, sound judgement and the application required to succeed in a very competitive and intellectually demanding environment.

Pupillage programme We like to recruit our junior members from those who have undertaken pupillage with us. We are therefore careful that our pupils acquire all the skills necessary to make them successful commercial chancery barristers. During a 12-month pupillage, a pupil will have, on average, four pupil supervisors with whom they will spend the majority of their time.

When and how to apply Please see our website (www.xxiv.co.uk) for application details for pupillages commencing in October 2019. The deadline for applications is Monday 27 November 2017. Keep up to date with our dedicated twitter feed www.twitter.com/xxivpupillage.

Mini-pupillages Chambers offers mini-pupillages throughout the year. Each lasts on average three days. Our website contains guidance on mini-pupillage applications.

Sponsorship/funding Up to a quarter of the pupillage the award may (upon application) be drawn down during the BPTC.

Pupillages funded	3
Tenants	42
Tenancies in last 3 yrs	3

Mini-pupillages   yes

Applications contact
Mr Edward Cumming

Remuneration for pupillage
Up to £65,000 each

Minimum qualifications
2.1 degree

Ten Old Square

10 Old Square, Lincoln's Inn, London WC2A 3SU
Tel: 020 7405 0758
Email: pupillage@tenoldsquare.com
Web: www.tenoldsquare.com
f tenoldsquare **𝕏** tenoldsquare

Description of Chambers Chambers is a leading commercial Chancery set which enjoys the highest reputation in the specialist areas of: private client work, including the administration of estates, capital taxation, charities, trusts and settlements, family provision, probate, court of protection and matrimonial finance; partnership; property litigation, including conveyancing, real property disputes, landlord and tenant, mortgages and securities, development contracts and manorial rights; company and insolvency; commercial litigation; financial services; banking; local government; and professional negligence.

Areas of work Private client, partnership and LLPs, property and commercial chancery.

Who should apply We are looking for a potential tenant. Candidates should have a real enthusiasm for our areas of practice, be of proven high academic ability and possess excellent powers of analysis, reasoning and presentation. In addition, the successful candidate will demonstrate sound judgement and be highly motivated. Our specific selection criteria are set out on our website and application form.

Pupillage programme The pupillage is structured so that our pupil can see the full range of chambers' work. Our pupil will have two pupil supervisors throughout the 12 months and will also sit with two other members of chambers. It is also likely that, throughout the pupillage, our pupil will undertake work for other members of chambers. Monitoring of a pupil's progress takes place at the end of pieces of work through discussion with their pupil supervisor and through monthly written reviews, rather than than by way of formal assessment.

When and how to apply The deadline for pupillage commencing October 2019 is likely to be 15 January 2018. Applicants should check chambers' website from December 2017 onwards for the definitive deadline. Applications must be made on chambers' application form, which will be available from chambers' website or from the clerks' room from December 2017. Shortlisted candidates will be invited for interview, will spend a day in chambers and will be asked to prepare a piece of written work.

We offer one 12-month pupillage.

Mini-pupillages Apply by application form, available on the website or from the clerks' room. Deadlines are 7 January, 15 July and 15 October.

Sponsorship/funding £60,000, with the option of drawing down up to a quarter in the year prior to pupillage.

Pupillages funded	1
Tenants	26
Tenancies in last 3 yrs	2
Mini-pupillages	yes
Remuneration for pupillage	£60,000

TEN OLD SQUARE

Old Square Chambers

10-11 Bedford Row, London WC1R 4BU
Tel: 020 7269 0300
Email: clerks@oldsquare.co.uk
Web: www.oldsquare.co.uk
🐦 oldsqchambers

Description of Chambers The defining quality of Old Square Chambers is excellence. This is the standard we set for ourselves in the delivery of services to our clients, and the criterion by which we assess prospective tenants and pupils. Many of our members hold part-time judicial positions, sit on specialist panels, act as mediators, and edit or contribute to leading practitioner texts. We are a highly specialised, forward thinking set, committed to expansion. Our objective is to select a small number of pupils with the aim of recruiting our tenants from them. Chambers operates an equality and diversity policy which fully complies with the Bar Standards Board's requirements. We are committed to ensuring all of our recruitment and selection processes are fair and that protected characteristics are safeguarded. We are based in Bedford Row but also operate from premises in Bristol. We offer pupillage at both locations.

Areas of work Our work is balanced between claimant and defendant or respondent, and includes the protection of individual rights. We work on behalf of trade unions, commercial organisations, the NHS and local and central government. In employment we cover all the relevant areas including: discrimination, collective action, individual rights, restraint of trade and human rights. We also have a thriving practice in the field of professional regulatory and disciplinary work, especially in the healthcare sector. In personal injury we have an excellent profile spanning all types of litigation. Particular areas of strength include catastrophic injury, disaster and multi-party litigation. In clinical law we have a number of expert practitioners encompassing all disputes affecting and involving the medical, dental, pharmaceutical and nursing professions. In product liability and health and safety compliance we engage in civil and criminal litigation of varying complexity as well as public inquiry work. In environmental law we represent corporate and individual defendants. Case experience includes prosecutions of major pollution incidents, permit breaches, marine regulation prosecutions, the release of hazardous or noxious substances and the escape of controlled waste. We also undertake human rights and public law work where it relates to our main fields of practice. Much of our work involves the use of European jurisprudence.

Who should apply We assess candidates on a number of criteria. These may change from year to year but generally include: intellectual ability (measured by academic or other achievement), potential as an advocate, interest in chambers' fields of practice, ability to cope with hard work and pressure, and interpersonal skills.

Pupillage programme Pupils are offered generous funding. Pupils will experience a wide variety of court and paperwork. There is also the opportunity to work closely with silks on complex and sometimes high profile cases.

When and how to apply As per Pupillage Gateway.

Mini-pupillages Apply online via our website.

Sponsorship/funding 2019 award will be £50,000, comprising of an award of £40,000 and guaranteed minimum earnings of £10,000, which may be exceeded depending on earnings in the second six. A draw down system facility is available for BPTC on application.

Pupillages funded	2
Tenants	79
Tenancies in last 3 yrs	6

Mini-pupillages   yes

Apply through Pupillage Gateway

Remuneration for pupillage
£50,000 including £10,000 guaranteed earnings

Minimum qualifications
2.1 degree preferred

OLD SQUARE CHAMBERS

Old Square Chambers

3 Orchard Court, St Augustines Yard, Bristol BS1 5DP
Tel: 0117 930 5100
Email: clerks@oldsquare.co.uk
Web: www.oldsquare.co.uk
🐦 oldsqchambers

Description of Chambers The defining quality of Old Square Chambers is excellence. This is the standard we set for ourselves in the delivery of services to our clients, and the criterion by which we assess prospective tenants and pupils. Many of our members hold part-time judicial positions, sit on specialist panels, act as mediators, and edit or contribute to leading practitioner texts. We are a highly specialised, forward thinking set, committed to expansion. Our objective is to select a small number of pupils with the aim of recruiting our tenants from them. Chambers operates an equality and diversity policy which fully complies with the Bar Standards Board's requirements. We are committed to ensuring all of our recruitment and selection processes are fair and that protected characteristics are safeguarded. Chambers operates from premises in Queen Square, Bristol and Bedford Row, London (see separate entry). The pupillage offered is at the Bristol premises.

Areas of work Our work is balanced between claimant and defendant or respondent, and includes the protection of individual rights. We work on behalf of trade unions, commercial organisations, the NHS and local and central government. In employment we cover all the relevant areas including discrimination, collective action, individual rights, restraint of trade and human rights. We also have a thriving practice in the field of professional regulatory and disciplinary work, especially in the healthcare sector. In personal injury we have an excellent profile spanning all types of litigation. Particular areas of strength include catastrophic injury, disaster and multi-party litigation. In clinical law we have a number of expert practitioners encompassing all disputes affecting and involving the medical, dental, pharmaceutical and nursing professions. In product liability and health and safety compliance we engage in civil and criminal litigation of varying complexity as well as public inquiry work. We also undertake human rights and public law work where it relates to our main fields of practice. Much of our work involves the use of European jurisprudence.

Who should apply We assess candidates on a number of criteria. These may change from year to year but generally include: intellectual ability (measured by academic or other achievement), potential as an advocate, interest in chambers' fields of practice, ability to cope with hard work and pressure, and interpersonal skills. We are looking for candidates with a strong link to Bristol who demonstrate a genuine desire to make Bristol and the surrounding area a long term-home.

Pupillage programme Pupils are offered generous funding and the level indicated may be subject to upwards review for pupils starting October 2018. Pupils will experience a wide variety of court and paperwork. There is also the opportunity to work closely with silks on complex and sometimes high profile cases.

When and how to apply As per Pupillage Gateway.

Mini-pupillages Apply online via our website.

Sponsorship/funding 2018 award will be £50,000, comprising of an award of £40,000 and guaranteed minimum earnings of £10,000, which may be exceeded depending on earnings in the second six. A draw down system facility is available for BPTC on application.

Pupillages funded	2
Tenants	79
Tenancies in last 3 yrs	6
Mini-pupillages	yes

Apply through Pupillage Gateway

Remuneration for pupillage
£50,000 including £10,000 guaranteed earnings

Minimum qualifications
2.1 degree preferred

Remember to cite *The Training Contract & Pupillage Handbook* on your application form if you apply to this chambers.

582 THE TRAINING CONTRACT & PUPILLAGE HANDBOOK

FIVE PAPER Ground Floor, 5 Paper Buildings, Temple, London EC4Y 7HB **Tel:** 020 7815 3200 **Email:** pupillage@fivepaper.com **Apply to:** Miss Joanna Brownhill	Leading set in *Chambers & Partners* and the *Legal 500*. Five specialist practice groups: property, commercial, employment, family and business immigration and regulatory.	PF 2 T 43 T_{L3Y} 3 MP yes
4 PAPER BUILDINGS First Floor, Temple, London EC4Y 7EX **Tel:** 020 7427 5200 **Email:** pupillage@4pb.com **Apply to:** The Pupillage Committee	4 Paper Buildings is an exclusive specialist family law set and has a reputation as one of the friendliest sets in which to undertake pupillage.	PF 3 T 79 T_{L3Y} 6 MP yes
5 PAPER BUILDINGS 5 Paper Buildings, Temple, London EC4Y 7HB **Tel:** 020 7583 6117 **Email:** clerks@5pb.co.uk Apply through Pupillage Gateway	We are a leading set, specialising in criminal law. Commercial fraud is an acknowledged strength. Other expertise includes trading law, public inquiries and disciplinary tribunals.	PF 2 T 46 T_{L3Y} 6 MP yes
9 PARK PLACE 9 Park Place, Cardiff CF10 3DP **Tel:** 029 2038 2731 **Email:** pupillage@9parkplace.co.uk **Apply to:** Mr Matthew Barry	9 Park Place is a leading set offering a wide spectrum of legal specialisation. Chambers offers two funded pupillages each year.	PF 2 T 60 T_{L3Y} 6 MP yes
30 PARK PLACE Cardiff CF10 3BS **Tel:** 029 2039 8421 **Email:** pupcom@30parkplace.co.uk Apply through Pupillage Gateway	A mutli-disciplinary chambers highly ranked in the major legal directories; offering expert legal advice and representation, across a wide range of practice areas.	PF 1 T 67 T_{L3Y} 18 MP yes
PARK SQUARE BARRISTERS 6 Park Square, Leeds LS1 2LW **Tel:** 0113 245 9763 **Email:** pupillages@psqb.co.uk **Apply to:** Mr Simon Clegg	PSQB is the largest multi-disciplinary Chambers on the NE Circuit. We offer exceptional training, resources and support in pupillage.	PF 2 T 125 T_{L3Y} 6 MP yes
PARKLANE PLOWDEN CHAMBERS 19 Westgate, Leeds LS1 2RD **Tel:** 0113 228 500 **Email:** pupillagecivil@parklaneplowden.co.uk **Apply to:** Mr Andrew Sugarman	We are likely to offer up to four pupillages across our civil and family practice areas to commence October 2019.	PF Up to 4 T 77 T_{L3Y} 6 MP yes
5 PUMP COURT Ground Floor, Temple, London EC4Y 7AP **Tel:** 020 7353 2532 **Email:** clerks@5pumpcourt.com Apply through Pupillage Gateway	Chambers is looking for one pupil who has a genuine interest in a common law pupillage and one who wishes to specialise in criminal law.	PF 2 T 57 T_{L3Y} 3 MP yes

PF = Pupillages funded / *T* = Tenants / *T_{L3Y}* = Tenancies in last 3 years / *MP* = Mini-pupillages offered

3PB

Chambers of Nigel Lickley QC, 3 Paper Buildings, Temple, London EC4Y 7EU
Tel: 020 7583 8055
Email: pupillage@3pb.co.uk
Web: www.3pb.co.uk

Description of Chambers Based in London, Winchester, Bournemouth, Oxford, Bristol and our newly opened Birmingham centre, 3PB is a modern, progressive set with an enviable reputation for our legal expertise. Our barristers and staff are professional, friendly and approachable and there is a good team atmosphere in chambers.

Areas of work We have both breadth and depth through the number and quality of our members. The work of chambers covers a broad spread of common law, commercial and chancery work. Our work includes contract, personal injury, employment, landlord and tenant, professional negligence, planning and local government. We also have a specialist family team who deal with financial remedies, private Children Act work and public law children work. In addition we have specialist teams in technology and construction, company and partnership, insolvency, education and intellectual property. Our chancery practitioners deal with matters ranging from probate disputes through to trusts and tax. In real property we are extensively instructed in boundary disputes, covenants, easements, village greens and planning. Our crime team is superb, dealing with all aspects of crime including the most serious murders and white collar crimes. We also have a number of members who are mediators and adjudicators, as well as a number who sit in courts and/or tribunals.

Who should apply Chambers seeks pupils with strong academic and intellectual abilities, coupled with a drive and determination to succeed and the ability to apply practical skills. We welcome applications from candidates from all backgrounds. Our marking system does not take into account A levels or which university a candidate has attended.

Pupillage programme We regard our pupils as the long-term future of our chambers and aim to recruit and retain the very best. We offer up to four funded pupillages each year and provide an unique internal training programme which not only covers advocacy exercises, drafting skills and marshalling opportunities, but also the practical and business skills required to maintain a successful practice. Chambers also pays for the compulsory external training. Pupils frequently appear in court during their second six, whilst continuing with their education.

When and how to apply We recruit through the Pupillage Gateway, with the time windows as advertised.

Mini-pupillages Applications for mini-pupillages are considered on their merits. Candidates must be over eighteen and have either undertaken or be in the process of undertaking tertiary education. Applications forms may be downloaded from our website.

Sponsorship/funding 3PB offers each pupil an award of £30,000 (presently under review). This is made up of a grant of £15,000 which is paid over the first six months in nine tranches. The first payment is made the month before pupillage commences in order to ensure that pupils have sufficient funds for their first month in chambers and a double payment immediately before the commencement of the second six. Once a pupil is able to accept instructions in his or her own right, chambers has ample work available. Pupils will have guaranteed earnings of £15,000 during their second six, with assistance from chambers if necessary.

Pupillages funded	3
Tenants	170
Tenancies in last 3 yrs	26

Mini-pupillages — yes

Apply through Pupillage Gateway

Remuneration for pupillage £27,000 (made up of £15,000 award and £12,000 guaranteed earnings)

Minimum qualifications 2.1 degree

4 Pump Court

Temple, London EC4Y 7AN
Tel: 020 7842 5555
Email: chambers@4pumpcourt.com
Web: www.4pumpcourt.com
🐦 4pumpcourt

Description of Chambers 4 Pump Court is one of London's leading sets of chambers, with a reputation for excellence in advocacy. We believe we offer an exceptionally friendly and relaxed environment in which to complete pupillage.

Areas of work The work of chambers covers virtually every aspect of commercial law, but with particular emphasis on insurance and reinsurance, professional negligence, construction and information technology and telecommunications.

Who should apply We look for candidates with sound academic qualifications (minimum 2.1), impressive academic references and the ability to express themselves clearly and attractively, on paper as well as orally.

Pupillage programme During their first six months, each pupil is assigned to two barristers for three months each. During their second six months, each pupil has only one pupil supervisor, but will usually be conducting his or her own cases as well.

When and how to apply By 13 January 2018 to begin October 2019. The application form is available on request (to Claudia Dine) or on the chambers' website.

Mini-pupillages Limited places available throughout the year upon application by completing the application form available to download from our website and return to minipupillage@4pumpcourt.com.

Sponsorship/funding Usually two funded pupillages with awards of £70,000, of which up to £15,000 may be advanced during the Bar Professional Training Course. Any fees earned in the second six months are in addition to the award.

Pupillages funded	2
Tenants	65
Tenancies in last 3 yrs	6

Mini-pupillages yes

Applications contact
Claudia Dine

Remuneration for pupillage
£70,000 plus earnings in
second six (October 2019)

Minimum qualifications
2.1 degree

Pump Court Tax Chambers

16 Bedford Row, London WC1R 4EF
Tel: 020 7414 8080
Email: pupils@pumptax.com
Web: www.pumptax.com
🐦 pumptax

Description of Chambers Pump Court Tax Chambers is the largest set specialising in tax law (35 members, 11 silks).

Areas of work Members of chambers undertake litigation and provide advice in relation to all areas of tax law, both personal and corporate. Members appear in courts at all levels from the tax tribunals to the Supreme Court and the CJEU.

Who should apply Anyone interested in practising in an area of law requiring an analytical mind and a grasp of other areas of law, especially trust law and European law. Tax advice provides intellectually stimulating challenges, while tax litigation (which is an increasing part of our work) often involves novel points of law, as well as complex statutory interpretation and factual analysis. Many recent developments in the law of restitution have been tested in tax cases.

Pupillage programme Chambers offers 12-month pupillages. Pupils generally spend their first 10 weeks with one pupil supervisor followed by four to six weeks with three other supervisors. They also spend time with silks and senior juniors. This allows them to see a wide variety of work and also gives members at different levels of seniority the opportunity to give them feedback.

When and how to apply Chambers keeps its membership of the Pupillage Gateway under review and has chosen not to participate in the Pupillage Gateway for pupillages starting in October 2019. Details of the application process will be pubished on our website in September 2017.

Mini-pupillages We welcome applications for mini-pupillages. Mini-pupillages of three days' duration are available throughout the year. Please apply by CV and covering letter, marked for the attention of the mini-pupillage secretary, by post or email. Further details (including details of deadlines for applications) are available on our website.

Sponsorship/funding Pupils are typically awarded £60,000, £12,000 of which can be drawn down during Bar school.

Pupillages funded	1-2
Tenants	35
Tenancies in last 3 yrs	2
Mini-pupillages	yes
Apply by CV	
Remuneration for pupillage	
Typically £60,000	
Minimum qualifications	
Generally, a 2.1 degree	

PUMP COURT
TAX CHAMBERS

Remember to cite *The Training Contract & Pupillage Handbook* on your application form if you apply to this chambers.

586 THE TRAINING CONTRACT & PUPILLAGE HANDBOOK

6 PUMP COURT
First Floor, Temple, London EC4Y 7AR
Tel: 020 7797 8400
Email: clerks@6pumpcourt.co.uk
Apply through Pupillage Gateway

Chambers' work is divided between four specialist groups: criminal law, planning and environmental law, civil litigation and family law. Chambers also has an annexe in Maidstone.

PF 0
T 40
T$_{L3Y}$ 5
MP yes

PUMP COURT CHAMBERS
3 Pump Court, Temple, London EC4Y 7AJ
Tel: 020 7353 0711
Email: j.lee@pumpcourtchambers.com
Apply through Pupillage Gateway

Large common law chambers based in London and on the Western Circuit, specialising in civil, criminal, family and international work.

PF 2
T 92
T$_{L3Y}$ 5
MP yes

---

1 PUMP COURT CHAMBERS
Elm Court, Temple, London EC4Y 7AH
Tel: 020 7842 7070
Email: agi@1pumpcourt.co.uk
Apply through Pupillage Gateway

Chambers is committed to removing inequality and promoting diversity and justice. We provide a specialist first class representation, particularly to publicly funded and unfunded clients.

PF 2
T 75
T$_{L3Y}$ 5
MP yes

QEB HOLLIS WHITEMAN
1-2 Laurence Pountney Hill, London EC4R 0EU
Tel: 020 7933 8855
Email: pupillage@qebhw.co.uk
Apply to: Mr Tom Kark QC

First-class set specialising in criminal law, professional disciplinary regulation, inquests and Inquiries, with an extensive in-house advocacy training programme.

PF 4
T 66
T$_{L3Y}$ 5
MP yes

QUEEN SQUARE CHAMBERS
56 Queen Square, Bristol BS1 4PR
Tel: 0117 921 1966
Email: pupillage@qs-c.co.uk
Apply to: Mr James Bromige

Chambers is located in Bristol and our members are instructed in cases nationwide, with a particular focus on the Western and Wales and Chester Circuits.

PF 1
T 39
T$_{L3Y}$ 6
MP yes

THREE RAYMOND BUILDINGS
Gray's Inn, London WC1R 5BH
Tel: 020 7400 6400
Email: pupillage@3rblaw.com
Apply to: Mrs Donna Garner

Leading set with a national and international reputation. Expertise in crime, fraud, extradition, public law, licensing/regulatory law, health and safety, professional discipline, police law.

PF Up to 3
T 51
T$_{L3Y}$ 6
MP no

5RB
5 Gray's Inn Square, Gray's Inn, London WC1R 5AH
Tel: 020 7242 2902
Email: pupillage@5rb.com
Apply through Pupillage Gateway

Chambers is particularly well known for expertise in all areas of media and entertainment law, intellectual property and sports law.

PF Up to 2
T 28
T$_{L3Y}$ 5
MP yes

RED LION CHAMBERS
18 Red Lion Court, London EC4A 3EB
Tel: 020 7520 6000
Email: clerks@18rlc.co.uk
Apply to: Miss Joanna Hardy

Red Lion Chambers is one of the leading sets specialising in criminal and regulatory law. Members of chambers undertake work of the highest quality for both the prosecution and defence.

PF 3
T 88
T$_{L3Y}$ 7
MP yes

PF = Pupillages funded / **T** = Tenants / **T$_{L3Y}$** = Tenancies in last 3 years / **MP** = Mini-pupillages offered

Quadrant Chambers

Chambers of Luke Parsons QC, Quadrant House, 10 Fleet Street, London EC4Y 1AU
Tel: 020 7583 4444
Email: pupillage@quadrantchambers.com
Web: www.quadrantchambers.com

Description of Chambers We are a leading set of barristers specialising in commercial law. We act as advocates in court, arbitrations and inquiries, and provide specialist legal advice to clients from around the world in a wide range of industry areas. A number of us also act as arbitrators and mediators. Many of us are qualified to practise in other jurisdictions, including Australia, the BVI, California, Germany, Hong Kong, New York and South Africa. Distinguished former members of Quadrant Chambers have gone on to chair high-profile public enquiries, and to sit as judges in the High Court (QBD, Commercial, Administrative and Admiralty Courts), DIFC Courts, European General Court, Court of Appeal, House of Lords, Privy Council and UK Supreme Court.

Areas of work We undertake all types of commercial law. We are market leaders in shipping and aviation, and have a very strong reputation in banking and finance, energy, commercial chancery, insurance and reinsurance, insolvency and restructuring, commodities and international trade, general commercial litigation and arbitration, sports and media. Our work has a strongly international flavour, and most of it involves international clients.

Who should apply We look for candidates with a very strong academic background. Successful applicants will generally have (or be predicted) a first class degree, and they must have/be predicted at least a high 2.1 to apply. Candidates must have excellent analytical abilities, outstanding written and oral communication skills and the ability to perform under pressure. They must also be able to demonstrate that they have the commitment, energy and robustness to succeed in the competitive world of the Commercial Bar. Successful candidates often read law for their first degree, and an increasing number also have postgraduate law degrees. However, these are not pre-requisites. We welcome applications from candidates who have studied any serious academic subject at university.

Pupillage programme We offer up to three pupillages of 12 months' duration each year. We aim to develop in our pupils the skills, knowledge and sound judgment they will need to become successful commercial barristers. During their first and second six months, pupils sit with up to three pupil supervisors and are exposed to a wide range of high quality commercial work. Tenancy decisions are made at the end of June. Pupils also undertake advocacy and written assessments throughout their pupillage.

When and how to apply Quadrant Chambers uses the Pupillage Gateway to manage its applications. Thereafter our process involves a series of interviews and a test set. Please see our website for further details.

Mini-pupillages Mini-pupillages are available in March/April, July, September and December of each year. Places are limited. Please see our website for details.

Sponsorship/funding Pupils receive an award of £65,000, part of which may be advanced during the BPTC year. Pupils also have the opportunity to do fee-earning work during their second six.

Pupillages funded	3
Tenants	62
Tenancies in last 3 yrs	5
Mini-pupillages	yes

Apply through Pupillage Gateway

Remuneration for pupillage
£65,000 (earnings not included)

Minimum qualifications
1st or high 2.1

Queen Elizabeth Building

Chambers of Lewis Marks QC, Queen Elizabeth Building, Temple, London EC4Y 9BS
Tel: 020 7797 7837
Email: clerks@qeb.co.uk
Web: www.qeb.co.uk

Description of Chambers QEB is a leading set of family law chambers, particularly well-known for dealing with the financial consequences of divorce, but with immense experience in all aspects of family law including: jurisdictional disputes, foreign divorces, pre-marital agreements, civil partnerships, injunctions both financial and domestic, private law child work, child abduction, Inheritance Act claims and disputes between former cohabitees. In addition some members practise in general common law with particular emphasis on personal injury and professional negligence work.

QEB has been established for well over 100 years and is consistently rated as one of the top-ranking sets for family law. Many members of chambers are listed as leaders in their field in the annual publications *Chambers & Partners* and *Legal 500*.

Members of QEB have been involved in many of the most important cases of legal principle, including: *White*, *Sorrell*, *Miller*, *Spencer*, *Marano*, *Robson*, *Schofield*, *Jones*, *Z v Z* (No.2), *Petrodel v Prest*, *Mittal*, *Cooper-Hohn*, *AB v JJB* (EMR Modification), *Arif v Anwar*, *Broomfield*, *A v B* (Art.19 and Seisin B 11a) and *Fields*. Many members of Chambers have continued into high judicial office. Currently, Lord Wilson sits in the Supreme Court, while Lord Justice Moylan sits in the Court of Appeal.

Who should apply The practice of family law is infinitely varied and clients come from all walks of life. International and conflict of laws issues arise increasingly often. An ability to deal not only with complex financial disputes, often involving commercial issues, but also with child-related or other emotionally fraught and sensitive situations, is essential. We are looking for applicants with a strong academic record (minimum 2.1 law or non-law degree save in exceptional circumstances), good legal and analytical skills, and an ability to communicate sensitively with a wide range of people at a critical time in their lives.

Pupillage programme QEB offers two pupillages each year. A pupillage at QEB offers top-quality training and very good financial support in a busy, friendly environment. A 12-month pupillage involves three pupil supervisors, but pupils are also encouraged to work with other tenants at all levels to gain a broad experience of our work. All our pupils are automatically considered candidates for tenancy and new tenants are only recruited from QEB pupils. Our reputation is such that where a pupil is not taken on, he or she is usually well placed elsewhere.

When and how to apply Chambers is a part of the Pupillage Gateway system. Applicants should apply in early 2018 for a pupillage beginning in September 2019. Please consult the Pupillage Gateway website for details of the timetable.

Mini-pupillages Applications for mini-pupillages are to be made by application form. Please consult our website at www.qeb.co.uk for full details.

Sponsorship/funding Chambers offers a pupillage award of £35,000 pa minimum, plus earnings in the second six and from devilling. Pupils do not pay chambers' expenses or clerks' fees. Chambers also funds the compulsory inn advocacy and practice management training courses.

Pupillages funded	2
Tenants	33
Tenancies in last 3 yrs	4
Mini-pupillages	yes

Apply through Pupillage Gateway

Remuneration for pupillage
£35,000 minimum (plus earnings in second six from devilling)

Minimum qualifications
2.1 degree, save in exceptional circumstances

Radcliffe Chambers

11 New Square, Lincoln's Inn, London WC2A 3QB
Tel: 020 7831 0081
Email: clerks@radcliffechambers.com
Web: www.radcliffechambers.com
🐦 radcliffechmbrs

Description of Chambers Described by the *Legal 500* as "a go-to set" for traditional chancery and commercial work. Radcliffe Chambers is a modern set of chambers based in Lincoln's Inn. We have 55 barristers, including five QCs, with many recommendations in the current editions of *Chambers & Partners* and the *Legal 500*.

Areas of work We are a top-ranked set for charity law and are highly regarded in the fields of real property, trusts and estates, pensions, company and insolvency, consumer credit and mortgages and landlord and tenant. Members also act in the related areas of professional negligence. We provide advice in contentious and non-contentious matters and appear before all levels of courts and tribunals including Court of Protection work.

Who should apply Candidates should have a strong academic record. You should possess at least a good 2.1 degree (this does not need to be in law) and be able to demonstrate a clear and genuine interest in practising at the Chancery Bar.

Pupillage programme For the pupillage year commencing October 2019, we will offer up to two 12-month pupillages, each of which carry a pupillage award of £60,000, plus any earnings generated during the second six months of pupillage, when you should expect to be undertaking your own caseload as well as completing your pupillage training. We are willing to consider any request for part of the pupillage award to be drawn down during the BPTC year. Chambers also pays for all training courses required during pupillage.

Our members undertake a wide range of traditional chancery and commercial work and we aim to give our pupils as much exposure to our different practice areas as possible. During your pupillage, you will sit with four different supervisors across different practice areas and you will also work with a number of other members, assisting them with their cases. Unlike most other chambers, Radcliffe Chambers has for many years operated a 'super pupil' policy. We have grown considerably in recent years and as a result of this growth we have decided to offer up to two funded pupillages for the pupillage year beginning October 2019, with a view to offering tenancies to both pupils at the end of the year if circumstances permit.

Our pupils are encouraged to gain as much advocacy experience as possible during their second six. In recent years, our second six pupils have been able to undertake a significant amount of their own court work.

When and how to apply Applications are made via a CV and covering letter addressed to our Pupillage Committee and the deadline for applications for the pupillage year commencing October 2019 is 5 January 2018. Your application should highlight (i) any awards or prizes you may have obtained, (ii) your legal experience (such as mini-pupillages, marshalling and other legal work experience), (iii) your experience and achievements in oral advocacy (particularly mooting and other legal advocacy) and (iv) your reasons for applying for pupillage (and, in particular, your reasons for wishing to join Radcliffe Chambers).

Mini-pupillages We offer a number of unassessed two-day mini-pupillages during the year. Applications are accepted from those in their second or third year of a law degree or on the GDL. Please see our website for further details.

Sponsorship/funding Radcliffe Chambers is a supporter of the Bar Council's Social Mobility Foundation placement scheme and a partner chambers of the Pegasus Access Scheme run by the Inner Temple.

Pupillages funded	2
Tenants	55
Tenancies in last 3 yrs	3
Mini-pupillages	yes
Apply by CV	
Remuneration for pupillage	£60,000
Minimum qualifications	2.1 degree

Radcliffe Chambers

REGENCY BARRISTERS CHAMBERS 45 Priestgate, Peterborough PE1 1LB **Tel:** 01733 315 215 **Email:** clerks@regencychambers.law.co.uk **Apply to:** Mr Nigel Sleight	Family law and civil litigation chambers.

PF 0
T 14
T_{L3Y} 1
MP no

SELBORNE CHAMBERS 10 Essex Street, London WC2R 3AA **Tel:** 020 7420 9500 **Email:** pupillage@selbornechambers.co.uk **Apply to:** The Pupillage Secretary	Chambers usually offers one 12-month pupillage.

PF 1
T 30
T_{L3Y} 3
MP yes

SERJEANTS' INN CHAMBERS 85 Fleet Street, London EC4Y 1AE **Tel:** 020 7427 5000 **Email:** jfarrell@serjeantsinn.com Apply through Pupillage Gateway	Serjeants' Inn Chambers is a busy, progressive and friendly set of chambers. Our principal practice areas include medical, police, regulatory and disciplinary and employment law.

PF 0
T 61
T_{L3Y} 4
MP yes

11 SOUTH SQUARE Gray's Inn, London WC1R 5EY **Tel:** 020 7405 1222 **Email:** clerks@11southsquare.com Apply through Pupillage Gateway	11 South Square is a leading set of barristers chambers specialising in intellectual property law as well as information technology and media and entertainment work.

PF 1
T 17
T_{L3Y} 2
MP yes

5 ST ANDREW'S HILL 5 St Andrew's Hill, London EC4V 5BZ **Tel:** 020 7332 5400 **Email:** clerks@5sah.co.uk Apply through Pupillage Gateway	A leading criminal set with an excellent reputation in financial and white collar crime. Chambers prides itself on a friendly, diverse and relaxed working atmosphere.

PF 2
T 62
T_{L3Y} 6
MP yes

ST IVES CHAMBERS Chambers of Nicholas Cole, 1-3 Whittall Street, Birmingham B4 6DH **Tel:** 0121 236 0863 **Email:** clerks@stiveschambers.co.uk **Apply to:** Mr Timothy Bowe	St Ives Chambers is an expanding general common law set with a strong local and national reputation across all practice areas.

PF Up to 3
T 37
T_{L3Y} 12
MP yes

9 ST JOHN STREET CHAMBERS 9 St John Street, Manchester M3 4DN **Tel:** 0161 955 9000 **Email:** ruth.bailey@9sjs.com Apply through Pupillage Gateway	Recognised as one of the leading sets of barristers, we have many members of chambers who are acknowledged leaders in their particular field of expertise.

PF 2
T 96
T_{L3Y} 7
MP yes

18 ST JOHN STREET CHAMBERS 18-20 St John Street, Manchester M3 4EA **Tel:** 0161 278 1800 **Email:** pupils@18sjs.com **Apply to:** The Chambers Manager	Chambers was founded in 1973 and has developed into a strong mixed set practising in the principal specialist groups: crime, civil, family and chancery/commercial.

PF Up to 4
T 74
T_{L3Y} 6
MP yes

PF = Pupillages funded / **T** = Tenants / **T**$_{L3Y}$ = Tenancies in last 3 years / **MP** = Mini-pupillages offered

Serle Court

6 New Square, Lincoln's Inn, London WC2A 3QS
Tel: 020 7242 6105
Email: pupillage@serlecourt.co.uk
Web: www.serlecourt.co.uk

Description of Chambers Serle Court has "a phenomenally good reputation that is really well deserved", is a "'first port of call' for a wide range of commercial chancery cases", offers "a variety of skill sets that others can't provide" and is home to "some of the biggest names at the Bar" – *Chambers & Partners*.

Serle Court is one of the leading commercial chancery sets with 64 barristers including 25 silks. Widely recognised as a leading set, Serle Court is recommended in 10 different areas of practice by the legal directories. Serle Court has a stimulating and inclusive work environment and a forward looking approach.

Areas of work Litigation, arbitration, mediation and advisory services across the full range of chancery and commercial practice areas including: civil fraud, commercial litigation, company, insolvency, offshore, partnership and LLP, trusts and probate, and property.

Who should apply Chambers is interested in well-rounded candidates from any background. Chambers looks for highly motivated individuals with outstanding intellectual ability, combined with a practical approach, sound judgment, an ability to develop good client relationships and the potential to become excellent advocates. Serle Court has a reputation "for consistent high quality" and for having members who are "highly intelligent, user-friendly, approachable and supportive" and seeks the same qualities in pupils. Chambers generally requires a degree classification of a good 2.1 as a minimum. Serle Court is committed to equality and diversity and encourages and welcomes applications from women, people of minority ethnic origin and people with disabilities, as well as candidates from other groups which are under-represented in the legal sector.

Pupillage programme Pupils sit with four pupil supervisors in order to experience a broad range of work. Chambers aims to recruit up to three pupils each year. Serle Court offers an excellent preparation for successful practice, a genuinely friendly and supportive environment, the opportunity to learn from some of the leading barristers in their field and a real prospect of tenancy.

When and how to apply Application deadline is 12.00 noon GMT on 17 January 2018 for pupillage to begin in 2019, although do check the Serle Court website in case this changes. Contact pupillage@serlecourt.co.uk for an application form or download one from the website at www.serlecourt.co.uk.

Mini-pupillages About 30 available each year. The application form is available at www.serlecourt.co.uk.

Sponsorship/funding Serle Court offers awards of £65,000 for 12 months, of which up to £22,000 can be drawn down during the BPTC year. Chambers also provides an income guarantee worth up to £120,000 over the first two years of practice.

Pupillages funded	Up to 3
Tenants	64
Tenancies in last 3 yrs	6
Mini-pupillages	yes
Apply via website	
Remuneration for pupillage	
£65,000	
Minimum qualifications	
Good 2.1 degree	

serle court

South Square

3-4 South Square, Gray's Inn, London WC1R 5HP
Tel: 020 7696 9900
Email: pupillage@southsquare.com
Web: www.southsquare.com

Description of Chambers South Square is a highly respected and successful commercial set involved in complex and high-profile international and domestic commercial litigation. Members are recognised as leaders in their fields in all the key legal directories and have acted in some of the most important commercial cases of the last decade – including Lehman Brothers, MF Global, Madoff, Northern Rock, Formula One and the LIBOR litigation. *Chambers UK* Bar Guide describes South Square as having "members with unrivalled talent and "excellent in everything they do".

Areas of work South Square's work is mainly focussed on financial and banking issues. We are the market leader for restructuring and insolvency, and widely recognised for our work in banking and finance litigation. Members also specialise in commercial litigation, company law and civil fraud related disputes. South Square's work has a significant international focus and members regularly appear in the courts and tribunals of international jurisdictions, notably the Cayman Islands, British Virgin Islands, Bermuda, Dubai, Hong Kong and Singapore.

Who should apply Chambers looks to recruit up to three high calibre pupils with a strong academic record and the potential to become an outstanding commercial barrister. The minimum academic qualification is a 2.1 degree. Pupils are selected from a broad range of backgrounds and experience, whether recent university graduates or those seeking a second career at the Bar. A number of our members have degrees in law, some have taken non-law degrees and then sat the CPE/GDL, and others have started their career in another sector before becoming a barrister.

Pupillage programme Pupils are welcomed into all areas of chambers' life and are provided with a structured programme designed to train and equip them for a successful practice in a dynamic and challenging environment. Pupils sit with a number of supervisors for periods of six to eight weeks to experience a range of practices and work. Pupillage is not run as a competition between pupils and chambers' approach is to recruit all pupils as tenants who meet the required standard.

When and how to apply The deadline for pupillages commencing in October 2019 is 20 January 2018. Applications must be on the chambers' application form which will be available to download from the website.

Mini-pupillages Chambers also offers five-day funded mini-pupillages carrying an award of up to £750, and two-day unfunded mini-pupillages. See the chambers' website for further details www.southsquare.com/pupillage.

Sponsorship/funding Pupils receive awards of £65,000 per annum (reviewable annually). £20,000 of the pupillage award may be paid in advance for living expenses during the BPTC. As a junior tenant you would receive a number of benefits including; subsidised travel and conference fees, no rent during your first 15 months of tenancy and no receipts charge for the first six months, subsidised membership of key professional associations for the first two years, and assistance and training in financial planning and business development.

Pupillages funded   Up to 3
Tenants   44
Tenancies in last 3 yrs   5

Mini-pupillages   yes

Applications contact
The Pupillage Administrator

Remuneration for pupillage
£65,000 (reviewable annually)

Minimum qualifications
2.1 degree

5 Stone Buildings

Lincoln's Inn, London WC2A 3XT
Tel: 020 7242 6201
Email: clerks@5sblaw.com
Web: www.5sblaw.com
🐦 5sblaw

Description of Chambers 5 Stone Buildings is one of the outstanding sets of Chancery chambers with many distinguished present and former members, including a number of current and former law lords. We have 33 members, of whom seven are silks. Chambers is consistently ranked highly in the legal directories and the vast majority of our members are recommended practitioners. When compared to the largest chancery sets, chambers is relatively small. We believe that our size and ethos enables us to ensure that pupils and young tenants are trained and clerked properly and are well prepared for the problems and opportunities which practice will throw at them. All members of chambers, however senior, are always willing to assist other members, however junior, and to provide advice and guidance when requested. Generous terms are offered to junior tenants in their first years of practice, including heavily subsidised rent and an income guarantee.

Areas of work Members' work covers a wide span of civil law with an emphasis on chancery work, from specialist wills, trust and probate, pension and revenue work through to real property and professional negligence. Chambers is instructed by a wide range of solicitors, from the largest City firms to sole practitioners outside London. Many members have practices involving work from the major offshore financial centres.

Who should apply Applicants should normally have at least a 2.1 degree. Our policy is only to offer pupillages to candidates whom we believe to be potential tenants. We welcome applications from law and non-law graduates alike.

Pupillage programme We aim to offer one 12-month pupillage each year and to recruit tenants from our pupils. Pupils will normally sit with at least three pupil supervisors during that period with a view to experiencing a wide range of work. Pupils are given regular feedback as to how they might improve or refine their work.

When and how to apply Chambers is not a member of Pupillage Gateway. Applications for pupillage commencing in October 2019 must be made in writing on chambers' application form, which can be downloaded from our website at www.5sblaw.com. Applications should be addressed to 'The Pupillage Committee' or sent by email to pupillage@5sblaw.com. Applications must be received by 4pm on 5 January 2018. Please see our website for full details of the recruitment process.

Mini-pupillages We offer a limited number of mini-pupillages each year for periods of three days. Details and a timetable for applications can be found on our website at www.5sblaw.com.

Sponsorship/funding Up to £60,000 per pupillage, £15,000 of which can be drawn down during the BPTC year.

Pupillages funded	1
Tenants	33
Tenancies in last 3 yrs	4
Mini-pupillages	yes
Applications contact	Chambers' Administrator
Remuneration for pupillage	Up to £60,000
Minimum qualifications	2.1 degree

5 Stone Buildings

Remember to cite *The Training Contract & Pupillage Handbook* on your application form if you apply to this chambers.

594 THE TRAINING CONTRACT & PUPILLAGE HANDBOOK

St John's Chambers

101 Victoria Street, Bristol BS1 6PU
Tel: 0117 923 4700
Email: officemanager@stjohnschambers.co.uk
Web: www.stjohnschambers.co.uk
🐦 stjohnschambers

Description of Chambers St John's Chambers is one of the largest and most prestigious barristers' sets in the South West, offering specialist advice and services in all major areas of civil law. St John's Chambers is recognised nationally as providing first-class legal advice and representation in the six core practice groups: commercial (company and commercial, property, wills, trusts and tax), personal injury, family, public and administrative law, clinical negligence and employment.

Areas of work Administrative law, agriculture and rural affairs, banking, construction and engineering, children, civil fraud, clinical negligence, company, commercial dispute resolution, court of protection, employment, environmental, family finance including ToLATA and Inheritance Act, health and safety, housing, industrial disease, inquests, insolvency, intellectual property, licensing, partnership, personal injury, planning, property and real estate, property and insurance litigation, professional negligence, regulatory and disciplinary, tax advisory and dispute resolution, travel litigation and jurisdiction disputes, town and village greens, wills, trusts and tax.

Who should apply St John's Chambers will be recruiting outside of the Pupillage Gateway. We look to recruit top quality applicants with the ability to analyse information quickly and to present arguments succinctly and persuasively. The typical successful applicant will have strong academic credentials (subject to any extenuating circumstances) together with experience of mooting, public speaking, debating or presentations and a desire to excel. We also welcome interest from suitably qualified professionals who are changing careers. While pupillage can offer experience across practice groups, market forces generally require specialisation as the norm once tenancy has been offered. Pupils are therefore expected to focus on key areas during pupillage.

Pupillage programme Each year the pupillage committee, with the heads of each practice group, defines the pupillage requirements for the following year. As a pupil at St John's Chambers, your pupillage will cover all necessary aspects of your specialist area(s).

When and how to apply Application dates and details will be found on the website from January 2018. Should you have any general enquiries about pupillage then please do not hesitate to contact Isabelle Mills at isabelle.mills@stjohnschambers.co.uk.

Mini-pupillages Mini-pupillages (non-assessed) are an opportunity to experience life at the independent Bar. Applications for mini-pupillage are considered on a quarterly basis. The ideal time to apply is: i) if you are studying law and you are a second year student or ii) you are in your third year or studying the BPTC, but we will consider applications before then, especially from non-law candidates. Please see our website for details. Student visits are not available.

Sponsorship/funding We offer two funded pupillages with awards each of £35,000 in the first 12 months. Three pupillages will be offered depending on recruitment needs. In general terms, funded pupillage means that chambers will guarantee a pupil's income each month for the 12-month period of pupillage. This is subject to a clawback to the extent of any fees actually received during the second six months of pupillage.

Pupillages funded	2
Tenants	83
Tenancies in last 3 yrs	7
Mini-pupillages	yes

Apply to
Check website for details

Remuneration for pupillage
£35,000

Minimum qualifications
2.1 and would consider 2.2 degree with extenuating circumstances

St John's
CHAMBERS

ST JOHN'S BUILDINGS 24-28a St John Street, Manchester M3 4DJ **Tel:** 0161 214 1500 **Email:** clerk@stjohnsbuildings.co.uk **Apply to:** Mr Mike Fry	A leading Manchester/Preston/ Chester common law set with a strong reputation and acknowledged collegial culture. Family, PI/clinical negligence, crime, employment, commercial and public/admin law. Modern, efficient and friendly.	PF 1 T 156 T_{L3Y} 10 MP yes
ST MARY'S CHAMBERS 26-28 High Pavement, Nottingham NG1 1HN **Tel:** 0115 950 3503 **Email:** clerks@stmarysflc.co.uk Apply through Pupillage Gateway	A well established specialist family law set practising throughout the East Midlands and beyond. Further expansion is expected.	PF 2 T 32 T_{L3Y} 4 MP yes
ST PAUL'S CHAMBERS St Paul's House, 23 Park Square, Leeds LS1 2ND **Tel:** 0113 245 5866 **Email:** clerks@stpaulschambers.com **Apply to:** Secretary of Pupillage Committee	Founded in 1982, St Paul's Chambers now comprises 39 tenants working in complementary areas of expertise, in order to provide a consistent service across a broad range of legal fields.	PF 0 T 44 T_{L3Y} 4 MP yes
ST PHILIPS CHAMBERS 55 Temple Row, Birmingham B2 5LS **Tel:** 0121 246 7000 **Email:** pupillage@st-philips.com **Apply to:** Ms Emily Smith	We are one of the largest regional and national sets in the country with offices in Birmingham, Leeds and London.	PF Up to 2 T 175 T_{L3Y} 20 MP yes
STAPLE INN CHAMBERS Second Floor, 7 Staple Inn, London WC1V 7QH **Tel:** 020 7242 5240 **Email:** pupillage@stapleinn.co.uk **Apply to:** The Pupillage Secretary	Application window for pupillage commencing October 2018 will open on 1 April 2018 and close on 6 May 2018. Details will be placed on the Pupillage Gateway.	PF 1 T 27 T_{L3Y} 5 MP yes
THREE STONE Ground Floor, Lincoln's Inn, London WC2A 3XL **Tel:** 020 7242 4937 **Email:** clerks@3sb.law.co.uk **Apply to:** Ms Constance McDonnell	A chancery and commercial set specialising in financial and property litigation and advice.	PF 1 T 30 T_{L3Y} 3 MP yes
4 STONE BUILDINGS Lincoln's Inn, London WC2A 3XT **Tel:** 020 7242 5524 **Email:** pupillage@4stonebuildings.com Apply through Pupillage Gateway	4 Stone Buildings specialise in litigation and advisory work in the fields of company law, commercial law, financial services regulation, insolvency and international trusts.	PF 2 T 36 T_{L3Y} 5 MP yes
9 STONE BUILDINGS Lincoln's Inn, London WC2A 3NN **Tel:** 020 7404 5055 **Email:** clerks@9stonebuildings.com **Apply to:** Mr Philip Brown	Rooted in commercial chancery practice, Chambers undertakes advocacy, drafting and advice in a range of property, insolvency, private client and commercial matters, domestically and overseas.	PF 1 T 24 T_{L3Y} 1 MP yes

PF = Pupillages funded / **T** = Tenants / **T**_{L3Y} = Tenancies in last 3 years / **MP** = Mini-pupillages offered

Chambers	Description	PF	T	TL3Y	MP
STONE CHAMBERS 4 Field Court, Gray's Inn, London WC1R 5EF **Tel:** 020 7440 6900 **Email:** pupillage@stonechambers.com **Apply to:** Mr Henry Ellis	Stone Chambers is a leading commercial and shipping set based in London and Singapore, specialising in international commercial litigation and arbitration. Accepts direct pupillage applications.	1	26	5	yes
STOUR CHAMBERS Mill Studio, 17a Stour Street, Canterbury CT1 2NR **Tel:** 01227 764899 **Email:** clerks@stourchambers.co.uk **Apply to:** Pupillage Coordinator	Chambers' specialisations are: family law and general civil law. Applications must be made on chambers' application form.	1	16	2	yes
SUSSEX CHAMBERS 5 Chiswick Place, Eastbourne BN21 4NH **Tel:** 01323 642102 **Email:** clerks@sussexchambers.co.uk **Apply to:** Miss Rebecca Upton	Criminal, family and general common law set.	1	12	1	yes
TANFIELD CHAMBERS 2-5 Warwick Court, London WC1R 5DJ **Tel:** 020 7421 5300 **Email:** clerks@tanfieldchambers.co.uk	Tanfield is a leading property law set and a 'force to be reckoned with' across all aspects of commercial and residential real estate litigation and ADR.	3	65	6	yes
FOURTEEN 14 Gray's Inn Square, Gray's Inn, London WC1R 5JP **Tel:** 020 7242 0858 **Email:** clerks@fourteen.co.uk Apply through Pupillage Gateway	A leading family law set, with practice teams in children law, family finance, the Court of Protection and international family law.	1	34	3	yes
TEMPLE COURT CHAMBERS 19-21 High Holborn, Gray's Inn, London WC1R 5JA **Tel:** 020 7353 7888 **Email:** clerks@templecourt.co.uk **Apply to:** Ms Sarah Bedford		1	18	6	no
TEMPLE GARDEN CHAMBERS 1 Harcourt Buildings, Temple, London EC4Y 9DA **Tel:** 020 7583 1315 **Email:** clerks@tgchambers.com Apply through Pupillage Gateway	Leading general common and public law set instructed by a wide range of solicitors including those representing government departments, insurance companies and trade unions.	2	67	6	yes
3 TEMPLE GARDENS Chambers of John Coffey QC, Temple, London EC4Y 9AU **Tel:** 020 7353 3102 **Email:** clerks@3tg.co.uk Apply through Pupillage Gateway	Chambers is well-established, specialising in all areas of criminal law. Chambers has achieved accreditation to Barmark as issued by the General Council of the Bar.	Up to 2	52	7	yes

PF = Pupillages funded / T = Tenants / TL3Y = Tenancies in last 3 years / MP = Mini-pupillages offered

3 Verulam Buildings

Gray's Inn, London WC1R 5NT
Tel: 020 7831 8441
Email: chambers@3vb.com
Web: www.3vb.com

Description of Chambers Sitting comfortably and spaciously in a newly refurbished and expanded row of buildings in Gray's Inn, 3VB is a large and highly regarded set of chambers, with its members being involved in many of the most important commercial cases of the day.

Areas of work 3VB is acknowledged to be one of the handful of top sets for general commercial litigation, banking and finance, and civil fraud and is very highly regarded in a range of fields, including international arbitration, insolvency and company law, insurance, IT and telecoms, energy and natural resources, construction, media and entertainment and professional negligence. Members of chambers practise in the UK and internationally, in litigation in a range of jurisdictions such as Bermuda, the Cayman Islands and Singapore and in international arbitration proceedings throughout the world.

Who should apply 3VB is looking for outstanding applicants from all backgrounds. There are no fixed requirements, but applicants are likely to have at least a high 2.1 from a good university in their undergraduate studies and will often have a first and/or a postgraduate degree. Applicants must also demonstrate strong written and oral advocacy abilities, which usually requires experience in mooting or similar activities, as well as a commitment to and an understanding of the commercial bar, in part by having done mini-pupillages at 3VB or similar sets (although we appreciate that this will not always have been possible). Finally, candidates will have good temperament, integrity, commercial sense and motivation.

Pupillage programme Pupils sit with four pupil supervisors for three months at a time. 3VB's pupil supervisors are high achievers at various levels of seniority and so pupils are exposed to a range of cases and to top-quality expertise from which to learn their skills, all in a friendly and encouraging atmosphere. Pupils sit in the rooms of their pupil supervisor and share their daily professional life. Whilst they have to work hard, it is not normally expected that pupils should work in the evenings or at weekends. Pupils also undertake a number of advocacy exercises during the course of pupillage, usually one each term. During the practising six, pupils are given the opportunity to undertake advocacy on their own account, in order to start building up experience and earnings.

When and how to apply 3VB has traditionally used the Pupillage Gateway, for which applications should be made in January 2018, but this is under review. Students should check the position on 3VB's website later this year.

Mini-pupillages 3VB accepts applications for short mini-pupillages which are assessed and an essential part of our pupillage selection procedure. We therefore strongly encourage those interested in 3VB to do a mini-pupillage prior to applying for pupillage. For further details on mini-pupillage and how to apply, visit the 3VB website.

Sponsorship/funding The pupillage award is currently £65,000 per annum, not including second six earnings. Up to £20,000 of this award can be drawn down during the year prior to pupillage.

Pupillages funded	Up to 4
Tenants	71
Tenancies in last 3 yrs	6
Mini-pupillages	yes
Apply to	Check website for details
Remuneration for pupillage	£65,000 for 12 months

3 VERULAM BUILDINGS
BARRISTERS

Wilberforce Chambers

8 New Square, Lincoln's Inn, London WC2A 3QP
Tel: 020 7306 0102
Email: pupillage@wilberforce.co.uk
Web: www.wilberforce.co.uk
🐦 wilberforcech

Description of Chambers We are one of the leading commercial chancery and business law sets in the UK. We are involved in some of the most commercially important and cutting edge litigation and advisory work undertaken by the Bar today. Our clients demand high intellectual performance and client-care standards but in return the reward is a successful and fulfilling career at the Bar.

Areas of work We offer a full range of advocacy, drafting, arbitration and mediation services to a wide variety of clients, both in the UK and across numerous international jurisdictions. Our core practice areas include commercial litigation, pensions, property, professional liability, trusts, tax, probate and estates, and arbitration/ADR.

Who should apply You should possess high intellectual ability, excellent communication skills and a strong motivation to do commercial chancery work. You need to be mature and confident, have the ability to work with others and analyse legal problems clearly, demonstrating commercial and practical good sense. We have a minimum requirement of a 2.1 degree in law or another subject, and we have a track record of taking on GDL students, as well as undergraduate law students, as pupils and as tenants.

Pupillage programme We offer two 12-month pupillages. We provide an excellent pupillage and operate a well-structured programme aimed at providing you with a broad experience of commercial chancery practice. You will sit with different pupil supervisors with whom you will be able to develop your skills. Our pupils are not in competition with one another and if you meet the requisite standard, then you will be offered tenancy.

When and how to apply We are not a member of the Pupillage Gateway. Please visit our website from November 2017 for an application form and further information on when to apply.

Mini-pupillages We run four mini-pupillage weeks with two weeks held in December, one at Easter and one in July. Please visit our website for an application form and further information on when to apply.

Sponsorship/funding A pupillage award of £65,000 (for pupillage starting in October 2019) is offered to all pupils. The award is payable in monthly instalments and up to £20,000 of the award may be drawn down during the BPTC year.

Pupillages funded	2
Tenants	66
Tenancies in last 3 yrs	5
Mini-pupillages	yes
Apply via website	
Remuneration for pupillage	£65,000
Minimum qualifications	2.1 degree

Wilberforce CHAMBERS

2TG Chambers of Neil Moody QC, Temple, London EC4Y 9AY **Tel:** 020 7822 1200 **Email:** kpoulton@2tg.co.uk Apply through Pupillage Gateway	2tg is a common law and commercial chambers. We specialise in banking, clinical negligence, employment, insurance, personal injury and professional negligence.	PF 3-4 T 61 T$_{L3Y}$ 7 MP yes
THOMAS MORE CHAMBERS 7 Lincoln's Inn Fields, London WC2A 3BP **Tel:** 020 7404 7000 **Email:** clerks@thomasmore.co.uk Apply through Pupillage Gateway	A successful and established common law set with an excellent reputation. We offer a broad and challenging pupillage covering a comprehensive cross-section of our work.	PF 1 T 39 T$_{L3Y}$ 4 MP yes
TRINITY CHAMBERS The Custom House, Quayside, Newcastle upon Tyne NE1 3DE **Tel:** 0191 232 1927 **Email:** info@trinitychambers.co.uk Apply through Pupillage Gateway	Busy provincial set with sites in Newcastle and Middlesbrough with significant specialisations including those indicated. Chambers has Barmark and Investors in People accreditation.	PF 1-2 T 71 T$_{L3Y}$ 10 MP yes
TRINITY CHAMBERS Highfield House, Moulsham Street, Chelmsford, Essex CM2 9AF **Tel:** 01245 605040 **Email:** clerks@trinitychambers.law.co.uk	Trinity Chambers is a busy and dynamic set focused in Chelmsford. Members specialise predominantly in family and civil law.	PF 0 T 23 T$_{L3Y}$ 4 MP yes
UNITY STREET CHAMBERS 5 Unity Street, Bristol BS1 5HH **Tel:** 0117 906 9789 **Email:** chambers@unitystreetchambers.com Apply through Pupillage Gateway	Applications should be made by way of covering letter and CV. Pupils are taken on with a view to tenancy.	PF 1 T 13 T$_{L3Y}$ 1 MP no
WESTGATE CHAMBERS 64 High Street, Lewes BN7 1XG **Tel:** 01273 480 510 **Email:** clerks@westgate-chambers.co.uk **Apply to:** Mr Christopher Prior	Chambers' principal areas of work are criminal, family and civil. Pupils will receive advocacy training throughout pupillage.	PF Up to 2 T 49 T$_{L3Y}$ 3 MP yes
15 WINCKLEY SQUARE Preston PR1 3JJ **Tel:** 01772 252828 **Email:** paulm@15wsq.co.uk Apply through Pupillage Gateway		PF 2 T 46 T$_{L3Y}$ 3 MP yes

PF = Pupillages funded / **T** = Tenants / **T$_{L3Y}$** = Tenancies in last 3 years / **MP** = Mini-pupillages offered

Useful information

Glossary

ABS Alternative business structures were brought in by the Legal Services Act in October 2011 and are licensed by the Solicitors Regulation Authority. ABSs enable lawyers to form partnerships with non-lawyers and allow companies to invest in law firms and provide legal services. See also 'Tesco law'.

ADR Alternative dispute resolution, which comprises various methods for resolving problems without going to court.

Advocacy The act of arguing or pleading in favour of something either orally or in writing. A key skill for lawyers.

Affidavit A written statement, the truth of which must be sworn before an officer of the court.

Annulment A legal decree stating that a marriage was never valid.

Appeal A request to a supervisory court, usually composed of a panel of judges, to overturn the legal ruling of a lower court.

Arbitration A method of alternative dispute resolution whereby the disputing parties agree to submit their differences to the judgment of an impartial person or group.

Articles of incorporation A document that must be filed in order for a company to incorporate. Among other things, it must include the name and address of the corporation, its general purpose, and the number and type of shares of stock to be issued.

Assistant/associate solicitor Next step on the career ladder after the two-year training period.

Associated office (Usually overseas) office with which a firm has an arrangement to share work and to second trainees.

Bad faith Dishonesty or fraud in a transaction, such as entering into an agreement with no intention of honouring its terms.

Bail The money that a defendant pays as a guarantee that he or she will show up in court at a later date.

Bankruptcy Another term for insolvency.

The Bar Term used to refer to the barristers' branch of the legal profession.

Bar Council Official body representing barristers in England and Wales.

Bar Standards Board Independent board responsible for regulating barristers in England and Wales.

Barrister A lawyer who has been called to the Bar and who appears in court to argue a client's case.

Beneficiary Person named in a will or insurance policy to receive money or property; person who receives benefits from a trust.

Black-letter law The principles of law which are generally known and free from doubt or dispute.

Board of directors The group of people elected by a corporation's shareholders to make major business decisions for the company.

Bolt-on A department (or even an entire smaller firm) that joins an existing firm. Generally, the larger firm will not have practised in the specialist area in which the newcomers excel.

Bond A document through which one party promises to pay another within a specified amount of time.

Boutique Small niche firm offering specialist advice on one or a few specific areas of law.

BPTC The Bar Professional Training Course, the vocational stage between degree and pupillage. It replaced the BVC in September 2010.

Brief Details of a client's case, prepared by a solicitor and given to the barrister who argues it in court.

Burden of proof The duty of a party in a case to convince the judge or jury that enough facts exist to prove the allegations in question.

BVC The Bar Vocational Course, which was replaced by the BPTC in September 2010.

Call to the Bar A formal ceremony following completion of the BPTC during which you are given the title of barrister (although you must complete pupillage before you can practise).

Case law The law created by judges when deciding individual cases. Also known as 'common law'.

Caveat emptor Latin for 'buyer beware', this principle gives the buyer full responsibility for determining the quality of the goods in question.

Chambers Offices of a group of barristers.

Chinese walls Procedures enforced within firms to restrict access to certain information and so avoid any awkward conflicts of interest.

CILEx The Chartered Institute of Legal Executives is the professional body that represents trainee and practising chartered legal executives. See also 'Legal executive'.

Citizens Advice Previously the Citizens Advice Bureau. A charity service offering legal and financial advice to the public.

The City The commercial and financial area in the centre of London.

Claimant Formerly 'plaintiff'. The person or body that initiates a lawsuit.

Codicil A supplement to a will.

Collateral An asset that a borrower agrees to give up if he or she fails to repay a loan.

Common law The law created by judges when deciding individual cases. Also known as 'case law'.

Contentious Legal situation where a dispute has arisen.

Contingency fee A fee arrangement in which the lawyer is paid out of any damages that are awarded.

Contract An agreement between two or more parties in which an offer is made and accepted, and each party benefits.

Copyright A person's right to prevent others from copying works that he or she has written, authored or otherwise created.

Corporate finance Area of law that involves, among other things, advising clients on mergers and acquisitions, takeovers and stock exchange flotations.

Corporation An independent entity created to conduct a business.

Counsel Barrister(s) acting for one of the parties in a legal action.

CPE Common Professional Exam, a conversion course for non-law graduates. More often referred to as the GDL.

CPS The Crown Prosecution Service is responsible for prosecuting criminal cases investigated by the police in England and Wales. Employs solicitors and barristers.

Creditor An individual (or institution) to whom money is owed.

Damages The financial compensation awarded to someone who suffered an injury or was harmed by another's wrongful act.

Debtor Person who owes money.

Decision The judgment rendered by a court.

Deed A written legal document that describes a property and outlines its boundaries.

Defamation Publication of a statement that injures a person's reputation. Libel and slander are defamation.

Defendant In criminal cases, the person accused of the crime. In civil matters, the person or organisation that is being sued.

Devilling Doing paperwork for other members of chambers.

Due diligence Investigation carried out to establish an accurate picture of a company's finances and market position.

Due process The concept that laws and legal proceedings must be fair.

ECHR The European Convention on Human Rights 1950 protects human rights within the member states of the Council of Europe; the European Court of Human Rights is an international judicial body responsible for upholding the convention.

Encumbrance Any claim or restriction on a property's title.

Equity partner A partner at a firm who owns a share of the business (and is liable for its failures).

Equivalent means Introduced in 2014 by the SRA, this allows anyone to apply to qualify as a solicitor provided that (i) their skills and legal work experience are equivalent to that which a qualifying solicitor would have attained following a training contract, and (ii) they have completed the LPC.

Escrow Money or documents, such as a deed or title, held by a third party until the conditions of an agreement are met.

Estate All the property that a person owns.

Evidence The various testimony and documents presented in court to prove an alleged fact.

Ex parte Latin term meaning 'by or for one party'. Refers to situations in which only one party appears before a judge.

Executor Person named in a will to oversee and manage an estate.

Expert witness A witness with a specialised knowledge of a subject who is allowed to discuss an event in court even though he or she was not present.

Fee earner A lawyer at a firm for whose time the firm charges.

First six The first six months of pupillage. During this stage the pupil will train under a barrister, but will not have rights of audience.

Force majeure When parties to a commercial agreement are excused from performance of the contract due to events that are beyond their control.

Franchise A business relationship in which an owner (the franchisor) licenses others (the franchisees) to operate outlets.

FTSE The Financial Times Stock Exchange. The FTSE 100 is an index of the top 100 companies in the country, based on share value and turnover.

GDL Graduate Diploma in Law, a conversion course for non-law students. See also 'CPE'.

GLS The Government Legal Service provides legal services across the spectrum of the government's activities. Employs solicitors and barristers.

Good faith To act honestly and without deception.

Human Rights Act 1998 Statute that requires public authorities to act in a way that is compatible with the rights guaranteed by the ECHR. It requires the courts to read and give effect to primary legislation in a way that is compatible with the convention rights.

Hung jury A jury that is unable to reach a verdict.

In camera Latin for 'in chambers'. Refers to a hearing or inspection of documents that takes place in private, often in a judge's chambers.

In-house Refers to a lawyer who works within a company (not a law firm) as a salaried employee.

Inns of Court Collective name for the four legal societies in London that have the exclusive right of admission to the Bar.

Interlocutory order Temporary order issued during the course of litigation. Typically cannot be appealed because it is not final.

Intestate To die without a will.

IPO Initial public offering is the first sale of stock by a listed company to the public.

Jackson reforms Civil costs reforms recommended in a report by Lord Justice Jackson that came into force on 1 April 2013. See also 'LASPO'.

JLD Part of the Law Society, the Junior Lawyers Division is a group for students, trainees and newly qualified solicitors.

Judgment A court's official decision on the matter before it.

Jurisdiction A court's authority to hear a dispute.

LASPO The Legal Aid, Sentencing and Punishment of Offenders Act 2012 introduced wide-ranging changes to the legal aid system and reformed the use of conditional fee agreements. Highly controversial.

Law clinic A free legal advice centre, usually staffed by volunteer lawyers and students.

Law Commission An independent body set up in 1965 to keep the law of England and Wales under review and to recommend reform where needed.

Law Society Official body representing solicitors in England and Wales.

Lawyer Umbrella term used to refer to both barristers and solicitors.

LDP Legal disciplinary practices – introduced by the Legal Services Act – allow the eight different types of 'official' lawyer, known as authorised persons (ie, solicitor, barrister, legal executive, licensed conveyancer, trademark attorney, patent attorney, notary and costs lawyer), to go into partnership. They also permit firms to have up to 25% of their partnership made up of non-lawyers.

Legal aid The provision of assistance, advice or representation to people who are otherwise unable to afford legal representation.

Legal apprentice An individual who joins a law firm straight from school, rather than going to university, to work in a role similar to that of a paralegal.

Legal executive A qualified legal professional who specialises in a particular area of law and often performs work that is similar to that of a solicitor. See also 'CILEx'.

Legal Services Act 2007 A law that has opened up the legal market by allowing lawyers to form new business structures and permitting corporations to move into the legal services market. See also 'ABS'.

Legal Services Board The independent body responsible for overseeing the regulation of lawyers in England and Wales.

LETR The Legal Education and Training Review report was published in June 2013, setting out 26 key recommendations for change, particularly in regard to quality, accessibility and flexibility.

Liability Legal responsibility, duty or obligation.

Libel Defamatory written statements or materials.

LLB Letters written after someone's name, showing that he or she has the degree of bachelor of laws.

LLC A limited liability company is a business structure that is a hybrid of a partnership and a corporation.

LLD Letters written after someone's name, showing that he or she has a doctorate in law.

LLM Letters written after someone's name, showing that he or she has the degree of master of laws.

LLP A limited liability partnership is essentially a hybrid between a general and limited partnership. An LLP protects partners from personal liability for the negligent acts of the other partners.

Lockstep A system by which partners' pay is decided by time served as partner in predictable sequence. Pay rises in a series of steps (eg, after one, three, five, seven and 10 years).

LPC The Legal Practice Course is the vocational stage between degree and training contract.

M&A Mergers and acquisitions. A merger occurs where two or more companies join as one. An acquisition is the takeover of one company by another.

Magic circle Term used to refer to the top five UK law firms: Allen & Overy, Clifford Chance, Freshfields Bruckhaus Deringer, Linklaters and Slaughter and May.

MDP Multi-disciplinary partnership. A combination firm offering the full range of professional services, particularly law and accountancy functions.

Mediation A method of alternative dispute resolution in which a neutral third party helps to resolve a dispute.

Mini-pupillage Work experience within a set of chambers.

Ministry of Justice The body responsible for prisons, judges and courts, and probation.

Moot A mock trial, designed to test advocacy skills.

Negligence A failure to exercise the degree of care that a reasonable person would have used in the circumstances.

Niche firm/chambers Firm or set that specialises in a certain area of law.

Non-contentious Legal situation where there is no dispute.

Notary An official authorised to certify, for example, deeds, contracts or copies of documents.

No win, no fee An agreement whereby a solicitor acting in a claim is entitled to be paid his or her fee only if he or she wins. Such payment is usually made by the loser or his or her insurance company. Also known as a 'conditional fee'.

Paralegal A non-lawyer who does legal work which often resembles that of a solicitor.

Partnership An association of two or more people who agree to share in the profits and losses of a business venture.

Patent A document issued to an inventor, detailing ownership, rights and the nature of the invention.

Period of recognised training Introduced in 2014 by the SRA to replace the term 'training contract' (although most firms still refer to it in this way), it refers to the two-year pre-qualification training period for a solicitor, normally spent in a law firm.

Perjury The crime of knowingly making a false statement while under oath in court.

Piercing the corporate veil The concept through which a corporation's shareholders, who are usually protected from liability for the corporation's activities, may be held responsible for certain actions.

Pleadings The allegations by each party of its claims and defences.

Power of attorney The authority to act legally for another person.

Precedent A previously decided case that is considered binding in the court where it was issued and in all lower courts in the same jurisdiction.

Prima facie Latin for 'at first sight', meaning that a matter appears to be self-evident on first examination.

Pro bono The giving of free legal advice and services.

Profits per partner A firm's total profit divided by the number of partners at the firm.

PSC Professional Skills Course, which must be passed while training to qualify as a solicitor.

Punitive damages Money awarded to a victim that is intended to punish a defendant and stop the person or business from repeating the type of conduct that caused the injury in question.

Pupil barrister A trainee barrister who is effectively practising, but is not yet fully qualified. Also known as a 'pupil'.

Pupillage The training period before qualifying as a barrister.

Pupil supervisor A barrister who oversees an individual's training during pupillage.

QC Queen's Counsel, a barrister who has been appointed counsel to Her Majesty on the advice of the lord chancellor. Also known as a 'silk'.

Qualifying sessions Run by the four Inns of Court, students must complete 12 qualifying sessions before they can be called to the Bar. Sessions can include dinners, workshops, moots and residential weekends. Formerly called 'dining'.

Receivership The appointment by a court of a receiver to take custody of the property, business, rents and profits of a party to a lawsuit pending a final decision.

Salaried partner Unlike an equity partner, a salaried partner is still an employee of a firm, though with enhanced status, influence and responsibilities.

Seats Periods of training during a training contract. Normally six months long each.

Second six The second six months of pupillage. The pupil continues to train under a barrister, but has rights of audience in all courts.

Secondment Placement with a law firm's client or to an overseas office.

Settlement The resolution or compromise by the parties in a civil case.

SIF The Solicitors Indemnity Fund, covering liability for claims made against its members.

Silk Another term for QC.

Slander Defamatory oral statements.

Solicitor A lawyer who provides clients with skilled advice and representation. Mostly works in private practice.

Sponsorship The payment of GDL and/or LPC fees by a firm to individuals who have been offered a training contract.

SQE The Solicitors Qualifying Exam, proposed by the SRA in 2015, would need to be passed by all prospective solicitors (whether coming through the university, equivalent means or apprenticeship route) in order to qualify. Currently under consultation and not due to come in before 2019.

Square Mile London's financial centre, as defined by London's old medieval walls.

Squatter A barrister who remains in chambers after pupillage, but not as a tenant.

SRA The Solicitors Regulation Authority is the body in charge of setting and maintaining standards for solicitors.

Stare decisis Latin for 'to stand by that which is decided'. Refers to the principle of adhering to precedent when deciding a case.

Subpoena An order compelling a person to appear to testify or produce documents.

Tenant A barrister based in a particular set of chambers after pupillage.

Tesco law Euphemistic term for both the Legal Services Act and ABSs, which allow companies (eg, supermarkets or banks) to provide legal services. See also 'ABS'.

Title Ownership of property.

Tort A civil wrong that results in an injury to a person or property.

Trademark A word, name or symbol used to identify products sold or services provided by a business.

Training contract The two-year pre-qualification training period for a solicitor. See also 'period of recognised training'.

Transaction A deal arranged by two sets of lawyers.

Tribunal A court or forum established to settle certain types of dispute.

Trust A legal obligation with respect to property given by one person (donor) to another (trustee).

Vacation scheme Paid, formal work experience within a law firm. Also known as a 'work placement scheme'.

White-collar crime Term referring to financial crimes, such as fraud or insider dealing, committed primarily by persons at management level.

White-shoe firm A traditional, long-established US firm.

Work placement scheme Paid, formal work experience within a law firm, usually for one or two weeks. Also known as a 'vacation scheme'.

Useful addresses

Association of Graduate Careers Advisory Services
Millennium House, 30 Junction Road, Sheffield
S11 8XB
Tel: 0114 251 5750
Email: info@agcas.org.uk
Web: www.agcas.org.uk

Association of Costs Lawyers
Herringbone House, Lion Road, Palgrave, Diss,
Norfolk IP22 1AL
Tel: 020 3174 0967
Web: www.associationofcostslawyers.co.uk
Email: enquiries@costlawyer.co.uk

Association of Taxation Technicians
1st Floor, Artillery House, 11-19 Artillery Row,
London SW1P 1RT
Tel: 020 7340 0551
Email: info@att.org.uk
Web: www.att.org.uk

Association of Women Solicitors London
74A Seven Sisters Road, London N7 6AE
Tel: 07760 272809
Email: awslondon1@gmail.com
Web: www.awslondon.co.uk

Bar Association for Commerce, Finance and Industry
BACFI, PO Box 4352, Edlesborough, Dunstable
Beds LU6 9EF
Tel: 01525 222244
Email: secretary@bacfi.org
Web: www.bacfi.org

Bar Council
289-293 High Holborn, London WC1V 7HZ
Tel: 020 7242 0082
Email: contactus@barcouncil.org.uk
Web: www.barcouncil.org.uk

Bar Standards Board
289-293 High Holborn, London WC1V 7HZ
Tel: 020 7611 1444
Email: contactus@barstandardsboard.org.uk
Web: www.barstandardsboard.org.uk

Black Solicitors Network
c/o Percy Short & Cuthbert, 402 Holloway Road,
London N7 6PZ
Email: enquiries@blacksolicitorsnetwork.org
Web: www.blacksolicitorsnetwork.co.uk

British Institute of Verbatim Reporters
Mary Sorene, 73 Alicia Gardens, Kenton, Harrow,
Middlesex HA3 8JD
Tel: 020 8907 8249
Email: sec@bivr.org.uk
Web: www.bivr.org.uk

Career Development Loans
Tel: 0800 100 900
Web: www.gov.uk/career-development-loans

Central Applications Board
Ground Floor, Suite 2, River House, Broadford
Business Park, Shalford, Surrey GU4 8EP
Email: applications@lawcabs.ac.uk
Web: www.lawcabs.ac.uk

Central Law Training Ltd
Wrens Court, 52-54 Victoria Road, Sutton
Coldfield, Birmingham B72 1SX
Tel: 0121 362 7705
Email: registrar@clt.co.uk
Web: www.clt.co.uk

Chartered Institute of Legal Executives (CILEx)
Kempston Manor, Kempston, Bedfordshire
MK42 7AB
Tel: 01234 841000
Email: info@cilex.org.uk
Web: www.cilex.org.uk

Chartered Institute of Patent Attorneys
95 Chancery Lane, London WC2A 1DT
Tel: 020 7405 9450
Email: mail@cipa.org.uk
Web: www.cipa.org.uk

Chartered Institute of Taxation
1st Floor, Artillery House, 11-19 Artillery Row,
London SW1P 1RT
Tel: 020 7340 0550
Email: comms@tax.org.uk
Web: www.tax.org.uk

The Directory of Social Change
352 Holloway Road, London N7 6PA
Tel: 020 7687 4200
Email: cs@dsc.org.uk
Web: www.dsc.org.uk

Citizens Advice
3rd Floor North, 200 Aldersgate Street, London
EC1A 4HD
Tel: 03454 040 506
Web: www.citizensadvice.org.uk

Local Government Association
Layden House, 76-86 Turnmill Street, London
EC1M 5LG
Tel: 020 7664 3000
Email: info@local.gov.uk
Web: www.local.gov.uk

Commercial Bar Association
3 Verulam Buildings, Gray's Inn, London WC1R 5NT
Tel: 020 7404 2022
Email: admin@combar.com
Web: www.combar.com

Employment Law Bar Association
Tel: 01895 256 972
Email: admin@elba.org.uk
Web: www.elba.org.uk

Council for Licensed Conveyancers
CAN Mezzanine, 49-51 East Road London N1 6AH
Tel: 020 7250 8465
Email: clc@clc-uk.org
Web: www.conveyancer.org.uk

European Commission
Europe House, 32 Smith Square, London
SW1P 3EU
Tel: 020 7973 1992
Email: comm-rep-london@ec.europa.eu
Web: http://ec.europa.eu/unitedkingdom

Criminal Bar Association
Suite 23, 30 St Dunstan's St, Canterbury CT2 8HG
Tel: 01304 849149
Email: aaron.dolan@criminalbar.com
Web: www.criminalbar.com

The Faculty of Advocates
Parliament House, Edinburgh EH1 1RF
Tel: 0131 226 5071
Email: info@advocates.org.uk
Web: www.advocates.org.uk

The Crown Office
25 Chambers Street, Edinburgh EH1 1LA
Tel: 01389 739 557
Email: enquirypoint@copfs.gsi.gov.uk
Web: www.crownoffice.gov.uk

Family Law Bar Association
1 Garden Court Family Law Chambers, Temple,
London, EC4Y 9BJ
Tel: 0207 427 5591
Email: admin@flba.co.uk
Web: www.flba.co.uk

Crown Prosecution Service
Rose Court, 2 Southwark Bridge, London SE1 9HS
Tel: 020 3357 0000
Email: enquiries@cps.gsi.gov.uk
Web: www.cps.gov.uk

Free Representation Unit
5th Floor Kingsbourne House, 229-231 High
Holborn, London, WC1V 7DA
Tel: 020 7611 9555
Web: www.thefru.org.uk

Useful addresses

Government Legal Service
GLS Recruitment Team, 11th Floor, Lower Castle Street, Castlemead, Bristol BS1 3AG
Tel: 0845 300 0793
Email: glstrainees@tmpw.co.uk
Web: www.gls.gov.uk

Gray's Inn
Treasury Office, 8 South Square, London WC1R 5ET
Tel: 020 7458 7800
Web: www.graysinn.org.uk

Inner Temple
Treasury Office, Inner Temple, London EC4Y 7HL
Tel: 020 7797 8250
Email: enquiries@innertemple.org.uk
Web: www.innertemple.org.uk

Lincoln's Inn
Treasury Office, Lincoln's Inn, London WC2A 3TL
Tel: 020 7405 1393
Email: mail@lincolnsinn.org.uk
Web: www.lincolnsinn.org.uk

Middle Temple
Treasury Office, Ashley Building, Middle Temple Lane, London EC4Y 9AT
Tel: 020 7427 4800
Email: members@middletemple.org.
Web: www.middletemple.org.uk

Institute of Barristers' Clerks
Queen Elizabeth Building, Temple, London, EC4Y 9BS
Tel: 020 3763 8999
Email: admin@ibc.org.uk
Web: www.ibc.org.uk

Career Development Institute (CDI)
Ground Floor, Copthall House, 1 New Road, Stourbridge, West Midlands DY8 1PH
Tel: 01384 376464
Email: hq@thecdi.net
Web: www.thecdi.net

Institute of Chartered Accountants in England and Wales (ICAEW)
Chartered Accountants Hall, Moorgate Place London EC2R 6EA
Tel: 020 7920 8100
Email: generalenquiries@icaew.com
Web: www.icaew.com

Institute of Chartered Secretaries & Administrators
Saffron House, 6-10 Kirby Street, London EC1N 8TS
Tel: 020 7580 4741
Email: info@icsa.org.uk
Web: www.icsa.org.uk

Institute of Legal Finance & Management
2nd Floor, Marlowe House, 109 Station Road, Sidcup, Kent DA15 7ET
Tel: 020 8302 2867
Email: info@ilfm.org.uk
Web: www.ilfm.org.uk

Institute of Paralegals
20-22 Bedford Row, London WC1R 4JS
Tel: 020 3034 1487
Email: office@theiop.org
Web: www.theiop.org

Institute of Trademark Attorneys
ITMA Office, 5th Floor Outer Temple, 222-225 Strand, London WC2R 1BA
Tel: 020 7101 6090
Email: tm@citma.org.uk
Web: www.citma.org.uk

Intellectual Property Bar Association
Web: www.ipba.co.uk

Junior Lawyers Division
113 Chancery Lane, London WC2A 1PL
Email: juniorlawyers@lawsociety.org.uk
Web: http://communities.lawsociety.org.uk/junior-lawyers

Law Centres Network
Floor 1, Tavis House, 1-6 Tavistock Square,
London WC1H 9NA
Tel: 020 3637 1330
Email: info@lawcentres.org.uk
Web: www.lawcentres.org.uk

The Law Commission
1st Floor, Tower, 52 Queen Anne's Gate, London
SW1H 9AG
Tel: 020 3334 0200
Email: enquiries@lawcommission.gsi.gov.uk
Web: www.lawcom.gov.uk

Law Society
113 Chancery Lane, London WC2A 1PL
Tel: 020 7242 1222
Web: www.lawsociety.org.uk

Law Society of Northern Ireland
96 Victoria Street, Belfast BT1 3GN
Tel: 028 9023 1614
Email: enquiry@lawsoc-ni.org
Web: www.lawsoc-ni.org

Law Society of Scotland
Atria One, 144 Morrison Street, Edinburgh
EH3 8EX
Tel: 0131 226 7411
Email: lawscot@lawscot.org.uk
Web: www.lawscot.org.uk

Legal Aid Practitioners Group
12 Baylis Road, London SE1 7AA
Tel: 020 7833 7431
Web: www.lapg.org.uk

The Magistrates Association
10A Flagstaff House, St George Wharf, London
SW8 2LE
Tel: 020 7387 2353
Email: information@magistrates-association.org.uk
Web: www.magistrates-association.org.uk

National Association of Licensed Paralegals
Lincoln House, 1-3 Brixton Road, London
SW9 6DE
Tel: 0845 8627000
Email: info@nationalparalegals.co.uk
Web: www.nationalparalegals.co.uk

Pupillage Gateway
The Bar Council, 289-293 High Holborn London
WC1V 7HZ
Tel: 020 7611 1321
Email: pupillagegateway@barcouncil.org.uk
Web: www.pupillagegateway.com

Personal Injuries Bar Association
Devereux Chambers, Devereux Court, London
WC2R 3JH
Email: weir@devchambers.co.uk
Web: www.piba.org.uk

Planning and Environmental Bar Association
4a Woodside Business Park, Whitley Wood Lane,
Reading, RG2 8LW
Tel: 0118 987 3345
Email: administrator@peba.org.uk
Web: www.peba.org.uk

Property Bar Association
5 Quernmore Road, London N4 4QU
Web: www.propertybar.org.uk

Revenue Bar Association
Temple Tax Chambers, 3 Temple Gardens, London
EC4Y 9AU
Tel: 020 7353 7884
Email: rba@templetax.com
Web: www.revenue-bar.org

Society of Asian Lawyers
Web: www.societyofasianlawyers.co.uk

Useful addresses

Solicitors Regulation Authority
The Cube, 199 Wharfside Street, Birmingham
B1 1RN
Tel: 0370 606 2555
Email: contactcentre@sra.org.uk
Web: www.sra.org.uk

Technology & Construction Bar Association
Web: www.tecbar.org

Universities and Colleges Admission Service (UCAS)
Rosehill, New Barn Lane, Cheltenham,
Gloucestershire, GL52 3LZ
Tel: 0371 468 0468
Web: www.ucas.com